W9-CGZ-089

GLOBAL SCIENCE

ENERGY • RESOURCES • ENVIRONMENT

Fourth Edition

John W. Christensen

Cherry Creek Schools
Englewood, Colorado

KENDALL/HUNT PUBLISHING COMPANY
4050 Westmark Drive Dubuque, Iowa 52002

Cover photos: Background photo courtesy of NASA.
Left photo courtesy of Interstate Power Co., Dubuque, IA.
Right photo used by permission of UNICEF.
Bottom photo courtesy of The National Renewable Energy Laboratory, Golden, CO.

Library of Congress Catalog Card Number: 94–78100

ISBN 0–8403–7483–6

Printed in the United States of America
10 9 8 7 6 5 4 3 2 1

Contents

Acknowledgments

Global Science: Energy, Resources, Environment has been developed over the last twenty-four years. Scores of friends, students, professional acquaintances, and fellow educators have made suggestions. No person is an island; hence, each of my ideas, no matter how novel, has been enhanced by comments of friends and associates. To the extent that I am aware of my intellectual debts, I have tried to acknowledge them and give proper credit. If I have left anyone out, I apologize.

A special thank you to the following organizations:

- The Colorado Section of the American Institute of Mining, Metallurgical & Petroleum Engineers (AIME) for financial help, encouragement and the duplication of the preliminary draft of this course.
- The Mineral Information Institute for financial support, encouragement in the development of all four editions, and continuing efforts to promote the use of this text.
- The Mining and Metallurgical Society of America (MMSA), the Seeley W. Mudd Memorial Fund of AIME, and the Society of Economic Geologists Foundation (SEG) for financial assistance which provided for numerous pilot schools and field tests.
- The National Science Teachers Association (NSTA) for choosing me as a writer for its *Project for an Energy-Enriched Curriculum* (PEEC) and for allowing me to use several of their activities in the text. A special thank you

to Dr. John M. Fowler, PEEC director, whose ideas and recommendations have been most helpful.

- The Colorado Institute on Population Problems for encouragement and financial assistance for expenses.
- Colorado's Cherry Creek School District for providing the atmosphere where such a course could be pioneered, and for binding the preliminary draft.
- To (Harvard) *Project Physics, Inc.* for encouragement and for financial help in the production of the initial phases of the course.
- To the many individuals and organizations that allowed the use of figures and illustrations I am most grateful.

The pilot testing of this program was a most ambitious undertaking. Generous financial assistance was provided by the Colorado Endowment for the Humanities; the National Endowment for the Humanities; the Kettering Family Foundation; Walter S. Rosenberry, III; the Richard King Mellon Foundation; The Frost Foundation, Ltd.; Joy R. Hilliard; Richard Ballantine; St. Mary Parish Land Company; MGA Inc.; and others.

The pilot teachers were most helpful with their suggestions, criticisms, and compliments when the project seemed overwhelming. They reinforced the fundamental belief that science is of value to all students and has an important message for all of us.

Dr. Charles Bottinelli's ability to organize and carry out teacher training workshops is unsurpassed. Dr. William L. Christen's work on reading level and format gave a new dimension to the program. Dr. Faith M. Hickman, an outstanding science curriculum specialist, wrote narrative, questions, lab activities and evaluations, all of highest quality.

To improve and expand the curriculum, generous in-kind support was provided by Public Service Company of Colorado; Pacific Gas & Electric; City of Colorado Springs Energy Department; University of Northern Colorado; Colorado College; Cherry Creek School District; and many others.

The development of the third edition enabled *Global Science: Energy, Resources, Environment* to become a national (global) curriculum that started as a dream. This could not have been done without the help of Jacqueline R. Evanger and many of the directors of the Mineral Information Institute (MII), and Dr. Carol Stone of The Stone Cottage, Alameda, California.

MII has provided important support for all the editions of this text, but most extensively during the development of the Third and Fourth Editions. In addition to coordinating the activities involved in preparing this latest edition, Mrs. Evanger's untiring efforts to convey ideas and concepts as clearly and meaningfully as possible brought flow and accuracy to the text. Her work was complemented by the artful, concise, editing of Dr. Carol Stone.

MII coordinated the work of thirty-two editors, each providing specific expertise to ensure accuracy and clarity in this latest edition. I will never have the luxury of meeting many of them, but I am truly indebted for their many hours spent reviewing the manuscript and diligently researching and preparing the comments that led to this finished text. Outstanding among these editors were MII directors, Paul Bailly, Ann Pierce Dorr, Page Edwards, Alfred Hoyl, John Goth, Scott Ingersoll, P. A. Meyer, C. Phillips Purdy, Jr., Geoffrey G. Snow and MII President Nelson Fugate, along with Martha Balbach for her keyboarding skills in bringing it all together in the manuscript. Thought, discussion, suggestions, debate, and a year and a half of hard work culminate in this fourth edition.

A very special thanks to my family who suffered through months and then years of research and writing. Thank you for your love, help, and understanding.

And finally, to all my students and those around the globe to whom this whole endeavor is dedicated, may the content help each of you prepare and plan for a better world.

—John W. Christensen

About the Author

John W. Christensen, who teaches environmental science in the Cherry Creek School District in Englewood, Colorado, pioneered in the development of global science materials as early as 1968. Broadening and improving these materials has involved study at resource-related facilities from coast to coast.

Mr. Christensen received his B.A. from Augsburg College in Minneapolis, Minnesota and his M.S. in Natural Science from New Mexico Highlands University, majoring in physics, chemistry, and mathematics. He has both attended and taught at numerous summer institutes across the nation supported by the National Science Foundation (NSF). In particular, he was on the writing team that produced Harvard Project Physics; also, he recently spent four summers on an NSF team focusing on the production of relevant classroom materials for uncommitted students. As a member of another writing team, Mr. Christensen spent two summers working on the National Science Teachers Association's Project for an Energy-Enriched Curriculum.

About the Mineral Information Institute and This Textbook

*"It's so incredibly impressive when you look back at our planet from out there in space and you realize so forcibly that it's a closed system—that we don't have any unlimited resources, that there's only so much air and so much water."**
—Edgar Dean Mitchell, Apollo 14 Astronaut

The resources people have to work with are those that were on the planet when humankind appeared—the air, the water, the mineral and the living resources. Humans are also blessed with mental resources that characterize our species—curiosity, the ability to reason, ingenuity, and intellect. Using our mental ability for solving problems requires getting the right perspective on them. Few of us have the perspective—the view of Earth as a sphere wrapped in clouds and water—that Mitchell got from his spacecraft. One of the aims of this textbook is to provide some measure of that perspective.

Perspective is the message of the foregoing quotation, of this textbook, and of the Mineral Information Institute. Though the lifestyle we enjoy today is based on the science and technology of the last two centuries, our society feels plagued by the undesirable side effects of its successes. Some members of our well-to-do societies feel hostile toward those who are responsible for our improved standard of living. Many have focused on the costs of scientific technology and ignored the benefits—perhaps because the benefits are so familiar that they are taken for granted.

The science writer Isaac Asimov once said that modern science need not be such a mystery to nonscientists. "Much could be accomplished toward bridging the gap if scientists accepted the responsibility of communication—explaining their fields of work as simply and to as many people as possible—and if nonscientists, for their part, accepted the responsibility of listening." In aiding with this book, the Mineral Information Institute has accepted the challenge of explaining to young people that mineral and energy resources can be extracted in an environmentally sound manner, while providing social and economic benefits. The Mineral Information Institute is striving to achieve its purpose so that more of our citizens will face with understanding the complicated scientific, technological, and societal issues that will confront them in the 21st Century.

Teachers and students are invited to inquire about other activities of the Mineral Information Institute and to participate in them.

Mineral Information Institute
475 17th Street, Suite 510
Denver, Colorado 80202

*Mitchell's comments are striking but not entirely accurate—the planet is not a closed system, as both energy and radiation leave and enter, and gasses leave the Earth.

An Open Letter to Students

My interest is in the future because I am going to spend the rest of my life there.
Charles F. Kettering

Dear Student:

You are living at an exciting time. During your lifetime, important decisions will be made, and you have a role in making them. These decisions will affect: the position of your country in the world of nations; your feeling of who you are and how you relate to others and the environment that surrounds you; the quality of life you will have; and, the amount of personal freedom you will enjoy. Many decisions will relate to how you use energy, resources, and our environment.

Wise decisions will depend upon how well you understand the issues. It is the purpose of this course to build a basic background for understanding energy, resource, and environment benefits and problems. *Global Science* is not just another science course. The questions we will discuss relate to today as well as tomorrow. You will find that the road you travel as you work through these pages can be an exciting journey.

Science is a tool at our disposal. It is a powerful tool. Science plays an important role for every living creature on Earth. Some of the questions this science course will discuss are:

- What is exponential growth?
- Does the Earth have a carrying capacity?
- Is there an energy, resource, and environmental concern?
- Can we live better with less? Do we have to?
- What are our alternatives?

It is true that people cause some of the concerns we will study. It is also true that people are keys to solutions. *Global Science* helps provide the vision of tomorrow. It describes alternatives and suggests possible solutions.

To be part of the solution you need to:

- understand how the scientific issues relate to you and your needs.
- have a vision of what a sustainable world might be like.
- act on what you know. That is something you do for yourself.

African environmentalist Baba Dioum said:
In the end, we will conserve only what we love. We will love only what we understand. We will understand only what we are taught.

Global Science teaches the wonders of our planet. Studying this text will not provide all the answers, but you will be much better prepared to face the challenges of tomorrow because of your experiences in this course.

John W. Christensen

Using This Textbook

Using a textbook to its fullest potential should be a goal you want to pursue. To help you use it properly, we want to point out the key features of this book.

As you open the book to Chapter 1, note the following features:

- **Marginal notes** on each page provide a clue into the content of the passages they match. Use them to help you find the important information in the text. They will also help you set up your notes.
- **Vocabulary** you need to know is placed in **bold face type** the first time a new key word appears in a chapter. This is done to draw your attention to that word. All key words are clearly defined in the glossary, which is located near the end of this textbook.
- **Key questions/ideas** are provided to give you an idea of what is important in the chapter. They appear as marginal notes in boxed format by the related sections of text. This will enable you to focus your attention on key ideas when they are being presented.
- **Charts, graphs, illustrations, and pictures** have been included to help you visualize the concept being discussed. Do not overlook these important aids.
- **Chapter summaries** are provided. Read them before you read the entire chapter. They will help you detect the most important ideas. Read them again at the end to help you put together all the different concepts of that chapter.
- **References** for further reading and research follow the Summary section.
- **End of chapter questions/problems** give you an opportunity to practice and apply what you have learned. Do these carefully and completely. ***Set A*** focuses on major concepts and specific ideas. ***Set B*** is more difficult and requires application of major concepts.

We believe these features will help you learn the most important ideas presented in this book. Using them to your advantage will give you an edge. Take time to look each of them over carefully and use them as you proceed through this textbook. We hope you enjoy your journey through this fascinating topic. As a result of this experience, you will become a more informed citizen of the world.

Key to the Symbols

Throughout the *Global Science* Student Edition, you will find symbols which will alert you to the features of the text or its use in combination with the other *Global Science* components.

? A question mark next to each question in the margin that is repeated in the end of the chapter questions.

A flask with the appropriate number next to each subhead for each laboratory activity that corresponds.

? A question mark at the beginning of the end of chapter questions to create the visual link with questions in the margin.

An open book lying flat at the chapter summary to indicate important reading material.

Goal

To build a firm understanding of the ecosystem concept.

A Grand Oasis in Space

The vast loneliness up here is awe-inspiring, and it makes you realize just what you have back there on Earth. The Earth from here (the Apollo-8 spacecraft) is a grand oasis in the big vastness of space.

—Astronaut James A. Lovell, Jr.

Why is our Earth called a global spaceship?

Our Unique Planet

We live on what has been called a global spaceship. Earth is like a spaceship because it travels through space alone, with no outside resources except sunlight.

With the exception of a few astronauts, all human beings are bound to Earth for life. Even those astronauts leave Earth only temporarily and under very special conditions. They need to return to the wonderful and delicate life-support system of Spaceship Earth.

Spaceship Earth: the grand oasis in space.

Most of us take Earth's life-support system for granted. We think little about it and observe it only casually. Since most of us will spend every moment of our lives on Earth, it makes sense to examine how our spaceship operates. Also, we need to see how our daily actions interact with our life-support system.

What is global science?

The overall goal of this course is to provide an understanding of our life-support system. Global science is the study of how individuals and societies use Earth's resources and influence the environment in their attempts to satisfy human wants. Through your study, you should gain a better understanding of the human struggle and a greater appreciation of our planetary home.

1.1 The Birth Event

What is the big-bang theory?

For centuries, humans have wondered how the universe began. Most scientists now think it began with a "big bang," when a dense piece of matter expanded with great violence. This chunk contained all the matter in the universe. The **big-bang theory** is supported by the observation that the vast majority of galaxies appear to be moving away from us as if everything is still expanding. Some scientists believe that gravity is slowing down this expanding by pulling back on the outward-moving stars and planets. The outward movement may eventually change to inward movement. Sometime in the far distant future, the big bang may be repeated.

What is the steady-state theory?

Another group of astronomers assumes the universe remains basically constant in appearance throughout space and time. This **steady-state theory** speculates that matter is being created continuously and spontaneously. Because of special problems, the steady-state theory has lost most of its following. But the idea of a universe with no beginning and no end still has appeal to some. Neither of these theories attempts to explain where all the original matter came from.

How was our sun formed?

Theories of the origin of our own solar system also are uncertain. The most popular theory is that our solar system originated as a cloud of slowly rotating gas and dust particles. Under the influence of its own gravity, the cloud began to collapse and spin faster. As the collapse proceeded, the cloud flattened into a disk of whirling particles. Most of the material slowly condensed into the disk's center and became our sun. The contraction heated the sun enough for atomic energy to begin. The energy source for almost all life processes was operating.

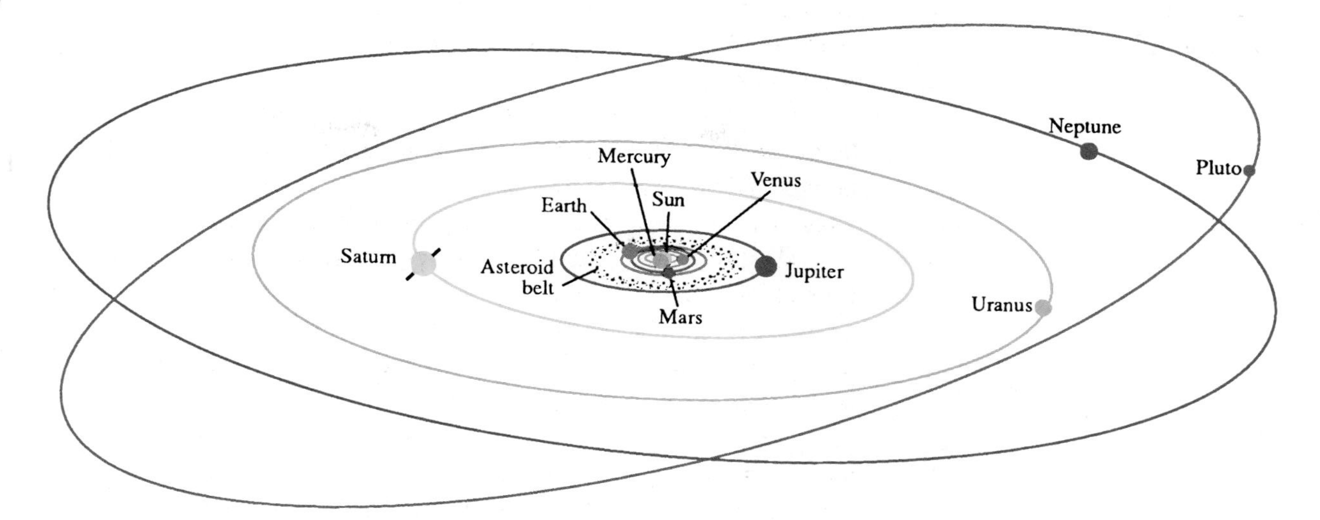

Figure 1.1 The solar system.

In regions far from the center of the disk, smaller condensations of particles became our solar system's planets. The planets formed in different ways, partly because of their distances from the sun.

How was the Earth formed?

Gravity pulled particles of matter together during the planet-forming process. Our early Earth was, most likely, one giant sphere having the same composition throughout. However, as time passed, the solid planet began to heat up. This was caused by (1) the energy released when chunks of matter slammed into the Earth, (2) the compression of the inside of the Earth as matter accumulated farther out, and (3) radioactivity from uranium, thorium and potassium. Eventually, the interior became hot enough for iron to melt. Iron, being denser than the other common elements of Earth, sank to the center and formed the molten core. This process released even more heat energy causing a large fraction of the Earth to melt.

List the four layers of the Earth.

As the iron and other dense materials sank, the lighter materials from which they separated floated outward to cool and form a primitive solid crust and mantle. Between the molten iron core and the mantle was the remaining liquid core. Uranium and thorium broke down to lighter compounds that accumulated in the crust. Much of the heat associated with that breakdown rose to the surface and was lost to space. This slowed down the melting process and left us with the layered Earth. (Figure 1.2) Thus our Earth was born.

1.2 A Grand Oasis

What was the impact of the launch of Sputnik?

In 1957, a "star" called Sputnik appeared in the heavens. It was bright and clear. Unlike real stars, Sputnik moved rapidly and did not twinkle. It was an artificial satellite that had been built and launched into orbit by the Soviet Union. The satellite's appearance caused a great

Figure 1.2 The Earth's layers. (*From Continents in Motion*, by Walter Sullivan. New York; McGraw-Hill, 1974.)

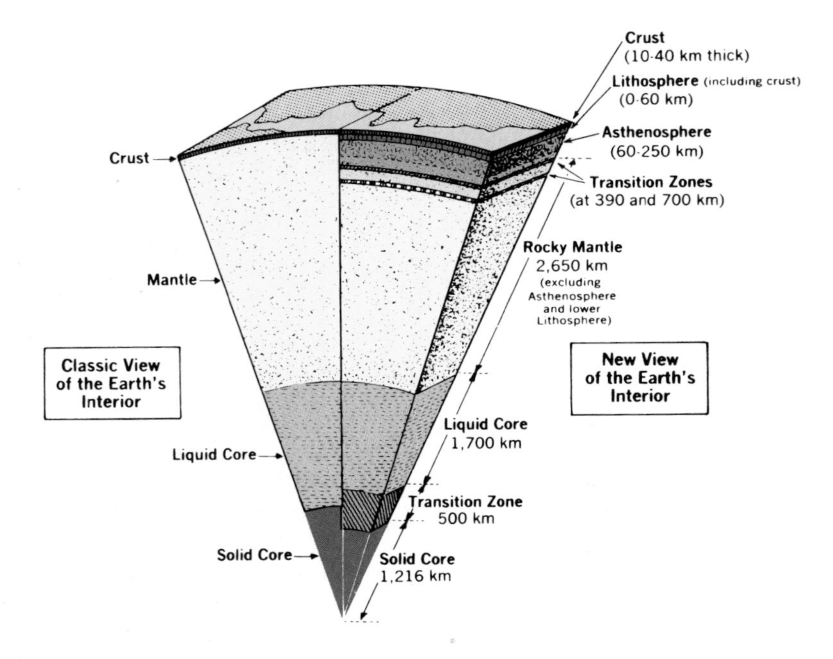

Figure 1.3 Computer fit of the continents around the Atlantic Ocean. (From Bullard, Everett and Smith, "The Fit of the Continents Around the Atlantic:" Philosophical Transactions of the Royal Society, London, A-258; 41 - 51, 1965.)

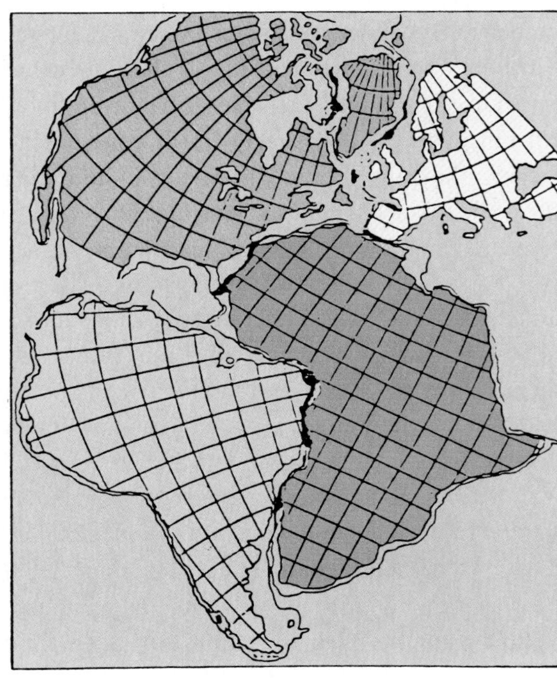

deal of flurry in the United States. A U.S. space program was begun with the goal of showing our technical strength to the world. On July 20, 1969, an American walked on the moon, and our hearts filled with pride. But the real significance of all this activity was quite unexpected.

What does "finite" mean?

Because of photographs taken from space, for the first time in human history we saw clearly that our Earth is finite. We live on a fragile, blue oasis in the dark void of space. One look at that blue planet forces the observer to conclude that we are all bound together.

The purpose of this course is not to speculate on how we began, but to examine how we relate to the world as it exists today. We are

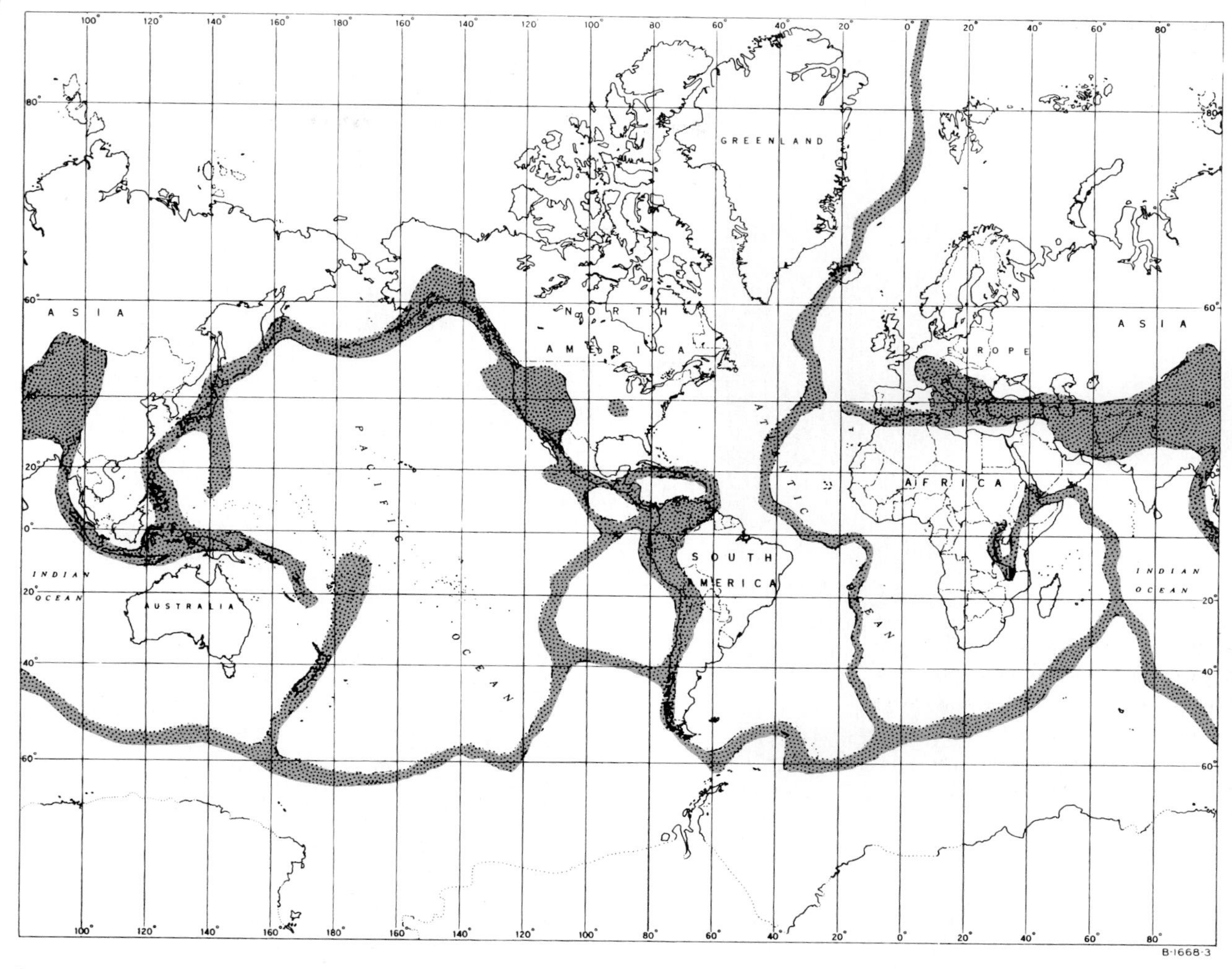

Figure 1.4 The Earth's seismic belts. (From U.S. Geological Survey (USGS), National Earthquake Information Service.)

living here and now. What is our function on this grand oasis? We must understand how we relate to our environment so that we can better exist with our surroundings, our neighbors and ourselves.

1.3 It's Always Changing

Earth feels firm beneath our feet. It is comforting to sense that stability and permanence. But that sense of stability is only an illusion. Consider the following:

Pangaea is the name given to the large continent shown in Figure 1.3.

1. The borders of the continents around the Atlantic Ocean all fit together like pieces of a jigsaw puzzle. (See Figure 1.3.)
2. Studies indicate the Earth's magnetic poles move about as the centuries pass.
3. Earthquake belts, active volcano belts and ocean trenches occur in definite zones on Earth. (See Figure 1.4.)

Traveling the Grand Oasis

science at work

You can't get away from Spaceship Earth, but you can vacation in areas that are remote or unfamiliar. Jim Sano helps people who *really* want to get away from it all—at least for three weeks or so. As President of InnerAsia Expeditions in San Francisco, California, Jim focuses on special-interest travel. Want to follow Marco Polo's route through China? Do research on rare butterflies in Micronesia? Jim knows how to help you take advantage of our widely diverse global ecosystems.

Most of InnerAsia's clients have unusual interests and a higher-than-average sense of adventure. They may want to explore an especially remote place such as Patagonia, or sample the cuisines of various provinces in China. Jim often assists filmmakers in finding inaccessible locations for movie sets. He helps scientists and students travel to areas where they can observe the unique characteristics of those areas.

It's interesting and challenging to arrange travel in these unusual lands and circumstances, and sometimes Jim's efforts aren't completely successful. One trip to the Himalayas, for example, was designed for people who wanted to look for the rare snow leopard. Reservations fell off quite a bit, however, when folks realized they'd spend most of their vacation hanging out in parkas and snowshoes at 15,000 feet with little chance of a hot meal, much less of seeing the beautiful leopard.

In arranging tours, Jim has help from a variety of experts. Usually a tour guide in San Francisco is responsible for the overall planning and logistics of the trip. In the destination locale, an accompanying tour leader, naturalist, scientist, professor, or other knowledgeable person handles the daily educational needs of the travelers. Translators, too, are often on hand. Local tour guides who live in the area may have little formal education but do know their country, its climate, and its culture.

Travelers signing up for one of InnerAsia's expeditions receive an extensive itinerary with detailed instructions for preparing for their excursion. Annotated reading lists help them study the geography, etiquette, environment and local culture of the country they will visit. On returning, travelers may continue studying about the country, using the lists as references.

Jim Sano's graduate work in biochemistry was a long way from the travel industry, but as he used computers in his education, he appreciated more and more their usefulness in data analysis and problem solving. Today computers help him with everything from airline reservations to market analysis. In planning his ad mailing lists, for instance, he uses a customized statistical database to identify potential customers, their geographical interests and spending limits. An online medical information service provides the latest information for travelers on subjects such as immunization requirements and current disease outbreaks.

Jim says there is little formal training available for a career in his type of travel, other than standard travel-agent instruction in handling packaged tours, airline reservations, and hotel arrangements. But if you're interested in learning and teaching about Earth's people, its ecosystems, and its geography, the travel industry may have a place for you. You might start as a guide in a museum, theme park, or state park. Look for experience handling groups of people, and develop your confidence and leadership abilities. When he was in college, Jim worked as a naturalist at Yosemite National Park, in charge of the naturalist programs at Tuolumne Meadows. Now he continues his role in education in other ways, aided by his computer skills.

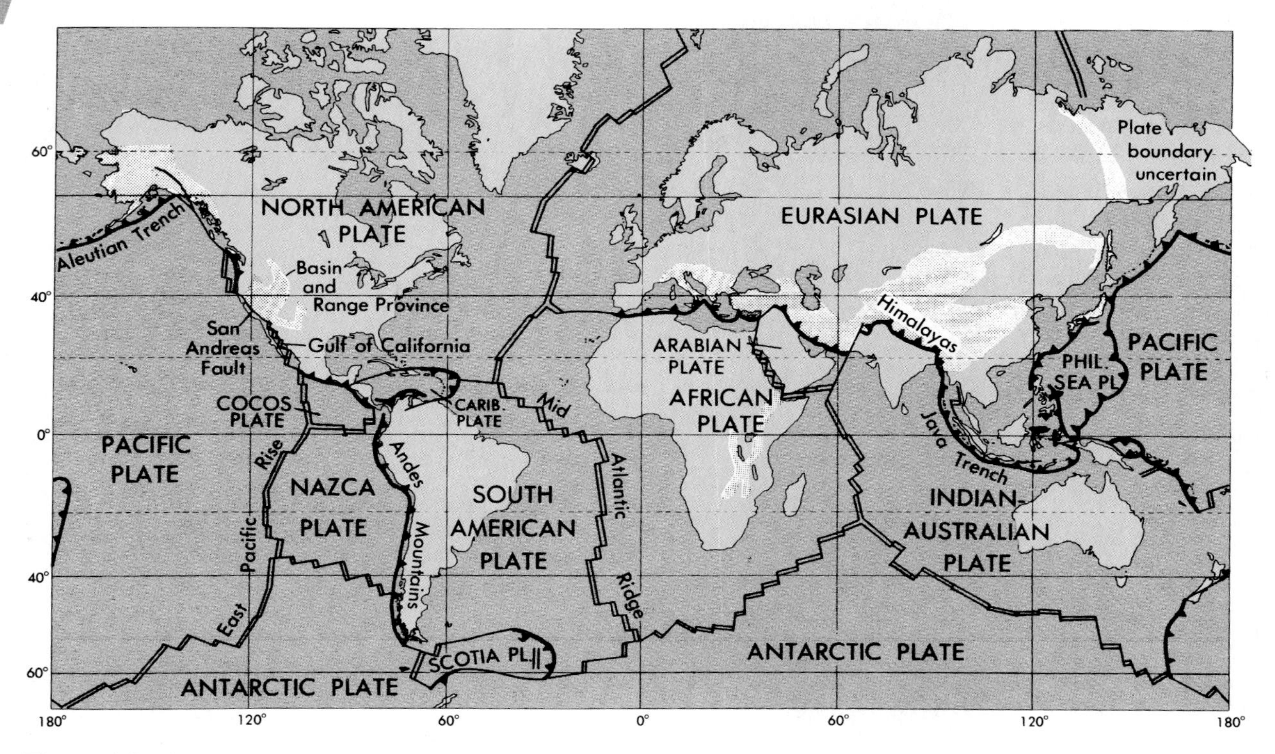

Figure 1.5 Lithosphere plates of the world. (USGS)

These strange and seemingly unrelated facts can all be explained if we assume that the Earth's apparently stable crust moves. This is the central idea of the **plate tectonics theory.**

? What are the major concepts of the plate tectonics theory?

According to the plate tectonics theory, the lithosphere, consisting of crust and rigid upper part of the mantle (see Figure 1.2), is divided into seven very large sections called plates. In addition, there are several smaller plates (see Figure 1.5). These plates float and move on a pliable layer called the asthenosphere.

Along the boundaries of moving plates, the crust is cracked and buckled. Earthquakes occur. Volcanoes spew forth gases, ash and lava.

How the atmosphere may have begun.

Volcanic gases (mainly water vapor, hydrogen, hydrogen chlorides, carbon monoxide, carbon dioxide, nitrogen, and sulfur dioxide), interacting with sunlight, eventually produced an ocean and a crude (non-oxygenated) atmosphere on the young Earth. Collisions with asteroids and comets may also have contributed to atmospheric gases. (See Figure 1.6.) Once we had an atmosphere, things changed. Conditions were right for the development of oxygen gas and for life, as we know it, to begin.

The continents are attached to plates which slowly move over the surface of Earth. Most of the dramatic geologic events that will happen during your lifetime will occur at plate boundaries.

The plates have continued to move. When a giant continent broke up millions of years ago, today's continents were formed. That explains why the boundaries can be fitted together like puzzle pieces, and why the magnetic poles show movement.

Figure 1.6 Volcanoes have contributed enormous amounts of water, carbon dioxide, and other gases to the atmosphere and materials to the continents. Sunlight broke water into hydrogen and oxygen. Photosynthesis by plants removed carbon dioxide and added oxygen to the primitive atmosphere, as it does today. (From *Earth,* 4th ed., by Frank Press and Raymond Siever. Copyright © 1974, 1978, 1982, 1986, W. H. Freeman and Company. Reprinted with permission.)

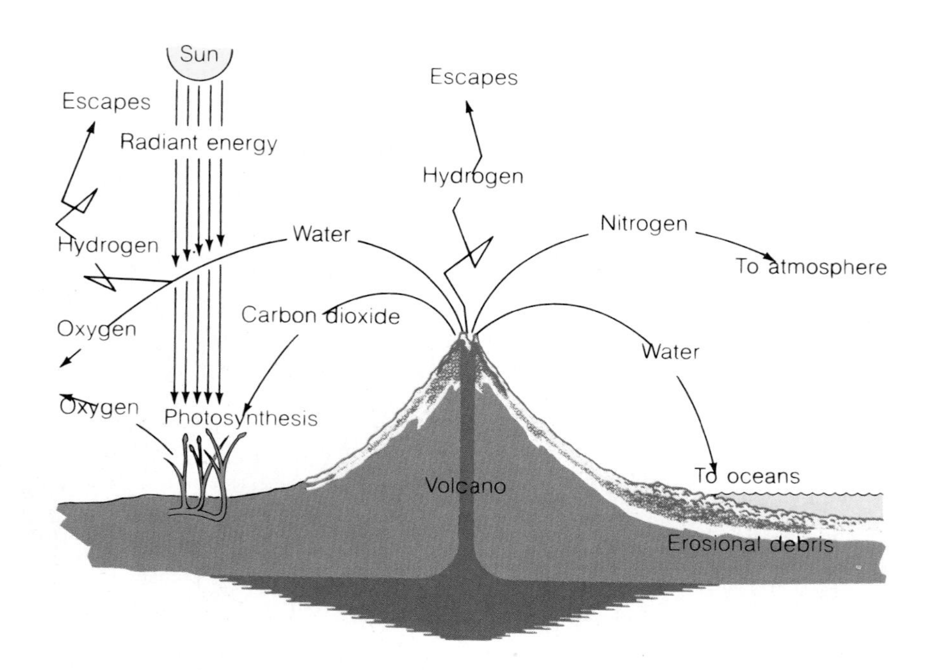

1.4 The Biosphere—Where All Life Exists

?

What is the ecosphere?

The biosphere and ecosphere are the same thing.

All life on Earth exists in a thin zone about nine miles thick. In this zone air, water, and rock meet, intermingle, and interact. This spherical shell of life is known as the **ecosphere** or **biosphere.** In it occur all relationships that bind together all living things.

The Earth itself can be divided into three areas—the **atmosphere** (air), the **hydrosphere** (water), and the **lithosphere** (rock). The ecosphere extends throughout much of all three areas, as shown in Figure 1.7.

1.5 The Sun—The Source of All Life

?

What happens to the solar energy that strikes the Earth?

The sun is the source of the radiant energy that supports the ecosphere. It warms the Earth and provides the energy for **photosynthesis** in plants. Photosynthesis is the process by which plants put together sugars and other carbohydrates from carbon dioxide and water. In carrying on photosynthesis plants produce the food and oxygen that sustain all life, including their own. For that reason, plants are called **producers.**

Figure 1.8 summarizes what happens to the solar energy that strikes the Earth. Note that 30 percent is directly reflected back into space. Forty-seven percent is converted into heat after being absorbed by such things as the ground, the oceans, and roofs. Twenty-three percent evaporates water and causes precipitation. About 0.2 percent drives all the winds, waves and convection currents. Less than 0.1 percent is used in the photosynthesis process. (See Figure 1.8.)

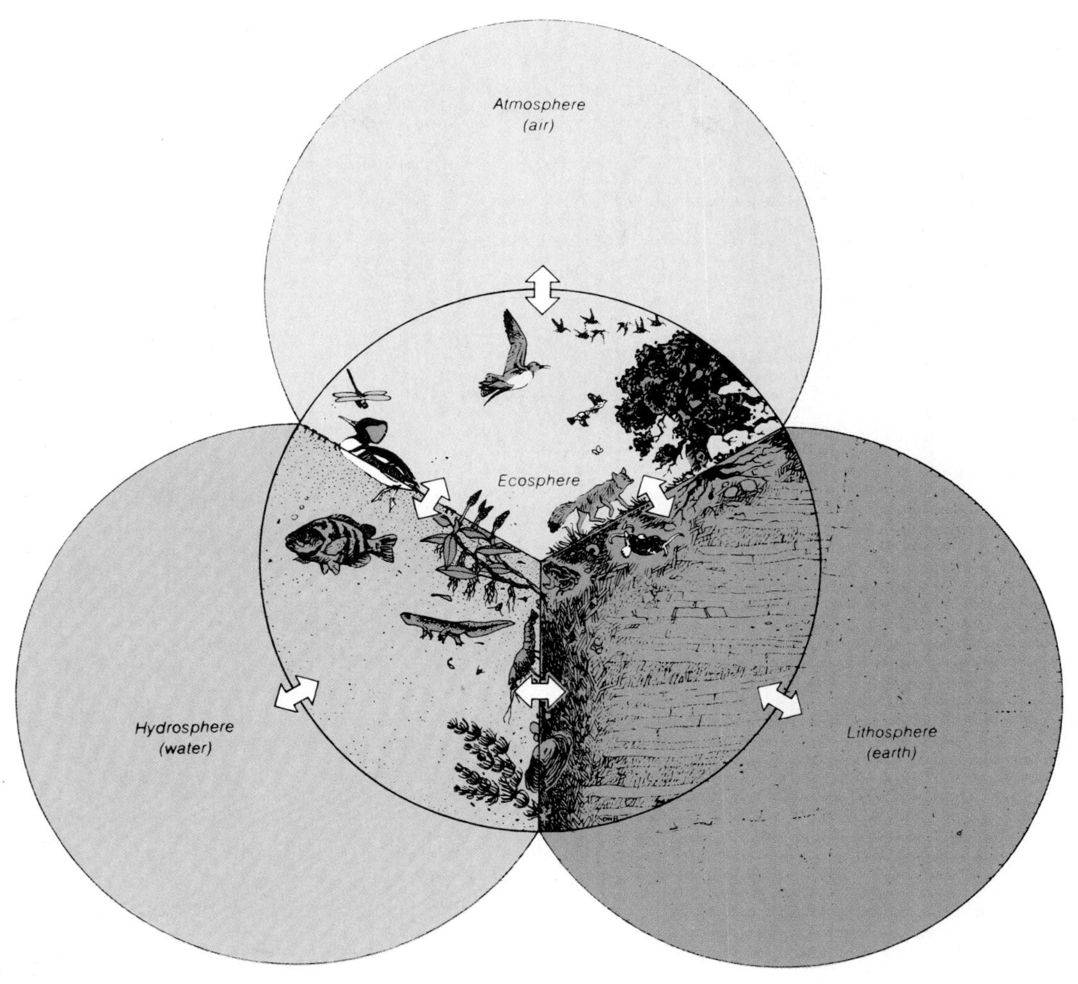

Figure 1.7 Our life-support system—the ecosphere. (From *Living in the Environment* by G. Tyler Miller, Jr. Copyright © 1975 by Wadsworth Publishing Co., Inc., Belmont, California 94002. Reprinted by permission of the publisher.)

1.6 Levels of Organization

Scientists classify matter according to size and function. Their classification scheme is referred to as **levels of organization.** This system of classification will be useful to us as we develop the concept of ecosystem. Figure 1.9 summarizes the relationships between the various levels. The levels of concern to us are defined as follows:

> **atom:** the smallest particle of an element that can exist as that element. (There are more than 100 fundamental substances called elements. They make up all matter.) Atoms are made up of still smaller parts—protons, neutrons and electrons.
>
> **molecule:** the smallest particle of a substance that can exist as that substance. Molecules are combinations of like or differing atoms.

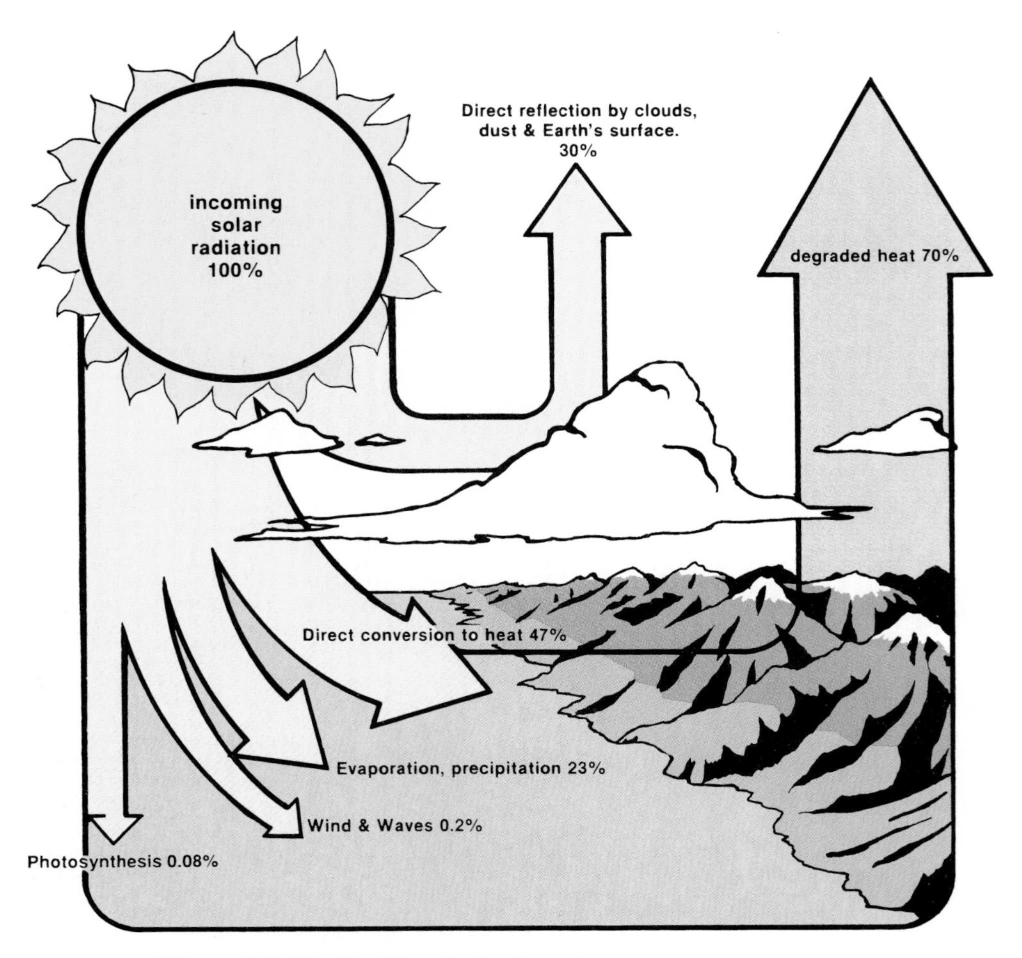

Figure 1.8 The Earth's solar budget. (Adapted from Hubbert, 1974, Figure 1, p. 11, with permission of the author. The 0.08 figure for photosynthesis is based on a literature search done by John W. Christensen.)

protoplasm: The substance making up living parts of a cell.
cell: a group of atoms and molecules interacting in an organized way to exhibit life.
tissue: a group of similar cells performing a similar function, example—muscle tissue, blood tissue.
organ: a group of tissues performing a similar function, example—the heart, the lungs.
organ system: a group of organs performing a similar function, example—the digestive system.
organism: any living thing.
species: a group of closely related organisms that can interbreed.
population: a group of the same type of organisms living in a certain area.
community: a group of populations living in a given area.

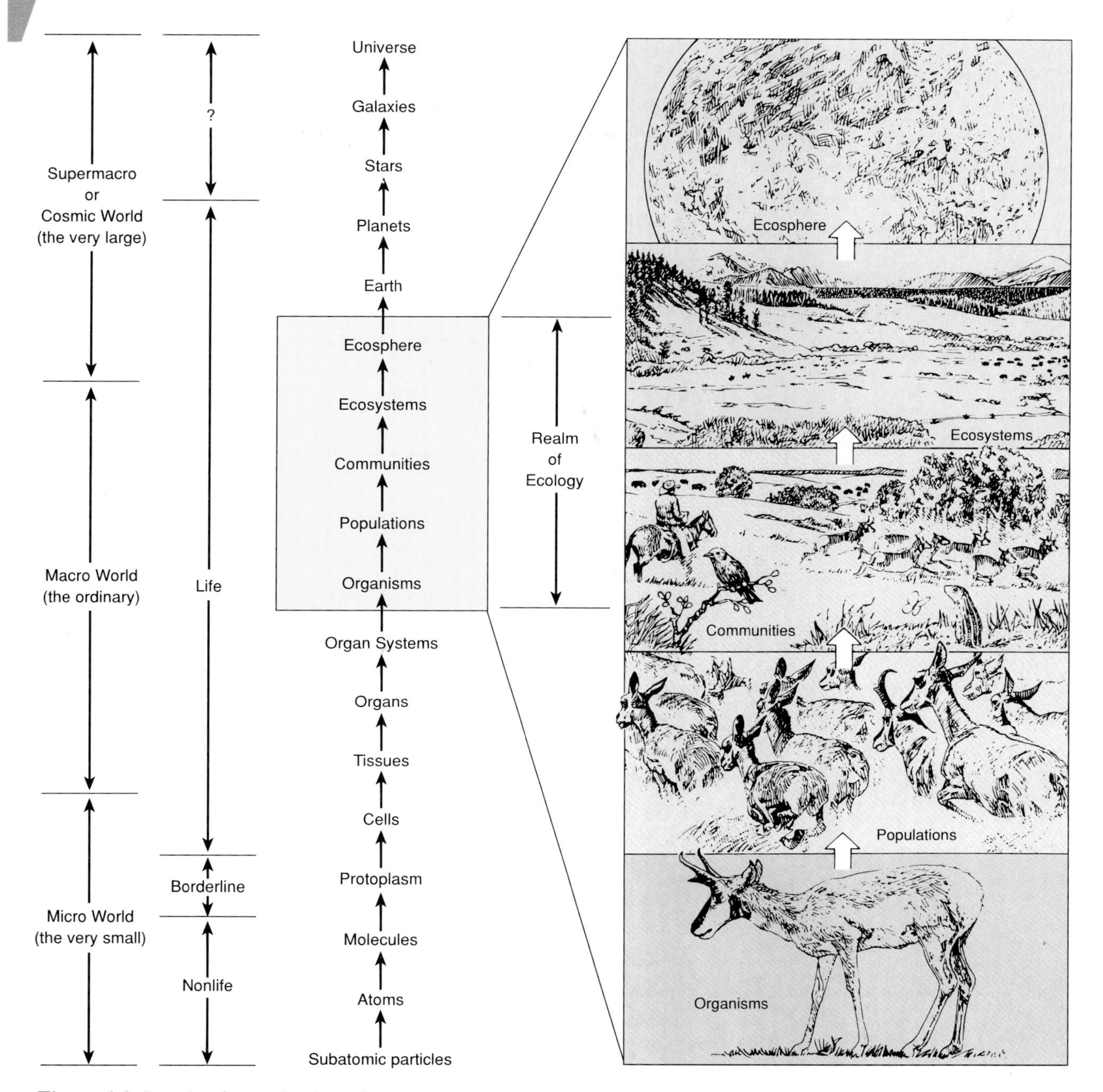

Figure 1.9 Levels of organization of matter. (From *Living in the Environment;* 2nd ed., by G. Tyler Miller, Jr. Copyright © 1979 by Wadsworth Publishing Co., Inc. Belmont, California 94002. Reprinted by permission of the publisher.)

ecosystem: any area of nature that includes living organisms and nonliving substances interacting by transforming energy to produce an exchange of materials between the living (biotic) and nonliving (abiotic) parts. Major ecosystems are often called biomes.

ecosphere or biosphere: the global ecosystem. The sum total of all the various ecosystems on the Earth.

Earth: a grand oasis in space.

An ecosystem is an area of nature that includes living organisms and nonliving substances interacting to produce an exchange of materials between the living and nonliving parts.

Patrick Balch

What is considered the realm of ecology? What do ecologists study?

1.7 Ecology and Ecosystems

It is possible to study single organisms without giving much thought to how and where those organisms live. For example, an anatomist may study the structure of an animal's bones, muscles, and organs without caring much about the life of the animal in its environment. It is also possible to study nonliving environments without worrying about the animals, plants, and other kinds of organisms that live there. For example, one may describe a desert in terms of its nonliving or abiotic parts. These would include rocks, sand, wind, temperature, rainfall, or elevation. A physical geologist or meteorologist might take this view.

Some aspects of organisms can only be understood in terms of their relationships to other organisms and the nonliving environment. **Ecology** is the study of those relationships. **Ecologists** are scientists who are concerned with why certain organisms are found in specific environments and the unique relationships and adaptations that make their life possible.

Environment: the sum of all the conditions and influences affecting the life, development and ultimately the survival of an individual organism or population.

Ecologists study the interactions that occur in ecosystems. Interactions occur between living things. This occurs when an animal eats a plant or another animal. Interactions also occur between the biotic and abiotic parts of the system. This happens when waste materials from living things decompose, returning minerals to the soil.

What is human ecology?

Human ecology is especially interesting to some scientists because human populations are so numerous, diverse, and widespread on planet Earth. Human ecology emphasizes the relationships among humans, other organisms, and their environments. Human beings are much more than biological animals. We socialize with each other. We exist in and interact in our neighborhoods. We are part of society as a whole. Human ecology seeks to bring together physiological, behavioral, sociological, political, economic, ethical, and spiritual factors and their interactions with agriculture and mineral and energy resources.

As shown in Figure 1.9, ecologists usually deal with five main levels of organization: organisms; populations; communities; ecosystems; and the ecosphere.

How are ecosystems defined?

In some ways, ecosystems are defined for convenience. The definition may change depending on what a person wants to study. The interactions occurring within a jar of pond water make up a rich and fascinating ecosystem. An ecosystem may be studied within any given area. All that is necessary is some boundary across which inputs and outputs of materials and energy may be measured. Thus, a student of ecology may investigate ecosystems like a forest, a pond, a rotting log, a garden, a culture of bacteria in a test tube, or the entire Earth!

What is an aquatic ecosystem?

What are biomes?

Ecologists generally group ecosystems on Earth into a few major types. **Aquatic ecosystems** include lakes, ponds, rivers, springs, swamps, marshes, estuaries, coral reefs, seas, and oceans. On land, the major ecosystems—often called biomes—are forests, grasslands, savannas (combinations of grasslands with scattered trees), chaparrals (shrublands), tundra, and deserts. These groupings are handy.

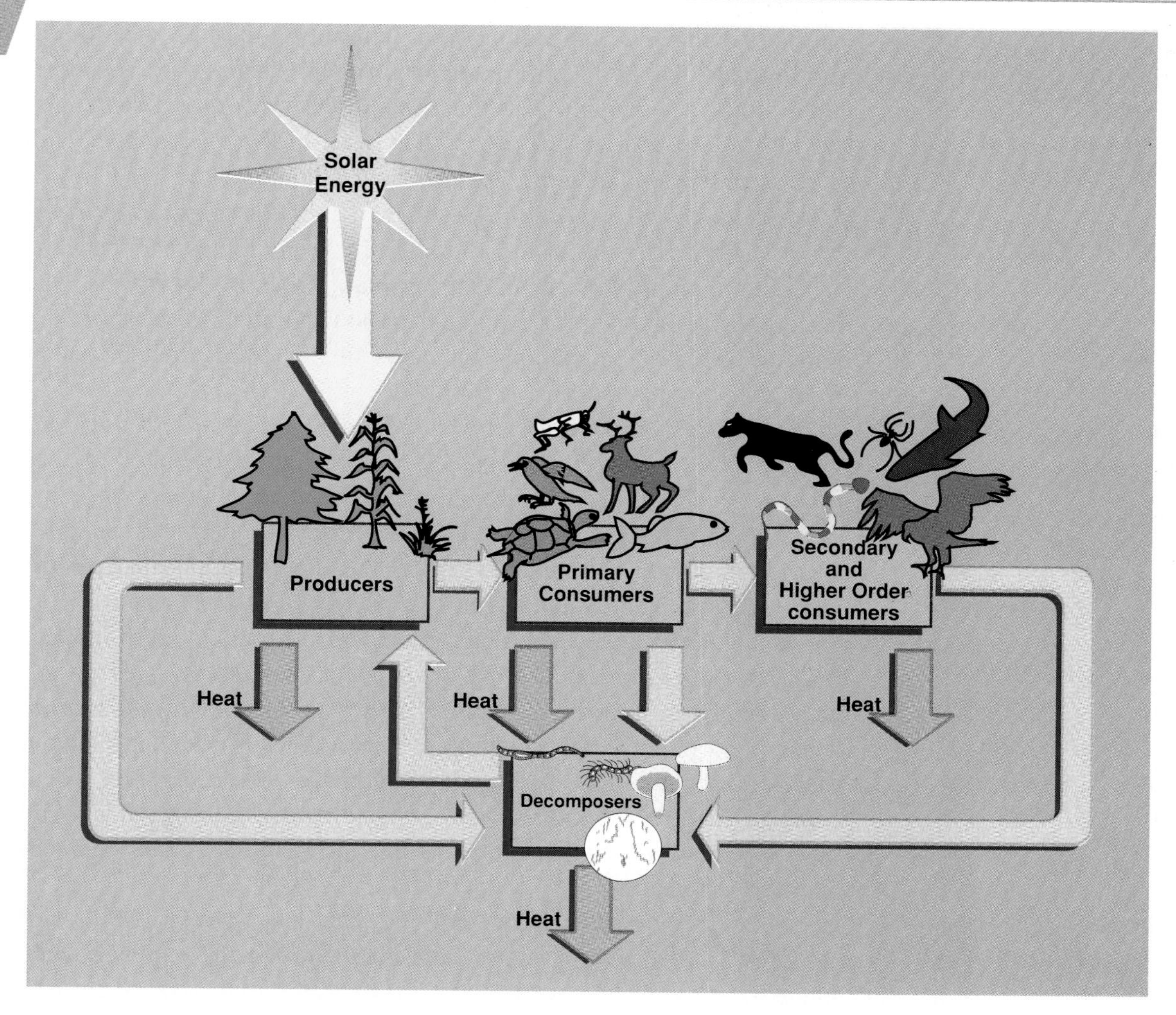

Figure 1.10 The basic components of an ecosystem. Orange lines show the cyclic movement of matter through the system. Red lines show the one-way flow of energy through the system.

Although no two forests are exactly alike, they have much in common. For that reason, an understanding of the natural laws at work on one type of forest helps predict what goes on in another.

The Ecosphere

All of the various ecosystems on Earth are connected to one another in the ecosphere. The ultimate goal of ecology is to find out how everything in the ecosphere is connected to everything else.

1.8 The Components and Structure of an Ecosystem

Figure 1.10 shows the basic parts of any ecosystem and how those parts are related. Notice in the center of the drawing, the grasshopper, deer, bird, fish, and turtle. These organisms are examples of **primary consumers** or **herbivores.** They are classed this way because they eat plants. In this ecosystem they get all their food materials and energy from producers. Producers are mostly green plants, as shown in Figure 1.10.

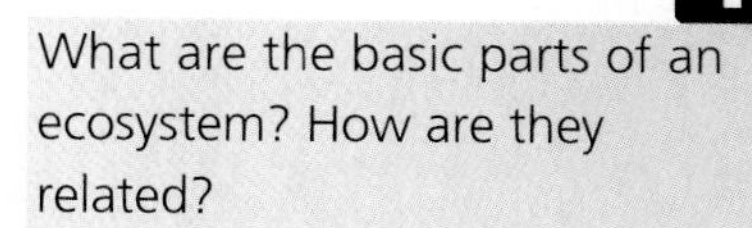

?

What are the basic parts of an ecosystem? How are they related?

What are producers, primary consumers, and secondary consumers?

What happens when a snake eats a grasshopper, or a hawk captures a snake? They obtain food without which they would die. Ecologically speaking, these **secondary consumers** are acting as **carnivores** (meat eaters). Some consumers are **omnivores.** They eat both plant and animal foods. The bear, living on a diet of both berries and fish, is a good example. So are you.

Whenever one organism eats another, energy is transferred. A series of such transfers is called a food chain. Many things happen when an animal eats a plant or another animal. Nonliving materials, like minerals, are taken in as part of the food. Animals cannot survive without molecules containing elements like calcium, iron, phosphorous, zinc, manganese, and so forth.

Why are minerals and energy flow important?

Along with these molecules in food, energy is transferred. No organism on Earth can live without a constant supply of energy. Plants trap the energy of the sun through photosynthesis. Photosynthesis occurs only in green plants and other producers. The energy of the sun is trapped in carbon compounds. This is the energy supply that powers nearly the entire ecosystem.

When an animal eats a plant, the energy is transferred to the animal. The animal breaks down plant-cell material and releases the energy trapped in the cell structure. This process is called **respiration.** There are still some other important interactions to consider. Without the work of **decomposers** or **microorganisms,** the ecosystem would cease to function. Decomposers break down the waste products and dead bodies of other organisms, both plant and animal. Nonliving substances are released.

What are decomposers?

After their release, these nonliving materials are recycled through the biotic parts of the system. This natural recycling happens when plants take the materials from the soil or water and absorb them into their tissues.

Note: Plants take in nonliving chemicals called soil nutrients. Soil nutrients are also called fertilizer or minerals.

The atmosphere is also important to recycling. Plants release oxygen as a by-product of photosynthesis. Animals breathe oxygen. Plants use oxygen in their own respiration. Furthermore, both plants and animals release carbon dioxide as a by-product of respiration. Carbon dioxide is a raw material (along with water) used by plants in the photosynthetic process. Some decomposers are responsible for food spoilage. Such spoilage of food is an age-old problem.

1.9 How Ecosystems Work

Ecosystems, regardless of size, consist of groups of organisms interacting in a variety of ways with each other and with the nonliving environment. Many of these interactions are driven by each organism's basic need for food.

Ecosystems consist of many communities living together in the same area. The place where an animal lives is called its **habitat.** What an organism does or how it affects and is affected by its habitat is called its **niche.** The niche idea is not easy to understand, but you might think of it as the animal's job. The grassland community is a

Special Focus

Food Preservation

Modern humans desire a variety of good food throughout the year. Because most people do not live in regions that have a yearlong growing season, and because transporting large quantities of food by air is very expensive, strategies for preserving food must be used.

The key to all these strategies is controlling **enzymes** and the growth of microorganisms. All living organisms produce enzymes. Enzymes are important in digestion. They also ripen fruits and vegetables and tenderize meats. They do this by breaking down starches, fats, proteins, and similar materials. If their action is not stopped, they make foods over-ripe. Microorganisms, too, are everywhere. They break down food for their own use. Food spoilage results from chemical changes and from the growth of microorganisms. Chemical spoilage is primarily the work of enzymes during storage. This spoilage may lead to a color change or result in bad odors, flavors, or textures.

Figure 1.11 This photo shows early Americans cutting ice on a frozen lake or river in the midwest. The ice was brought to an ice house and covered with sawdust. It was then removed as needed throughout the year. (From the archives of the Grout Museum of History and Science, Waterloo, Iowa. Assistance provided by the Ice House Museum, Cedar Falls, Iowa.)

How rapidly foods spoil depends on temperature, humidity, the nature of the product, and the type of containers in which they are kept. Storage temperature is the primary factor affecting storage life. A chemical law states that the rate of natural chemical reaction doubles every time the temperature rises 18° F(10° C). Applying this law to food storage means the general quality loss of 70° F storage (for a given length of time) would be almost twice the quality loss for the same product stored at 52° F.

Prehistoric people quickly realized the temperature relationship. They stored food in cool caves or cold springs. Much later, early pioneers used root cellars and storage in cool basements. Later, iceboxes became popular. Blocks of ice could be cut from lakes in the winter and stored in piles of sawdust all summer long. Today, mechanical refrigerators provide preservation with very little effort on the part of the consumer. Convenience is maximized, food is preserved, and fresh fruits and vegetables can be enjoyed all year long.

Prehistoric people also dried food in the sun. This removed water from the food. (Water is necessary for microbial growth.) Dehydration techniques have improved through time so that one can now obtain a great variety of foods in that form. Dehydrated apples, apricots, pears, eggs, milk and vegetables all have excellent flavor. Another technique is curing, the preservation of food by salting or smoking. Curing slows the growth of microorganisms inside food and on food surfaces.

Smoking meat, poultry and fish removes moisture and adds preservatives. The food is hung in a smokehouse over a slow-burning fire.

Sugar and salt, in large amounts, slow the growth of microorganisms. Both sugar- and salt-cured hams are popular items at meat markets. A similar technique is pickling, the preserving or flavoring of food in any brine, vinegar or spicy solution.

The most significant advance in food preservation was canning. Canning is the process of cooking food and sealing it in airtight metal or glass containers. The heat process that cooks the food also destroys the microorganisms (bacteria, yeasts and molds) that can spoil it. Chemicals such as salt and sugar are not needed to preserve canned food, but may be added to prevent undesirable chemical reactions which might change an appealing color or flavor.

Continued

In canning, sealing keeps out microorganisms and helps prevent oxidation of the food. An advantage of the airtight seal is that it provides a safety factor. The consumer will hear a rush of air when a sealed can or jar is first opened. If the can is swollen or leaking, the seal has been broken. Bacteria have been admitted to the container, the food has spoiled (releasing gases), and the contents must be thrown away.

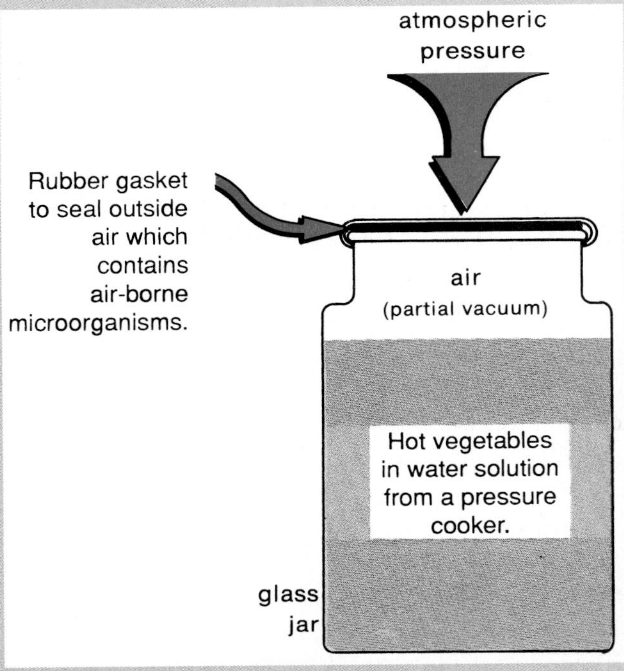

Canned foods can sit on shelves for months, even years. When opened, the contents will taste as good as the day the containers were sealed.

Freezing is a popular method of food preservation. Freezing preserves food and kills most microorganisms.

New plastic packaging materials allow food-processing companies to meet consumer needs for pre-portioned meals that require no freezing or refrigeration, and can be heated in microwave ovens and served directly from the package. These materials are composed of several different layers of plastic, each of which serves a specific function in protecting the food from damage, moisture, or oxygen.

The plastic is formed into shallow trays or bowls, filled with product, and a lid is sealed on. The packages are then heat processed to cook the product and kill bacteria. The shallow tray shape provides both a convenient serving dish and allows the package to be heat processed very quickly. The fast heat processing allows the product to have a fresher taste and texture without the need for any additives. The heat process, airtight seal, and barrier properties of the package eliminate the need for preservatives and allow the product to retain its safety and quality for a year or more.

atmospheric pressure
Rubber gasket to seal outside air which contains air-borne microorganisms.
air
(partial vacuum)
Hot vegetables in water solution from a pressure cooker.
glass jar

Figure 1.12 The principle of food canning.

Figure 1.13 Green beans in the canning process. (Photo courtesy of the Pillsbury Company.)

habitat suitable for antelope. It includes nutritional grasses, and open spaces across which the antelope can escape its predators. If you were to study all the activities of the antelope, you would be studying the niche of the antelope. The boundaries of an ecosystem are determined by the environment. That is, as the environment (moisture, soil type, temperature and wind) changes, so does the ecosystem.

The boundaries may be the result of change in moisture, such as that found between a marsh and the adjacent dry land, or between a grassland and an adjacent forest. The separation of ecosystems is not often as distinct as that between a pond ecosystem and the adjacent forest ecosystem.

Ecosystems are dynamic (changing) systems in which there is a constant movement of energy and materials. However, within this flow of energy, environmental resources and organisms tend to be in balance. If the primary consumers eat too much grass (or too many of the producers) and deplete their food reserve, then many of the consumers will die, until a balance is reached between the number of consumers and the amount of food available. Figure 1.14 summarizes the major components and processes in an ecosystem. Refer to it as you read the remainder of this section.

An ecosystem has five interacting components: 1) plant nutrients, 2) producers, 3) primary consumers, 4) secondary consumers, and 5) decomposers. The whole system is powered by solar energy.

In the photosynthesis process, plants use solar energy to rearrange carbon dioxide molecules, water molecules, and selected minerals into plant bodies (cells). In the process, oxygen is released. Photosynthesis is summarized by the following general equation:

carbon dioxide + water + minerals + energy ——> plant cells + oxygen

Respiration is the reverse of photosynthesis. It may be represented by the following general equation:

Note: Photosynthesis stores energy. Respiration releases energy.

food + oxygen ——> energy + carbon dioxide + water + minerals

Thus as consumers process food, they give off carbon dioxide, water, and a variety of minerals. Figure 1.15 shows how photosynthesis and respiration interact.

In terms of energy, ecosystems are open systems. (Energy must continually be brought in from outside.) Energy is continually lost to the environment as organisms use food and minerals for growth and maintenance. This energy is continually replaced by the sun which is the primary source of energy for almost all ecosystems. This is amazing when one remembers that less than 1% of the sun's energy that reaches the Earth actually ends up being captured by plants. Animals and plants use this energy as needed, by breaking down the energy compounds in their cells with special enzymes and releasing the energy for body needs.

How does energy move in an ecosystem?

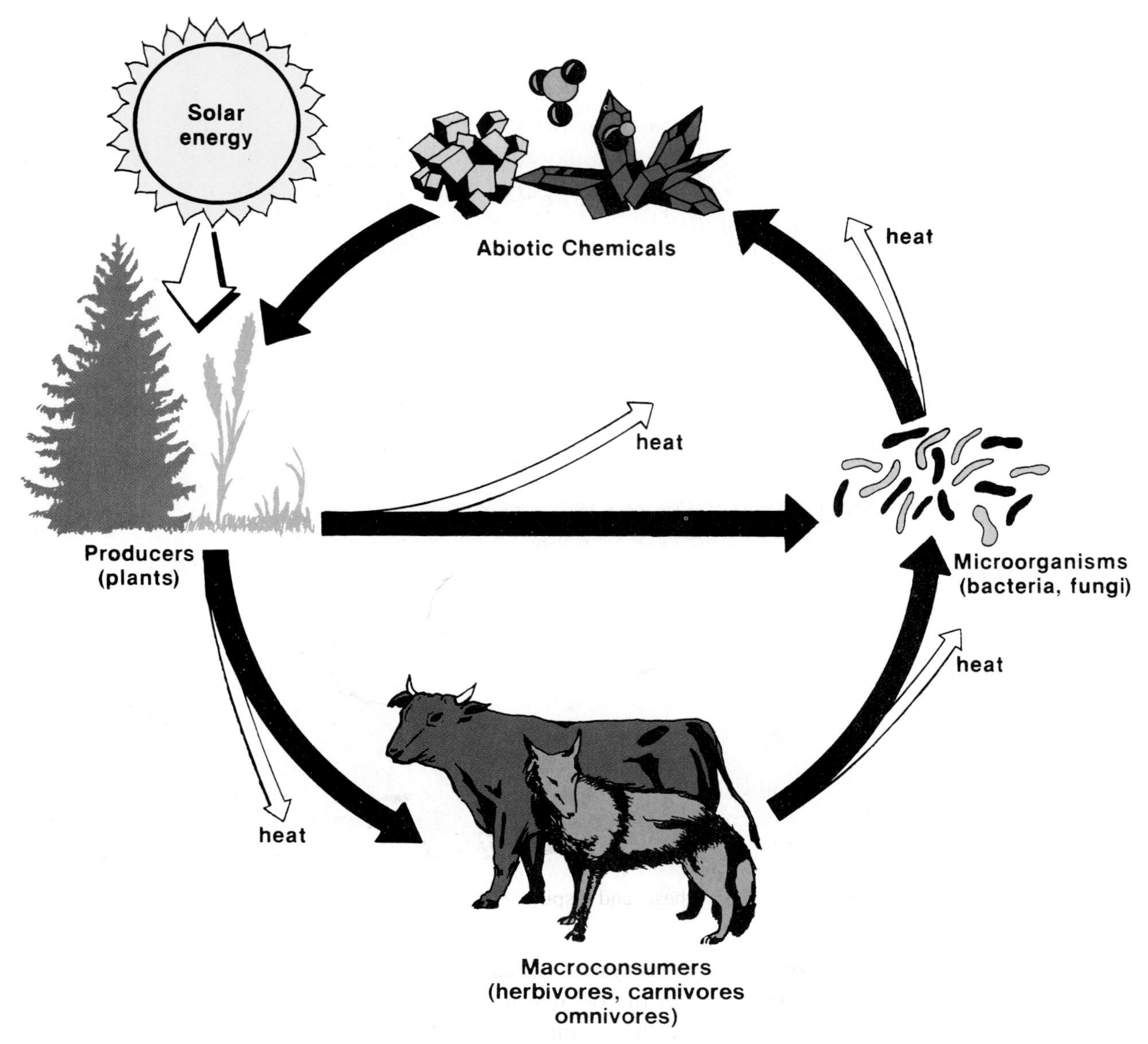

Figure 1.14 A summary of energy flow and matter recycling in ecosystems. Dark arrows indicate movement of matter. White arrows show energy flow.

Energy is passed from one organism to another through a food chain. Producers, green plants, transfer a certain portion of their energy to the herbivores or primary consumers such as rabbits or cows. They in turn pass on a portion of their energy to the carnivores, or secondary consumers. Each time energy is transferred, some is "lost" as heat. We say it is "lost" because it is not available for use by living things in moving about, growing, reproducing, or carrying on other life functions. But much of that heat is used by the organisms, especially the animals that must maintain a constant body temperature. Also, much energy is used at each step by the plant or animal for its own needs. Only about 10% of the energy it takes in is passed on to the next link in a food chain. (See Figure 1.14.)

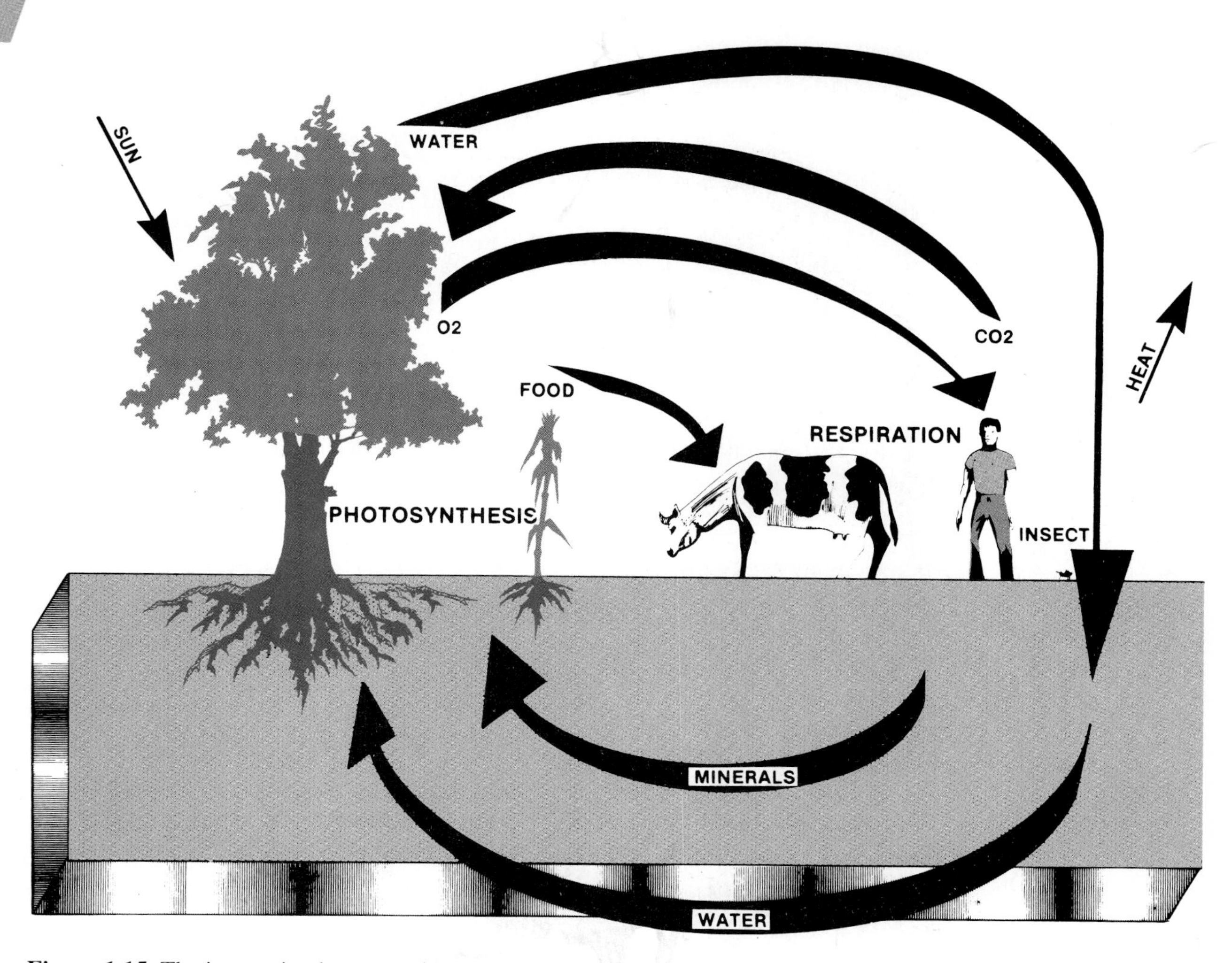

Figure 1.15 The interaction between photosynthesis and respiration.

Wastes do not accumulate greatly in an ecosystem because of the work of the decomposers. They break down the organic material in wastes and dead organisms. In this process, the decomposers obtain the energy they need for their life processes. The result of this decomposition is that minerals and water are released to the soil and carbon dioxide and other gases to the atmosphere. Because these materials are recycled, ecosystems are generally considered closed systems in terms of matter. These, in turn, become the raw matter for photosynthesis. The cycle repeats over and over. Death becomes life renewed.

How do decomposers function in an ecosystem?

In terms of matter, why is an ecosystem a closed system?

1.10 Ecological Succession

Although ecosystems are excellent units to study, they can be difficult to understand because they are continually undergoing change. This change, called **succession,** occurs in all ecosystems. Succession is the gradual replacement of one community with another. Succession occurs because each stage modifies the environment and prepares the way for the next stage. (See Figure 1.16.)

What is succession? Why does it occur?

Figure 1.16 Ecological succession. Over time, an area of bare soil may change until it can support a mature forest. Natural processes produce this change. (From Wildlife Management Institute.)

What is a climax community?

Succession is usually not obvious, unless a drastic event such as a forest fire eliminates a major area or community. After the fire, a gradual replacement of the vegetation occurs over a number of years. The first arrivals in this replacement usually consist of short-lived plants (annuals) which thrive over several years. This may be followed by the emergence of perennials (plants living longer than one year), shrubs and short-living trees.

The process culminates with a mature stage dominated by long-lived species. This stage is referred to as the **climax community.** A community may take many months, years, or hundreds of years to reach its mature state. This is because of differences in the length of growing season, climatic conditions, and nutrients and energy available.

The climax community remains relatively stable unless it is disturbed or the climate changes. The general pattern of succession is similar in all ecosystems, though the organisms differ. The sequence of stages follow an orderly pattern. Communities become more complex as succession progresses. Succession is summarized in Figure 1.16.

1.11 Stability in Ecosystems

?

Why are natural ecosystems stable?

If left to themselves, ecosystems can go on indefinitely (as long as the sun lasts). Nature does cause change, but this succession is usually gradual, orderly, and predictable. Occasionally a volcanic eruption or sudden change in climate changes ecosystems abruptly. Change caused by current human activity is also extensive and fast. We need to examine these changes in terms of their ecological impact.

Young communities, whether natural or artificial, tend to have large numbers of a few species. For example, when a farmer plants a corn field, (s)he works very hard to eliminate the weeds. By doing this, the farmer keeps the species composition simple by growing only corn. The corn field is called a **monoculture.** The farmer works very hard to keep succession from occurring and to keep out insects.

All the plants in a monoculture are members of the same species.

Most species in a new ecosystem have seemingly unlimited access to nutrients, and there are few consumers. For those reasons production is typically high, while diversity is low.

In nature, if plenty of food and nutrients are available, young populations tend to flourish and rapidly spread throughout the community. The community undergoes development and change, finally reaching the stable, climax system of plants and animals.

Figure 1.17 Ear rot of corn. (University of Illinois, College of Agriculture, Cooperative Extension Service)

Populations in climax communities are smaller, but there are many different kinds of species. This increased diversity leads to a complex system of food webs and food chains and tends to provide a degree of stability to the system that was not present in the young community. With more habitats, niches, and diversity of species, there is less chance that a small change in any one component of the ecosystem will adversely affect the total system. Even the loss of one species has relatively little effect.

What is diversity?

Why does it make an ecosystem more stable?

This is not true in the farmer's corn field. Should one organism, such as ear mold, attack the corn, the farmer may lose a large portion of the crop. That is the price a farmer may pay for the benefit of high production. Less diverse ecosystems are not as stable as more diverse ones. A diverse system conserves its nutrients, is resistant to pest and disease invasion, and can withstand a fairly wide range of climatic variation. This strength results from diversity. If one species is wiped out, there are many others to take its place.

What related problems come with a monoculture?

Monocultures, such as an orange grove or a wheat field, also must have their nutrients replaced by fertilizers (or, plants having nitrogen-fixing bacteria must be planted in alternate years to restore the soil). They lack resistance to pests and disease. Farmers usually protect them with chemical herbicides and pesticides. They are also threatened by unusual changes in weather (dry spells and cold snaps) and are likely to require artificial and expensive irrigation and shielding.

Nitrogen-fixing bacteria make nitrogen available for plant use.

Diversity is an important characteristic of all natural ecosystems. Community diversity is simply defined as the number of different kinds of living things.

What is meant by diversity?

If you constructed a fresh-water aquarium and added only a few kinds of organisms, such as a few water plants and a fish, the system would not be very diverse. You would have to feed the fish. Little change could occur.

Figure 1.18 A monoculture, such as this field of wheat, requires considerable human intervention to keep it healthy.

However, if you fill the aquarium with pond water, the ecosystem will be diverse. This is because the pond water has many different kinds of microscopic organisms, and may also include fish, snails, and water plants. A food chain, with its pathways for energy flow, is now present. There is food for each organism. They depend on each other. The ecosystem in the aquarium will change through time. The microscopic plants and animals will multiply. Within several weeks, your aquarium will reach a balance where each species is dependent upon the physical environment and other organisms for food. Organisms that die will be recycled as they decay and become food for others.

Why is diversity important?

Diversity is also important for human survival. It provides stability to ecosystems and helps to preserve nature. Many of the diverse items found in natural ecosystems are vital or useful to us. For example, quinine from the bark of a South American tree (cinchona tree) is used for treating malaria which is caused by mosquitoes. Some of the plants now endangered by human destruction of forests may provide other drugs we need.

1.12 Limiting Factors in an Ecosystem

What are limiting factors?

The **limiting factors** in an ecosystem restrict organisms in their productivity and survival. Organisms are clearly limited by their own physical and biological needs. A fish out of water will not survive. Humans cannot survive without adequate drinking water. For any organism, the requirement that is most deficient in an ecosystem is often the single element that determines the size and success of a particular plant or animal species.

When any limiting factor is below the critical minimum or exceeds the critical maximum for a population, the population's growth is slowed and usually halted. For example, the element phosphorus is needed in biological systems for building molecules that store energy.

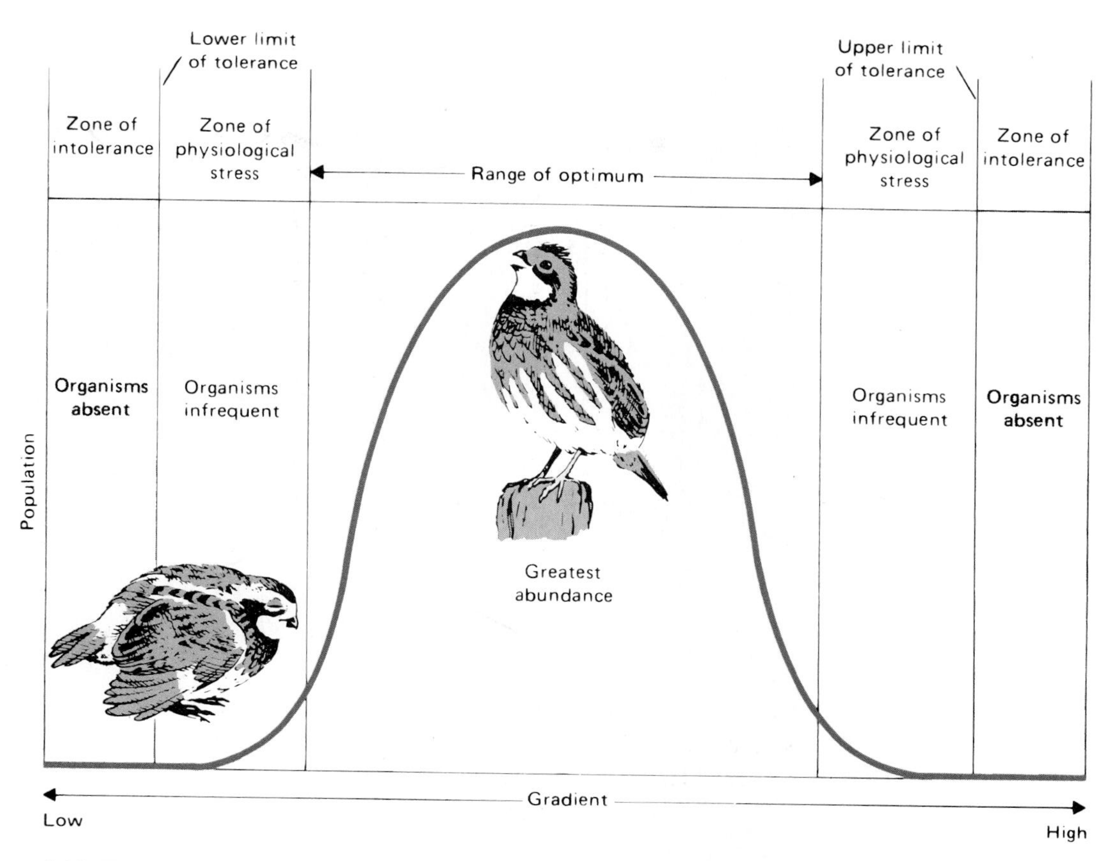

Figure 1.19 The law of tolerance. The success of an organism is limited by either too little or too much of a requirement. Organisms live within a range of abundance called the limits of tolerance. (From *Ecology and Field Biology* by Robert L. Smith. Copyright © 1980 by Robert Leo Smith. Reprinted by permission of Harper & Row, Publishers, Inc.)

Phosphorus is often present in only small amounts in otherwise adequate ecosystems. Hence, it is often a limiting factor. Iron is another element that is limiting to plant growth because many soils are iron deficient.

What is the law of tolerance?

Species tend to occur in an area relative to their ability to tolerate the habitat and its associated physical environment. For example, some species grow in shaded environments, but others must have full sunlight. (See Figure 1.19)

These limits of tolerance for different factors vary with species. The interrelationships often become very complicated. In a nitrogen-rich soil environment, a limited water source is not as critical for plant growth as in a nitrogen-poor soil environment. Cottonwood trees are usually found growing near streams or permanent water sources. However, they are usually not so close to the water source as their relatives, the willows. Willows may remain submerged for several weeks and survive. Cottonwoods cannot stand much more than a week or two of total submersion in water. Therefore, tolerance ranges are often used to describe a species' success in a particular environment.

Figure 1.20 The limitation and distribution of three tree species along a moisture gradient.

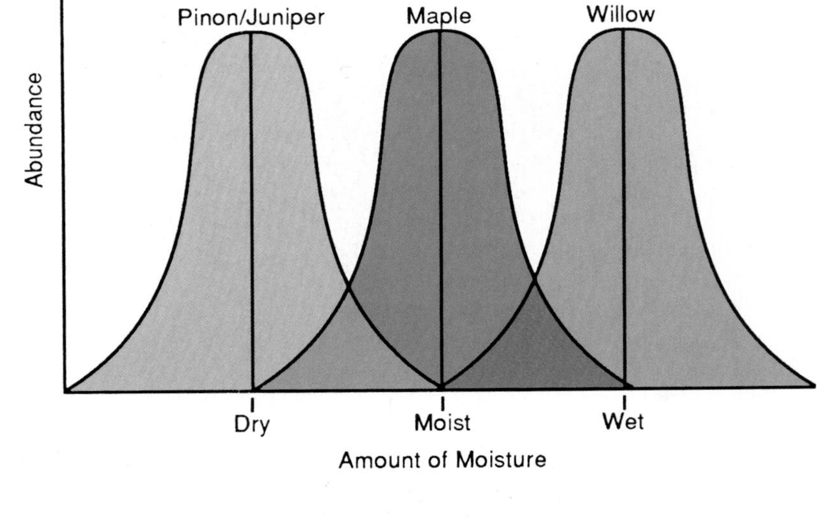

All species tend to show similar curves relative to particular environmental factors to which they have adapted. Figure 1.20 demonstrates the limitation and distribution of three species along a moisture gradient (gradual increase or decrease).

The human species has been able to manipulate limiting factors in a manner that has permitted population size and length of life to increase. Increased medical care, disease control, quality and quantity of food, and a health-conscious population all lead to longer life spans and more people. This, however, has brought about other problems that place great stress on our natural resources. Without population control, limiting factors will eventually become significant and limit the population.

What factors determine the make-up of an ecosystem?

What determines the combination of plant and animal types found in a particular ecosystem? Why is one area a desert, another a forest, and still another a grassland? The kind of ecosystem occurring in a particular place at a particular time is brought about by temperature, precipitation, surface features, and soil type. Figure 1.21 relates such abiotic variables to the type of ecosystem expected. Note that little moisture and high average temperatures result in a desert. How might human activity change this picture? Does Figure 1.21 suggest any of the difficulties that people are likely to encounter in projects like "farming the deserts"?

The law of limiting factors.

One important ecological principle may help answer that question. The factor that is most *deficient* in an ecosystem determines the presence (or absence) of any given plant or animal. (That is known as the **law of limiting factors.**) It is said that people can live without air for three minutes, without water for three days, and without food for three months. Whether or not those time estimates are accurate, the law of limiting factors is in effect. A human being can perish very quickly in an environment where water and food are abundant, but air is in short supply. Similarly, where air and food are plentiful but water is scarce, death is just as certain. In this case, water (not air) is the limiting factor.

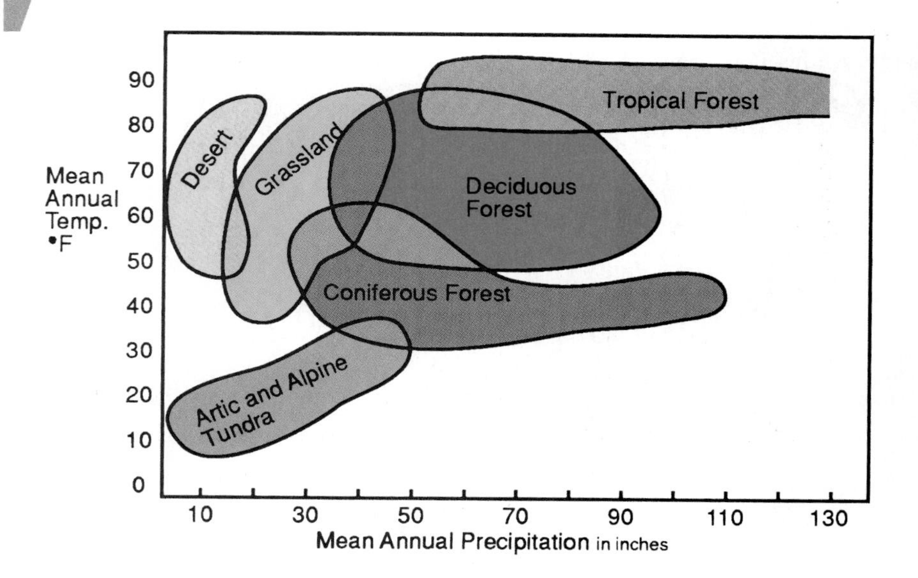

Figure 1.21 The influence of temperature and precipitation on biome types.

Geography and Life

What are biomes? Why are there different biomes on Earth?

Huge **terrestrial** (land) ecosystems that have similar climate, plants, animals, and soil type are called **biomes.** Examples are forests, deserts, grasslands, woodlands, and tundra. The terrestrial portion of the biosphere is divided into a series of biomes, as shown in Figure 1.22. From this figure we see the biomes span entire continents with many of their division lines roughly parallel to latitude lines. The same biome tends to occur in the same latitudinal range. All of the biomes occur in both the northern and southern hemisphere with the exception of Arctic tundra, which is rare in the southern hemisphere. (There is little land at that latitude in the southern hemisphere.) Terrestrial biomes are identified by either the major plants that dominate the landscape or the climate of the area.

Why do aquatic ecosystems differ?

The term "biome" refers only to ecosystems on land. However, a similar division can be used for aquatic ecosystems. The major division is into freshwater and marine. Marine life zones are often classified as open ocean, coral reefs, and estuaries. Major differences between them are the result of the concentration and type of dissolved nutrients. This is related to salt content of the water, water temperature, depth of sunlight penetration, and closeness to land areas and freshwater discharges.

1.13 Terrestrial Ecosystems (Biomes)

Biomes are usually separated by temperature (radiation) and moisture gradients. For example, a moisture gradient is illustrated by traveling from the southeastern United States to the Southwest. This trip can take one from a rainy, humid environment (the eastern deciduous forest biome of South Carolina) to a very dry biome (the desert of the Southwest). Or, someone who traveled from the hot biome of southern

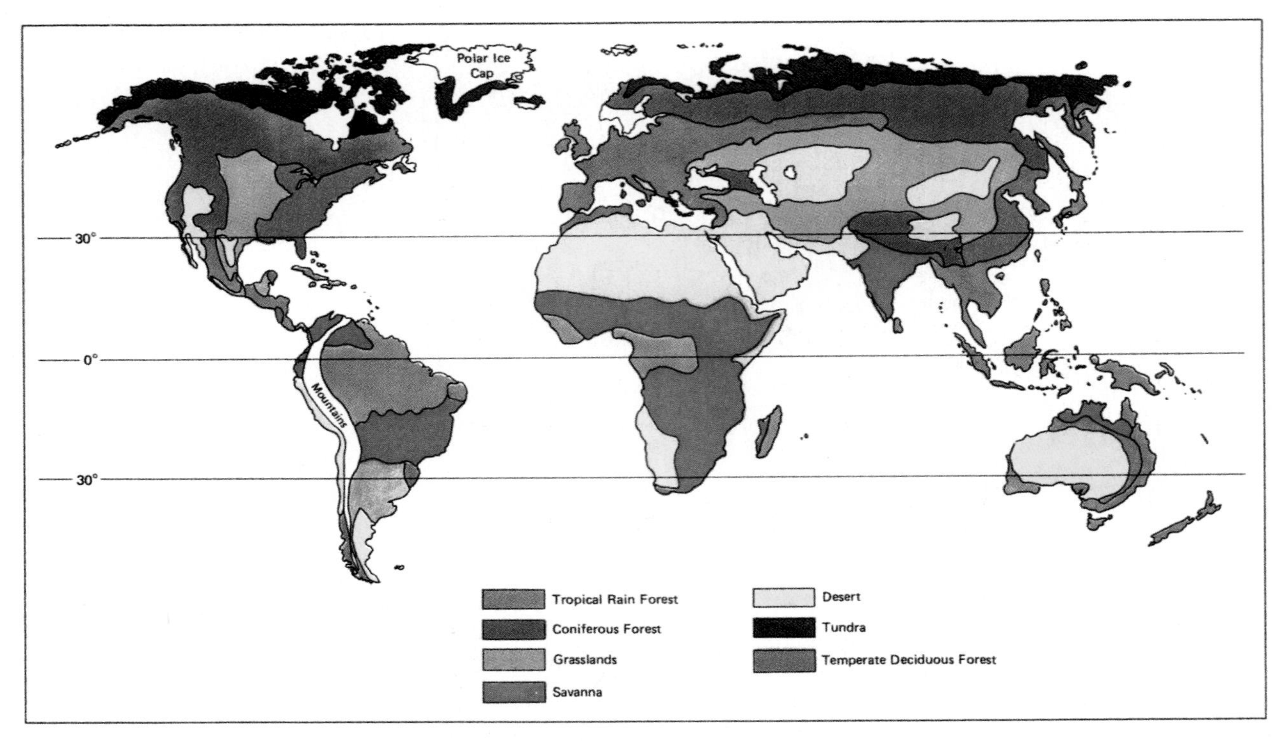

Figure 1.22 The vegetative biomes of the world. (Reproduced by permission from D. K. Northington and J. R. Goodin, *The Botanical World, St. Louis, © 1984, The C. V. Mosby Co.)*

Florida to the cold Arctic Circle would pass through the eastern deciduous forest, the northern coniferous forest, and into the tundra. This represents a temperature (radiation) gradient.

a. Tundra

Arctic tundra.

The region north of the tree line and south of the Arctic Circle is known as the **arctic tundra.** This area is unique in that the angle of the sun is low for much of the year. This results in long nights during the winter and increases to nearly 24 hours per day of daylight during a short summer. The few plant species must survive a cold, severe climate. The growing season in the arctic tundra is often less than 60 days. This does not allow trees the time required to store food until the next growing season. For this reason, only dwarfed trees are seen here.

Why are trees unable to grow in the tundra?

Precipitation rarely exceeds 10 inches (25 centimeters) a year. Low temperatures freeze the soil permanently as deeply as 100 to 1,500 feet. Only a top layer 2-14 feet thaws during the summer. The frozen soil beneath, called permafrost, does not allow root or water penetration. Consequently, water collects on the surface and forms many lakes. This further reduces the chance for tree growth. Tundra does not have the structured vegetation that other biomes do. Habitats and niches are restricted. Hence, tundra is the least complex of all the biomes. Most of the plants are dwarfed and occur in marshy plains.

Figure 1.23 Arctic tundra. (Will Troyer/Visuals Unlimited)

Figure 1.24 Alpine tundra. (Photo by Ivo Lindauer.)

Mosses and willows are common. Many of the animals are large, such as caribou. Having small surface area in proportion to their body mass ratio helps them conserve body heat.

Alpine tundra.

At lower latitudes, **alpine tundra** also occurs on the mountain tops and in high mountain valleys above the timber line. Alpine tundra is common throughout the high mountains of the North American continent. At a higher altitude, the colder air produces conditions much like those at a higher latitude.

b. Northern Coniferous Forests

Northern coniferous forests.

South of the tundra (or levels lower than alpine tundra) lies the northern coniferous forest. This is often called the **taiga** or **boreal forest.** The taiga also stretches across to Europe and Asia. The climate of this region is less severe than the tundra. However, it remains cool to cold

Figure 1.25 Northern coniferous forest (taiga).

with more precipitation and a longer growing season. The coniferous, needle-leaved trees that conserve moisture, such as spruces, pines, and firs, dominate this biome. Aspen and birch also are common, especially where disturbances have occurred and succession is in progress. Because much of the northern United States was covered by sheet glaciers during the Ice Age, it contains many bogs and lakes. The area is dominated by black spruce, white spruce, hemlock, several different pine species, tamarack, and alder thickets (Figure 1.25). Most of these are evergreens. Soils of this region tend to have deep litter layers, are acidic, and are usually mineral deficient. The dense forests that grow on these soils allow little light to pass through. Little vegetation, other than moss and fern, grows on the shady forest floor.

This biome is a haven for large mammals including deer, elk, moose, bear, wolverine, marten, lynx, fox, and wolf. Smaller mammals such as weasels, snowshoe hares, moles, chipmunks, shrews and bats, a variety of birds including juncos, jays, warblers and nuthatches thrive in this biome. Much of the original forest was harvested by logging in the late 1800s and early 1900s. The trees were converted to useful and necessary things such as houses, wagons, and ships, or were used for fuel. Today, the use and management of forests is more important than ever because of the diminished supply and slow growth rate.

c. Deciduous Forest

What are deciduous trees?

Much of the eastern half of the United States is dominated by the temperate deciduous forest biome (Figure 1.26). As the name suggests, the temperature of this biome is moderate. Its climate is characterized by humid, warm summers and cold winters. Abundant moisture is evenly distributed throughout the year. Annual rainfall averages from 75 to 150 centimeters. The forests are dominated by broadleaf

Figure 1.26 Temperate deciduous forest. (Carl Bollwinkel)

deciduous trees which lose their leaves each year. The soil is rich, with much accumulation of litter (such as fallen leaves). There is little fluctuation among the stable populations of this forest. The dry uplands are dominated by oak and hickory. Maple, basswood, and beech take over habitats that are moist. Cottonwood, willow, elm, and sycamore thrive in stream and river habitats.

The eastern deciduous forest provides a lush habitat for many different organisms. White-tailed deer, red deer, and skunk are common, as are squirrels. Although present, Black bears are rarely found. Many bird species, such as woodpeckers, vireos, flycatchers, and ravens, also live there. Insects, which are very diverse and common, provide an extensive food source for the birds.

Clearing the lands for farming, cutting the hard wood for lumber and building towns and cities have greatly reduced the extent of this biome. Little of the original forest exists today.

d. Grasslands

Why aren't trees common on grasslands?

Grasslands, which are often called prairies, occur where precipitation is too sparse to support tree growth but does not fall below 10 inches (25 centimeters) per year (Figure 1.27). In the United States precipitation ranges from 20 in. (50 cm.) per year on the eastern edge to 10 in. (25 cm.) per year on the western and southern edges.

Grassland regions are usually found in the interiors of continents such as the great plains of North America, the pampas of South America, the steppes of Russia and Asia, and in isolated spots of Europe. They occur in both temperate and tropical climates.

Grasslands are thought to have covered nearly half of the land area of the world at one time. Most of the grasslands today are now farmlands and are frequently referred to as "the breadbaskets of the world." Typically, the fertile soils of these lands produce the wheat

Patrick Balch

Figure 1.27 Pronghorn in the Thunder Basin National Grassland in Wyoming. (USDA Forest Service.)

and corn we use for flour and breakfast cereals. The North American grassland supported great herds of bison which, for the most part, have been replaced by cattle and sheep. Other animals include antelope, coyotes, foxes, badgers, prairie dogs, ground squirrels, rattlesnakes, and spadefoot toads. Meadowlarks and prairie chickens are very common. They have little impact on the large populations of insects that occupy this ecosystem. The major herbivores and consumers of the grasslands are the insects, which consume thousands of tons of plant material each year. These include grasshoppers, locusts, and aphids. The herds of wild grazing animals and today's grazing livestock seem to have little effect on the grasses which developed under grazing pressure over several million years.

e. Deserts

What special adaptations do desert plants have?

Generally, regions that receive less than 10 inches (25 centimeters) of precipitation annually are identified as deserts. However, rate of water loss is even more important. Desert vegetation varies considerably, but much of it consists of shrubs having a variety of special adaptations for conserving water. Many annual plants are found in the desert. Annuals can complete most of their life cycle when there is moisture, and then survive the drought in seed form. Their seeds are resistant to moisture loss. There is a great variety of plants because of a great variety of desert conditions. In Death Valley, found in California's Mojave Desert, the precipitation is often below 2 in. (5 cm.) per year. The lush woodlands of the Sonoran Desert in Arizona receive nearly 20 in. (50 cm.) of precipitation each year during the two rainy seasons, but dry out greatly during the dry seasons.

Deserts occupy about one-seventh of Earth's land surface. The largest desert is the Sahara Desert in Africa. It covers more than 3,000,000 square miles. Drought, overgrazing by livestock and woodcutting for fuel are increasing the size of the Sahara. The next largest is the Gobi Desert (in Mongolia and China) which covers 500,000 square miles.

Man has had less impact on the deserts of the world than on other ecosystems. However, the expansion of irrigation projects and

Figure 1.28 Plants of the hot desert. (From Smith-Southwestern, Inc. Tempe, Arizona.)

Figure 1.29 Animals of the hot desert. (From Smith-Southwestern, Inc. Tempe, Arizona.)

increase in human population, along with city growth, windfarms, livestock grazing, off-road-vehicles, backpacking, hiking, camping and other recreational activities, have a severe effect on these regions. The ecosystems of deserts are easily damaged.

f. Tropical Forests

Why are rain forests so valuable to us?

In areas of the world where there is no freezing and moisture is plentiful, a lush tropical growth is present. The tropical regions occur near the equator. These forests contain the greatest diversity, both plant and animal, of any ecosystem on Earth. They contain thousands of different tree species (compared with less than one hundred in other types of forests). Soils of these forests are typically thin and poor. The few nutrients resulting from decomposition are quickly taken up by plants. Where the trees are burned or otherwise eliminated, the nutrients are washed away with the heavy rain runoff.

Figure 1.30 Lowland tropical rain forest in Costa Rica. (Robert L. Sanford, Jr.)

The largest rain forests occur in the Amazon Basin of South America, where average tree height exceeds 100 feet. These forests serve as major reservoirs for the production of atmospheric oxygen and the consumption of carbon dioxide. Today, they are seriously threatened by the expansion of human populations into the forest. Large expanses are being cleared for farming and grazing. Some are being cut for lumber.

Tropical seasonal forests are found where a dry season occurs. Most of the trees in these forests are deciduous and semi-deciduous. They lose their leaves during the dry season. This forest type may be found on the Pacific side of Mexico and Central America.

g. Shrublands

Shrublands.

Much of the arid and semi-arid lands of the world are covered by shrubby vegetation. The climate of these regions is often described as having hot, dry summers and cool to cold, wet winters. These major land ecosystems are found in temperate as well as semi-tropical regions. The "chaparral" ecosystem, for example, is found best developed along the California coast. The dense stands of shrubs growing there have hard, thick waxy leaves that are drought resistant. These stands are frequently subject to fire, which aids in the maintenance of the ecosystem.

Figure 1.31 Chaparral.
(R. F. Ashley/Visuals Unlimited)

1.14 Aquatic Ecosystems

How do the three major aquatic ecosystems differ?

Aquatic ecosystems cover more than 70% of the Earth's surface and consist of a vast storehouse of energy, nutrients and living organisms. Aquatic ecosystems of the world may be divided into inland waters and oceans. Ecologists often separate them into three major groups (freshwater, marine and estuary) which are identified on the basis of differences in salt content. **Marine** waters are salty, and estuaries contain a mixture of fresh water and oceanic salt water.

a. Freshwater

Freshwaters are those inland waters that have very little or no soluble salts. They may be described as either flowing or standing waters. Standing waters may be puddles, ponds, or lakes. Flowing waters are divided into springs, brooks, streams, and rivers.

Springs and brooks.

Small flowing springs are usually cool and contain much dissolved oxygen. They give rise to brooks, which often contain leaves and other decaying material but little plankton. Many insects seek this habitat to carry out reproduction and early development. Predators such as small fish and trout do well in these small flowing waters.

Plankton: microscopic floating plant and animal organisms of lakes, rivers, and oceans.

Phytoplankton: free-floating, mostly microscopic, aquatic plants.

Brooks come together to form streams that are larger and slower and provide better habitat for plankton. Food chains originating from the phytoplankton support a much larger and a more diverse population of organisms. These populations increase and become more complex as streams form small rivers (creeks) that become larger rivers and provide the ultimate habitat in flowing water. Rivers are erosional and carry a great deal of sediment consisting of undecomposed organic matter, clay, silt, sand, and gravel. The sediments are deposited along the banks and at the mouth of the river. These deposits become the very fertile soils that make up some of the best agricultural lands of the world.

Standing waters.

Standing waters (puddles, ponds, bogs, and lakes) all have one thing in common. Their water is contained. The water may vary from little salt content, such as in the Great Lakes, to a large salt content,

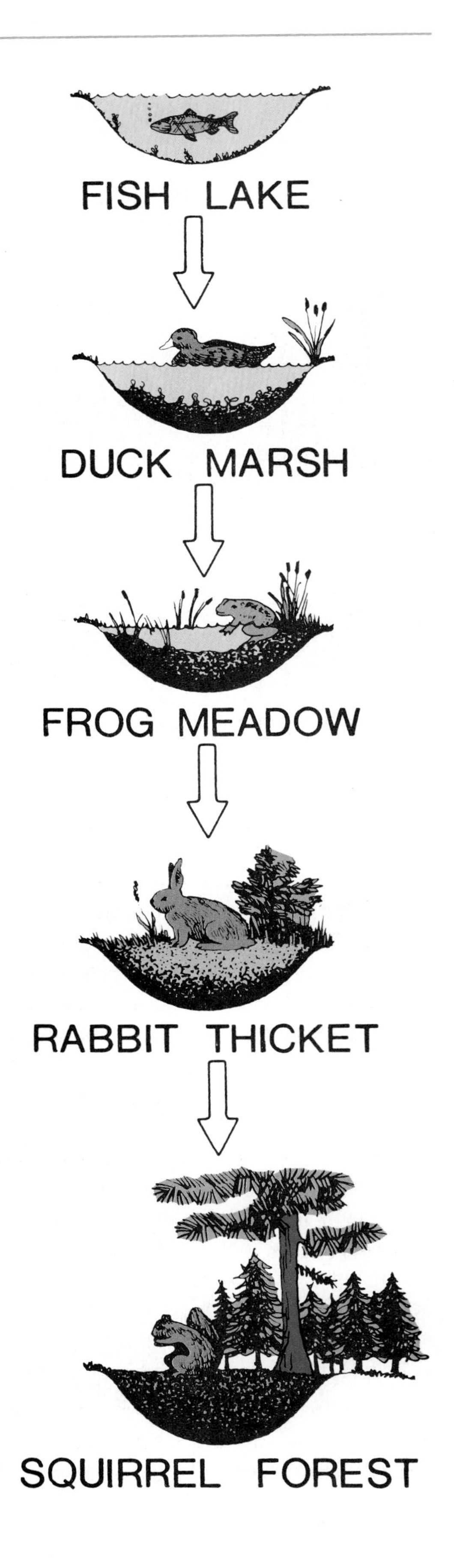

Figure 1.32 The ecological succession of a freshwater lake. As landscapes change through ecological succession, new habitats develop. (From Wildlife Management Institute.)

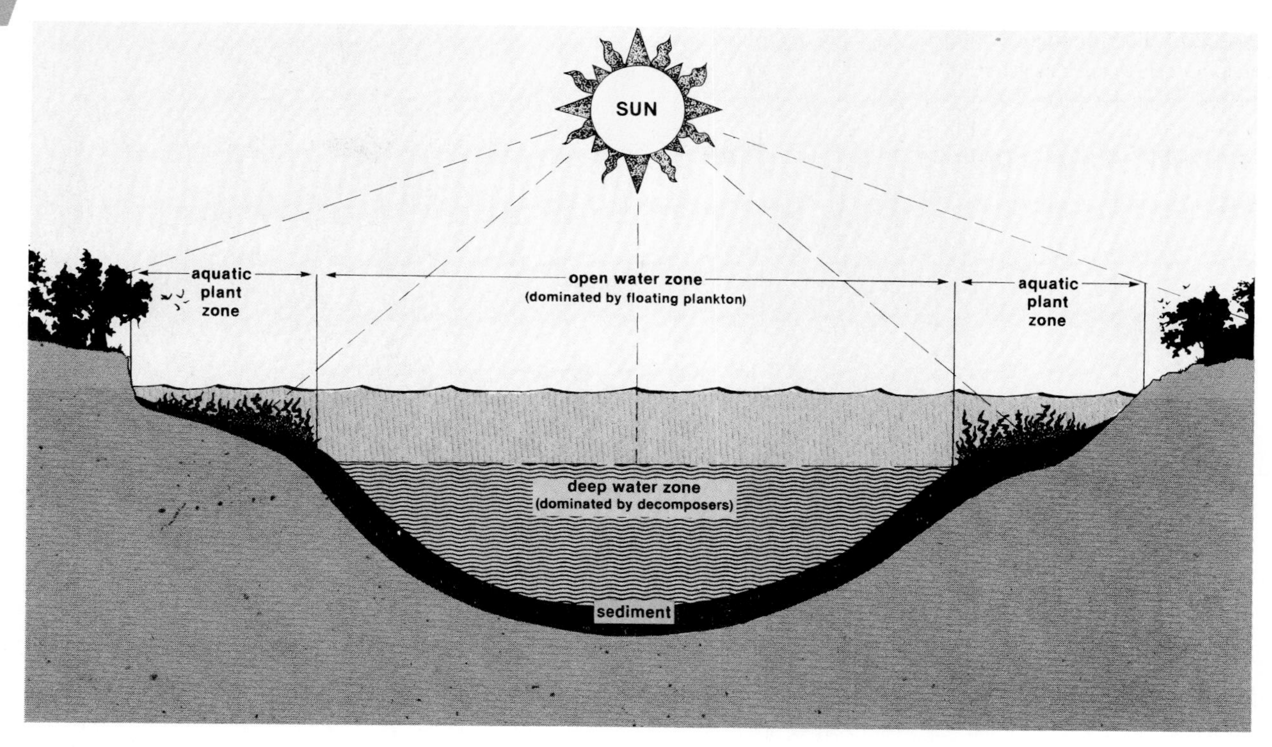

Figure 1.33 The three zones of life in a freshwater lake.

such as that of the Great Salt Lake in Utah. All standing waters are temporary in the sense that some day they will become filled with sediments and provide the basis for a forest or grassland. This process of succession occurs at various rates but is normally accelerated in warmer climates with longer growing seasons.

Sketch a cross-section of a lake and label the three zones.

Ponds tend to be shallow and often less than one acre in size. Light penetrates to the bottom providing the energy for photosynthesis. Lakes are deeper than ponds, and much larger.

Swamps.

Swamps and bogs are shallow, wet, land areas that contain trees and shrubs growing in their midst. They tend to contain considerable organic matter in various states of decomposition. Since bogs and swamps are shallow, much photosynthesis can occur, and healthy producer populations are established. They provide the food for many organisms. Swamps and marshes are frequently the breeding and rearing habitats for many insects, birds, amphibians, reptiles, shrimp, and other crustaceans.

b. Marine Waters

Oceans.

All oceans of the earth are connected and are described as one large ecosystem. The oceans absorb a great deal of solar energy during warm seasons and release this energy slowly during the cold seasons. This provides a stabilizing effect on the Earth's climate. The dissolved salts and minerals of the ocean increase with depth and nearness to the

Figure 1.34 Life in a freshwater stream. (Monte Dolack Graphics)

Figure 1.35 Diatoms. (Kenneth L. Weik)

equator. Next to the shoreline and near the mouths of rivers, ocean salinity is less. Here, tides and wave action circulate the nutrients from the shallow water and provide a more fertile habitat.

Oceans have zones similar to those of lakes. These zones are more complex since the oceans are so deep. Most productivity occurs along the continental shelf, the shorelines, and in the estuaries where nutrients are plentiful.

The open ocean is often described as a desert. However, a considerable amount of photosynthesis occurs near the surface. Because the oceans are so vast, they are the major photosynthetic ecosystem of the world. Small phytoplankton, diatoms, are responsible for much of this production.

Figure 1.36 Tidal salt marsh in southern Florida. (Harold Hungerford)

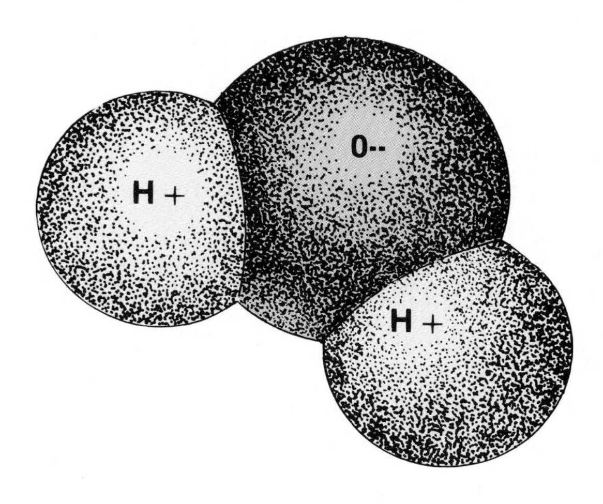

Figure 1.37 A model of a water (H_2O) molecule.

c. Estuaries

What are estuaries?

Estuaries are transitional zones between fresh water and the open ocean. They often occur in bays or coves, sheltered from direct wind and oceans waves. They contain seawater that is diluted by the fresh-water inflow and mixed by the tides, which serve to remove waste and nutrients. These regions are extremely productive compared to other natural ecosystems and provide a nursery for many sea animals. Figure 1.36 shows a typical estuary.

Water For Life

Both oceanic zones and land biomes are characterized by the amount of sunlight and the amount of water they receive. The various combinations of solar energy and water, in turn, determine the number and kinds of plants that can grow there. In the pages that follow, you will be introduced to the unique properties of water that make it so important to the biosphere.

Water's special qualities come from the unique shape of the water molecule (Figure 1.37). Each molecule contains two atoms of hydrogen and one atom of oxygen. Because they are arranged as shown, one side of the molecule has a positive charge, and the other side has a negative charge. If two such molecules come together, the positive side of one is attracted to the negative side of the other. So, water molecules cling together. That accounts for the high boiling point, surface tension, and other characteristics that make water important in the biosphere.

1.15 The Wonder of Water

?

What properties of water enable it to support life on Earth?

a. Abundance and Structure

From space, Earth is seen as the "blue planet." The blue color is caused by the vast amount of water. Oceans cover 71% of the globe, and water is also found in lakes, rivers, streams, in soils, and in underground reservoirs. Some water remains frozen as ice caps and glaciers, and some is found in the atmosphere as water vapor. Water is the most abundant compound in all living organisms. Without water there would be no life.

b. Physical States

The three physical states of water.

Picture a winter day with snow on the ground and air temperatures slightly above freezing. As snow, water is frozen in the form of ice crystals. Ice also forms a solid layer on top of the pond. Liquid water is in the pond below the ice and in the snow as water percolating through the melting snow. Water also exists as a gas in the form of water vapor, both within the snow and in the air above the snow. Thus, water exists in three different physical states as a solid, a liquid, and a gas at normal climatic temperatures, and all three forms of water can be present at the same time (Figure 1.38). Even though water exists in all three forms 80% of all water on our planet is liquid.

Ice.

Ice is the only substance in the world that expands when it freezes. This is inconvenient to a car owner whose radiator freezes and cracks. However, if water did not expand when it freezes, ice would not float on water, and the world would become a gigantic ice ball. Lakes would freeze from the bottom up, and icebergs would sink to the bottom of oceans where they could not melt. Each winter would add more layers of ice until even the oceans would freeze.

The form or physical state of water depends upon the speed of motion of its molecules. Molecular speed is tied to temperature. In the solid state, water molecules are relatively quiet with little energy. Ice crystals have geometric, six-sided shapes, like snow flakes. When molecules are activated by heat, water becomes a liquid. The molecules are close together, yet slip around freely, giving liquid water its flowing motion. At high temperatures, molecules move about violently, spreading out to form water vapor, an invisible gas (Figure 1.39).

Figure 1.38 The three physical states of water can be present at the same time. Identify locations of the three states of water in the photograph of Arctic icebergs. Water vapor cannot be seen, but its location can be determined. (Konrad Steffen)

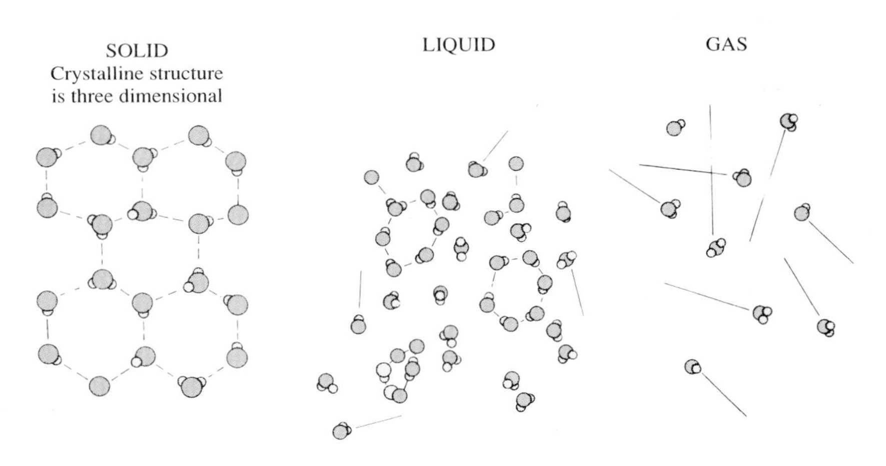

Figure 1.39 Bonds between water molecules in their three different physical states. Water molecules move about violently at high temperature. (From *Marine Biology* by H. V. Thurman and H. H. Webber, copyright © 1984 by Scott, Foresman and Company. Reprinted by permission.)

c. Heat Capacity

What is heat capacity?

Water has an extremely high heat capacity. Heat capacity is the ability of a substance to absorb a great deal of heat without itself becoming extremely hot. For example, an empty pan heated on a stove quickly becomes red hot. But, if a pan of water is heated, the pan becomes hot but not red-hot, and the temperature of the water rises only a few degrees.

Figure 1.40 Sphere-shaped drops of water cling to a blade of grass. (Dick Thomas/Visuals Unlimited)

Water absorbs five times as much heat per gram as rock for a given change in temperature. Because of water's high heat capacity, oceans act as huge reservoirs of solar warmth. Oceans moderate climates of nearby land masses, first by absorbing and then slowly giving off heat. For example, Florida and the Sahara Desert are at the same latitude and receive a comparable amount of sunlight. However, Florida surrounded by water has a moist, balmy climate, but the Sahara gets blistering hot during the day and cold at night.

How does water's heat capacity help moderate climate?

In addition to water's ability to carry and store heat, water requires a large amount of heat to change its physical state. Heat is necessary to melt ice, and even more heat is needed to change water from liquid to water vapor. A block of ice in a closed chest cools food because heat from the food is absorbed by the ice. As ice absorbs heat it melts, using the absorbed heat energy to break bonds holding the ice crystals together.

This same principle works in climate control. When hot, dry air passes over water, the water absorbs heat from the air. The air is cooled and the water is warmed. If the water is warmed enough to evaporate, it is converted to vapor. The water absorbs much heat because energy is required to break bonds between water molecules before gaseous vapor can move rapidly and expand.

The high heat capacity and the large amount of heat required to change water from one physical state to another are important in world climate and in the water cycle.

d. Surface Tension

If you watch a drop of water fall from a spout, you notice it clings to the tap, stretches very thinly, then finally lets go. Immediately it forms a sphere-shaped drop (Figure 1.40). Likewise, raindrops form droplets of water rather than a small stream of water. This ability of water molecules to stick together is called **surface tension.**

What is surface tension?

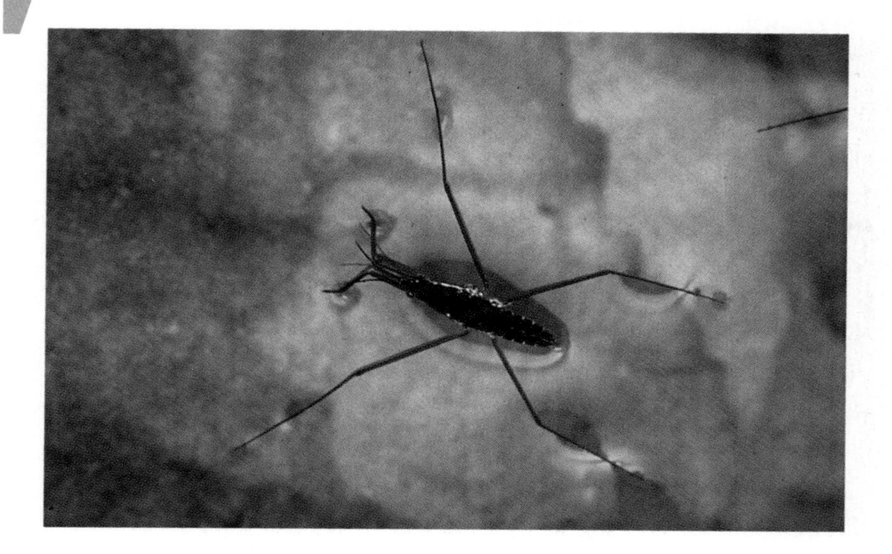

Figure 1.41 This water strider utilizes water's surface tension to run across the surface of a pond. (P. Starborn/Visuals Unlimited)

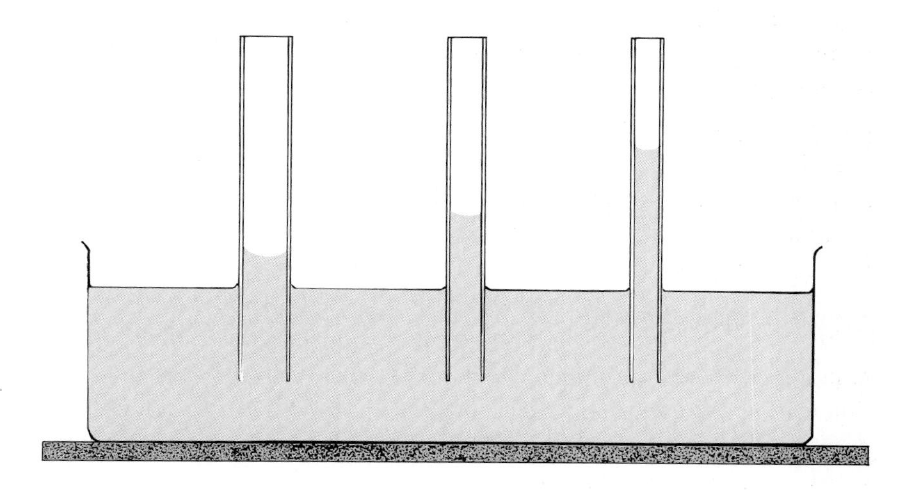

Figure 1.42 A demonstration of capillarity. When water is placed in the device shown, it rises higher in the narrowest tube than it does in the wider tubes.

Because water has a high surface tension, water forms a "skin" upon which materials that are actually more dense than water can float. Surface tension makes it possible for some insects to run around on the surface of water (Figure 1.41).

The attraction between positive and negative sides of water molecules not only causes surface tension, but also causes water to adhere to other surfaces, wetting them. The wetting ability of water is important in the movement of water upward through small cracks in soil and through small tubes in plant roots and stems. Water's movement through hair-width tubes is called **capillarity.** A good example of capillarity is observed when one end of a piece of paper toweling is dipped in water. The towel quickly absorbs water and becomes wet all over because water travels up the small fibers within the towel.

What is capillarity?

e. Water as a Solvent

Water seldom exists in its pure form. Pure water is a clean, colorless, tasteless, odorless liquid. Most tap water is not pure but contains

Why is water an excellent solvent?

Water transports nutrients through the tissues of living organisms.

How does water clean itself?

dissolved materials, and often has a distinct odor and taste. Distilled water is water from which all dissolved substances have been removed. Thus distilled water is pure water. It has no taste, and people often describe this lack of taste as "flat."

Because its molecules have positive and negative "poles," water easily dissolves many substances. Water is the nearest thing to a universal solvent. The water in lakes, rivers, and oceans is really a weak solution of various substances dissolved in water. Given enough time, water can and does dissolve nearly everything.

Each drop of rain is an independent sphere, like a tiny bullet that can break away tiny fragments of hard soil and even some rocks. As rain strikes the Earth, accumulates, and becomes a flowing liquid, it surrounds and moves fine particles of soil. Water carries the soil particles into streams and rivers to flood plains, deltas, and the sea.

Nutrients are carried through tissues of plants and animals in a watery solution. Life activities take place in a watery medium. We need to drink water to stay alive, yet our bodies become dehydrated if we drink sea water. As the Ancient Mariner said woefully, "Water, water everywhere, nor any drop to drink."

Even though water dissolves many substances, its molecules are not chemically changed by the dissolved materials. When water vaporizes, it sheds its impurities. If this did not occur, water could be made permanently dirty, and life as we know it would be impossible. Because of its power as a solvent and its ability to clean itself, water is important in all of our lives.

?

How is water recycled in the biosphere?

1.16 The Water Cycle

Water used by plants, animals, and people is never destroyed; it is used and reused by living and nonliving forms. Most of the precipitation falling on land is eventually carried to the sea. From land and sea surfaces, water evaporates to the atmosphere. There it circulates and forms clouds. Plants and animals also give off water as a vapor. Water falls back to Earth as rain, snow or sleet and the water cycle is complete.

The water cycle or **hydrologic** cycle is the Earth's vast natural plumbing system. Because of water's heat capacity, the hydrologic cycle is also a heat exchange system powered by the sun.

a. Precipitation

Precipitation, in the form of rain or snow, is the source of water in the hydrologic cycle. All precipitation starts as atmospheric water vapor. Water vapor cools as it rises. Finally, as molecules lose enough heat, they condense as liquid water droplets or freeze, forming minute ice crystals. For water vapor to condense or freeze, cool temperatures are needed. The water droplets or snow crystals form around minute dust particles or ice crystals. As microscopic particles of frozen and liquid water become large enough to be seen, they form clouds. Droplets and ice crystals combine into large water drops or snowflakes. Finally, they become so heavy that they fall as rain, snow, or sleet.

b. Groundwater

During a rainstorm, water is absorbed by the soil in a process called infiltration. As soil becomes wet during a rainstorm, the rate of infiltration decreases. How far water sinks into the ground depends on the surface vegetation, the soil development, and the types of rock beneath the soil (Figure 1.43).

Describe infiltration.

Water in the underground part of the hydrologic cycle is known as **groundwater.** Groundwater is water in cracks and rocks, and in spaces between pieces of gravel and grains of sand. Water moves through pores, holes, and cracks in the soil to the rock from which soil is derived. Seams and minute spaces between particles of weathered rock become fewer and fewer as depth increases. Finally these openings are so few or so small that movement of water becomes impossible.

Some rocks have a great number of natural pores and spaces making for permeability (allowing water to seep to a great depth). For example, pores between grains of sand in sandstone permit movement of water, as do buried gravel layers. Such an underground water-soaked area is called an **aquifer.** An aquifer may be an underground zone of gravel or sand, a layer of sandstone, or a zone of highly shattered or cracked rock. Beneath an aquifer is a zone of impermeable and watertight rock. Aquifers are natural underground reservoirs for water. Many areas depend upon aquifers as a major source of domestic and agricultural water.

What is an aquifer?

Unlike the water in lakes or reservoirs built by man, aquifer groundwater is not freeflowing. When water enters an aquifer, its route back to the ocean may be delayed for thousands of years.

The top level of water in an aquifer is called the **water table.** Water seeping down from the rain-soaked surface will sink to the water table but no further. It collects above the impermeable layer, filling all the pores and cracks of the permeable portions until it overflows into streams. The water table in an area may rise during the spring when there is more water seeping into the ground than is being used, and fall in summer when more water is being used than is being added.

Define water table.

c. Runoff

Not all water from a rainstorm infiltrates the soil. Some runs off the ground surface into streams, lakes, and reservoirs. It is called runoff. The flowing water in streams and rivers, and water stored in natural lakes, wetlands, and reservoirs, is called **surface water.** Precipitation on land eventually flows back to the ocean as runoff. In this way the land returns water carried to it by clouds that drifted in from the ocean. Water also is discharged from underground water, but surface runoff occurs at a much faster rate.

What is surface water?

d. Evaporation

Following a rainstorm, puddles dry up, water droplets on sidewalks and plants dry up, and the soil surface also dries. Water absorbs heat

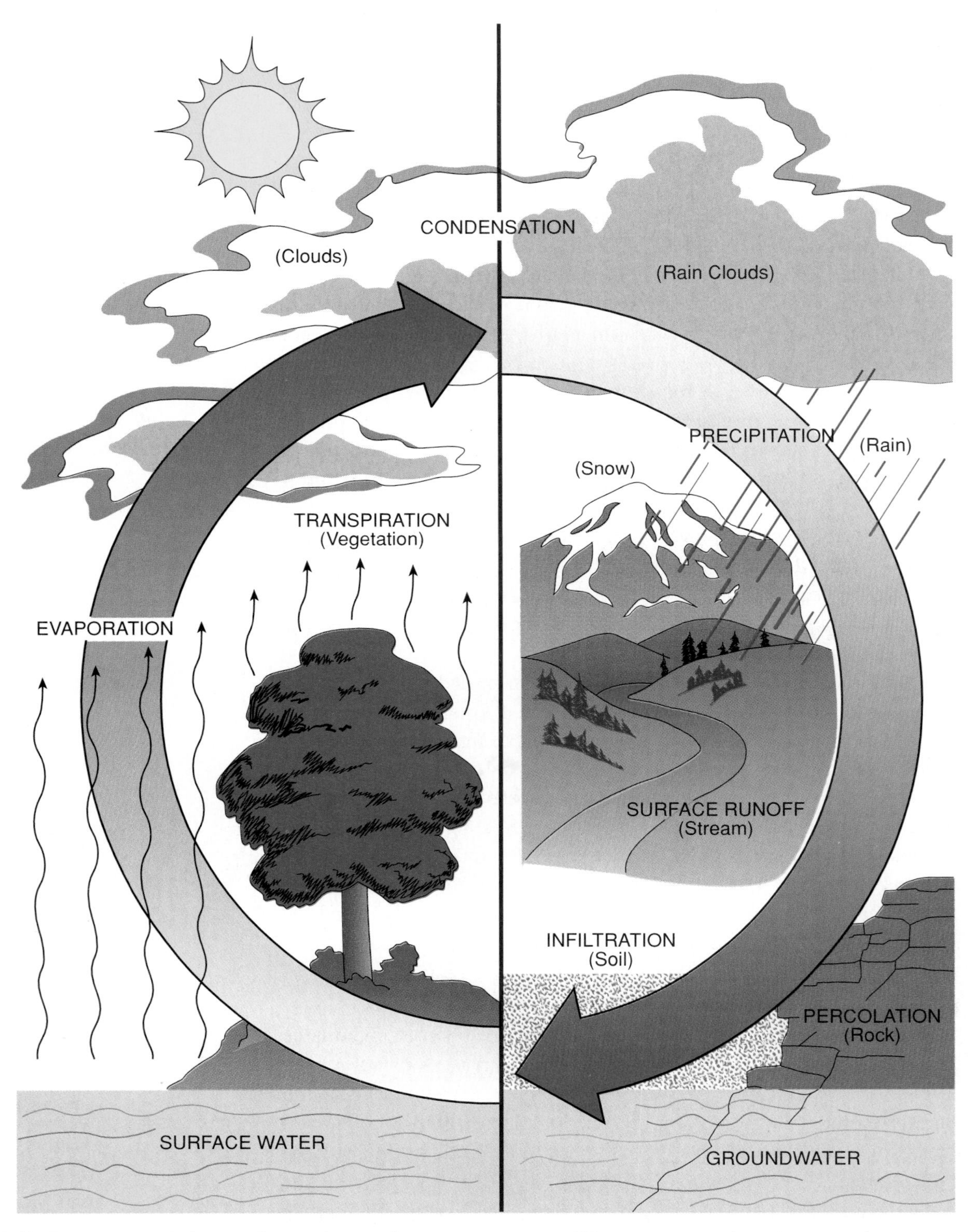

Figure 1.43 The water cycle is one of nature's most important processes. Water evaporates into the atmosphere, condenses, falls to Earth as rain or snow, and flows to the oceans to begin the cycle again. Energy to keep the cycle moving comes from the sun. (Source: *Compton's Encyclopaedia,* a division of Encyclopaedia Britannica.)

from the sun and changes from liquid water to gaseous water vapor. Water vapor rises, condenses to form clouds, and falls back to Earth as precipitation.

As water evaporates, all impurities dissolved in it are left behind, so water vapor contains only pure water. Because vaporization purifies water, it can be used over and over again. Without this important step, water would be a limited nonrecyclable resource.

Huge amounts of water also evaporate from plants. Water rises from the soil into roots, stems, and finally into the leaves. Water evaporates from the leaves moving through small openings in the leaf into the surrounding air. This process is called **transpiration.** An eastern deciduous forest loses water in transpiration equal to 20 inches (50 centimeters) of rainfall per year. An acre of corn transpires 15 inches (38 centimeters) of rainfall during its growing season.

Describe transpiration.

e. Renewal Time

In order to use water wisely as a renewable resource, we need to know: "How long does it take for water in a given part of the Earth to renew (or clean) itself?"

The freshwater available for human use consists of groundwater and runoff from streams and rivers. Rivers renew themselves relatively rapidly, but the renewing of underground water is much slower. Pollution of ground water, with its slow renewal rate, can impact the future of humankind for centuries.

Human Needs and Wants

1.17 The Basic Needs of Humans

What are the basic needs of all humans?

From the study of ecosystems, we see that for life to continue, certain conditions must exist. Like other animals, humans have certain basic needs. They are:

a. Water

Water is needed to transport nutrients to the cells and carry waste products away. Evaporating water helps moderate body temperature. The producers and consumers we rely on also require water for their life processes.

b. Shelter

On Earth, gravity holds our atmosphere in place and makes possible the biosphere, our global home. In addition, almost all humans live in houses that moderate climate changes and make life much more pleasant. Anyone who ventures out of the biosphere must take shelter along. Even during space walks, astronauts' suits provide conditions needed for human life.

Humans, being biological organisms, have certain basic needs. These are water, air, shelter, food, minerals, and decomposers.

c. Air

A mixture of gases (nitrogen, oxygen, carbon dioxide, and other gases) make up air. Nitrogen is required for building structural protein, enzymes, and other organic molecules. In addition, nitrogen dilutes the oxygen in our atmosphere. That is, it slows down combustion, allowing materials to burn at a controllable rate. And, nitrogen prevents certain respiratory problems. Oxygen is required for the breakdown of food. Carbon dioxide is essential for the photosynthesis process.

d. Minerals

Foods cannot be grown without minerals. For instance, soils that have no trace of molybdenum will grow no plant life at all. Potassium, iron, zinc, manganese, selenium, and germanium, as well as other minerals, not only provide the necessary nutrients for plant life, but through the food chain, provide the minerals essential for a healthy human body.

e. Food

Humans need a variety of foods. Plants and animals provide carbohydrates and fats for energy, proteins for energy and tissue building, vitamins that perform specific biological functions, and minerals that are indispensable for life (although not required as an energy source). Finally, the interaction of producers and consumers regenerates the atmosphere and soil.

Have you thanked a bacterium today?

An ecosystem is a remarkable self-sustaining entity that uses and reuses the matter it contains. An ecosystem is powered by the energy that flows through it.

f. Decomposers

The organisms of decay (mainly bacteria and fungi) recycle sewage, dead plants, and animals and keep the soil fertile.

This is a rather brief list of things that most of us take for granted. Yet these are our basic needs. These are the things we must have for life and that are provided in our ecosystems. We will continue to have them as long as we treat our Earth and its ecosphere with care.

1.18 The Social Requirements of Survival

Humans need social interactions to survive.

Even if all our basic needs were met, most humans could not survive as individuals alone. For some reason, most of us require companionship—an exchange of ideas and feelings.

Interaction is necessary, but sometimes it leads to conflict. Conflict can lead to destruction. Because of this humans have developed techniques for attempting to resolve conflicts and punish destructive behavior.

The Special Focus that follows shows how one group of people endured both physical danger and isolation from the outside world. As you read it, notice what strategies they used to cooperate and to deal with the stressful situation.

Special Focus

Surviving An Antarctic Winter

By Robert Reinhold
The New York Times

SOUTH POLE STATION, Antarctica—The events of Aug. 17, 1979, will not get into the official history books, but they were something of a psychological milestone in the history of the South Pole. Outside, temperatures dipped to 71 degrees below zero in a blinding blizzard, but inside, emotional temperatures among the crew of 16 men and one woman, after nearly half a year of total darkness, were reaching the flash point.

Foaming at the mouth and roaring drunk, a member of the crew who has recently learned of his father's death, piles into the galley in rage. He yells and begins to smash cups wildly. Blood and glass are everywhere. Soon he spies his rival for the affections of the station's lone woman and charges with a two-by-four, then runs out into the blizzard. It is hours before the mayhem ends, with gashes, bruises and frostbite.

In the three days of eerie calm that followed, Andrew Cameron, the 22-year-old supply man who witnessed all this, reflects in his diary: "Most people would never winter over if they knew what it really is like. Well the truth of it is that it can be fun at times but the deep dark winter with hopeless isolation for eight months is a sheer mental hell." He wonders how the crew, afflicted by deep jealousies and divisions, can survive another three months.

Though an extreme example, that night of violence underscores the powerful mental effects of protracted isolation. And many psychologists believe the unusual nature of Antarctic isolation in which a small group of scientists and support personnel is confined to a tiny life-sustaining cocoon surrounded by an impenetrable hostile environment that permits no quick escape may hold lessons for an approaching age of prolonged space travel and space colonization.

"Isolation is a kind of stress—it brings out the best and worst in people," said Dr. Jay T. Shurley, a psychiatrist who spent several years studying the denizen of the South Pole . . .

Though the Navy does the screening, the entire winter crew belongs to the United States Antarctic Research Program, an arm of the National Science Foundation. Seven of the 17 are scientific personnel making observations of the weather, upper atmosphere and geophysical phenomena. The rest are support workers—a cook, engineers, mechanics, a doctor—employed by a private contractor, ITT Antarctic Services Inc., of Paramus, N.J. . .

Psychologists say the best candidates for isolation are hard-working personalities, somewhat diffident, with higher than average intelligence and education, and without close family ties. Above all, they say, isolated personnel should be competent in their work, since criticism can be devastating in such confines. They must be flexible and tolerant of other people's habits and beliefs.

Probably the best bets are "professional isolates," the kind of men who work on offshore oil rigs and Alaskan pipelines. Such men do not relate well to women and seem to thrive on isolation.

"Some of the people who are most gung-ho for this experience are not well adapted," said Cameron. "They tend to be misfits, seeking something they'll not find. And when the bubble bursts, their depressive experience is very difficult for others to handle. This is the big league of isolation."

As for Andrew Cameron, now living in Gaithersburg, Md., he says it took him nearly a year to calm down from the winter. Toward the end he wrote in his diary: "I am sick of this chunk of ice. I want to get out of this cesspool. Let me get the hell out of here. I want to go home." Today he calls it "the greatest year of my life."

Note: Scientific knowledge and skills are only part of what it takes to survive in a situation like the one just described. Independence and absorption in work are helpful. As this account illustrates, social skills in human relations and conflict resolution are also important. The same type of skills will be needed when attempting to resolve problems related to population, food supply, pollution, resource distribution, and land use at local, regional, and global levels. Keep this in mind as you study these problems in upcoming chapters.

Questions to Ponder

1. How might survival in this Antarctic episode be related to the Voyage to Mars situation described in the laboratory manual?
2. Does it take more than scientific knowledge to survive in Mars/Antarctic-type situations? Explain.
3. According to the article, what does stress bring out in people? Give examples.
4. What are the best personal traits to have if cooperation among individuals is a major goal?
5. What lessons do these accounts (Mars/ Antarctica) teach us that might be applicable to the resolution of conflicts related to regional and global pollution, food supply, and land use?

Besides scientific knowledge, what is necessary for achieving the good life?

1.19 Our Quest for the "Good Life"

Most people want more out of life than mere existence. In addition to their basic needs, most humans desire:

- To love and be loved
- To do meaningful work and feel useful in society
- To learn new things and teach them to others
- To benefit from a variety of healthful foods
- To enjoy clean air and water
- To have modern day conveniences
- To seek the beauty and meaning of life
- To help rid our planet of disease
- To promote world peace and rid our planet of war
- To relax and enjoy life on occasion

To achieve some of these desires, the ability to interact and resolve conflicts is important, and the wise use of our natural resources is essential. In the remainder of this course, we will examine the challenge of obtaining and using these resources. We also will speculate about how related issues might be resolved. By understanding resources and their uses, designing and using new technology, learning from mistakes of the past, and improving our abilities to communicate, we are more likely to assure the "good life" for ourselves and our children.

The Principles and Values of Human Ecology

As humans seek to achieve the good life, we use the Earth's natural resources. In many cases, this use has caused environmental damage. Sometimes we have lacked knowledge of how the Earth functions; at other times we have failed to value the wise use of resources.

To harm the environment less in the future, and to correct our mistakes of the past, we need to know the scientific principles that govern the behavior of matter and energy in living and nonliving systems. Scientific principles are based on logic and supported by evidence.

Further, we need to make decisions from an Earth-sensitive viewpoint. That viewpoint includes knowing and using scientific principles, but it also includes making value judgments. Values may change from one generation to the next, or from one country to another. Scientific principles come from scientists, but the values of human ecology have been contributed by many kinds of people. The value statements below come from a variety of sources—from scientists, from politicians, from spiritual leaders, from biologists, and from this book's author. All of them, however, reflect concern for the Earth and its future.

Some of the scientific principles and value statements relating to human ecology are listed below. As both groups of statements will be emphasized throughout this course, you should know them well.

Scientific Principles

Law of Conservation of Matter: Matter can be neither created nor destroyed, though it can be rearranged. The law implies that everything must go somewhere (there is no "away") and that Earth itself is finite.

First Law of Thermodynamics: Energy can be neither created nor destroyed. However, it can be transformed from one form to another.

Second Law of Thermodynamics: Once energy and other resources are used there is an overall decrease in their future usefulness. "Useful" means objects can be moved or electricity can be generated and profit can be made.

Principle of Diversity: The greater the diversity of a natural system, the greater its stability.

Law of Continual Change: Everything is becoming something else.

Optimum Size Principle (Brontosaurus Principle): Up to a point, the bigger the better. Beyond that point, benefits may be reduced.

Interrelatedness: Everything is connected to everything else, and so you can't do one thing without affecting other things. Humans, too, interact with each other and everything around them.

Value Statements

Matter/Energy Quality: Matter and energy are more useful when they are highly concentrated, such as in mineral deposits, petroleum, or bright sunlight.

Wise Resource Use: High quality resources should not be used on low quality tasks.

Rights of Future Generations: Our environment does not belong to one generation alone. It was used by our ancestors, passed on, and will be given to future generations. We are charged with the responsibility of passing it on in the best possible condition.

Responsibility for Pollution: Every person must be responsible for their contribution to pollution.

Nature Knows Best: In many cases, but not always, Nature provides the best solutions to problems of human ecology. (Nature doesn't really "know" anything, of course. It just is.)

Minimal Change: In using a natural resource, we should choose the least harmful method. Damage repair should be planned for.

True Cost: The market price of anything should include all present and future costs of harmful effects on society and the environment.

Your Environment Is You: In the words of Winston Churchill, "We shape our buildings (environment) and afterwards our buildings (environment) shape us."

Ideas Unlimited: The creativity of the collective human mind is nearly limitless. If humans understand the laws that govern our ecosphere and live within their limits, human creativity should enable us to enjoy a comfortable living on our planet for an indefinite period.

Equity: All humans are created with equal rights to live in dignity and peace and to have a meaningful existence. Everyone is entitled to a fair share of the world's resources and is obligated to share the world's responsibilities.

Technology—Part of the Problem, Part of the Solution: Our use of technology, not the technology itself, aids or harms the environment. We should proceed into the unknown with caution and refrain from action when ignorant of the consequences.

Goal of Society: A major goal should be to live both in comfort and in harmony with nature.

Give Earth a Chance: No national goal, however urgent, no political or economic necessity, however pressing, can possibly justify the risk of bringing all human history to an end.

Our technological dependence is strong and widespread. Technology has helped us achieve the highest standard of living in the history of humankind. Technology has also contributed to many of our environmental problems. You, as a student, citizen, and potential leader, perhaps as a future decision maker, parent, or engineer, are challenged to use your creativity as we attempt to fashion a better future for our children.

Summary

We live on a global spaceship. It seems permanent and firm beneath our feet. This is only an illusion. Processes within the Earth cause the lithospheric plates to move. As they move, new minerals are brought to the Earth's surface, and volcanoes add gases to our atmosphere. The atmosphere (air zone), hydrosphere (water zone), and lithosphere (rock zone) make up the ecosphere (life zone). The ecosphere is the global ecosystem that supports all life.

In an ecosystem, living organisms and nonliving substances interact to produce an exchange of materials between the living and the nonliving. The sun provides the energy that is necessary for this exchange to occur. Plants store energy and minerals. Animals (including humans) directly or indirectly take these from plants for their needs. Finally, decomposers break down dead organic material and return minerals (nutrients) to the soil. Thus the cycle is complete. It is repeated over and over again. As humans, we are totally dependent on this process.

In addition to existing, most humans want a little more out of life. We desire peace, beauty, and love. Our ability to interact reasonably with our fellow human beings will determine the degree to which these desires are realized. We also desire various material comforts (homes, cars, appliances). Our understanding of the laws that govern the use of energy and mineral resources will ultimately determine how many of us will be able to enjoy these creature comforts. These laws are the focus of Chapter 2.

References

Aber, John D. and Jerry M. Melillo. *Terrestrial Ecosystems* (Philadelphia: Saunders), 1991.

Akin, Wallace E.. *Global Patterns: Climate, Vegetation and Soils* (Norman: University of Oklahoma Press), 1991.

Carson, Rachel. *Silent Spring* (New York: Fawcett World), 1970.

Colinvaux, Paul A. *Ecology* (New York: John Wiley), 1986.

Goldsmith, Edward, et al. *Imperiled Planet: Restoring Our Endangered Ecosystems* (Cambridge, MA.: MIT Press), 1990.

Leopold, Aldo. *A Sand County Almanac* (New York: Oxford University Press), 1949.

Lieth, Helmut and Robert H. Whittaker, eds. *Primary Productivity of the Biosphere* (New York: Springer - Verlag), 1975.

Miller, G. Tyler, Jr. *Living in the Environment,* 7th ed. (Belmont, CA: Wadsworth), 1992.

Northington, David K. and J. R. Goodin. *The Botanical World* (St. Louis: Times Mirror/Mosby College Publishing), 1984.

Odum, Eugene P. *Ecology and Our Endangered Life-Support Systems* (Sunderland, MA: Sinauer), 1989.

Press, Frank and Raymond Siever. *Earth,* 4th ed. (New York: W. H. Freeman), 1986.

Ricklefs, Robert E. *Ecology,* 3rd ed. (New York: W. H. Freeman), 1990.

Smith, Robert L. *Elements of Ecology,* 4th ed. (New York: Harper & Row), 1990.

End of Chapter Questions

Set A

1. Why is our Earth called a global spaceship?
2. You are taking a course in global science. What is global science?
3. Summarize the big bang theory.
4. Summarize the plate tectonic theory.
5. Why must we understand how we relate to our environment?
6. What is the ecosphere?
7. How do volcanoes contribute to air pollution?
8. Name the three spherical layers that make up the ecosphere.
9. Name the source of energy that sustains all life on Earth.
10. What is photosynthesis?

11. In five steps, account for 100% of the solar energy that strikes the Earth.
12. In an ecosystem, materials are exchanged between the living and nonliving parts.
    Give an example of what this means.
13. Write an equation for respiration and explain why it is the opposite of photosyntheses.
14. An ecosystem has five interacting parts. List them and tell what makes the whole system function.
15. Start with the sun and explain how energy flows through an ecosystem.
16. Explain why a meadow in a national park is more stable than a corn field in Iowa.
17. Give an example of a five-step food chain.
18. What is ecological succession and why does it occur?
19. What are biomes?
20. Why do aquatic ecosystems differ?
21. Why will trees not grow in the tundra?
22. What special adaptations do desert plants have?
23. What properties of water enable it to support life on Earth?
24. How is water recycled in the biosphere?
25. List the two primary things that an ecosystem does.
26. Give an example of a monoculture.
27. Chemicals are recycled in ecosystems. What does this mean? Give an example, assuming a plant needs a certain type of iron compound.
28. Name the organisms that obtain food material and energy from the breakdown of animal wastes and the remains of dead organisms.
29. The energy source that drives the ecosphere is the ____________ .
30. List the six basic needs of human beings. Make a drawing which shows how these needs relate to each other.

Set B

31. What are the two theories that describe the formation of the universe? In what ways do they differ?
32. One of the most significant products of the space program is the photograph of Earth surrounded by space. What important idea does this photograph help us to realize?
33. Give three pieces of evidence which support the plate tectonic theory.
34. Locate where you live on Figure 1.4. Have earthquakes occurred near your home town? Would you say you live in an area that is as active with earthquakes as the western coast of the United States or South America? Why or why not?
35. What is occurring along the Mid-Atlantic Ridge today?

36. The plates shown in Figure 1.5 can "slide around" because they rest on a pliable layer. But they would not move unless some force or forces actually "pushed" them. What do you think such forces might be? Give reasons for your answer.
37. Only a fraction of the energy from the sun's rays actually reach the Earth. Of the portion that does, almost all is unavailable for use by living things. Name three ways in which energy is "lost." What is the only way in which energy is retained in the ecosystem?
38. All organisms in an ecosystem may be classed as either producers, consumers, or decomposers. Yet only two of these classes are necessary for a fully functional ecosystem. Which two? Explain your answer.
39. In which of the following categories do you belong: producer, herbivore, parasite, omnivore, microconsumer? Explain why you do not belong in the categories you have not chosen.
40. Are the basic needs of human beings the same or different from those of other living things? Explain your thinking.
41. When astronauts travel beyond the nine mile thick ecosphere, they leave behind the natural systems that provide for their basic needs for survival. What must the astronauts take with them in order to survive outside the ecosphere? Explain how some of the survival problems are solved through artificial environments.
42. A deciduous forest is more diverse than a field of corn. Explain what is meant by that statement.
43. Why is the deciduous forest considered a stronger ecosystem than the corn field? Give specific examples of things which could happen in a forest and a corn field and how each ecosystem would respond to that occurrence.
44. Energy is tied up in waste products and in previously living materials. Decomposers live on the energy they obtain from breaking down the molecules in these materials. At the same time, they release nonliving molecules and elements back into the soil and atmosphere. Name some of the abiotic components of the ecosystem that are freed in this manner.
45. What is meant by the following statement: "We're all in it together."?
46. Give an example of the "Brontosaurus Principle" that relates to modern life. Explain.
47. Is the right to live in a clean environment an inalienable right? Should it be protected by the Constitution?
48. Should all of us be held responsible for our own pollution? Why, or why not? If so, how?
49. Does our environment also belong to future generations?
50. Select one of the Fundamental Laws and Principles of Human Ecology as the subject or a short paper. Your paper should either explain the meaning of the "law" or "principle," or you should "editorialize" about the subject.

51. "Equity" suggests that rights and responsibilities go hand-in-hand, and that one's "fair share" of the Earth's resources is equal to the effort one puts into conserving these resources. United States citizens constitute about 5% of the world's population, yet account for approximately 30% of the world's average annual resource consumption. Write an essay explaining:
    a. what Americans might do to meet their responsibilities for resource conservation better than they do now; and,
    b. how the lifestyle of the average American might change if resource consumption were to drop by one-half.
52. Technology is sometimes blamed for deterioration of environmental quality (examples: air and water pollution), and for resource depletion (energy consumption by equipment and machines, transportation, and households). Technology, while part of the problem, can also be part of the solution. Give some examples of the ways technology might be employed to reduce resource losses and improve environmental quality.
53. In your opinion, what does it mean to "live ecologically"? Do people need to change their behavior to "live ecologically"? If so, how?
54. Do you think it is possible to live in harmony with Nature? Explain.
55. Relate the following statements to the success of humans in achieving the "good life."
    - If you eat, you are involved with agriculture.
    - If you interact with people, you are involved with sociology.
    - If you live the "good life," you are involved with mining.

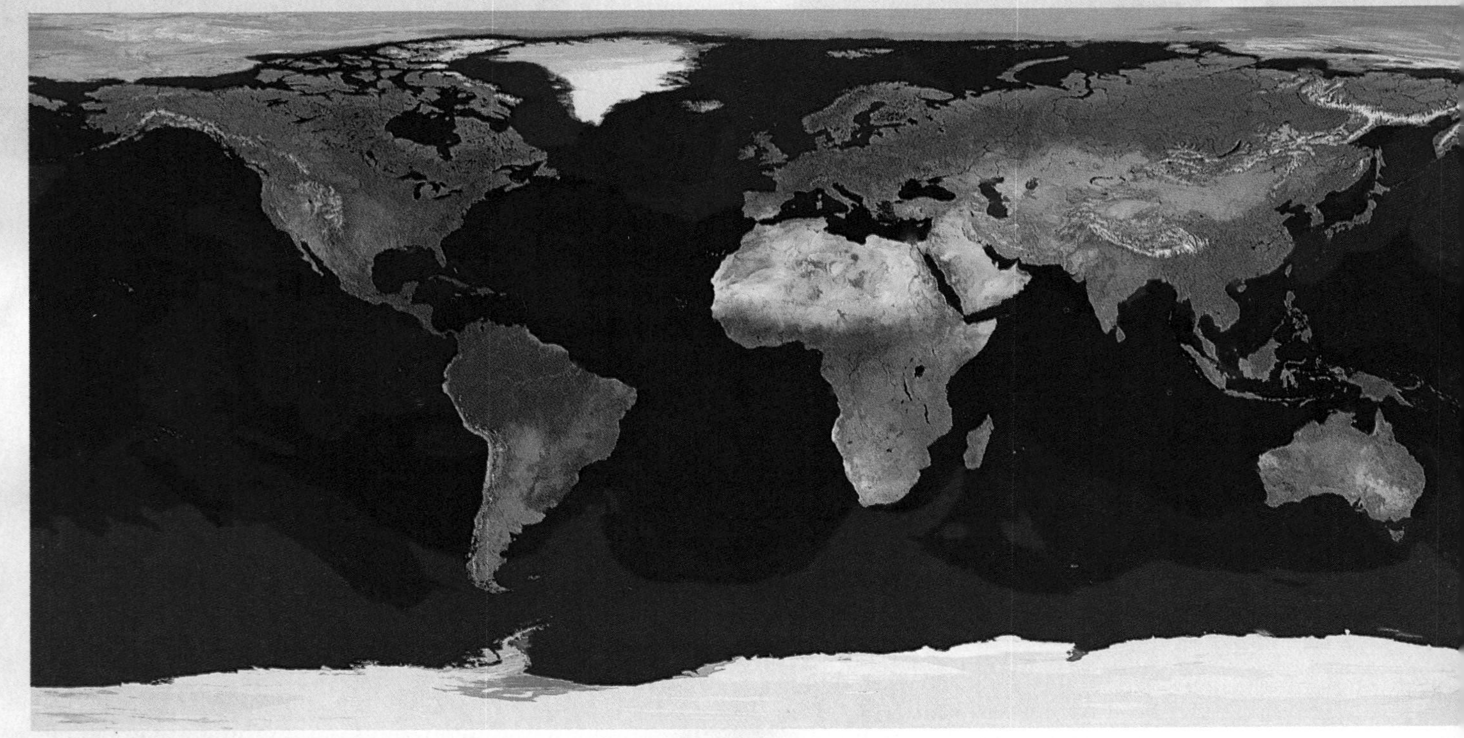

SATELLITE COMPOSITE VIEW OF EARTH
By TOM VAN SANT and the GEOSPHERE™ PROJECT
Santa Monica, California
With assistance from NOAA, NASA, EYES ON EARTH
Technical direction Lloyd Van Warren
Source data derived from NOAA/TIROS-N Series Satellites
Completed April 15, 1990

Goal

To build an understanding of the laws that govern our use of energy and mineral resources.

Basic Energy/ Resource Concepts

Before I flew, I was already aware of how small and vulnerable our planet is, but only when I saw it from space, in all its ineffable beauty and fragility, did I realize that humankind's most urgent task is to cherish and preserve it for future generations.

—Sigmund Jahn, Soyuz 31.

The GeoSphere Image This spectacular image of Earth marks a milestone in history. We see the Earth revealed, unobstructed by clouds. Through the use of NOAA weather satellites, hundreds of individual satellite images from space were combined to produce this image of the world. Drainage and relief features are enhanced. The composite, like a jigsaw puzzle, was assembled over a 10-month period and completed on April 15, 1990.

?

What are energy and matter?

Energy and Matter

As you have seen, Earth is isolated in space. But in one way, it is continually renewed from the outside. Energy is both all around us and inside us. Energy is carried to the Earth in the rays which come from the sun. It is locked for a time in the bodies of all growing things. It is released from these bodies in countless ways as life on Earth continues. Because of our sun, energy is always available. That energy flows through our ecosystem and makes life possible for all of Earth's creatures, including ourselves.

Why are energy and minerals important?

Energy is what makes things go, makes people go, makes nations go. Our lifestyle and our standard of living are based on energy and resource use. Without an adequate and varied supply of minerals, we'd have no automobiles or air planes. Without sufficient energy in the proper form, they wouldn't run. We use coal to fire our power plants, natural gas to heat our homes, electricity to power our refrigerators, machines, television sets, radios, and so on. Our appetite for energy and minerals seems to have no end. The wants and needs of the rest of the world for such resources are also growing.

Why is a knowledge of energy and resource related laws important?

This chapter is a foundation for understanding energy and resource use. Certain laws govern our behavior when it comes to obtaining and using our resources. We must understand these laws if we are going to understand basic ideas about energy, resources, and the environment. With this knowledge, we can make intelligent plans for the future.

Before we examine the laws governing the use of energy and mineral resources, we must first add to our vocabulary. We need to know the meanings of the terms mass, matter and energy.

What is mass?

Mass is a measure of the amount of "stuff" in an object. More precisely, mass is a measure of an object's resistance to change. Try throwing first a golf ball, then the metal shot used by the track team. Which one goes farther? The answer is obvious. The metal shot is composed of a lot more stuff. It has a much larger mass than the golf ball. Therefore, it resists change in its state of motion. It is much harder to throw, but once going, it is also much harder to stop. Would a drag race between a Trans-Am and a heavily loaded semi be very interesting? Why not?

What is matter?

Matter is anything that occupies space and has mass. All the objects that we see, touch and feel are composed of matter.

What is energy?

Energy is the capacity to take action. It is the ability to move matter around. Energy is necessary to maintain life and a vibrant society. When our energy supplies are low, gasoline is harder to get, people lose their jobs, and homes are cooler in the winter. All life would cease without energy.

2.1 Kinetic and Potential Energy

A moving car has energy. So does a tank of gasoline. However, we distinguish between them. They are different because the car must move to have energy, but the tank of gasoline doesn't have to move.

Figure 2.1 The sun is the most important of all our energy sources. Without it, there would be no life on Earth. (Dick Thomas/Visuals Unlimited.)

Figure 2.2 The kinetic energy possessed by this race car is made possible by the energy stored in the fuel that powers it. (Roger Penske, Detroit Diesel Corporation.)

Potential energy is stored energy.

Potential energy is stored energy. It is energy that has the ability to produce motion. A tank of gas, a bowl of cereal, a stick of dynamite, and a compressed spring are all examples.

Kinetic energy is the energy possessed by an object that is moving.

The energy that a mass has because of its motion is termed **kinetic energy.** The moving car, a falling rock, and an avalanche are all examples. The kinetic energy, KE, of a mass, m, moving at a velocity, v, is given by the equation:

$$KE = \frac{1}{2} mv^2$$

What is work?

How do objects obtain kinetic energy? The answer is, we must do work on them. **Work** is defined as the product of a force times the distance through which it acts. Thus,

$$\text{Work} = \text{force} \times \text{distance}$$
$$\text{or } W = F \cdot d$$

If a mass is at rest and we apply an unbalanced force (F) over a distance (d), our work will cause the mass to gain an amount of kinetic energy that is given by:

$$F \cdot d = \Delta(KE) = \frac{1}{2} mv^2$$

(where Δ is a mathematical symbol meaning "change in").

Potential energy is stored energy.
Kinetic energy is the energy possessed by an object that is moving.

In terms of matter, the Earth is a closed system. In terms of energy, the Earth is an open system.

2.2 Closed and Open Systems

A system is a region that is under study. For the purpose of the study, the region is surrounded by a boundary. The boundary may be imaginary.

You learned in chapter 1 that in terms of matter, the Earth is essentially a closed system. In terms of energy, however, the Earth is an open system. What we mean by these two important statements will be made clear with some definitions and examples.

Definitions

closed system: a system where nothing enters or leaves, a system where everything is used and reused.

open system: a system where things both enter and leave.

steady state: a system in which properties are constant because substances are entering and leaving at the same rate.

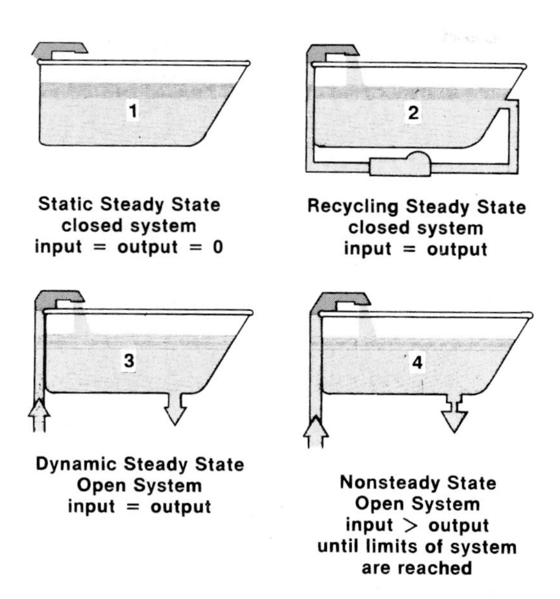

Figure 2.3 Four states of a bathtub. (Adapted from *Living in the Environment* by G. Tyler Miller, Jr. Copyright © 1975 by Wadsworth Publishing Co., Inc., Belmont, California 94002. Adaption approved by the Publisher.)

In Figure 2.3, a series of bathtubs show the relationship between the concepts of open systems, closed systems, and steady state systems. Through the following questions you will discover what these relationships are:

Examples. Which tub is more like:

a. the world's present population situation?
b. the world's present food situation?
c. the quantity of water in the world's oceans?
d. a lake with an inlet and an outlet?
e. the world's present mineral resource situation?
f. the average temperature of the Earth?
g. zero (no) population growth?
h. your average weight?
i. an efficient recycling program?
j. a no-growth economy?

See the footnote at the bottom of the page for suggested answers.

2.3 The Concept of Carrying Capacity

What is meant by carrying capacity, and how does this idea relate to us?

In terms of matter, the Earth can be viewed as a closed system. The fact that the Earth is finite implies the idea of carrying capacity. The carrying capacity is the maximum number (population) of any given

answers:
a—4, b—3 (we're eating it as fast as we're growing it), c—2 (it's being replenished as fast as it evaporates), d—3, e—1 (we're neither gaining or losing minerals, more about that later), f—3 (we radiate away as much energy as we receive), g—3, h—3, i—2, j—2 or 3.

Figure 2.4 Cows and carrying capacity.

organism a given ecosystem can support. When we talk about the carrying capacity of the Earth, we're almost always talking about the human population.

Why is the idea of "carrying capacity" important?

Relate Figure 2.4 to this statement.

The concept of carrying capacity was well illustrated by former Congressman Morris K. Udall of Arizona:

> "You know that if you put 10 cows on 1000 acres you may have 10 cows forever. The grass will grow. The trees will be green and bright and produce oxygen. The brooks will babble. But if you exceed the carrying capacity of that land, 15, 20, 30 cows, whatever it is, sooner or later you won't have any grass or any trees or any cows. The Earth has a carrying capacity, too. I don't know what it is. My guess is that it is something less than 3½ billion people in terms of the long-range use of the resources that can sustain generation after generation on this planet."

We now have a human population of more than five billion. Was Udall right? For some people in modern countries, food and other resources seem as plentiful as ever. For many in other countries,

Figure 2.5 Matter cannot be destroyed, but it can be rearranged and reused. We must design for recycling. (Institute of Scrap Recycling Industries, Inc.)

however, even food and water are scarce. Even in the United States, homelessness and poverty are present. For people everywhere, there are problems related to pollution.

In terms of people, no one number represents the Earth's carrying capacity. The number of people the Earth can support depends on their standard of living, their energy use, their mineral demands, their type of diet, and their demand for such things as open space, peace and quiet. In general, as the standard of living rises, the carrying capacity falls.

As the standard of living goes up, the Earth's carrying capacity goes down.

As you may remember from chapter 1, the *Brontosaurus Principle* states that to everything there is an optimum size. How does this principle relate to carrying capacity?

2.4 Conservation Laws

There are several conservation laws in nature. A conservation law is a law which states that in a closed system some quantity (such as total mass or energy) remains conserved (unchanged) forever. One such law is **the conservation of matter-energy:** the total amount of matter plus energy in the universe is constant.

On Earth, this conservation law is important to us because it relates to our use of energy and resources. It is dealt with briefly in the next two sections.

2.5 The Conservation of Matter

The law of conservation of matter states: the total mass of Earth is constant. This is because Earth is neither gaining mass nor losing mass. Another way of stating the law of conservation of matter is: matter can neither be created nor destroyed, but it can be rearranged.

?

What do the laws of conservation of matter and conservation of energy tell us?

Some Questions to Think about:

1. The conservation of matter is often stated: "There is no 'away'." What does this mean? How does this relate to you? How does this relate to current waste disposal problems?

Questions to think about.

2. In doing the "Voyage to Mars" lab, many students want to bring an oxygen-making machine along, "Just plug it in and it makes oxygen." Why isn't this a good idea?
3. What do you think about a pollution control device that one can attach to the tailpipe of a car to "eat up" pollutants?
4. If there is no "away," why doesn't trash build up in Nature?

2.6 The Conservation of Energy

The law of conservation of energy states: energy can neither be created nor destroyed. It can be transformed (changed) from one form to another. This statement is also known as the first law of thermodynamics.

The first law of thermodynamics = the conservation of energy.

Changes in Energy

What do we mean when we say mass is conserved?

Before we analyze the first law of thermodynamics, let's briefly describe the various forms of energy. Although energy appears around us in many forms, there are only six basic forms of energy that power the universe.

What are the six forms of energy?

2.7 Six Forms of Energy

a. Mechanical Energy

How is mechanical energy shown by objects?

Mechanical energy is the energy of an object as shown by the object's movement, its position, or both. Mechanical energy is the most familiar form of energy. The moving pistons in an engine have mechanical energy and do work by making wheels go around. A hammer moving toward a nail has mechanical energy. It has the ability to force a nail into a board. A boulder on the edge of a cliff has mechanical energy because of its position. It has the potential of moving something, if only a little soil, through a distance before it comes to rest.

Standard atmospheric pressure is 1.03 kg/cm^2 (14.7 lb/in^2).

b. Heat (Thermal) Energy

When you rapidly rub your hands together, your hands get warm. The mechanical energy of rubbing is transformed (changed) into heat.

Scientific evidence of the equivalence between mechanical work and heat was provided by the experiments of a Scottish physicist, James Prescott Joule. His most famous experiment used an apparatus in which slowly falling weights turned a paddle-wheel in an insulated container of water (see Figure 2.7). Friction between the paddle-wheel and the water warmed the water. He measured the temperature increase.

Joule is honored by having the present unit of energy named after him. In current scientific units, one kilocalorie of heat energy is equal to 4184 joules of mechanical work.

From this and similar experiments, Joule concluded heat was a form of energy. The quantity of energy required to raise one pound of water one Fahrenheit degree required the use of 772 foot • pounds of mechanical work.

An important understanding came out of these experiments. The mechanical work did not disappear. It reappeared as heat energy! The notion began to grow. Energy did not disappear—ever. This realization finally led to **the law of conservation of energy.**

Figure 2.6 "Big Muskie," a Bucyrus-Erie® 4250-W is the world's largest walking dragline. This giant machine weighs 27 million pounds or more than 150 Boeing "727" jet liners. It is as wide as a football field. Why? So it can do a huge amount of work. Each filling of its 220 cubic yard bucket moves enough material to more than fill two average size railroad coal hoppers. (Courtesy of Bucyrus-Erie Co., South Milwaukee, Wisconsin.)

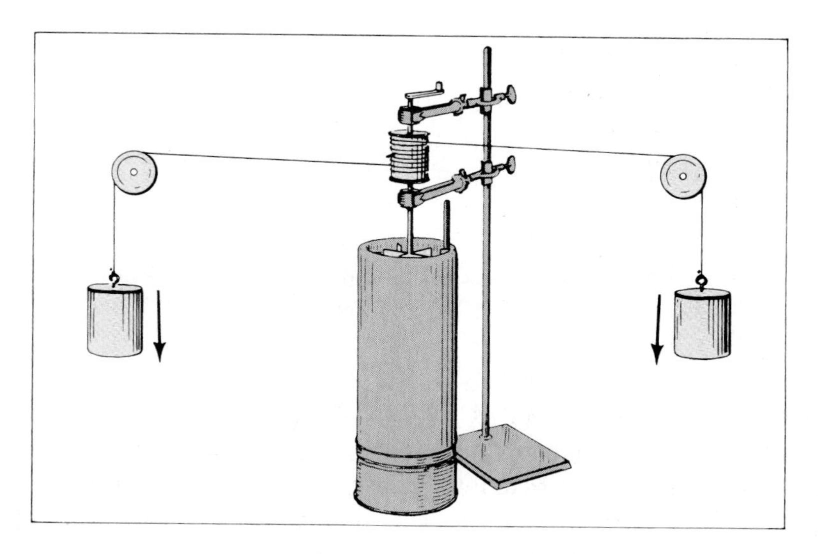

Figure 2.7 The apparatus for a Joule experiment to observe the conversion of mechanical energy to internal (thermal) energy. (From Physical Science Study Committee, *Physics*, Boston: D.C. Heath & Company.)

Another idea came after Joule's experiments. Heat energy actually is kinetic energy of moving molecules. Temperature is a measure of this motion. It was found that for gases at low pressure:

$$\frac{1}{2} mv^2 = kT$$

where k is a constant that relates the kinetic energy of the molecules to the Absolute (or Kelvin) temperature scale. Hence we see that as the temperature increases, the molecules of a substance move faster. As the substance cools down, its molecules move more slowly.

On the Absolute (or Kelvin) scale, 0° is so cold that all molecular motion stops at that temperature.

Figure 2.8a The electromagnetic spectrum.

Frequency, cycles/sec.
10^2 10^6 10^{10} 10^{14} 10^{18} 10^{22}
Power
Microwaves
Visible
X-rays
Radio Broadcast Antenna
Electric Heater
X-Ray Tube
Sun Lamp
Power Lines
Dish Antenna
Light Bulb
Radio
Infrared
Ultraviolet
Gamma rays
10^4 1 10^{-4} 10^{-8} 10^{-12}
Wavelength, meters

a

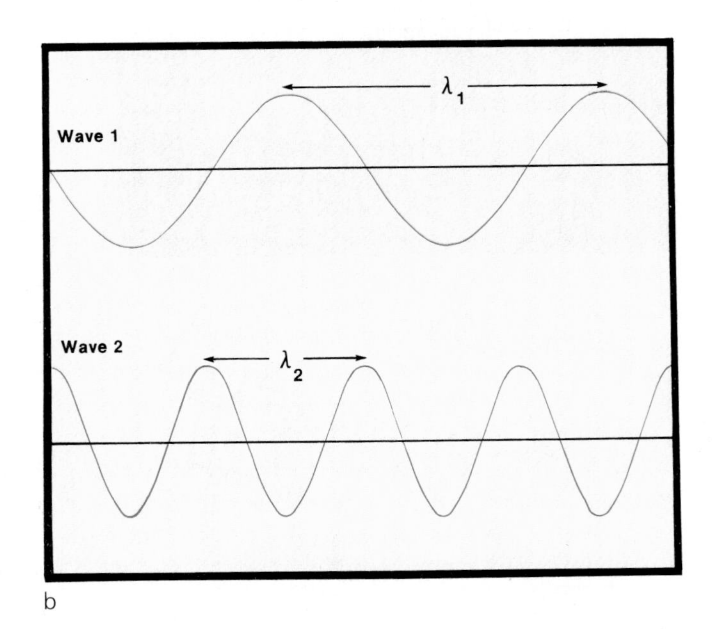

b

Figure 2.8b The relationship between frequency and wavelength for waves of constant velocity. As frequency increases, wavelength decreases. The wavelength of Wave 1 (λ_1) is twice that of Wave 2. However, the second set of waves have twice the frequency.

c. Radiant Energy (Including Light)

Radiation is produced when electric charges change speed.

Radiant energy is the energy of electromagnetic waves. Light, radio waves, infrared radiation, microwaves, x-rays, and gamma rays are all examples. Such waves are sent out by accelerating electric charges. If electric charges (in a wire) move back and forth fast enough, radio waves will leave the wire. Electrons, accelerated by the high temperatures that exist in the hot filament of a light bulb, send out visible (light) radiation.

Electromagnetic radiation.

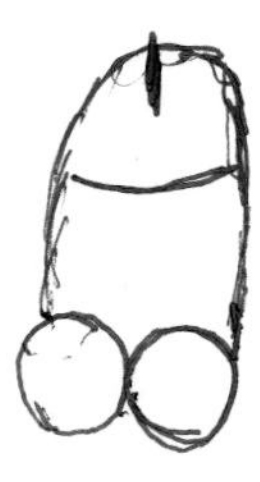

Electromagnetic radiation is characterized by two properties: The frequency (f) and the wavelength (λ). These waves move with the constant velocity (c), the velocity of light. These three quantities are connected by the relationship $c = f \cdot \lambda$. λ and f are inversely related. This means a "long wavelength" radiation (large λ) must have "low frequency" (small f). Figure 2.8a shows the familiar examples of electromagnetic radiation. Within a certain range of frequency and wavelength, electromagnetic radiation is visible as light.

Solar radiation.

As to energy, our most important form of radiation is solar (from the sun). Solar radiation includes not only visible light, but also the rest of the electromagnetic spectrum.

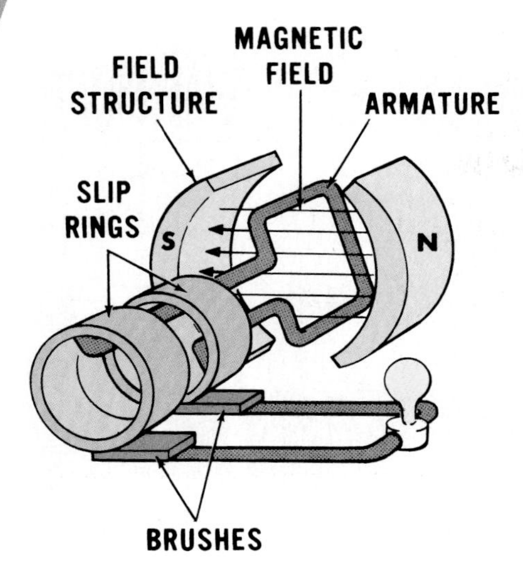

Figure 2.9 Electrical energy—an A.C. generator. The forced rotation of the coil (called the armature) between the poles (N and S) of the magnet induces alternating current in a closed circuit). (Copyright © 1966. Used by permission of the 3M Company.)

The fact that radiation is a form of energy can be shown in a variety of ways. We know by simple experiments with a magnifying glass that we can concentrate the sun's rays and start a fire. A solar cell changes the sun's energy into electrical energy.

d. Electrical Energy

The three forms of energy we have dealt with so far—mechanical, heat and radiant energy—are known to us because they are used in those forms. We are very familiar with their "end uses." Moving trucks or buses, heating buildings, lighting rooms, and cooking foods with microwaves are examples of such end uses in which these forms of energy appear.

Electrical energy.

Another well-known form of energy is never an "end use." Electrical energy is always an intermediate form. We only see its effects, such as the light from a light bulb, the heat in a toaster, or the work done by an electric motor.

Why is electrical energy such a popular form of energy?

Electrical energy is useful because it is so easily converted to other forms of energy. In fact, electrical energy is converted and used as it is generated. It is difficult and expensive to store it. We will discuss the meaning of this later.

Magnetic field: the space near a small magnet (or current-carrying body) in which a moving charge or another small magnet experience a force on themselves if placed there.

Electrical energy is a special kind of kinetic energy. It is the energy of electric charges, usually electrons, in motion. Passed through a wire, this current can cause heating. If the wire gets hot enough, it will glow and produce light. An electric current can establish a magnetic field. This field can cause a motor to turn if it is properly regulated.

How is electrical energy produced?

Electricity is most commonly produced when the magnetic field that passes through a closed electric circuit (usually a coil) is caused to change. You can produce some electricity this way by doing the experiment "How Electricity Is Generated." The basic principles involved are illustrated in Figure 2.9.

Figure 2.10 Chemical energy for your tank. As we move into the future, there may be increasing percentages of alcohol in the gasoline we buy. (National Renewable Energy Laboratory (NREL).)

e. Chemical Energy

Where does chemical energy originate?

Chemical energy is the energy that is stored in the chemical bonds holding molecules together. Common examples of chemical energy are the energy that is stored in food, in dried plant material, in crude oil, and in natural gas and coal. Figure 2.10 illustrates our need for chemical energy.

Through photosynthesis, plants capture the sun's energy. This energy is used to combine carbon dioxide and water into more complex molecules. These more complex molecules lock up solar energy in their chemical bonds. When the molecules are broken up as we digest food and burn fuel, the energy is released. With that energy, muscles can move and the body can do work.

f. Nuclear Energy

How is nuclear energy released?

Nuclear energy is the most difficult form of energy to release. This form of energy is locked in the nuclei of atoms. It is caused by the movement of the nuclear particles. Nuclear energy is released when these particles are rearranged.

Nuclear energy is released in two ways. One is the combination of small nuclei to make bigger ones. This combination is called **fusion.** The other is the breakdown of a larger nucleus into smaller nuclei. This breakdown is called **fission.** Both of these reactions could provide large amounts of energy in the future. We will discuss them further in later chapters.

Where does energy come from?

The six forms of energy we have described are summarized in Table 2.1. Review it carefully. The information will be very useful as you progress through this course.

Table 2.1 Six Forms of Energy

Energy Form	Definition	Examples	Common Units of Measure*
Mechanical	Kinetic: the energy of a moving object Potential: stored energy	A ball moving through air, energy stored in a wound-up spring	joule (J) foot • pound (ft • lb)
Heat	The energy of the random motion of the particles of a substance	The warmth of a campfire, or a hot bath	British thermal unit (Btu) calorie
Radiant	Energy carried as wave motion, produced when charges are accelerated	Solar energy, used for photosynthesis by plants or causing a sunburn	watt • hour (wh) kilowatt hour (kWh)
Electrical	The energy associated with magnets, electric circuits, and in combinations of the two	Energy for running a television, lamp, refrigerator, toaster, or radio	kilowatt • hour (kWh)
Chemical	The energy stored in chemical bonds (the energy of foods and fuels)	Energy in gasoline that runs your car; food that gives you energy	*Energy Density* calories/mole (cal/mol) calories/gram (cal/g) Btu/pound (Btu/lb)
Nuclear	The energy locked in the nucleus of an atom, caused by the movement of nuclear particles	Reactions used in atomic weapons, nuclear medicine, and nuclear reactors	tons of TNT

* The common units are defined in Section 2.9.

2.8 Energy Transformations

Each form of energy can be converted or transformed to the others. However, some transformations are more difficult to accomplish than others. Chemical energy can be changed to heat and heat can be changed to mechanical energy. Can you think of other transformations? Figure 2.15 summarizes some of these transformations. What forms of energy or transformations are not shown?

Burning gas to heat water and to make steam is an example of changing chemical energy to heat energy. Using steam to run a turbine involves changing heat energy to mechanical energy. Using the turbine to turn an electric generator involves changing mechanical energy to electrical energy. Using that electricity to operate a light bulb converts electrical to radiant energy. These transformations are illustrated in Figure 2.16.

Special Focus

Remote Sensing: New Visions of Earth

> Man must rise above the Earth to the top of the atmosphere and beyond, for only then will he fully understand the world in which he lives.
>
> — Socrates, *ca* 450 B.C.

Remote sensing is the science and art of obtaining information about an object, area, or phenomenon through measurements made from a distance. For example, a person can determine whether or not a metal object is hot by placing a hand near the object. If it is hot, the heat can be felt without touching the object. In a similar way, remote sensing devices measure electromagnetic radiation reflected or emitted from features of interest. Photography, for instance, uses an optical lens to record visible light on film.

Any remote sensing system consists of parts which collect, record, store, and finally process and analyze information. See Figure 2.11.

Human beings have eyes and ears to serve as sensors (collectors), and brains to record, store, analyze and interpret information. Yet as "remote sensors" we are very limited. Our senses can detect only a fraction of the electromagnetic spectrum. We do not see or hear X-ray, ultraviolet (UV) and infrared (IR) radiation, microwaves, or radio waves. To make up for our human limitations, scientists have developed sophisticated technologies for detecting and analyzing electromagnetic radiation. These remote sensing technologies can gather detailed information by processing wavelengths we cannot perceive.

If these detecting devices are placed on satellites and aimed properly, we can gather a great deal of information about our Earth.

Digital remote sensing systems convert records of electromagnetic energy to numeric values and

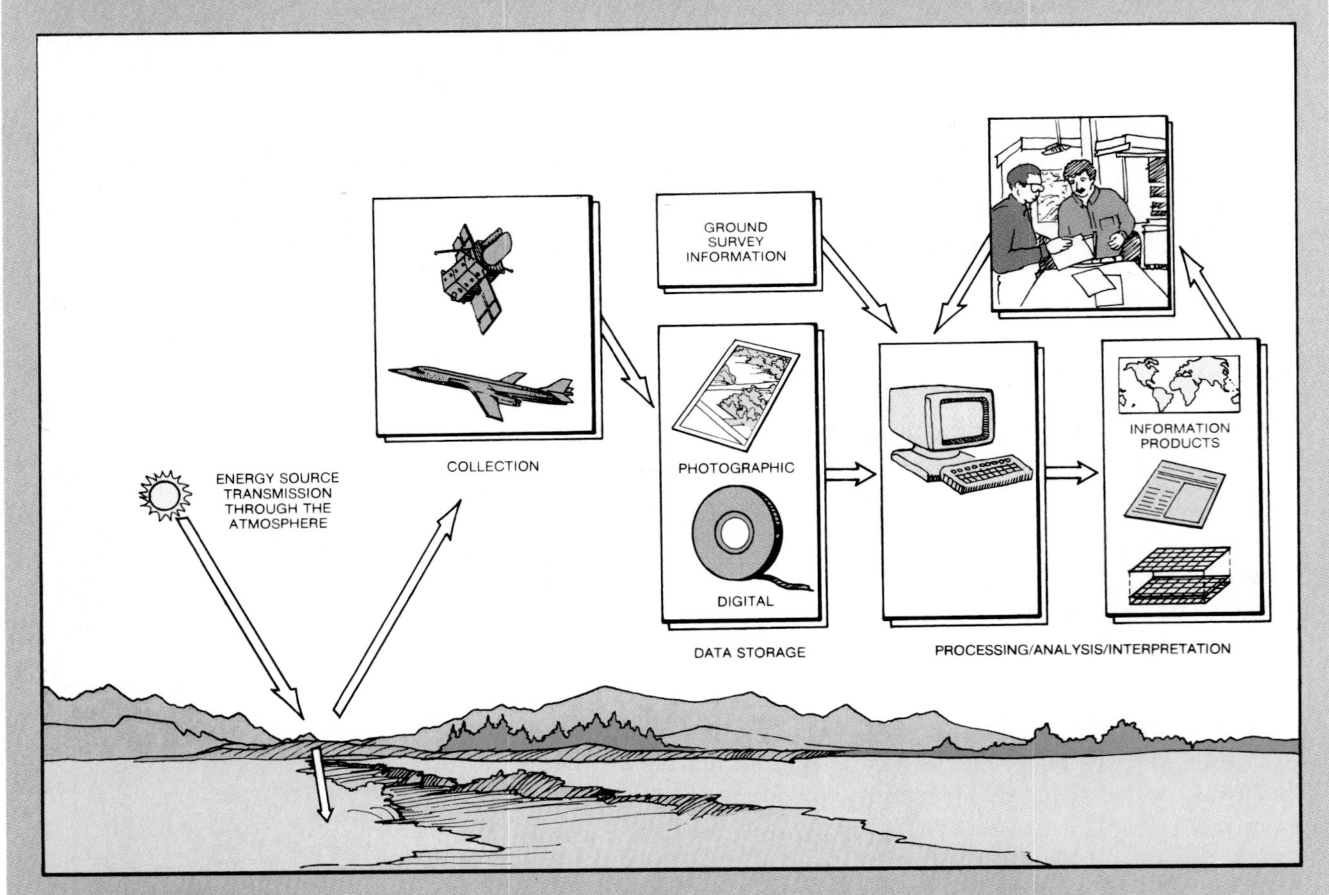

Figure 2.11 The major components of a remote sensing system. (Denver Museum of Natural History.)

Figure 2.12 The Landsat remote sensing satellite. (From Earth Observation Satellite Company, Lanham, Maryland.)

store them on a magnetic tape. Remote sensing satellites beam their data back to Earth where it is picked up by a receiver. To display digital data, a computer program translates each number on the magnetic tape into a pixel or small shaded box. Rows of pixels form scan lines; a series of scan lines builds up an image or picture.

An ever-expanding number of fields of study make use of remote sensing technologies. These include agriculture, climate studies, demographic studies, forestry, geologic mapping, land-use classification and monitoring, mineral resource exploration, oceanography, resource management, tectonics, and many others. The fields listed will all be areas of study in *Global Science*.

Remote sensing provides much valuable information about biomes and the impact humans have on them. The African continent is the subject of constant research, as drought cycles and desertification cause worldwide concern. Desert ecosystems are extremely delicate and do not recover readily from stress. Increasing demand for livestock grazing land, firewood, and cropland, coupled with changing climate, virtually assures that desert areas will continue to expand. Remote sensing plays a part in monitoring desertification by providing periodic data which helps form a basis for planning corrective measures. Figure 2.14 shows the kind of display that can be made available to planners.

Technology has enabled us to escape the bonds of gravity and atmosphere. Views of the Earth's sphere suspended in space reinforce the idea that despite political, philosophical, and geographic boundaries, the planet on which we live is a single entity. Remote sensing is a tool that can help us better manage and enjoy that entity.

Figure 2.13 Topography of the Earth generated from synthesized digital databases. Color-coded topographic contours have been overlain on top of a black and white shaded relief map to give an indication of both relative and absolute relief. The continental data illustrated in the image were acquired by several methods including field measurements and satellite altimetry; the bathymetric (oceanic) data were acquired using down- and side-looking sonars. The resulting image depicts the topographic relief that would be observed from space if the oceans were completely transparent. The color scale, shown at the bottom of the figure, illustrates the linear distribution of colors from 11 km below sea level to 9 km above sea level. (Source: Margo H. Edwards, Raymond E. Arvidson, Washington University in St. Louis, and James R. Heirtzler, Woods Hole Oceanographic Institute.)

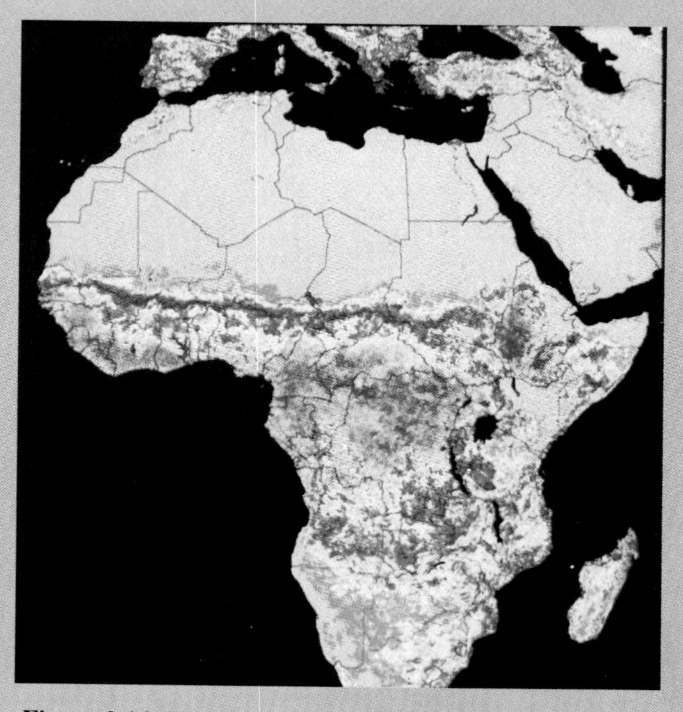

Figure 2.14 This map shows vegetation density in Africa. It was made with the data from eight 21-day composites. The Sahara Desert of northern Africa is seen to be nearly devoid of vegetation, while the rain forests of central Africa show very high densities. The sharp transition between these two regions is also clearly visible. (NASA/GSFC.)

Figure 2.15 Various energy transformations.

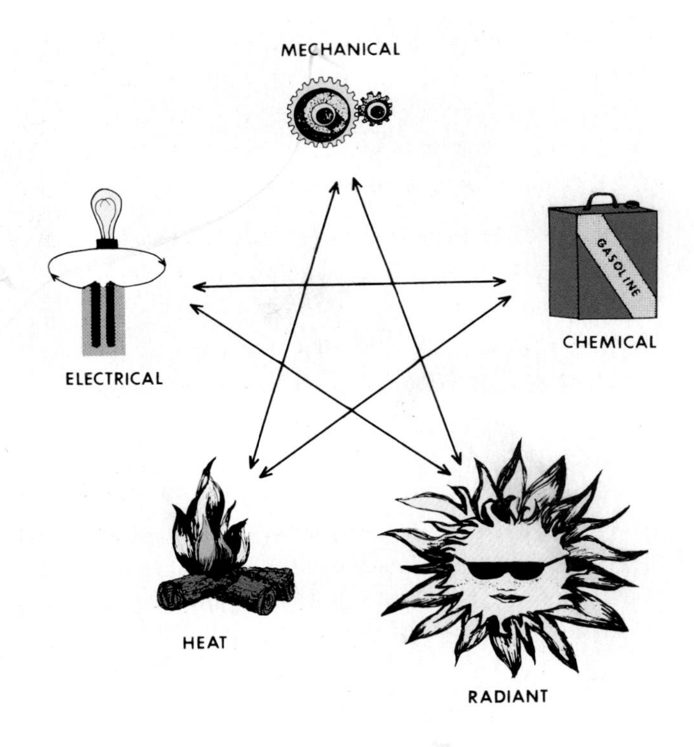

Figure 2.16 A series of energy transformations make possible the delivery of electricity to your home. (Courtesy Avco Everett Research Laboratory, Inc., Everett, Massachusetts.)

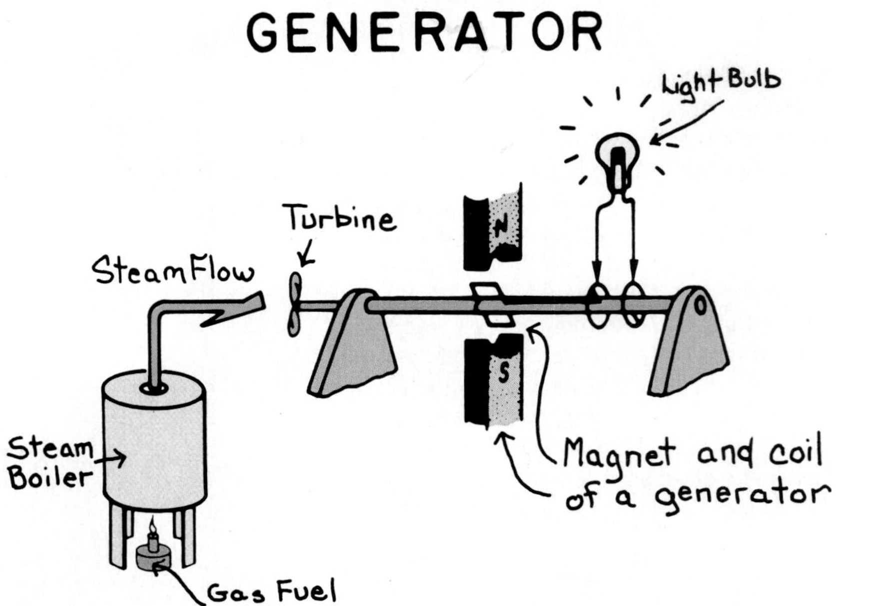

2.9 Energy Units

Energy is found in six different forms. The good news is, they are all directly related. The bad news is, we have several different units for measuring energy in the English and metric systems. The good news is, conversion factors allow us to change from one unit to another. The more common energy-related units are:

calorie (cal) The amount of heat necessary to raise the temperature of one (1) gram of water one Celsius degree at standard atmospheric pressure.

British thermal unit (Btu) The amount of heat required to raise the temperature of one pound of water one Fahrenheit degree at standard atmospheric pressure.

footpound (ft•lb) The amount of work done or energy used when a force of one pound acts through a distance of one foot.

joule An internationally accepted unit equal to about three-quarters of a foot•pound.

barrel of oil (bbl) The amount of energy that can be obtained through the burning of one barrel (42 U.S. gallons) of oil.

ton of TNT The amount of energy stored in or released by one ton of trinitrotoluene (TNT).

watt•hour (wh) The amount of electrical energy that will light a 10-watt bulb for six minutes. One kilowatt•hour of electrical energy will light a 100 watt bulb for ten hours.

2.10 Conversion Factors

Since energy is conserved during transformations, the various energy units are directly related. This means that they can be readily converted to each other by simple mathematical calculation. This is done using conversion factors. The conversion factors used in this course are the following:

Table

1 cal = 3.968×10^{-3} Btu = 4.184 J

1 kcal = 1000 cal = 1 dietetic Cal = 3.97 Btu

Btu = 252.0 cal = 772 ft•lb

1 ft•lb = 1.285×10^{-3} Btu = 0.3239 cal

1 J = 0.2389 cal = 0.7376 ft•lb

1 ton of TNT = 1.04×10^{9} cal = 4.14×10^{6} Btu

1 bbl = 5.8×10^{6} Btu

1 kWh = 3413 Btu = 1.341 horsepower (hp) = 1000 wh

Conversion factors enable us to change from one energy unit to another.

You can get some practice making energy unit conversions by doing some of the problems at the end of this chapter. If you need to refresh your mathematical memory (or learn something new), see Appendix 6.

Figure 2.17 A solar home utilizing flat-plate collectors.

?

What are the five primary sources of energy?

2.11 Energy Sources

Energy is available from the sun and other sources. As it is transformed, its usefulness is lessened.

At first it seems that our energy comes from a great variety of sources. A close analysis reveals that ultimately all our energy comes from only five primary sources. They are described below.

a. The Sun

The sun.

Most solar radiation is used as it arrives on Earth. Some is stored in chemical bonds and used later. The sun is basically a huge fusion reactor that radiates energy in all directions. Only a tiny fraction of the sun's energy arrives at the Earth, but that is still a huge amount of energy. Measurements outside the atmosphere indicate that Earth intercepts 1.353 kilowatts of power per square meter perpendicular to the sun's rays. That means that the total solar radiation intercepted by the Earth's surface area of 1.275×10^{14} square meters is 1.73×10^{17} watts!

Even though 30% of the energy never actually reaches the surface (being reflected from clouds, ice, etc.), the remainder warms the Earth. It also evaporates water and drives the water cycle. It drives all the winds, waves, and the Earth's weather system. Finally, it provides the energy for all photosynthesis and thus for plant and biological change.

How does the sun contribute to a variety of solar energy options?

At the Earth's surface, the solar input is approximately 1.0 kilowatt per square meter. Although very spread out, this power density can accomplish many useful tasks.

Current solar radiation makes possible a variety of energy options that are attracting significant interest in the United States. These include solar heating and cooling of homes (See Figure 2.17), solar-powered electric generating plants, wind power, and the use of temperature differences in the ocean to generate electricity. Each of these will be discussed in some detail in Chapter 9.

How is solar energy stored for future use?

Stored solar energy. Solar energy is stored in living plants (when they photosynthesize food) and in animals (when they eat plants). Significant quantities of energy are available to us from this source.

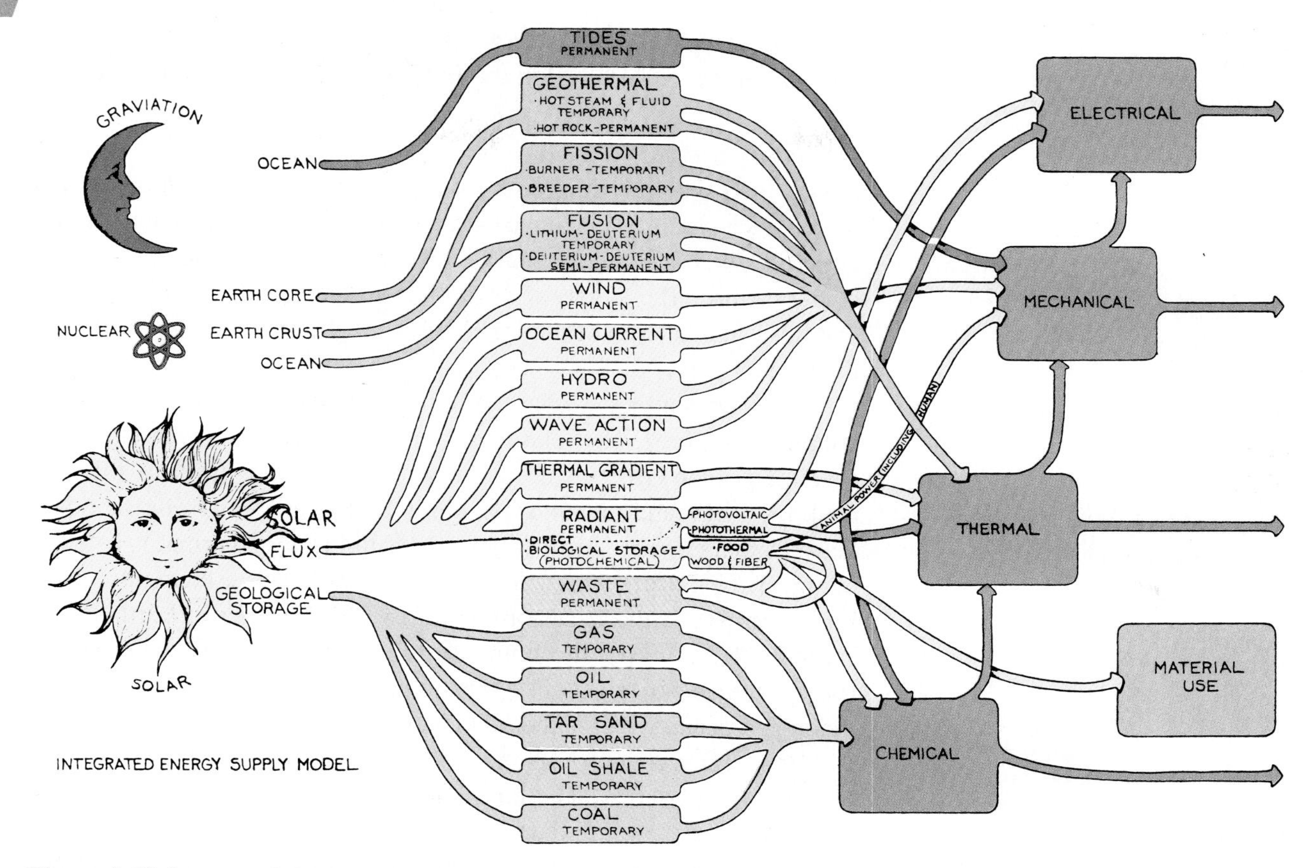

Figure 2.18 Integrated energy supply model. (From Office of Energy Research and Planning, State of Oregon.)

Decomposing plant and animal waste can be converted into methane gas and alcohol. Methane can be directly substituted for natural gas.

Solar energy is stored in plants that have recently died (dead wood and hay) and in trash (wood and plastic). Solar energy is stored in plants that died many millions of years ago forming fossil fuels (oil, gas, coal, oil shale, and tar sands).

At present rates of use, United States coal supplies could provide most of our energy needs for the next 500 years.

Modern societies run primarily on oil, gas, and coal. Unless we learn to tap other sources of energy, our reserves of fossil fuels will ultimately be exhausted.

b. Tides

This energy originates in the gravitational system of the earth, our moon, and the sun. The tides offer us a fascinating energy option. The applications are primarily of local interest.

c. Earth's Heat

The heat stored just below Earth's surface is caused by tremendous subsurface pressures and by the energetic decay of radioactive substances. This **geothermal** source is being used to provide steam to turn generators and supply electricity.

Earth's heat.

Fission fuels.

d. Fission Fuels

The energy stored in unstable uranium and thorium nuclei can be released and used to produce electricity. Uranium and thorium compounds can be extracted from the Earth's crust like other minerals.

e. Fusion Fuels

Deuterium and tritium are forms of hydrogen, the lightest element.

All energy available to humans on Earth ultimately comes from five primary sources: the sun, the tides, the Earth's heat, fission fuels, and fusion fuels.

Fusion involves the combining of very light nuclei to make larger ones. Since stability is gained in the combining process, energy is released. Deuterium and tritium have been found to be the easiest light nuclei to fuse. The supply of deuterium in the world's oceans is huge. Tritium is made from lithium which, although rare, can be mined from the Earth's crust.

The five sources we have summarized are shown in the left-hand column of Figure 2.18. Solar is divided into current sunshine (the solar flux) and solar energy stored in the ground in the form of oil, gas, coal, oil shale, and tar sand. Fusion is listed partly as from the ocean because that is where most of the deuterium is. Geothermal is listed as being in the Earth's core (actually from radioactive elements in the Earth's crust) as the heat comes from within the Earth. Earth's crust contains the uranium, thorium, and lithium that are raw materials for fission and fusion reactions. The gravitational attraction between the moon and ocean water is the major cause of the tides.

The center column lists the various energy options that come from the beginning sources. The boxes at the right represent the usual final forms of energy from all sources. The flowlines or arrows show the paths of the most common transformations. For example: Natural gas, which is stored *solar* energy, can release the *chemical* energy stored in its molecular bonds and give off heat (*thermal* energy). This heat can boil water, and the resulting steam can turn a turbine. The *mechanical* energy of the turbine can be used to power a generator that produces *electrical* energy. We also see that the *radiant* energy of the sun can cause a photovoltaic (solar) cell to convert solar energy directly into electrical energy. A fuel cell can generate electricity from hydrogen and oxygen without a steam-turbine phase. Try to identify other energy transformations on your own.

?

Why does the second law of thermodynamics suggest that modern societies create problems as they use their energy and mineral supplies?

2.12 The Second Law of Thermodynamics (Forms 1–3)

The first law of thermodynamics states that energy can neither be created nor destroyed. Thus, we are neither gaining nor losing energy! If this is the case, why should we worry about running out of energy? There's just as much energy now as there has always been!

What does the second law of thermodynamics tell us?

We know that when we fill our car's tank with gasoline and drive around, we lose something. If we didn't lose energy, what did we lose? The answer to this question is given by the second law of thermodynamics. We will state this law three ways. Each statement will add to your understanding of what the law says. (Mathematics can be used to show that all three statements are the same. However, proving this is beyond the scope of this course.)

Form 1: In any conversion of energy from one form to another, there is always a decrease in the amount of useful energy.

Useful energy is energy which can *easily* be used to move objects or to generate electricity. Moving objects and producing electricity are what modern societies prefer to do with the major portion of their energy resources.

What we mean by losing usefulness can be better understood by doing Exercise 2.1, "The Agony of (da) Heat."

Remember not to write in your textbook. Use a separate piece of paper for your answers.

Exercise 2.1 The agony of (da) Heat.

Examine the heat engine shown and then answer the questions below. The engine is enclosed in a perfectly insulated box (heat cannot enter or leave). The chamber at the left contains a very hot gas; the chamber at the right contains a cold gas. The paddlewheel's axle is mounted and turned on nearly frictionless bearings. Turning the generator and lighting the bulb requires only a tiny amount of energy. To start the heat engine, the valve is opened.

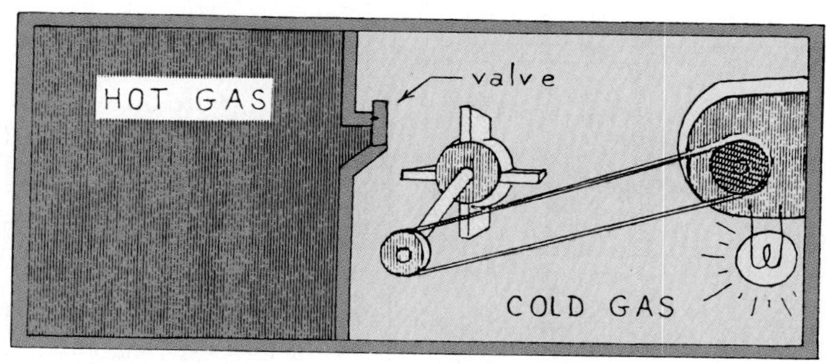

1. Why does the bulb light when the valve is first opened? ______________________________

____

2. What happens to the brightness of the bulb as time goes on? ______________________________

____

Why? ______________________________

3. Is energy lost as time goes on? ______________________________

What does change as time goes on? ______________________________

4. What is the direction of heat flow in this experiment? ______________________________

5. Is the heat flow spontaneous? ______________________________

6. When the valve was first opened, the energy did two useful tasks. List them. 1. __________ 2. __________
7. Complete the definition of useful energy. Be very general in stating what useful energy can do.

<u>Useful (quality) energy</u>: Energy which can easily be used to ______________ or ______________.
<u>Hint</u>: The answer to Question 6 will help you.

8. Using the definition of useful energy in Question 7, one may conclude that as energy is used (transformed) it goes to (less ___, more ___) useful forms. "X" the correct response.

(Adapted from PEEC Packet: *There is Enough Energy, So What's the Problem?* National Science Teachers Association, Washington, D.C.)

Remember not to write in your textbook. Use a separate piece of paper for your answers.

Exercise 2.2

Choosing Disorder

If one is to relate The Second Law of Thermodynamics to real world happenings and understand the concept of energy quality, one must first have a good grasp of what is meant by disorder. The following exercise will help you gain that grasp.

Shown below are six *pairs* of pictures. Choose the picture in each pair that represents the most disordered state and write "**MOST DISORDERED**" in the blank provided. Then answer the True-False question at the bottom of the page.

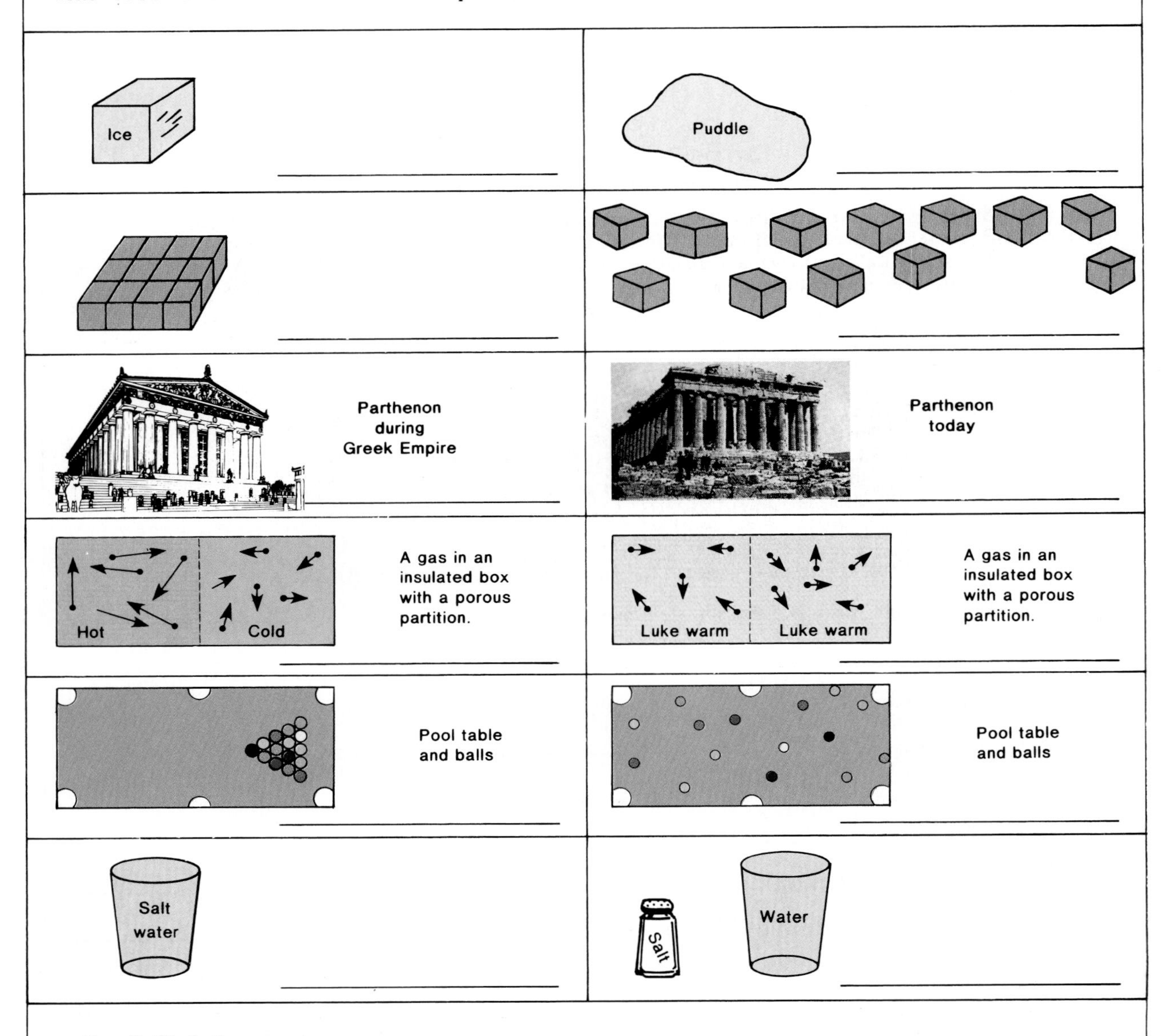

T or F: Circle the correct response.

The most disorderly arrangement is the arrangement in which the particles of matter are all "doing their own thing." Hence the most disorderly state is the most probable state.

Source: PEEC Packet: *There is Enough Energy, So What's the Problem?* National Science Teachers Association, Washington, D.C.

Remember not to write in your textbook. Use a separate piece of paper for your answers.

Exercise 2.3

It's a One Way Street

Synonyms: randomness ⟷ disorder ⟷ chaos ⟷ entropy.

Place 100 pennies "heads up" on a board. Flip the board over and allow the pennies to fall randomly to the floor. Take data on what happened by filling in the chart below. Do this ten times and then answer the questions.

Note: Your closed system consists of 100 pennies, the board and the floor.

Classification: 90–100 heads or tails = highly ordered.
70– 89 heads or tails = somewhat ordered.
50– 69 heads or tails = disordered.
H = heads, T = tails

Trial	Start	End	Classification
1	100 H	______	
2	100 H	______	
3	100 H	______	
4	100 H	______	
5	100 H	______	
6	100 H	______	
7	100 H	______	
8	100 H	______	
9	100 H	______	
10	100 H	______	

Questions:

1. As the pennies fall to the floor, they go to a more ____________ state.
2. To get the pennies back into an orderly arrangement, we must supply ____________________ from outside our closed system.
3. Plants, as they grow, create order by taking CO_2 and H_2O and combining them into structured (orderly) plant material. Do plants violate The Second Law of Thermodynamics by creating order? Why or why not?

____

____

4. If there is as much copper in the world today as there has always been, why are we "running out" of copper?

____

____

Remember not to write in your textbook. Use a separate piece of paper for your answers.

Exercise 2.3—*Continued*

5. **Why can't automobile exhausts be readily recycled and changed back into gasoline again?**

____

____

6. **Comment on the statement, "Little children are truly entropy's little helpers."**

____

____

7. **Relate the following equation to Form 3 of the Second Law:**

$$\text{plants} \overset{\text{balance}}{\rightleftharpoons} \text{animals (including man)}$$

Source: PEEC Packet: *There is Enough Energy, So What's the Problem?* National Science Teachers Association, Washington, D.C.

The least useful form of energy is low temperature heat. This is heat that is near the temperature of our surroundings. That's why we throw so much of it away. The purpose of the cooling towers at electric power generating plants is to discharge low temperature heat into the atmosphere. The fins on gasoline engines are there to help dissipate (dump) heat. The radiator in your car is another example. Can you think of other examples of ways we throw away heat?

The word spontaneous means occurring by itself, without help.

Form 2: Heat cannot of itself flow from cold to hot. It spontaneously flows from hot to cold.

What is meant by "The Agony of (da) Heat"?

Looking at the second law of thermodynamics in this way was also illustrated in "The Agony of (da) Heat." Work (the moving of objects) can only be accomplished when there is a difference in the energy content of objects. When the universe reaches a constant temperature, there will be *no* difference in energy content, and life anywhere in it will cease. This is referred to as "the heat death of the universe." Why must it occur? If people manage their affairs well, how long can humans survive on planet Earth? (*Answer:* As long as the sun lasts. The heat death of our sun is expected in about 5 billion years or so).

Form 3: In any closed system, randomness always tends toward a maximum.

Some synonyms for randomness are chaos, disorder, and entropy. You will find these words used interchangeably in the materials that follow. The meaning of disorder and of Form 3 of the second law will become meaningful to you as you do Exercises 2.2 and 2.3.

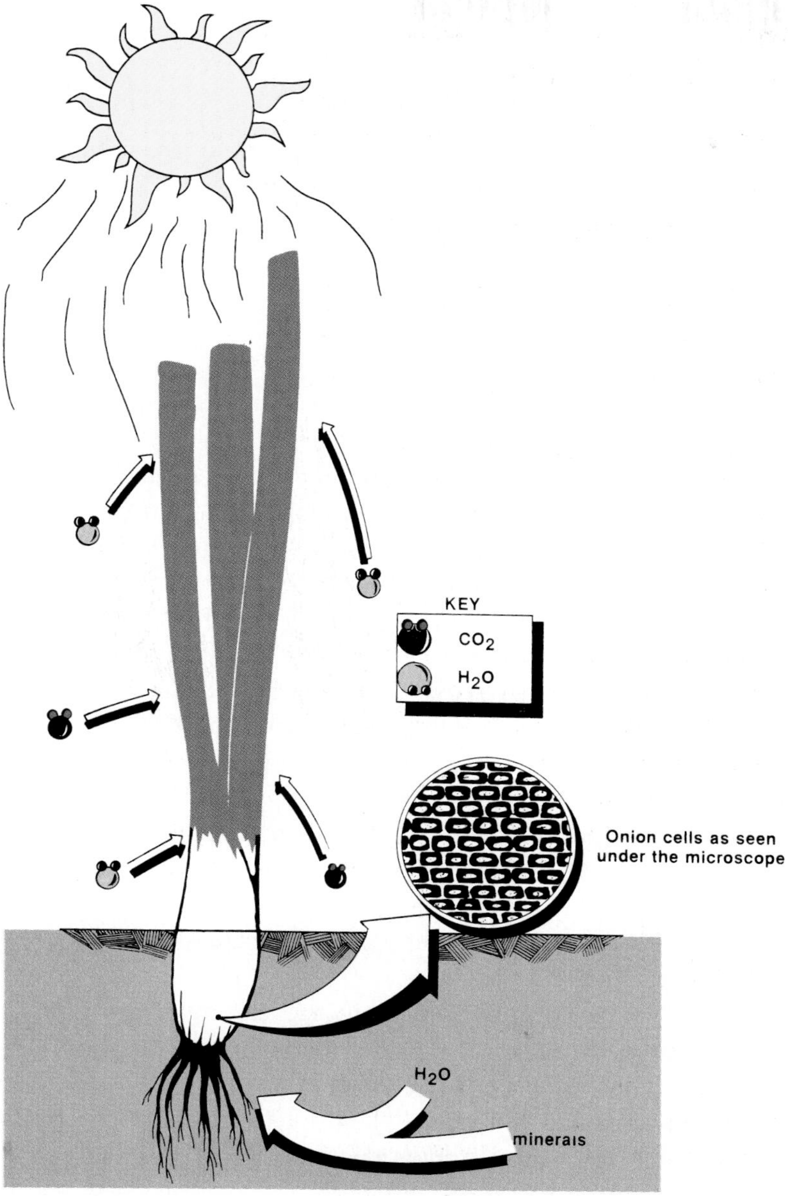

Figure 2.19 Photosynthesis implies order. Consider the onion.

At first glance, plants seem to violate Form 3 of the second law of thermodynamics, because they create order as they grow. The random movement of carbon dioxide and water molecules is converted to orderly plant structures in the photosynthesis process.

Figure 2.19 illustrates this concept. It must be remembered, though, that the second law of thermodynamics describes the behavior of closed systems. A plant is not a closed system. To make food and grow, it must be supplied with energy from the outside.

This idea can extend to the biosphere as a whole. The sun provides energy. Plants capture that energy for a time and store it in their orderly cell structures. Animals (including humans) utilize this store of energy to perform their life functions. In the process, they break down plant material and create disorder. If order and disorder can be better balanced, humans can live on Earth as long as the sun provides adequate energy.

2.13 Energy and Efficiency

What do we mean by high efficiency?

An *efficient* person gets a lot done with little effort. The definition of an efficient machine is the same. The efficiency of a machine is the ratio of the desired output (work or energy) to the input.

$$\text{That is: efficiency} = \frac{\text{useful energy or work out}}{\text{energy or work in}} \times 100\%$$

The first law of thermodynamics places a limit on how high efficiency can go. Since you can't create energy, no efficiency can be greater than 100 percent. You can't get more useful work out of any process than energy you put into it. You can't get something for nothing. In most real world situations, efficiencies are much less than 100 percent.

Certain types of friction are useful and necessary, such as that between a pulley and belt, or between your automobile tires and the road surface.

In industry, much energy is wasted as heat caused by friction. For that reason, industrial engineers try to reduce friction. Their efforts have included machining smooth surfaces, developing new lubricants, inventing better electrical conductors, and so on. Though the losses may be small, they are still there.

Any device that converts heat energy into mechanical energy is called a heat engine. Heat engines are important. The internal combustion engine in our cars, jet engines and the coal fired steam turbines at electric power plants are all examples. Unfortunately, heat engines are very inefficient.

Why are heat engines inefficient?

Figure 2.20 lists the efficiencies of various energy converters. Devices that are inefficient are located at the bottom of the illustration. Devices with high efficiency are located at the top. Note that electric motors, generators and batteries are highly efficient. Heat engines are inefficient devices. Heat engines made of metal must be quickly cooled. This also adds to their inefficiency. Devices that are used for lighting are also very inefficient.

2.14 System Efficiency

Let's examine the system for lighting an incandescent light bulb, using energy that originally comes from coal. Refer to Figure 2.21 as you read the next three paragraphs. The numbers refer to the related sections of the figure.

The coal that is mined contains a certain amount of energy. But energy was used to mine the coal. This energy must be counted as part of the input. After washing and sorting, the coal must next be transported to the power plant. It takes energy to transport coal. This must be added to the input side of the ledger.

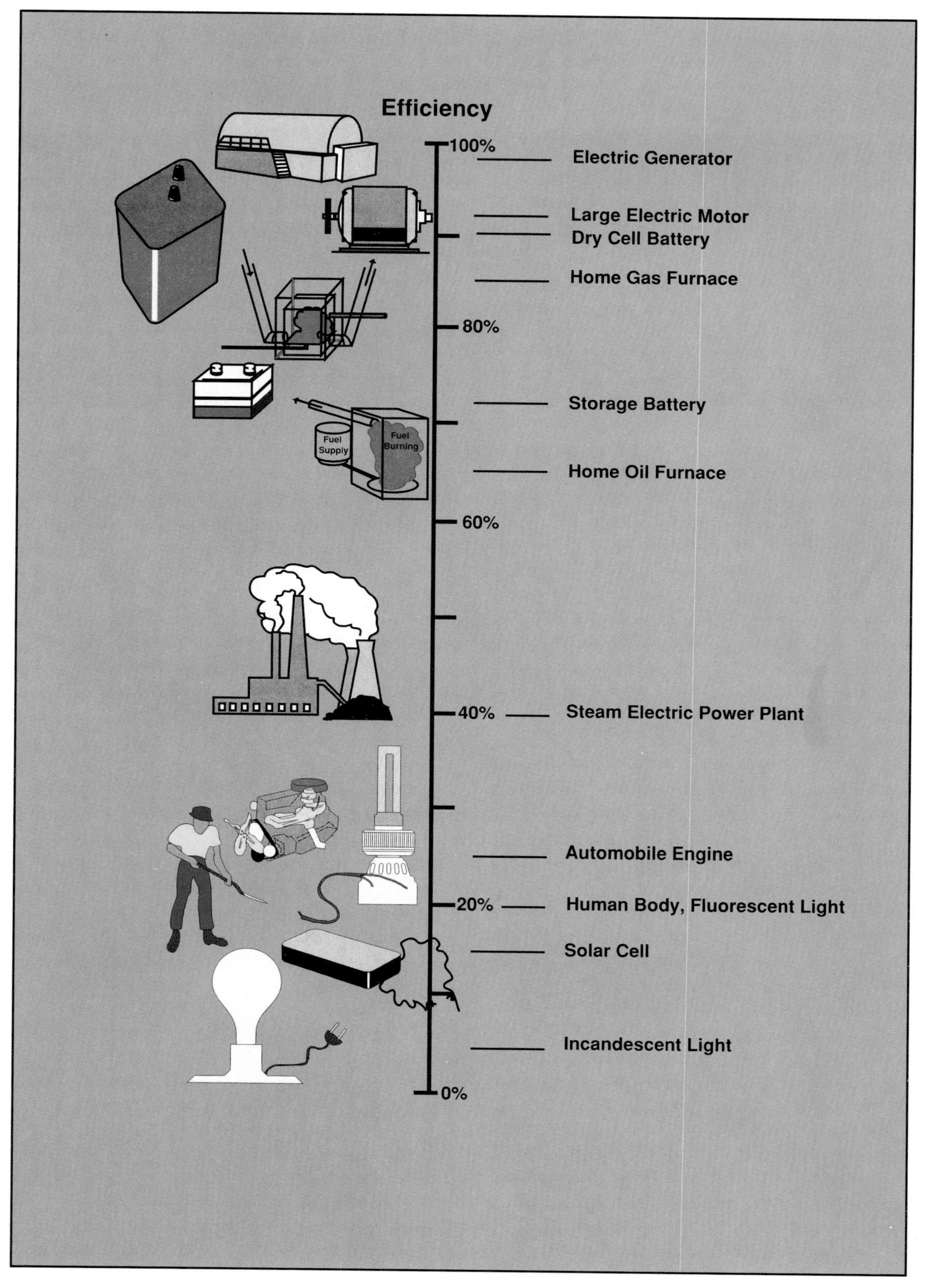

Figure 2.20 The energy efficiency of some common energy conversion devices used by modern society.

Figure 2.21 A coal-fired electric power generating plant. (National Coal Association.)

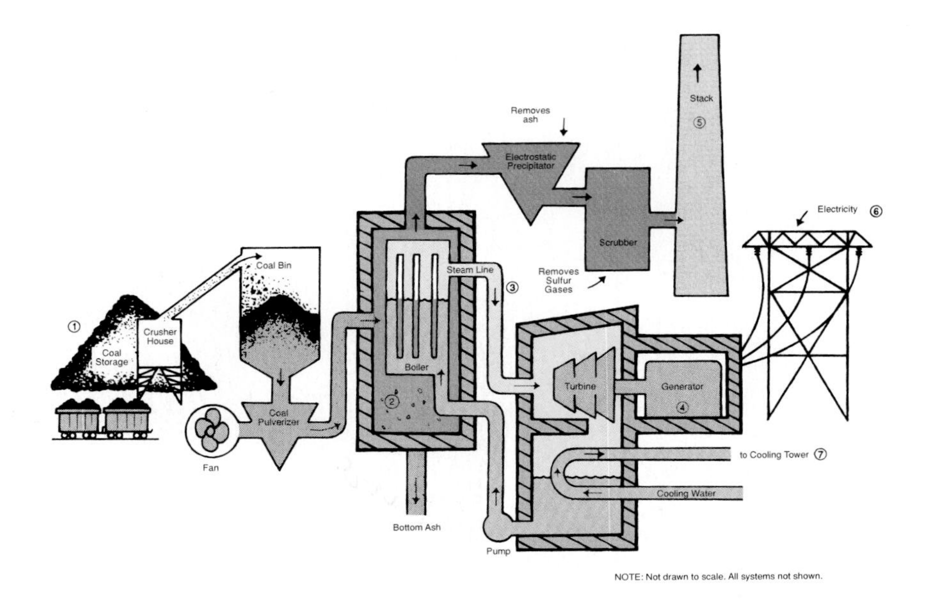

Why is the lighting of an electric bulb so inefficient?

Coal (1) is burned in the furnace (2) at the electric power plant. The heat produced is used to create steam. The steam (3) turns a turbine which turns the generator (4). Each of these conversion steps has its own efficiency. In the end, only about one-third of the energy of the coal at the plant appears as electrical energy (6). The other two-thirds is wasted as heat. It goes up the stack (5) with the hot exhaust gases or into the cooling tower (7). Turbines won't work unless the pressure is high where the steam goes in, and low where it leaves. Without the pressure difference, the steam could not act on the turbine blades. To create this difference, the steam-escape side of the turbine must be cooled. The cooling water both condenses steam and carries heat away. It is this heat that utilities release into the environment (air, lakes, or rivers). Some energy is used internally for running the plant and the pollution control devices, or for other functions.

The electrical energy must now be transported over high voltage transmission lines (6) and a lower voltage distribution system. It must flow through transformers to step the voltage up or down. Energy is lost in transmission. It heats up the conductors and disappears into the surroundings.

The remaining energy now arrives at the lamp. Figure 2.22 illustrates the whole process from generating plant to your home. At this point, most of the energy is lost in the process of heating the lamp filament to incandescence. Only 5 percent of it is actually converted to visible light. Thus only 5 percent of the energy that goes into the room illuminates its target. This illuminating energy is finally absorbed by some object and converted into heat.

We described this process to make a point. If we are to use energy to obtain light, the efficiency of the process does not depend just on the efficiency of the final conversion. Instead, it depends on the efficiency of each step of the flow. The cumulative efficiency of the

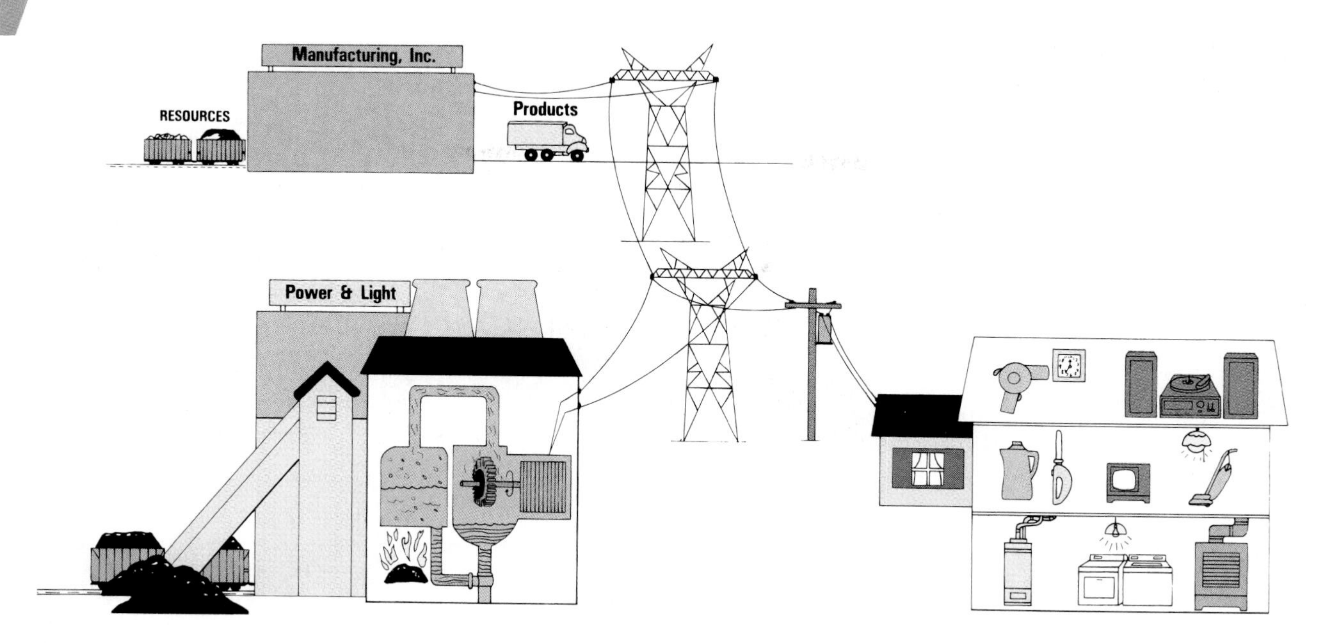

Figure 2.22 Generation, transmission and distribution of electricity. (Adapted from *Coal in Your World, National Coal Association.*)

Step	Efficiency of Step (in percent)	Cumulative Efficiency (in percent)
Production of Coal	96	96
Transportation of Coal	97	93
Generation of Electricity	33	31
Transmission of Electricity	85	26
Lighting, Incandescent (fluorescent)	5 (20)	1.3 (5.2)

Figure 2.23 Energy system efficiency of electric lighting (from coal-fired generation). (*From Energy-Environment Source Book,* by John M. Fowler, Washington, D.C.: National Science Teachers Association, 1975.)

whole process is called the **system efficiency.** It is the real measure of how efficiently we are using our energy sources. In the case of lighting the incandescent bulb, it is only 1.3 percent.

Why is the concept of "system efficiency" so important?

The concept of system efficiency is very important in understanding the energy problem. Many of our energy conversion processes require several steps. For example, to produce electricity, we usually mine, crush, and transport coal. Then we burn it to turn a turbine to turn a generator. Finally, the electricity must be brought to our homes by wires. It is then transformed to some end use, such as lighting a bulb.

In every energy conversion, a "heat tax" must be paid. The price we pay for energy is influenced by how many loss factors are involved in the conversion of that energy into its end use form.

At each conversion of energy along some path, some energy is "lost" in the form of waste heat. This waste heat is discharged into the atmosphere or into our rivers and lakes by the electric utility plants. It is given off by the wires that carry electricity, "lost" from our poorly insulated houses and commercial buildings, "lost" by inefficient furnaces, and "lost" to the atmosphere by the inefficient engines of our automobiles. In each conversion of energy in a multi-step process, a

Figure 2.24 Energy system efficiency of the automobile. (From *Energy-Environment Source Book*, by John M. Fowler, Washington, D.C.: National Science Teachers Association, 1975.)

Step	Efficiency of Step (in percent)	Cummulative Efficiency (in percent)
Production of Crude Oil	96	96
Refining of Gasoline	87	84
Transportation of Gasoline	97	81
Thermal to Mechanical-Engine	25-30	20-24
Mechanical Efficiency-Transmission (includes auxiliary systems)	50-60	10-15
Rolling Efficiency	60	6-9

Figure 2.25 Energy system efficiency of water heating. (From *Energy-Environment Source Book*, by John M. Fowler, Washington, D.C.: National Science Teachers Association, 1975.)

Step	Efficiency of Step (in percent)	Cummulative Efficiency (in percent)
Electric (coal-fired)		
Production of Coal	96	96
Transportation of Coal	97	93
Generation of Electricity	33	31
Transmission of Electricity	85	26
Heating Efficiency	92	24
Natural Gas		
Production of Natural Gas	96	96
Transportation of Natural Gas	97	93
Heating Efficiency	64	60

The overall efficiency of a system is equal to the product of the efficiencies of the various steps in the process.

"heat tax" must be paid because some of the energy is "lost" as far as future use is concerned. As a result, the overall system efficiency is equal to the *product* of the efficiencies of the various steps in the process. (See Figures 2.24 and 2.25 for examples.)

Figure 2.23 reveals the best strategies for improving system efficiency. Replacing the incandescent light (efficiency 5 percent) with a fluorescent light (efficiency 20 percent) is one of those strategies.

2.15 Net Energy

How do we determine if we get our "energy's worth?"

Energy system analysis encourages us to look at each step of the process of energy transfer from source to end use. We need to determine if we are getting our "energy's worth." In this examination we usually confine our bookkeeping to direct energy input and loss. We take into account the gasoline and diesel fuel used to run mining equipment and transport vehicles. However, we do not take into account the energy used to build the trucks and tractors, or to build the buildings, transmission lines, transformers, etc.

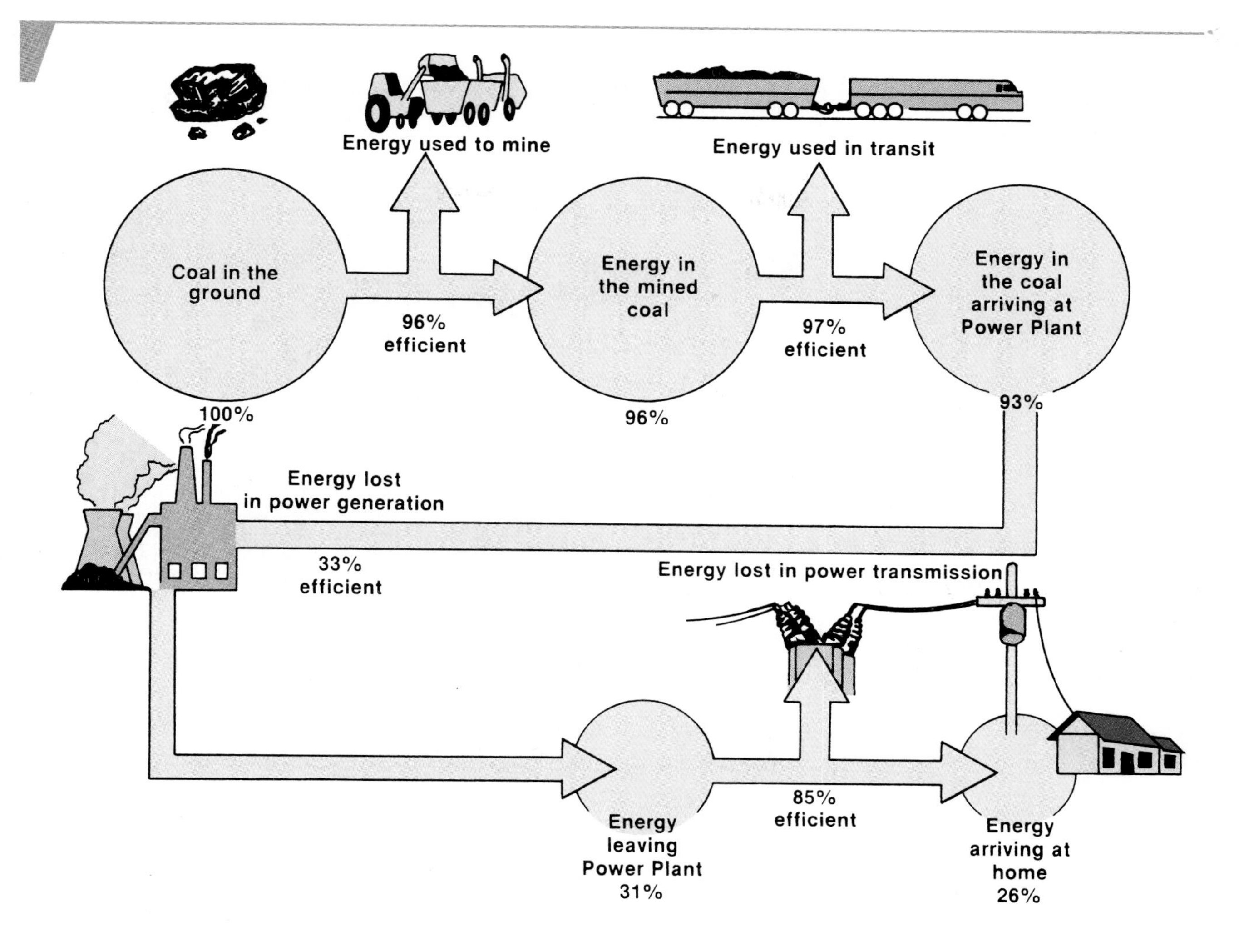

Figure 2.26 The efficiency of electric power delivery systems.

When coal was mined with a pickaxe and transported by wagon to a residential stove, the indirect energy input could be neglected. The wagon load of coal had much more energy in it than was used in any of the equipment.

This is no longer the case. Even in the case of coal there is a significant amount of energy expended in building the huge shovels and drag lines, the trucks, train cars, and power plants.

When we move beyond coal to uranium we have an even more energy-intensive process to consider. It takes enormous amounts of energy to enrich the uranium in the fuel rods and build the thick stainless steel vessel which surrounds a nuclear reactor.

Figure 2.26 traces the flow of energy from a coal mine to a home. The size of the circles represents the amount of useful energy available. In terms of usefulness, a significant price is paid for the luxury of having electricity available at the flick of a switch.

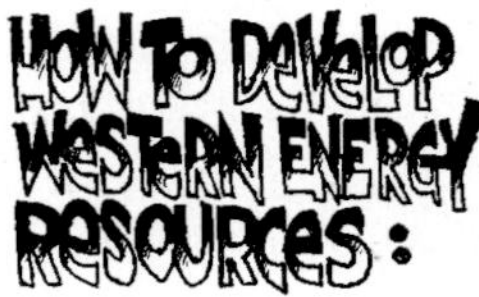

Figure 2.27 Net energy analysis.
(Mike Keefe, *The Denver Post*.)

What is meant by "net energy"?

The *net energy* of an energy production system is the ratio of the total energy produced over the lifetime of the system to the total energy (both direct and indirect) used to produce that energy. The larger this ratio, the better.

The fact that energy production now requires massive and complex equipment makes it useful to add to our efficiency measures the concept of **net energy**. The net energy of an energy production system is the ratio of the total energy produced over the lifetime of the system to the total energy, direct and indirect, used to produce that energy.

Net energy is clearly a useful tool for analysis. It is of no benefit to us, for instance, to employ a system for which the ratio is less than one. We should also look skeptically at ratios near one, because they indicate we are running in place.

Unfortunately, net energy studies are hard to do. Indirect energy measurements are hard to obtain. In the past, we have not computed the energy needed to manufacture a truck or build a power plant or drill an oil well in the ocean. Such studies are now being undertaken. Relate the concept of net energy to Figure 2.27.

Matter and Energy in Natural Systems

Ecosystems are dynamic (changing) systems in which there is a constant transfer of energy and materials. Energy flows through ecosystems in one-way paths. Matter flows along with energy, but is recycled. As energy flows, a balance is established between the environmental resources and the organisms present. If the first-order consumers eat too many of the producers and therefore deplete their food reserve, then many of the first-order consumers will die. This continues until a balance is reached between their population and the amount of food available.

2.16 Energy Flow in Nature

How is an ecological system like a human-built system?

The energy flow in natural ecosystems is governed by the same laws that operate in human-built systems. Energy is changed from one form to another. However, the total amount never changes. With living things, energy is lost to the environment as heat. This is much like burning fuel to run an engine, or using electricity to light a bulb. Energy must be transformed to drive either living or human-built systems. The chemical energy stored in carbon compounds must be changed to the mechanical energy of movement whether we are talking about the food that moves a person or the gasoline that powers a car.

Furthermore, efficiency is just as important in natural systems as it is in the energy systems people have created. The same principles appear again. No conversion is ever 100 percent efficient. Some energy is always lost (as heat). The final efficiency of a series of energy changes is the product of all the intermediate efficiencies. Figures 2.28 and 2.29 have a lot more in common than may at first seem apparent. Can you see how they show the same idea?

Figure 2.29 shows that a certain amount of energy arriving on the surface of a green leaf is captured in the sugar molecules plants produce through the process of photosynthesis. In photosynthesis, a plant converts solar energy to chemical energy which it stores in its cells. Plants and animals are able to use this stored energy to perform their daily functions. Special enzymes break down the energy compounds and release the energy for body needs.

Photosynthesis is nowhere near 100 percent efficient! Whatever energy is trapped in this way is all the energy that the ecosystem has. It's the living equivalent of a full tank of gas. If the tank were not constantly refilled by the sun and the action of green plants, the ecosystem would "run out of gas" very quickly.

When a primary consumer eats a plant, energy is transferred and transformed. The chemical energy stored in the plant food materials is changed to kinetic energy. This helps move the organism, and heat energy is released into the environment. Some of the plant's energy is stored in the bones and tissues of the animal.

If the animal is eaten, its energy becomes available to the secondary consumer (or carnivore). Since there is energy loss at each transfer, the total amount of energy available to secondary consumers is always less than what was available to primary consumers. Likewise, the total amount of energy available to primary consumers is always less than what came from the sun, or even what the plants trapped through photosynthesis.

Why is less energy available for secondary consumers than for primary consumers?

A food chain is the transfer of energy from one organism to another. Producers, green plants, transfer a certain portion of their energy to the herbivores or primary consumers such as rabbits or cows. However, a major portion of the energy (often as much as 90%) is lost in the transfer, usually in the form of heat energy. At each of the following steps in the food chain, another 90% of the energy is lost. This is one of the reasons that there are not very many animals at the top of the food chain, for it takes much energy to support them. It also explains why animals spend much of their time eating and behaving in ways that conserve energy.

Figure 2.28 Diagram of an electric power plant showing how energy flows through from coal to alternating current. (National Coal Association.)

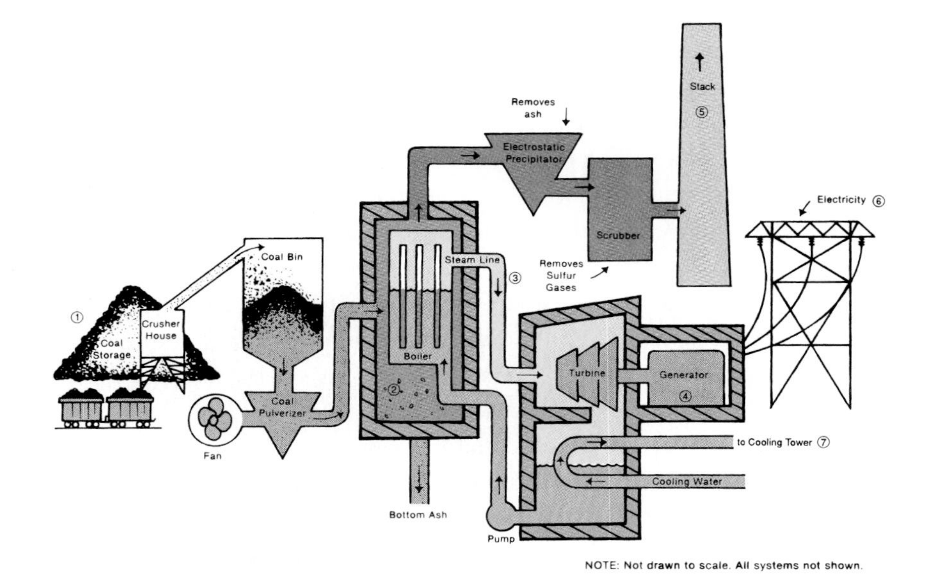

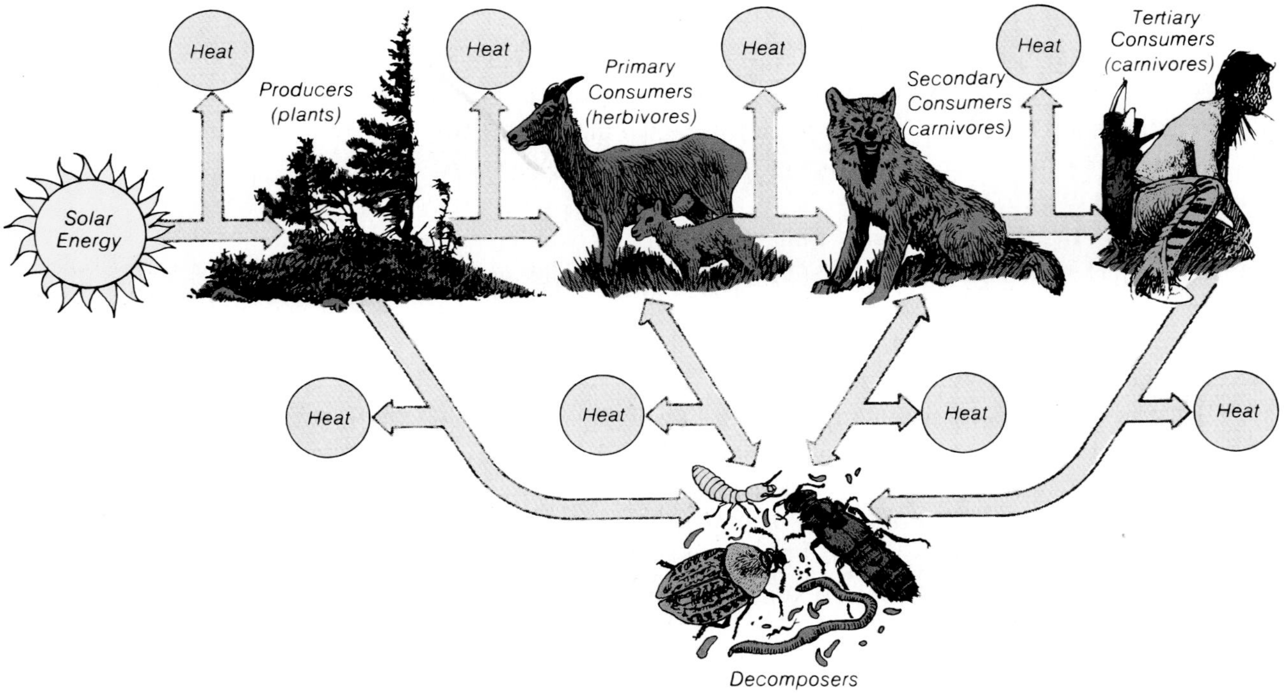

Figure 2.29 A simple food chain showing how energy flows through various trophic levels. (From *Living in the Environment* by G. Tyler Miller, Jr. Copyright © 1975 by Wadsworth Publishing Co., Inc., Belmont, California 94002. Reprinted by permission of the publisher.)

The relationships just described are sometimes drawn as an **energy pyramid,** showing producers on the bottom and secondary or tertiary consumers on the top. Figure 2.30 shows in graphic form the relationships just described.

Food chains usually become diverse and web-like instead of linear. Secondary consumers may have many choices and sometimes

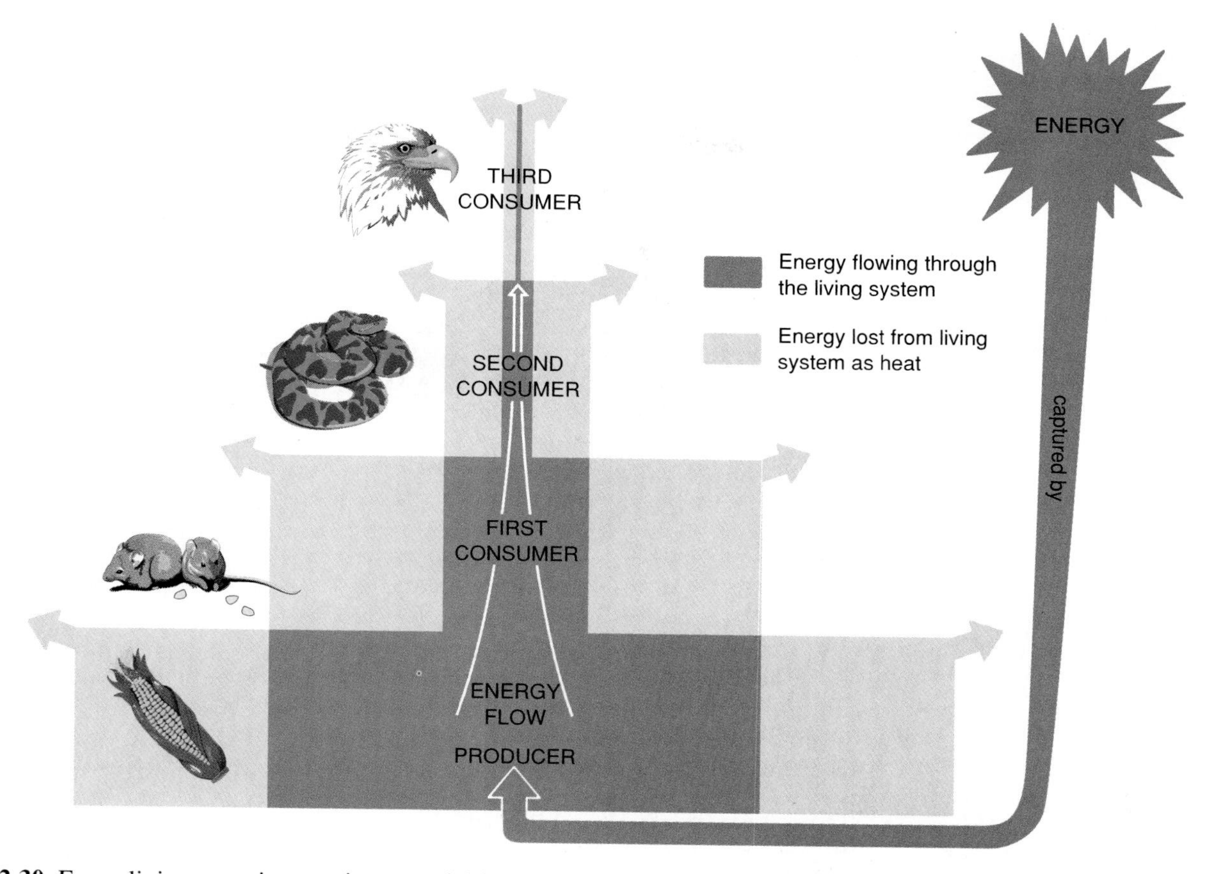

Figure 2.30 Every living organism carries on activities that result in the release of energy. Therefore, each following consumer level obtains a smaller percentage of the energy that was trapped by the producer. (From *Biological Science: An Ecological Approach, Green Version,* 3rd ed., 1973.)

become primary consumers as well. (Omnivores eat both plants and animals.) When this occurs, we say we have a food web. Figure 2.31 illustrates one such web. As the animals die, their remains are converted to minerals, gases, and heat by the decomposers that break them down. Much of the decomposition energy is lost to adjacent material or to the atmosphere. The heat created in a compost pile is one example of this energy release.

Energy is "lost" in the form of heat each time it is transferred from one organism to another. The amount of energy available to primary consumers is always greater than the amount available to secondary or tertiary consumers.

What is the system efficiency of an ecosystem? The answer varies depending on the type, variety, and number of plants and animals in a system and how they interact with abiotic factors. In general, the more plant life present, the greater the energy flow through an ecosystem. Warmer climates typically support more plant life than cooler ones. Lower elevations are usually more productive than higher ones. Some ecologists have, despite all the variables, calculated average values for ecosystem efficiency. This is the topic of the next section.

2.17 The Productivity of Ecosystems

Ecosystem efficiency is expressed in terms of productivity. The basic function performed by any ecosystem is the creation by photosynthetic

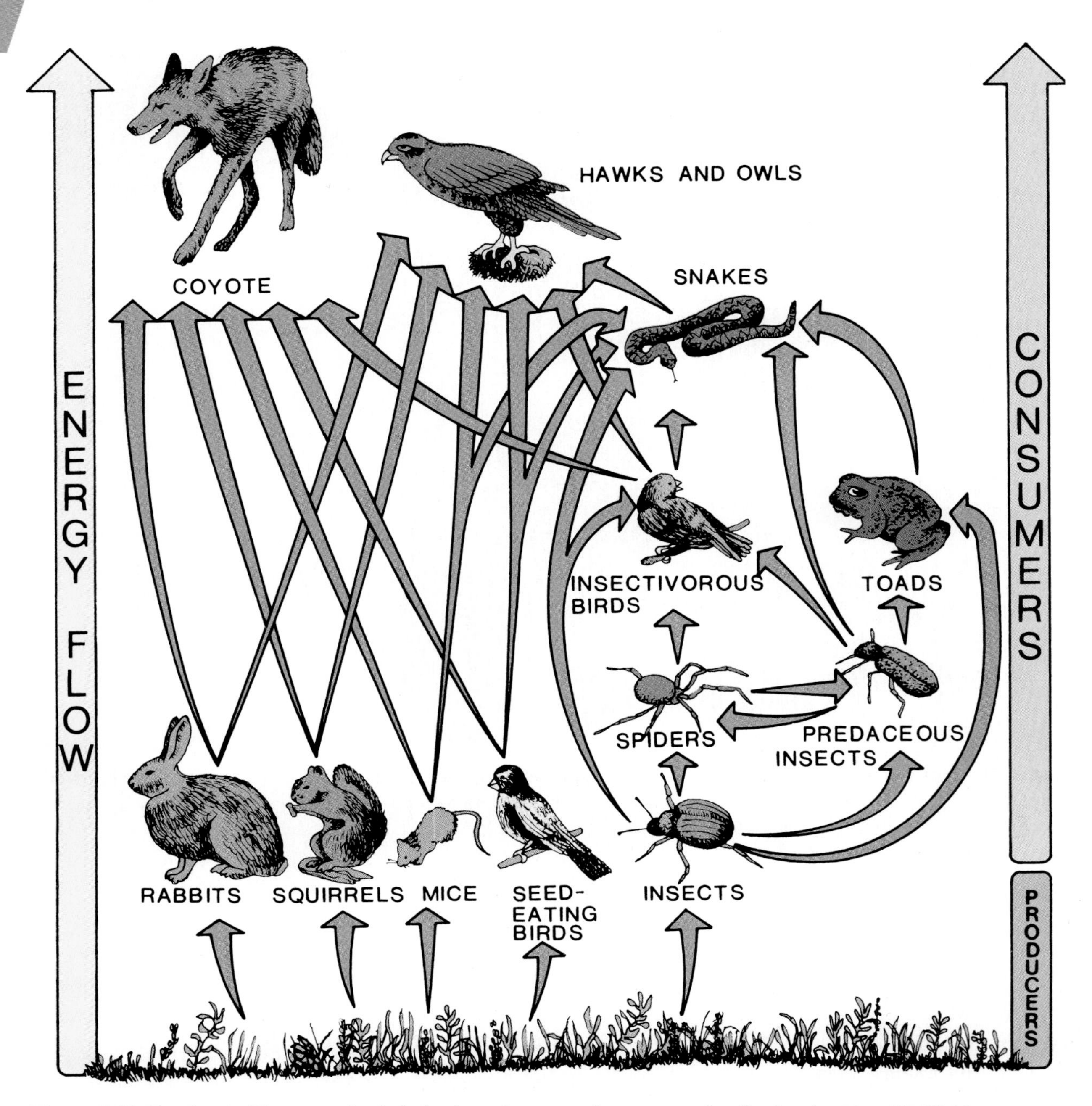

Figure 2.31 Food web. The many food chains in a given area form a complex food web. (From Wildlife Management Institute.)

What is primary productivity?

plants of organic matter incorporating the energy in sunlight. **Primary productivity** is the rate at which photosynthetic plants create organic matter.

Gross primary productivity refers to the total organic matter fixed during photosynthesis. However, in the process of living, each plant consumes some of that matter (in respiration), to obtain the energy needed for its own life functions.

The remaining portion, net productivity, is available for harvest by animals (including humans) and for breakdown by decomposers.

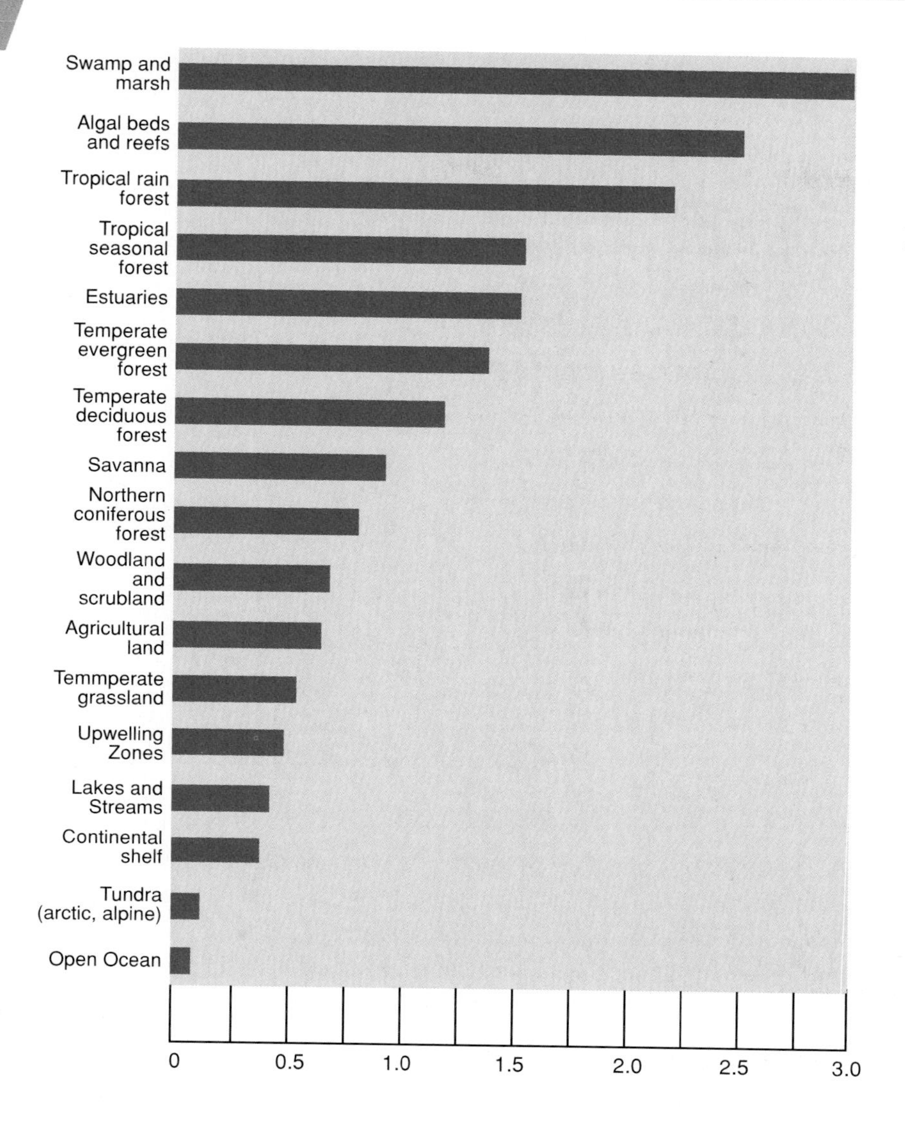

Figure 2.32 Average net primary production efficiency of ecosystem types. Data is in kilograms dry biomass/square meter/year. (From Lieth, Helmut and Whittaker, editors, *Primary Productivity of the Biosphere*, New York: Springer-Verlag, 1975.)

Net primary productivity is that part of the total or gross primary productivity of photosynthetic plants that remains after some of this material is used in the respiration of those plants. Net primary productivity provides the energetic and material basis for the life of all organisms besides plants themselves. It is their ultimate source of food and minerals.

Net primary production is most commonly measured as dry biomass (amount of organic matter) produced per area unit per time. It is expressed as grams per square meter per year ($g/m^2/yr$). Net production of ecosystem types in the world is expressed as metric tonnes (1000 kg) of dry matter per year.

Figure 2.32 shows the average net primary production efficiency of the Earth's major ecosystem types. Production is expressed in terms of kilograms of dry biomass of living organisms present per square meter per year.

From Figure 2.32 we see that tropical rain forests have very high average production per area, and the open oceans rank very low.

Why are tropical rain forests so important to us?

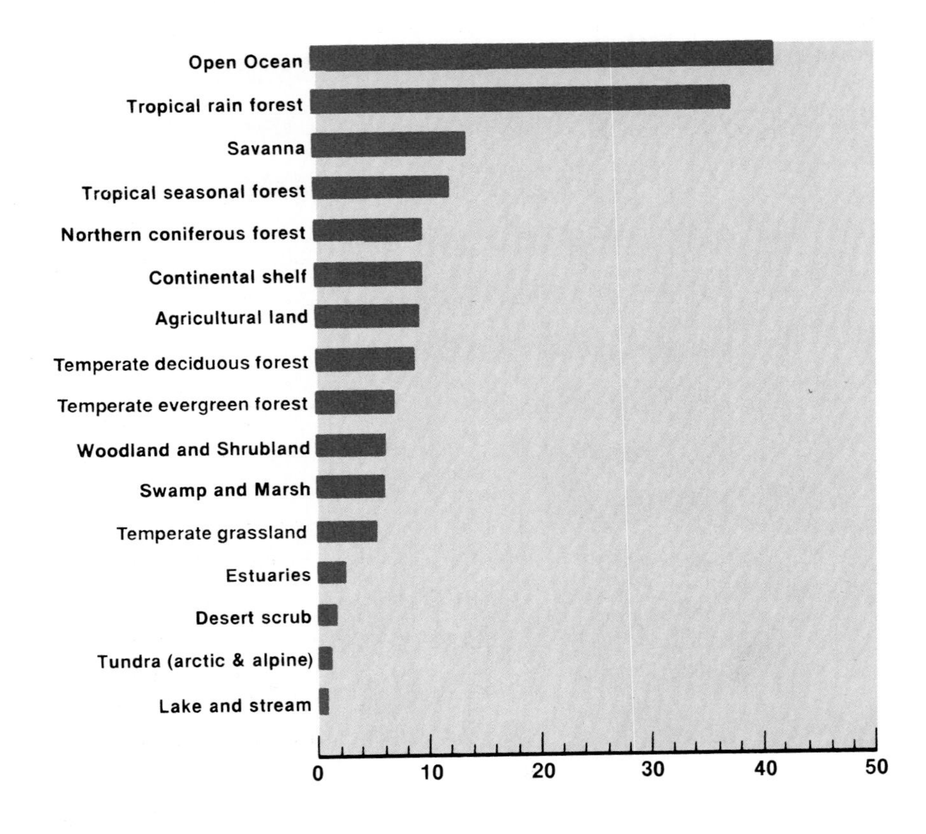

Figure 2.33 World net primary productivity by ecosystem type. Data is in billion metric tonnes dry biomass/year. (From Lieth, Helmut and Whittaker, editors, *Primary Productivity of the Biosphere,* New York: Springer-Verlag, 1975.)

As you might expect, ecosystems in warmer climates are generally more productive than those in cooler regions. These data also show that ecosystems at lower elevations are more productive than those higher up. In general, areas at high elevations are colder than those below. Land communities are much more productive than those of the oceans, because land makes possible an extensive community structure that retains nutrients and supports leaf surfaces.

Another very useful way to express production is to sum up the net primary production of an ecosystem over its full area. This gives us a figure for its total production per year. Figure 2.33 shows world net primary production by ecosystem type. From this figure, we see that even though the open oceans have a very low production per square meter, their overall contribution to world net primary production is the largest. This is because about 65% of Earth's surface is open ocean.

Tropical rain forests rank a close second in net primary production, even though they cover less than 3% of the Earth's surface, or about 9 million square kilometers. A major source of the world's oxygen supply, the tropical rain forests make a priceless contribution to the maintenance of life on Earth. They are a living storehouse of diverse genetic material. Their value to the maintenance of human life on Earth cannot be overemphasized. Unfortunately, these vital areas are being cleared for agriculture and other human uses. Every year nearly 200,000 square kilometers are lost. At this rate, how much longer will they last?

If we are to survive, we must fully appreciate our bond to the natural world. This realization will be reflected by wise long-term use and conservation of the biosphere.

 2.18 Resource Recycling in Nature

Why are the water, carbon, and nitrogren cycles important to human life?

There are many chemical cycles in nature. The main ones are the carbon, nitrogen, water, and mineral cycles (see Figure 2.34). You have already looked at the water cycle (Figure 2.35) in Chapter 1. The carbon and nitrogen cycles are described below.

a. The Carbon Cycle

The carbon cycle.

The **carbon cycle** is summarized in Figure 2.36. This cycle includes two processes: photosynthesis and respiration. During photosynthesis, plants convert carbon dioxide and water into carbohydrates and oxygen gas. The carbohydrates represent a rich store of energy. This energy is used in respiration as carbohydrates are broken apart again to yield carbon dioxide and water. Respiration is used by all organisms that can live in the presence of oxygen. Thus, they all return some carbon dioxide to the atmosphere. Some carbon is tied up in fossil fuels such as coal and petroleum. It returns to the cycle as carbon dioxide when these fuels are burned. Carbon is also tied up in minerals, such as limestone.

Photosynthesis.

The **photosynthesis** process is represented by the following equation:

$$\text{photosynthesis: } 6CO_2 + 6H_2O + \underset{\text{energy}}{\text{solar}} \longrightarrow \underset{\text{glucose}}{C_6H_{12}O_6} + 6O_2$$

Glucose (a sugar) is a carbohydrate and contains mostly carbon and hydrogen. In this process, solar energy is trapped in glucose for later use by plants and animals.

Respiration.

The process of **respiration** is represented by the following equation:

$$\text{respiration: } C_6H_{12}O_6 + 6O_2 \longrightarrow 6CO_2 + 6H_2O + \text{energy}$$

In this process, plants and animals break up food molecules to obtain the energy they use in living. Note that respiration is the reverse of photosynthesis.

b. The Nitrogen Cycle

The nitrogen cycle.

The **nitrogen cycle** traces the circulation of the nutrient that is often the limiting factor for plant growth. This cycle is summarized in Figure 2.37.

Atmospheric nitrogen is useless to plants. It does not react or combine readily with other elements. Nitrogen must be supplied in

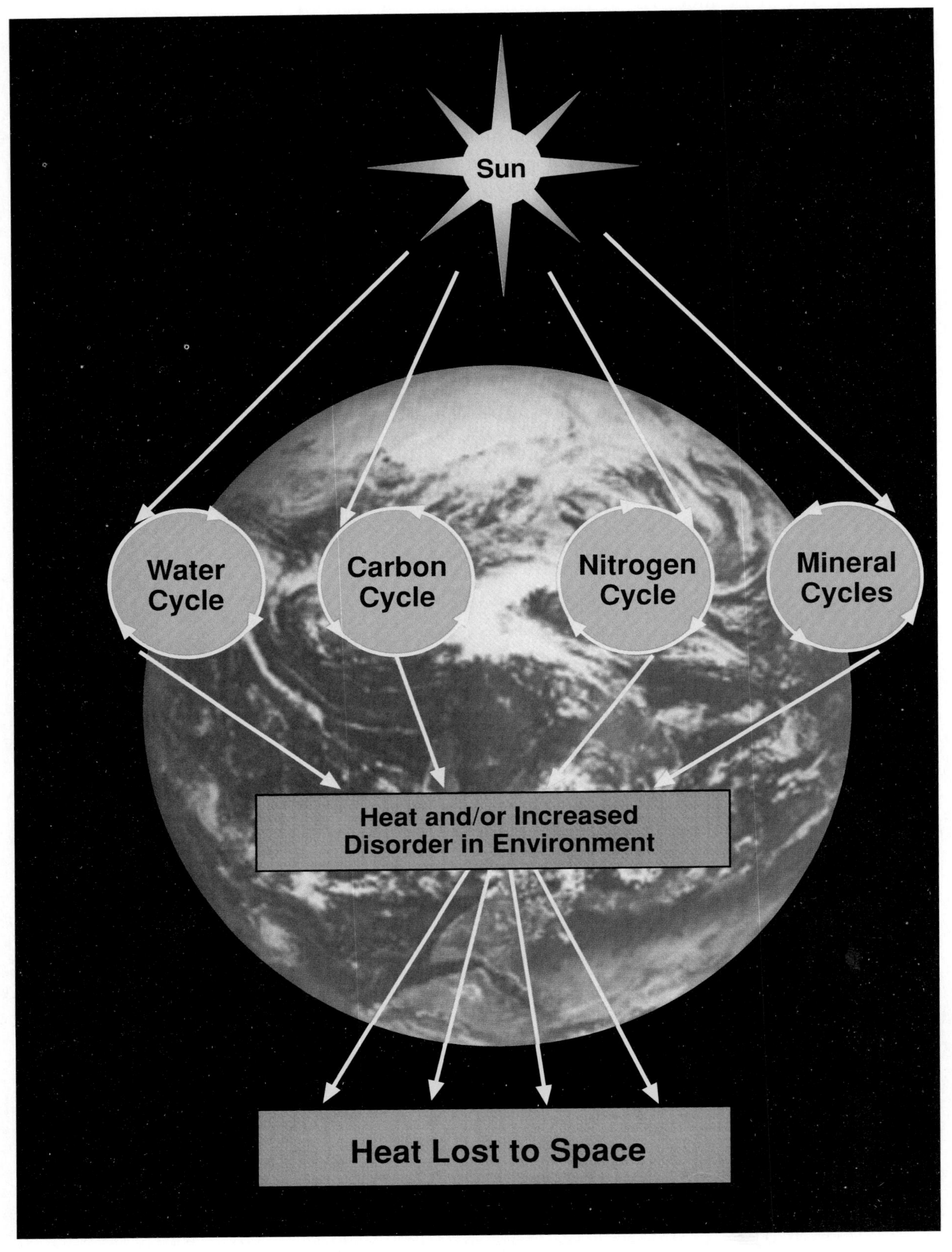

Figure 2.34 All life on Earth depends on the recycling of chemical nutrients and the one-way flow of energy through the biosphere. The sun provides the energy for both of these processes.

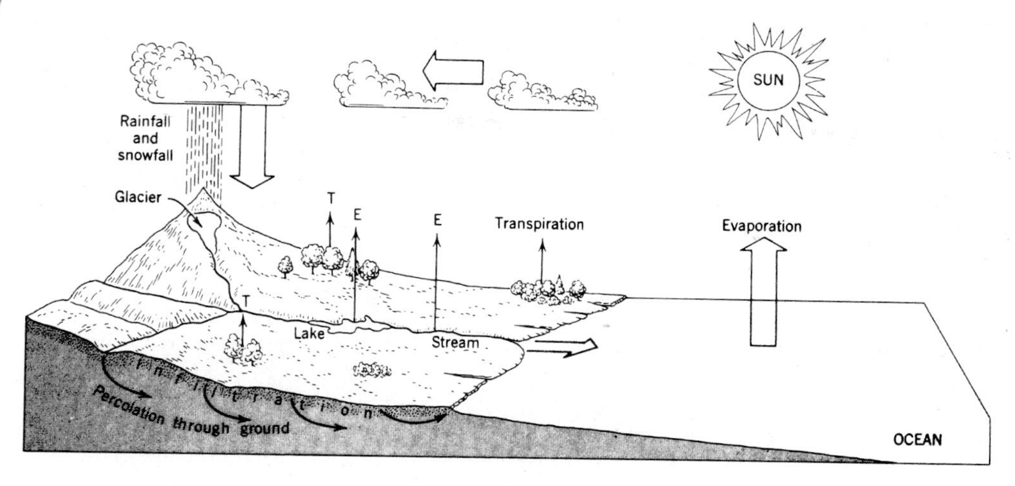

Figure 2.35 The water cycle. E = evaporation; T = transpiration by plants. (From *Physical Geology* 2nd ed., by R. F. Flint and B. J. Skinner. Copyright © 1977 by John Wiley and Sons, Inc. Reprinted by permission of the publisher.)

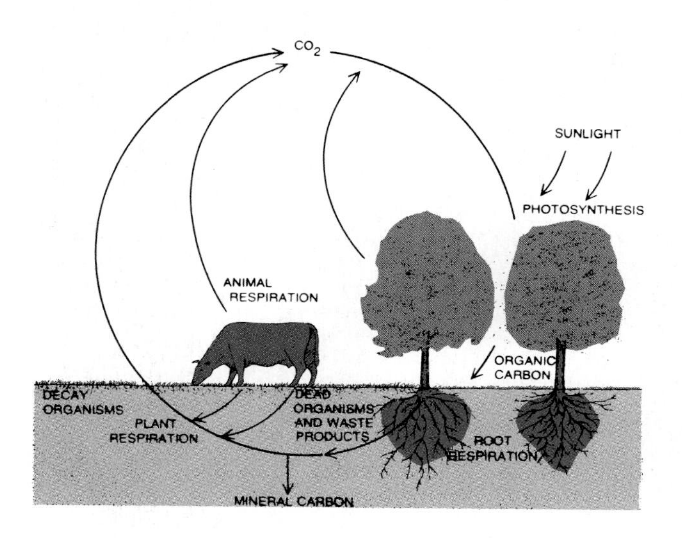

Figure 2.36 The carbon cycle. (From "The Cycles of Plant and Animal Nutrition" by Janick, Noller and Rhykerd. Copyright © 1976 by Scientific American, Inc. All rights reserved.)

"fixed" or combined form, as in ammonium ions (NH_4+) or nitrate ions (NO_3-). A little nitrogen is fixed by lightning and other processes in the atmosphere. Much more is fixed by bacteria, notably those that live in the root nodules of legumes. Nevertheless, the pool of available nitrogen in most soils remains small. The element is removed by leaching and by bacteria that return it to the atmosphere. It is lost through the harvesting of crops. To compensate for these losses, animal manure or nitrogen fixed industrially is applied to the soil as fertilizer. Industrial fixation has become a major component of the nitrogen cycle.

Natural ecosystems recycle all critical elements so that plants (producers) are continually supplied with minerals they need. Farmers add fertilizers to replace minerals.

Legumes are a group of plants that include peas, beans, and clover.

Energy Flow in a Modern Society

We will now consider the energy flow through the United States from a system efficiency point of view. A schematic diagram is provided in Figure 2.39. A new energy unit, the **Quad,** is used here. One Quad equals one quadrillion (10^{15}) Btu.

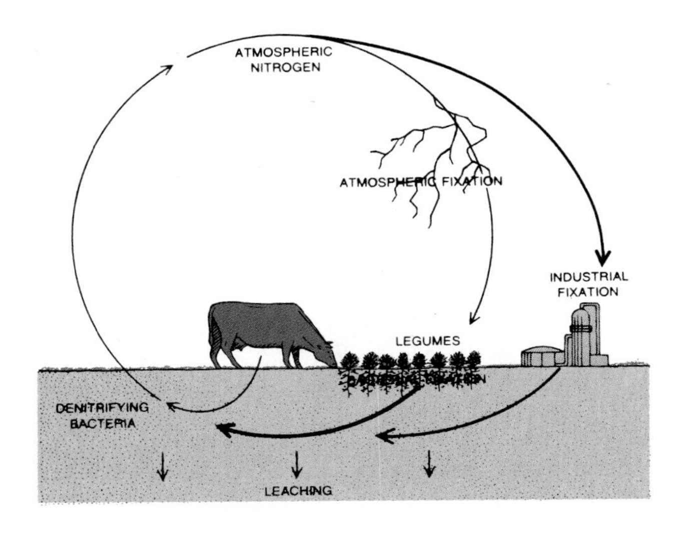

Figure 2.37 The nitrogen cycle. (From "The Cycles of Plant and Animal Nutrition" by Janick, Noller and Rhykerd. Copyright © 1976 by Scientific American, Inc. All rights reserved.)

Figure 2.38 Nodules are clearly visible on the roots of these soybean plants. The nodules contain nitrogen-fixing bacteria. (USDA.)

2.19 The Quantity of Energy

Energy flow in the United States

We see in Figure 2.39 that the total input into the U.S. energy system is 81.5 Quads (Q) [Nuclear 6.6 + Hydro 3.1 + Natural Gas 20.2 + Coal 18.8 + Petroleum 32.6 + Other 0.2]. Of the 30.1 Q that went for the generation of electricity, 21.0 Q, or more than two-thirds of it, were lost. Over-all, of the 81.5 Q input to the system, 50.0 Q were lost and only 31.5 Q actually produced the end use work or heat. The overall efficiency of the system, therefore, was 39 percent; a little more than 60 percent of the energy is lost as far as the intended purpose is concerned. What does the future hold? Electricity and transportation, the two most wasteful sectors, are growing rapidly. However, a thermodynamic analysis of the American economy indicates we could, with real commitment, achieve an efficiency of over 60%.

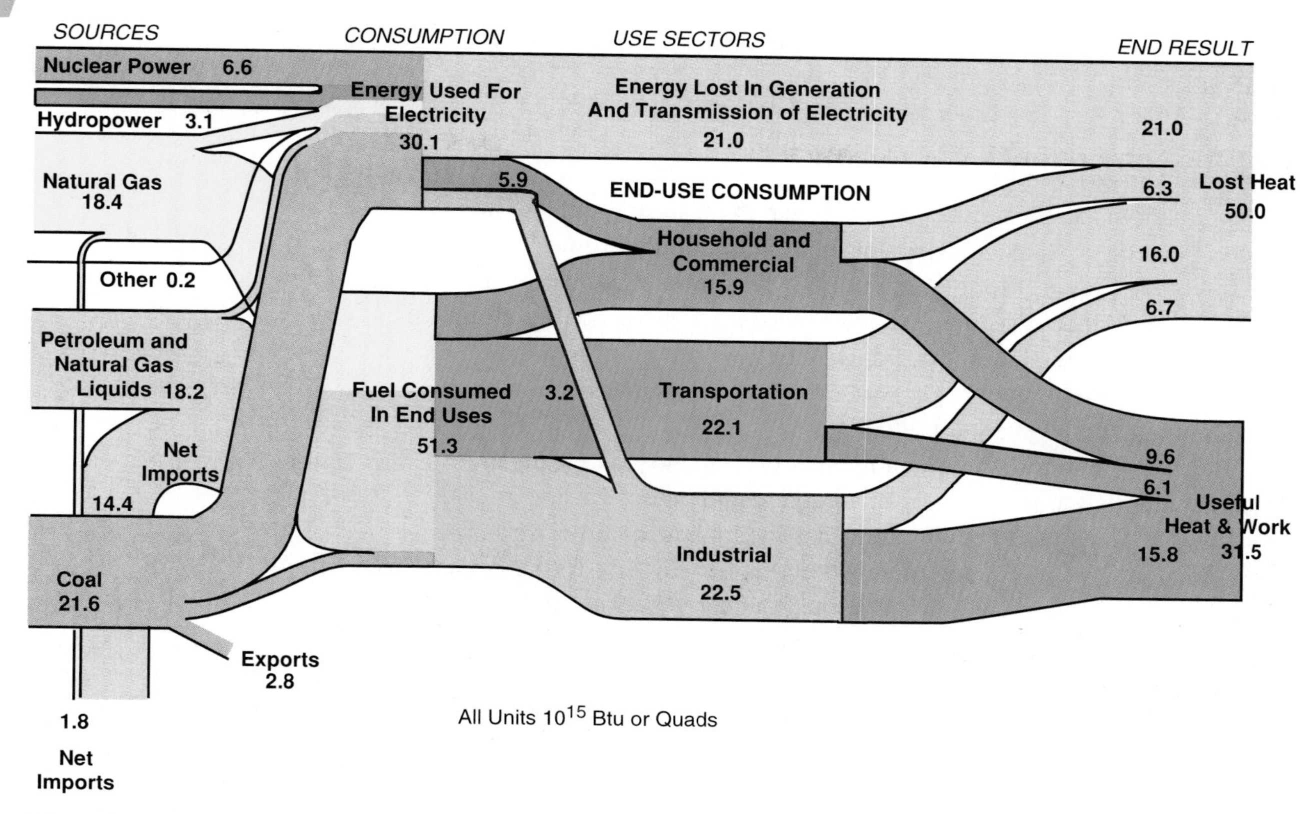

Figure 2.39 The flow of energy through the U.S. from primary sources through the use sectors to end result. The width of the bars is proportional to the amount of energy. The contributions of solar electricity, geothermal and wind power are presently too small to show. The contribution of passive solar heating may be significant, but it is not shown because it is difficult to estimate. The estimated 2.4 Q of wood energy consumed by industry (1.55 Q) and residences (0.85 Q) is not included because this historically has not been done. Using the historical method makes it easier to compare data from one year to another. We say apples are being compared to apples. (Source: Earl Cook, updated primarily using data from the U.S. Energy Information Administration. The estimates of sector efficiencies are best guesses from several sources.)

Ultimately, heat is the end product of all our energy conversions. The electric energy that is produced and delivered to homes and industry is eventually converted to heat directly (in heaters, toasters, and ranges) or indirectly (by the friction in electric motors, for instance). The kinetic energy of moving cars and trucks is converted to heat by brakes, air resistance, and other factors.

Furthermore, the heat quickly becomes low-temperature heat in air and water. What happens to all this low-temperature heat? It ends up being radiated out from Earth into the vast reaches of space.

Conclusions

What are the implications of losing all this heat? One strategy for energy conservation could be to move toward processes that don't involve heat energy as a middle step. That is, we could become less dependent on heat engines. We need conversion techniques to go from chemical or radiant energy directly to electrical. We need new technologies. We could make heat engines more efficient by making them

What are the implications of losing so much heat?

out of different materials that can tolerate very high temperatures. In the meantime, we must be content with trying to plug some of the leaks. This is what better home insulation and higher mileage cars are all about.

2.20 The Concept of Energy Quality

Energy quality is an idea that is central to the interests and goals of advanced societies. Much of what these societies consider the "good life" involves moving things around (mechanical energy) and using electrical appliances. (Have you tried washing clothes on a scrub board?) We consider mechanical and electrical energy to be high in quality. Hence, high-quality energy is energy which can easily be used to move things or to generate electricity.

Energy quality (usefulness).

Organized energy is high quality energy. "Organized" means that the molecules and atoms of the system under study are behaving in an orderly way. Thus, mechanical energy has the highest quality. When a car is in motion all the molecules and atoms are moving forward at least, in part. Electrical energy is high quality energy because the electrons in the wires move in a predictable (non random) way.

Energy quality is also high when energy is concentrated. Gasoline and sugar are ranked high on the quality scale. Energy is concentrated in their highly structured chemical bonds. Because you can make steam and cook with it, focused sunlight is high quality energy.

Ambient temperature heat (heat at a temperature near that of the surroundings) has the lowest quality. You can't move things with it. You can't cook with it. You can't even heat with it. Cars and electric power plants are designed to release it into space. That is why we lose so much usefulness as these devices operate.

Energy quality defined.

The quality of an energy source is a measure of its ability to be used to produce mechanical or electrical energy.

Ranking sources of energy.

It is difficult to rank all sources of energy on a quality scale. A crude ranking would look something like this:

mechanical energy	HIGH	
electrical energy	|	
focused sunlight	|	Energy Quality
gasoline	|	(usefulness)
coal	|	
wood and crop wastes	|	
normal sunlight	|	
ambient temperature heat	LOW	

We need to ask what kind of energy should be used to accomplish a particular task. It makes little sense to cut butter with a chain saw. To minimize our losses and get the most from the energy sources we have, we should match the quality of our energy sources to the quality of the task to be performed. Only high-quality tasks should require the consumption of high-quality energy sources.

People use energy to accomplish certain tasks. We want to move the car, watch TV, heat the house, and cook dinner. The task accomplished is called the end-use.

It also is useful to rank the tasks (or end-uses) we use energy for in terms of quality. That ranking looks like this:

Task		
mechanical motion (move vehicles, move products, run industry.)	HIGH	
electrical devices (lighting, electronics, communications, motors, appliances)	|	Quality of Task
heat: T > 100° C (cooking, steam production)	|	
heat: T < 100° C (home heating)	LOW	

It makes sense to match energy sources to end-use tasks. High quality sources should be saved for high quality tasks. Using high quality energy to do low quality tasks is wasteful, both from an energy and economic point of view. One can kill flies with a sledge hammer, but much effort has been wasted. Exercise 2.4, "Matching Source to End-Use," will give you more practice with this concept.

2.21 Strategies for Resource Users

Can you suggest some strategies for using resources that individuals and societies should consider as they look to the future?

Strategies for resource users include: redefining the good life (emphasizing activities that consume less); redesigning our technology; developing new, more acceptable energy sources; and matching the quality of our energy sources to the quality of the tasks to be performed.

NOTE: From this point in the text, proposed solutions to resource/environmental problems will appear in boxed format.

In this chapter we learned that energy can be neither created nor destroyed. It is merely transformed from one form to another. However, in these transformations, energy quality (or usefulness) is lost as matter proceeds to its most probable (most disordered) state. Thus we don't have an energy crisis, we have a quality crisis.

In an energy-dependent society, it makes sense to try to manage that quality. Furthermore, we need to stretch out our losses. Instead of losing energy's usefulness over decades and centuries, we need to extend its usefulness to as long as the lifetime of our sun (or other stars). We need to develop a resource use policy. This can be done by a variety of techniques:

1. Changing our life-styles (doing things that consume less, and recycling wastes).
2. Redesigning our technology (more efficient cars, energy-efficient homes and buildings).
3. Developing new energy sources.
4. Matching the quantity and quality of our energy sources to the quantity and quality of the tasks to be performed.

Here Today, Still Here Tomorrow

science at work

England, 1709. Imagine an old, shabbily dressed junk man, carrying a worn and stained bag of cast-off shoes, looking up at Queen Anne's palace. Now, it is today. The junk man's great-great-grandson kneels before Queen Elizabeth II, who taps him on each shoulder with her ceremonial sword and says solemnly, "I dub thee Sir Recycler."

Bill Cohen has watched the salvage business acquire new dignity; yesterday's "rags-and-bones" junk dealers are today's superstars. Bill knows about the importance of recycling, because he owns and runs ABC Recycling Industries, Inc., in Santa Clara, California. His company is one of many in the United States working to conserve the world's resources and decrease pollution from manufacturing—and making a living at it, too.

Businesses such as Bill Cohen's collect or purchase various discarded materials, separate and package them, and forward them to end-user companies for reuse. Take aluminum, for example. ABC repackages discarded aluminum cans, pots and pans, automobile and aircraft parts, screen doors, and so on, according to the specifications of end users such as Alcoa. The end-users melt down and recast these materials—sometimes as pure aluminum, sometimes combined with other metals to make alloys. ABC sends other materials, too, on this journey to recovery. Copper wire, sheeting and solar panels; brass doorknobs and valves; stainless steel sinks and pipes; zinc and lead—all can be reclaimed and reformed. Your family probably saves glass bottles, plastic jugs, newspapers, cardboard, and computer paper. These and many other materials are removed from the waste stream at Bill's company and used in new products or as fuel.

Up early most days, Bill enjoys the hands-on involvement with his business. After reviewing the weights of yesterday's collections, and current prices offered by end-users, he's outside with his workers, supervising packaging operations and shipments. Ten percent of ABC's suppliers are businesses recycling industrial waste; but 90 percent are "just folks"—scout troops, community organizations, families who collect their own recyclables, and even scavengers who wheel in shopping carts full of stuff found in alleys and vacant lots. Bill usually pays cash for the "junk" he collects.

Bill got started in recycling in Canada. His father was an early recycler: He and one truck provided "curb service" for folks wanting to get rid of things they weren't using any more. Bill worked in a neighbor's recycling business, learning it from the ground up. Later, he started his own company with one truck, just like his father.

Bill thinks his industriousness, perseverance, and natural curiosity about science in general have helped him in studying recycling methods and economics. To keep up on modern advances in industry and its uses for recycled material, he attends seminars and trade shows. One kind of information he needs for meeting his customers' needs is the physical properties of metals and other minerals. For example, one company might want materials that are very ductile (capable of being drawn out), for making wire. Another might need metals that transmit electricity quickly. Still another might be combining different materials to create a new alloy with certain properties. The more Bill knows about the properties of the materials he recycles, the better service he can provide to the companies. It also helps him decide whether materials must be separated from one another.

Recycling is a real equal-opportunity field, Bill says, and it needs the participation of more people who want to decrease pollution, conserve the Earth's resources, help produce useful and efficient products, and provide jobs. As one way to begin, he suggests starting out in government recycling programs.

Remember not to write in your textbook. Use a separate piece of paper for your answers.

Exercise 2.4

Matching Source to End-Use

Directions: In this exercise, you will be given pairs of source to end-use strategies. Select the strategy that represents the best source to end-use match from an energy quality standpoint. Give your reason for making the selection.

Pair I:

A A home is heated electrically (resistance strip heater). The electricity is produced at a nuclear generating plant.

B. A home is heated by burning methane gas in a furnace. The methane gas is produced in a bioconversion plant and delivered to homes through a pipeline network.

Choice ____ . ____

____

____

____

Pair II:

A. Electricity is restricted to such uses as powering electronic devices, electrochemical processes and electric motors in home appliances. Bigger tasks such as heating homes and transporting goods and people must be accomplished by various solar options.

B Electrical consumption is expanded to include the heating of homes because of the increased scarcity of natural gas. Electricity is produced in coal-fired and nuclear power plants.

Choice ____ . ____

____

____

____

____

Source: PEEC Packet: *There is Enough Energy, So What's the Problem?* National Science Teachers Association. Washington, D.C.

These are not easy changes to make. They are simply easy to list. The beginning of change starts with awareness. As we become more aware of our actions and their consequences, the desire to change grows.

There is no one best route into the future. The path we follow is not clearly marked and understood. Perhaps some of your new insights into the nature of energy and the laws that govern its flow will help you make a more successful journey.

Summary

A small number of laws govern our use of energy and mineral resources. We can neither create nor destroy matter, we can only rearrange it. We can neither create nor destroy energy (first law of thermodynamics). We can, however, transform energy from one form to another. There are six forms of energy: heat, radiant, mechanical, electrical, chemical, and nuclear.

As we go through life, we continually rearrange matter and transform energy. The second law of thermodynamics summarizes what happens in the process. Most human activity results in matter becoming more disordered or scattered. It requires our deliberate and constant action to slow this process down. As we use (transform) energy, it goes to less useful forms. This means our energy supply is continually losing its ability to move objects and/or generate electricity. Energy ultimately ends up as low-temperature heat and is radiated into space. We cannot stop these natural tendencies, but we can slow them down. In the process, we increase the benefits to be gained from our finite energy and mineral supplies. Wise use could result in some sort of human life on Earth lasting as long as the sun.

Major Concepts

Primary Sources	Energy	Forms
1. Sun		1. Mechanical
2. Geothermal		2. Electrical
3. Tidal		3. Chemical
4. Fission		4. Heat
5. Fusion		5. Light
		6. Nuclear

Major Concepts

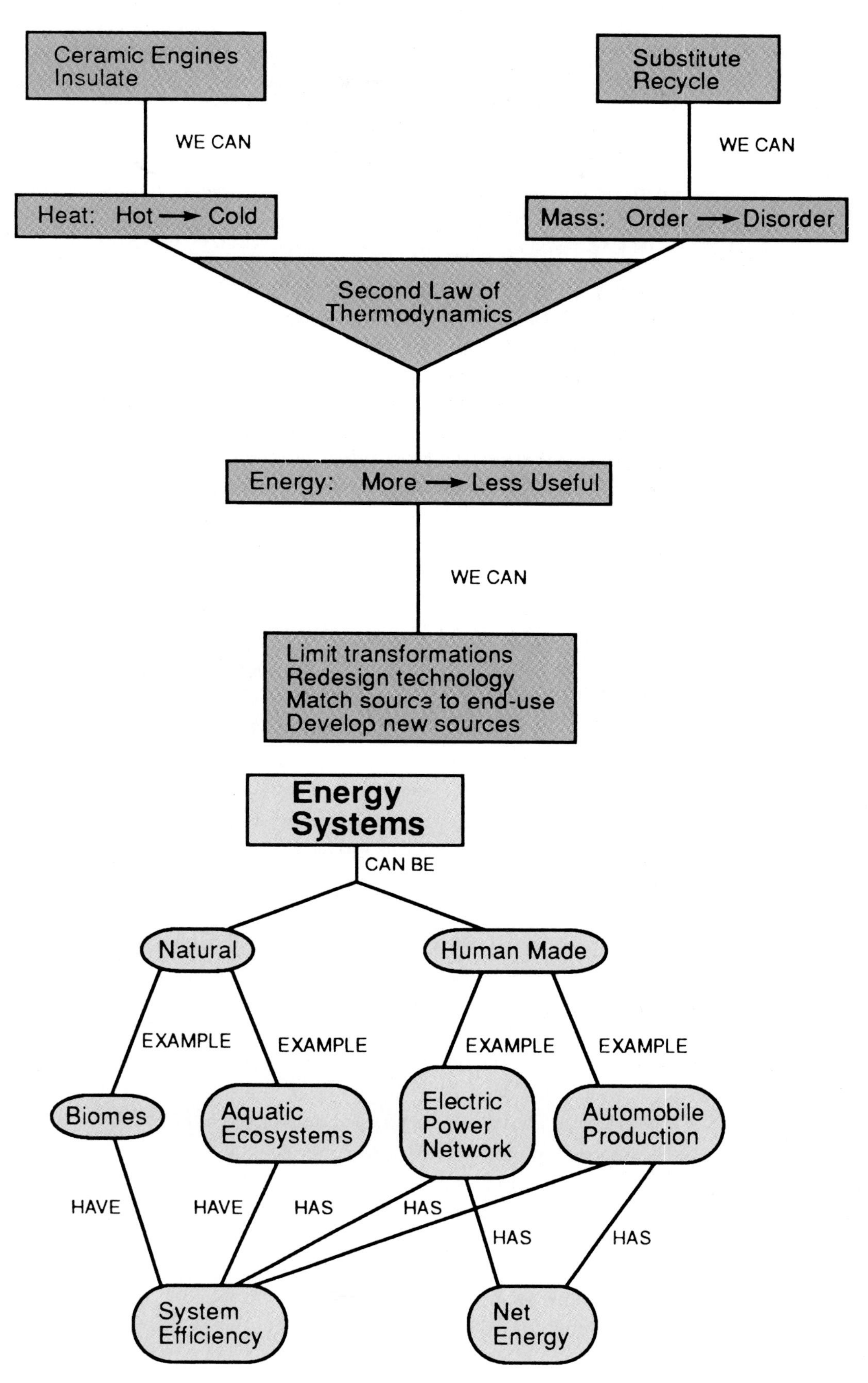

References

Bolin, Bert and R. B. Cook. *The Major Biogeochemical Cycles and Their Interactions* (New York: John Wiley), 1983.

Fowler, John M. *Energy and the Environment,* 2nd ed. (New York: McGraw-Hill), 1984.

Gates, David M. *Energy and Ecology* (Sunderland, MA: Sinauer), 1985.

Glasby, G. P. Entropy, pollution, and environmental degradation. *Ambio,* 17:330–335, 1988.

Kormondy, E. J. *Concepts of Ecology,* 3rd ed. (Englewood Cliffs, N. J.: Prentice-Hall), 1984.

Lieth, Helmut and Robert H. Whittaker, eds. *Primary Productivity of the Biosphere* (New York: Springer-Verlag), 1975.

Miller, G. Tyler, Jr. *Living in the Environment,* 7th ed. (Belmont, CA: Wadsworth), 1992.

Odum, Howard T. and Elisabeth C. Odum. *Energy Basis for Man and Nature,* 2nd ed. (New York: McGraw-Hill), 1981.

Post, Wilfred M. et. al. The global carbon cycle. *American Scientist,* 78:310–326, 1990.

Romer, Robert H. *Energy: An Introduction to Physics* (San Francisco: W. H. Freeman & Co.), 1976.

Smil, Vaclav. *General Energetics: Energy in the Biosphere and Civilization* (New York: John Wiley), 1991.

End of Chapter Questions

Set A

1. Why do you buy gasoline? Relate your reason to the definition of energy.
2. How does the NASA photo of Earth illustrate that Earth is a closed system (in terms of matter)?
3. Explain why Earth is an open system in terms of energy.
4. Relate the concept of carrying capacity to a meadow that contains a herd of deer.
5. If the conservation of matter is such a simple concept, why do we have "solid waste" and "hazardous waste" problems?
6. Many communities have aluminum can recycling centers. How does this change the amount of aluminum on Earth?
7. State the law of conservation of energy and list the six forms of energy.
8. Give an example of a household appliance which changes electrical energy into heat.
9. Give an example of a process that involves at least three energy transformations.
10. What are conversion factors and how are they used?
11. Put each of the following in categories of "potential energy" or "kinetic energy" or both. Briefly explain why you chose that category for each item.
    - **a.** one gallon of gasoline
    - **b.** a flying arrow
    - **c.** a rock balanced on cliff
    - **d.** a charged battery

e. a dynamite stick
f. a pitched baseball

12. Name the five sources from which all our energy comes.
13. Nuclear fusion does not generally occur on Earth under natural conditions, yet no ecosystem could function without fusion energy. How can this be so?
14. Name the ways in which solar energy has been stored for later use.
15. Which type of stored solar energy have we been using the most during the past several decades?
16. As your car moves down the highway, energy is not lost, even though you are using up gasoline. Where does the gasoline's energy go? If energy isn't lost, what is?
17. Iron is mined from an area of concentrated iron ore and made into thousands of different products, all of which will eventually end up in hundreds of dumps. Which form of the second law of thermodynamics does this illustrate? Explain your answer.
18. Use form 3 of the second law of thermodynamics to explain why we are "running out" of some metals such as silver.
19. Things tend to go from an orderly condition to one of disorder. To reverse this process, what must be provided?
20. Is energy more useful when it is concentrated or when it is spread out? Why?
21. Why can't the efficiency of a device be over 100%?
22. Why are the items at the top of Figure 2.20 more efficient than those placed at the bottom?
23. Why are steam (electric) power plants, automobile engines, and incandescent light bulbs so inefficient?
24. Why do energy systems become more inefficient as more steps are added?
25. If a net energy ratio for a process is less than one, what does that indicate about that process?
26. Using the concept of net energy, explain how using a chain saw to cut wood for a stove could result in an actual energy loss in the system.
27. Explain why vegetarians use food energy more efficiently than nonvegetarians.
28. Why don't lions hunt mice?
29. Elephants and blue whales are the largest of all animals on Earth. Both are vegetarians. Why do meat-eaters not get as large as elephants and blue whales?
30. Why are there more rabbits than coyotes?
31. What is net primary productivity?
32. Why are tropical rain forests so important to us?
33. Write the reaction below using chemical symbols and draw an arrow to indicate the direction of the reaction for respiration.
    Carbon dioxide + Water—Glucose + Oxygen

34. Both plants and animals respire, but only plants photosynthesize. If plants and animals are to live in balance in a closed ecosystem, what tasks must plants and decomposers carry out?
35. Explain how the water cycle is powered by the sun.
36. The United States economy is only 39% efficient. Where does the other 61% of the energy that is fed into the economy go?
37. What can be done to improve our use of energy?
38. Why have some scientists compared heating a home with electricity to "cutting butter with a chain saw"?
39. List some ways that we (as individuals and members of society) can increase the amount of time high-quality energy will be available for our use.

Set B

40. Using the concept of net energy, explain how farming swamps or deserts could actually use more energy than would be delivered in the form of food. In your opinion, would the "trade" be a good one?
41. People who take drastic measures to solve simple problems are sometimes said to be "killing flies with sledge hammers." Give examples of energy uses that you think fit into this category. Explain your reasoning.
42. Classify each of the following as either a closed or an open system, giving reasons for your judgments: professional football; a gas forced-air home heating system; an apple pie left on the counter to cool; a pure culture of bacteria sealed in a test tube; the Milky Way galaxy; the universe.
43. Game management laws in most states allow hunting of large and small game animals. Such laws are usually enacted under the assumption that, left unchecked, animal populations will exceed the carrying capacity of their habitats, resulting in large-scale die-offs of the animals or invasion of human areas. What are the laws in your state? Look in your library for information and arguments which support or refute the "hunting and game management" assumption mentioned above.
44. Some have suggested that a living organism defies the entropy law. Why is that claim invalid?
45. It is important to distinguish between renewable and nonrenewable sources of energy. If an energy source is renewable, it means we/nature can produce another supply before our present supplies run out. Nonrenewable sources cannot be replaced. When they are used up, there is no more. Give some examples of both kinds of energy sources.

End of Chapter Problems ?

Set A

1. A mover slides a refrigerator across a smooth floor. He exerts a 75-pound force while pushing it 4 feet. How much work has he done in moving the refrigerator?
2. How many calories are required to raise the temperature of 8 grams of water 7 Celsius degrees?
3. How many calories of heat will be given off when 200 grams of water cool from 80 to 20 degrees Celsius?
4. A small solar panel raised the temperature of 4.4 pounds of water 20 Fahrenheit degrees. How many Btus of heat were absorbed by the water?
5. How many foot-pounds of work would be required to produce 250 Btus of heat?
6. How many Btus would be the equivalent of 0.07 kWhs of electrical energy?
7. Convert 1720 joules to calories.
8. Assume that all of the work done by the mover in Problem 1 went to overcome friction between the refrigerator and the floor. How much heat was generated by the time the mover had done 193 ft-lbs of work? (Hint: give your answer in Btus.)
9. A quantity of energy can be measured in many different units, but the amount remains the same. Find the equivalent of 1 kilowatt•hour of electrical energy in:
   a. Btus
   b. calories
   c. foot•pounds
   d. joules
   e. barrels of oil
10. Out of the 17.6 quadrillion kilocalories of energy used by the U.S. in 1983, how much ultimately ended up as heat radiated into space?
11. If the energy input of a system is 50 calories and the output is 25 calories, what is the system efficiency?
12. Calculate the system efficiency of operating an electric car from the original energy stored in coal. On a separate piece of paper, write the steps, and their percentage of efficiency, and calculate the cumulative efficiency percentage.

	Efficiency	
Step	Step	Cumulative
a. Produce coal	96%	96%
b. Transport coal	97%	____
c. Generate electricity	33%	____
d. Transmit electricity	85%	____
e. Charge storage battery	73 ~~93%~~	____
f. Operate large electric motor	93%	____

13. Calculate the system efficiency for space heating with electric heaters, fuel oil, and natural gas. Fill in the blanks, as you did in Question 12. From a total energy use perspective, which system uses energy most wisely?

Step	Efficiency	
	Step	Cumulative
Electric (Coal fired)		
a. Coal production	96%	96%
b. Coal transportation	97%	_____
c. Electricity generation	33%	_____
d. Electricity transmission	85%	_____
e. Heater efficiency	95%	_____
Fuel Oil		
a. Crude oil production	96%	_____
b. Fuel oil refining	90%	_____
c. Fuel oil transportation	97%	_____
d. Furnace efficiency	63%	_____
Natural Gas		
a. Natural gas production	96%	_____
b. Natural gas transportation	97%	_____
c. Furnace efficiency	75%	_____

Set B

14. Most of the energy that escapes from the Earth is infrared radiation. A typical frequency for such radiation is ten trillion Hz (ten trillion cycles per second). Calculate the wavelength of this heat radiation. (Hint: the speed of light is 300 million meters per second.)

15. If 2500 kilocalories of food energy show up as work done by an individual, how much work is done in joules?

16. What is the frequency of radiant energy produced by a ham radio operator who is broadcasting on the 15 meter band? (Radio waves travel at the speed of light: 300 million meters/second.)

17. The surface of the Earth receives solar energy at the rate of 128 quadrillion watts. Of this, 0.0757% is converted to stored energy by plants in the photosynthesis process. Determine the rate at which plants fix energy photosynthetically. Give your answer in watts. Determine how much energy this is on a daily basis. Finally, to make the answer more meaningful, convert your answer to barrels of oil equivalent per day.

18. How much of the energy represented by a felled tree ends up as heat for a cabin that is heated with a wood-burning stove? Base your answer on the following data:

Step	Efficiency of Step
a. Production of wood (cutting and trimming)	66%
b. Wood/logs transportation	98%
c. Wood stove	25%

19. During 1979 (a peak year for oil imports), the United States imported approximately 8 million barrels of oil per day (8 mb/d). How many barrels of oil per year is this? Convert this annual rate to quads. (One quad is one quadrillion Btus.) The U.S. consumed 78 quads of energy in 1979. What percent of our energy came from imported oil that year?

20. If the average adult eats 3,000 kcal of food per day and is capable of doing 150,000 foot•pounds of work in a day, how efficient is the average adult?

Kennecott Corporation

Goal

To learn how mineral deposits are formed, located, and mined. To understand why minerals are important and how to manage them properly.

Mineral Resources

In the beginning, we mine the Earth seeking those minerals that are the foundation of our material well-being. We change minerals into those things that are an important part of our world. Used wisely and well, they will take us into a promising future.

—American Mining Congress

Mineral Formation, Extraction, and Use

Humans want more from life than just scratching out a meager existence. We all seem to want to experience the good life, including some material comfort and convenience.

?

What is a mineral?

Providing material comfort starts with the removal of minerals from the Earth. A **mineral** is a substance occurring naturally in the Earth that has an orderly internal structure, a consistent and distinctive set of physical properties, and a composition that can be expressed by a chemical formula.

Most minerals are inorganic, such as quartz and gypsum. A few are organic, such as tar sands and coal. Materials extracted from minerals are used for making building materials, tools, and machines. Minerals are required in the production of fertilizers and the various herbicides, pesticides, and repellents used in modern agriculture. Plastics and certain drugs come from organic minerals. Minerals are even necessary in the mining, milling, and refining of minerals themselves.

Most people pass their days with no thoughts of the role mining plays in their lives. They know where to buy the things they want, but seldom consider the origins. Food comes from a grocery . . . electricity from a wall socket . . . tools from a hardware store . . . cars from a dealer . . . appliances from a department store . . . and so on. If we think of how these things are created, many of us would probably begin with farms, factories and electric power stations. Our horn of plenty starts with a hole in the ground. We are in trouble if we forget that.

The human population is large and growing. So is our desire for "creature comforts." This places a tremendous demand on our mineral resources. Unlike farmland, mines bear no second crop. Our mineral resources are essentially nonrenewable.

In this chapter we will examine how mineral deposits are formed. We will then learn how useful minerals are located, mined, and refined. We will learn about the important roles minerals play in modern societies. Finally, we will learn why managing resources properly and caring for our environment are essential. Various strategies for meeting these goals will be examined.

Minerals are generally cold, solid materials. Many originated, however, in hot liquids flowing out of a violently moving Earth.

3.1 Plate Tectonics Theory

As you know from chapter 1, the uppermost layer of the Earth (the lithosphere) consists of a series of plates. These plates float on and are moved by a flexible layer called the asthenosphere.

What happens when plates move?

As the plates move, three kinds of events may occur: a) plate creation; b) plate destruction; and c) plates sliding past each other. See Figure 3.1. These events contribute to major geologic activities on Earth—earthquakes, volcanoes, and orebody formation.

a. Plate Creation

Molten material from the asthenosphere moves up into the void created when plates move away from each other. This brings new

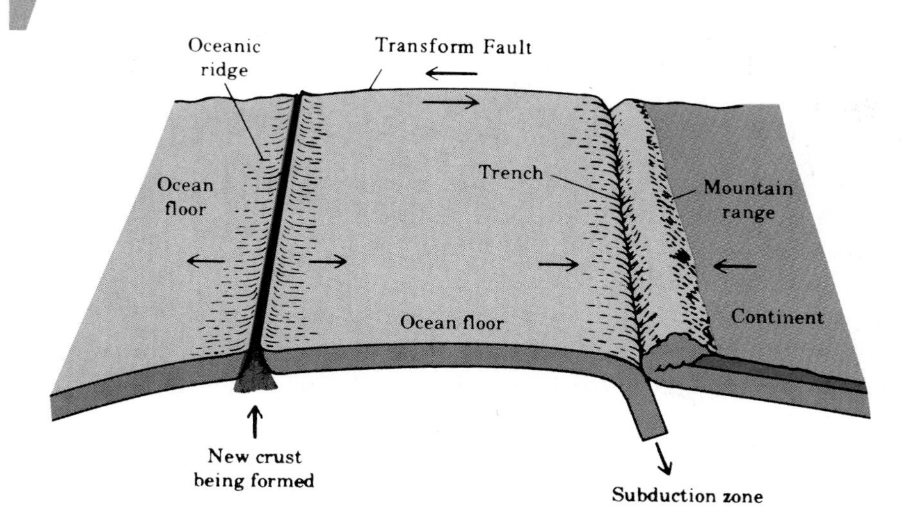

Figure 3.1 Plate movement. (From *Earth Sciences*, by Arthur Beiser, New York: McGraw-Hill, 1975.)

Figure 3.2 The mid-Atlantic Ridge surfaces in Iceland resulting in a landscape marked with volcanic features. (Charles Preitner/Visuals Unlimited)

minerals to the Earth's crust and results in the creation of new plate material. The Mid-Atlantic Ridge is one of the regions where this type of process is occurring.

b. Plate Destruction

Plate destruction occurs when plates collide. Since the Earth's size isn't changing, one of three events must occur when plates collide (Figure 3.3). The three possibilities are tied to the fact that oceanic crust is younger and more dense than most continental crust.

1) When oceanic crust meets oceanic crust, one of the plates is always more dense than the other. This causes it to slide under the less dense plate and slowly melt as it is **subducted** (pulled under). Earthquakes occur. Volcanoes erupt near the boundary of the collision. It is believed that this type of activity caused the Aleutian Island chain. These islands form the southwestern portion of Alaska. See Figure 3.3A.

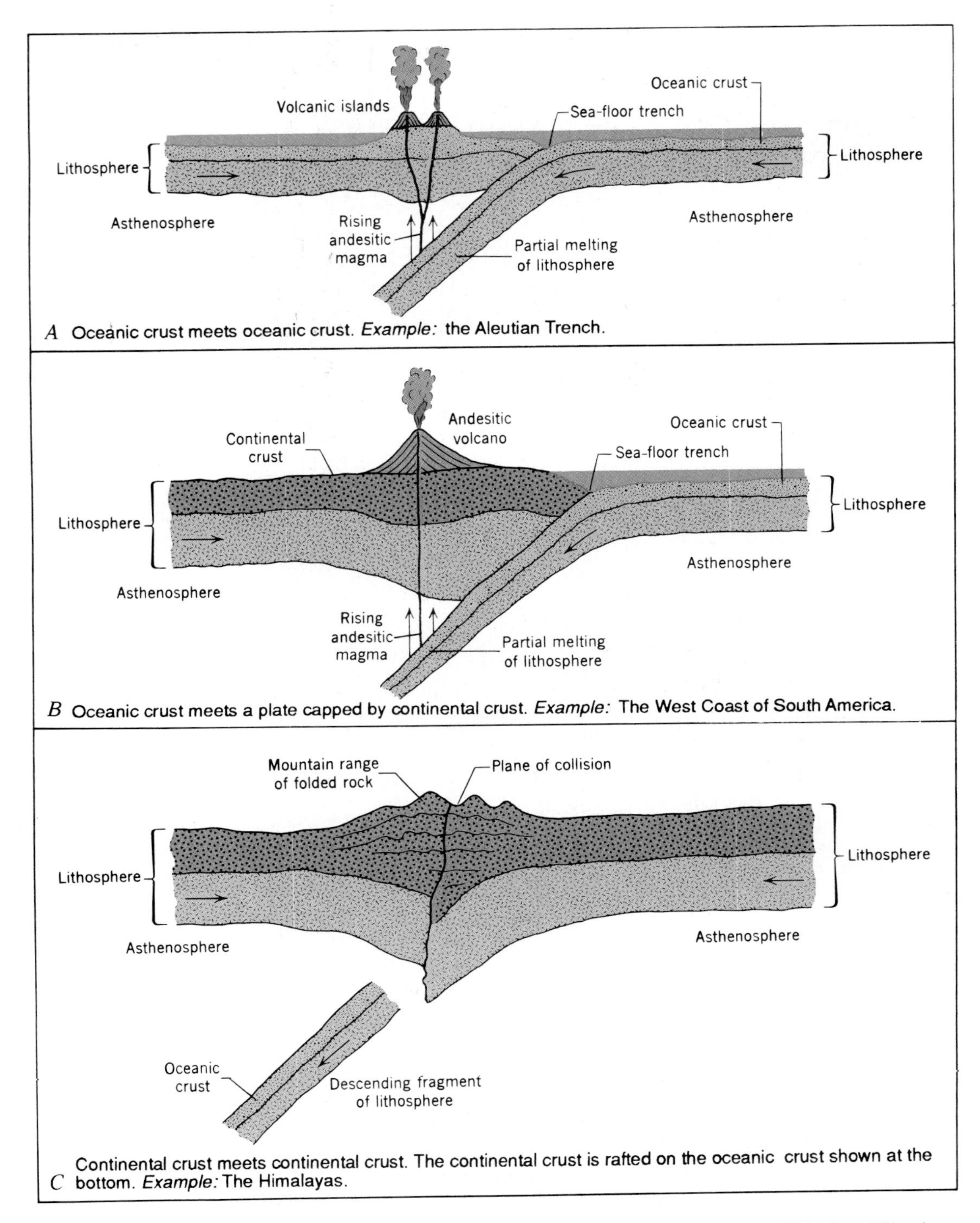

Figure 3.3 When plates collide. (From *Physical Geology*, 2nd ed. by R. F. Flint and B. J. Skinner, copyright © 1977 by John Wiley & Sons. Reprinted by permission of John Wiley & Sons, Inc.)

2) When oceanic crust meets continental crust, the denser oceanic crust is subducted. Volcanic and earthquake activity are also associated with this event. It is believed that the Andes Mountains, stretching the entire length of South America, are the result of such movement. See Figure 3.3B.

Figure 3.4 Aerial view of the San Andreas Fault. (John D. Cunningham/Visuals Unlimited)

3) When continental crust meets continental crust, the collision is spectacular. This is because continental crust has too low a density to be subducted. Since it can't go down, it buckles, cracks, and moves upward, forming the highest mountains on Earth. The Himalayas are located along the Tibet-India border where the Indian-Australian Plate is colliding northward with the Eurasian Plate. Subduction occurs below the mountains because the continental crust is rafted on top of oceanic crust. Earthquakes continually accompany this process. See Figure 3.3C.

c. Plate Sliding

When plates slide past each other, tremendous earthquakes can occur. This is because the movement is not slow and steady. Instead, immense pressures can build up. Geologic pressure can only build to a certain level. Then rapid movement occurs and the pressure is relieved. This type of activity is occurring along the San Andreas Fault in California as the Pacific Plate moves north relative to the North American Plate.

What may cause the plates to move?

The cause of plate movement is the subject of intense study and debate among geologists. Many geologists believe that heat from deep within the Earth thrusts up molten material in huge pipelike plumes. These plumes create convection currents within the asthenosphere. Figure 3.5 illustrates this model.

Where does most of the Earth's heat originate?

What causes the heat in the first place? Most of the heat within the Earth seems to originate from the breakdown of radioactive elements in rock. The heat given off is trapped. Since it has nowhere to go, it builds up and eventually melts the rock around it. Once a large volume of liquid is produced, unequal forces result in plumes. The plumes in turn drive the convection cells that move the plates.

Figure 3.5 Convection cell models.

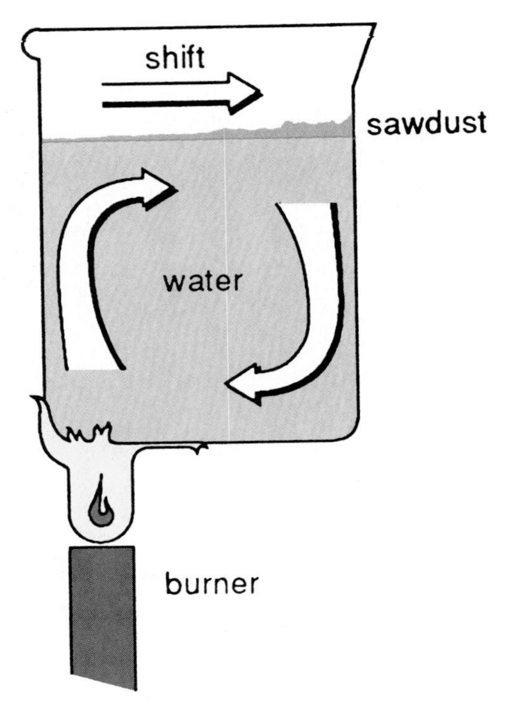

A convection cell in a beaker.

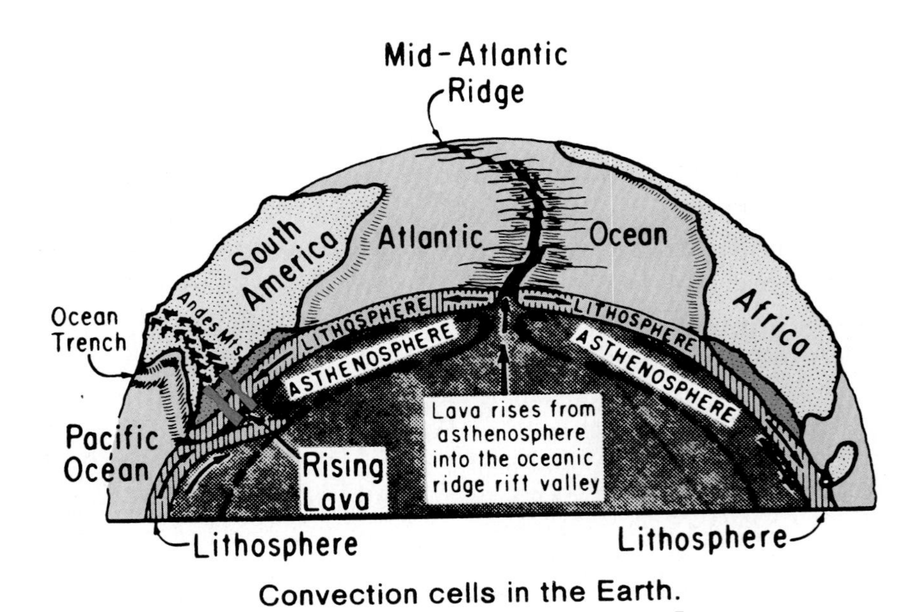

Convection cells in the Earth.

(Courtesy American Association of Petroleum Geologists.)

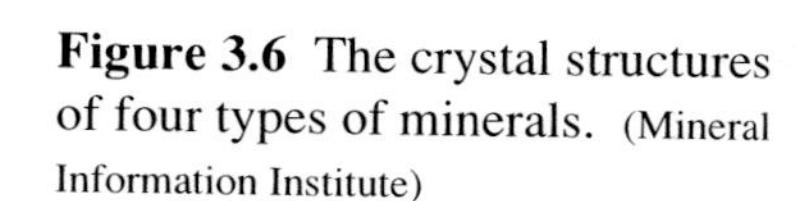
Figure 3.6 The crystal structures of four types of minerals. (Mineral Information Institute)

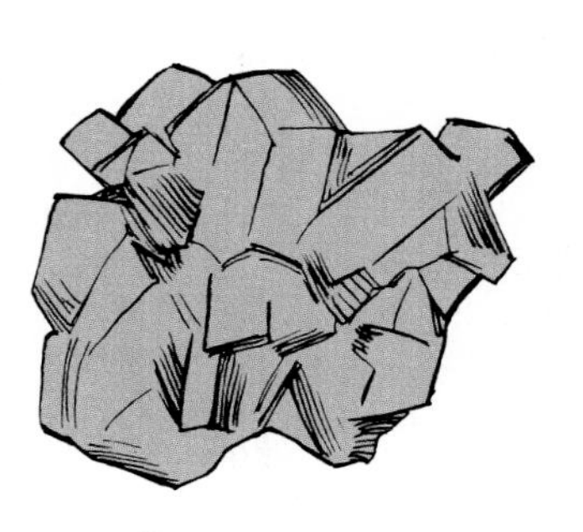

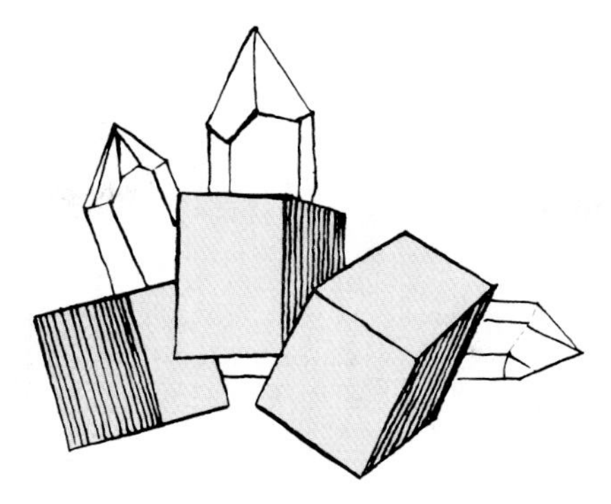

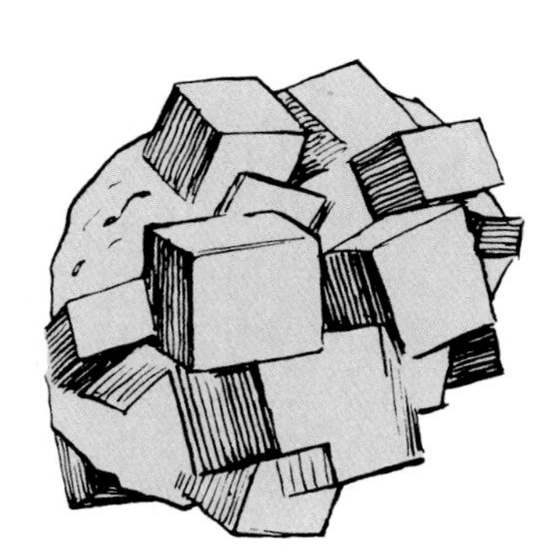

The separation or subduction of plates is generally accompanied by the eruption of volcanoes, which brings new minerals to the Earth's crust from the interior. If the geologic conditions are right, these minerals become concentrated, and potential ore bodies are formed.

 3.2 Minerals: The Ingredients of Rocks

A mineral is a naturally occurring, crystalline, usually inorganic material that has a definite internal structure, and hence a definite set of properties. This means that the mineral is put together in a particular way. Its structure is not random. Figure 3.6 shows the crystal structures of four different minerals.

Crystal: A solid form of a substance in which the atoms of which it is made are arranged in a definite pattern, so that its outer surfaces are plane faces in a symmetrical arrangement.

Minerals with such beautiful structures are difficult to find. One reason is that weathering (resulting from the forces of wind, water, and gravity) wears down the sharp edges of all such minerals exposed at the surface. Most spectacular mineral samples are found in cavelike openings underground.

Name	Composition	Hardness	Color	Cleavage	Luster	Other
Olivine	$(Mg,Fe)_2SiO_4$	> knife	a light green glass	none—conchoidal fracture	Glassy	Small grains, granular
Pyroxene	$(Mg,Fe)SiO_3$	between knife & teeth	black, dark green	Yes, 90°	Glassy	The cleavage angle is key
Amphibole	CaFeMgAl(Al,SiO) OH	between teeth & fingernail	black	Yes, 55°	Glassy	The cleavage angle is key
Biotite (mica)	$K(Mg,Fe)_3AlSi_3O_{10}(OH)_2$	< fingernail	Black, opaque	Yes, one perfect thin layer	like that of cellophane	A black mica common in granite
Muscovite (mica)	$KAl_3Si_3O_{10}(OH)_2$	< fingernail	clear, transparent, silvery	Yes, one perfect thin layer	like polished chrome	A clear mica, thin flakes
Potassium feldspar (orthosclase)	$KAlSi_3O_8$	harder than knife	Flesh colored, pinkish, white	Yes, $\simeq$ 90°	Glassy	Common in many granites
Sodium rich Plagioclase (feldspar)	$NaAlSi_3O_8$	harder than knife	White to gray translucent	Yes, $\simeq$ 90°	Glassy	A white-type feldspar

Figure 3.7 Common minerals and their properties. You may wish to consult a Periodic Table to identify the composing elements. (See chapter 8.)

Several thousand kinds of minerals have been identified, but most are very rare. Only a few occur in concentrations high enough to be mined economically. Minerals provide the materials for the products and conveniences modern societies want: machinery and tools to produce the goods we need, transportation that is safe, rapid and fuel efficient; buildings that are energy efficient (cool in the summer, warm in the winter); medicines and surgical instruments; and the many household items and appliances that help make life easier and more healthful, such as refrigerators, garbage disposals, washing machines, toilets, hair dryers, color TVs, radios and computers. The great diversity of minerals makes identification difficult for the beginner.

Name	Composition	Hardness	Color	Cleavage	Luster	Other
Calcium rich Plagioclase (feldspar)	$CaAlSi_3O_8$	about knife hardness	Violet & blue iridescent, dark glassy	Yes, ≅ 90°	Greasy	Some iridescent, some like moss agate
Quartz	SiO_2	harder than knife	Whitish translucent—with some color	None	Greasy, glassy	Very common
Kaolinite	HAlSiO(OH)	very soft!	White, opaque	One perfect—not noticeable	None	Earthy smell
Calcite	$CaCO_3$	between fingernail & teeth	clear to slightly yellow-translucent	3 perfect rhomboid	Glassy	Bubbles with dilute HCl
Dolomite	$Ca,Mg(CO_3)_2$	between fingernail & teeth	White or gray	3 perfect rhomboid	Pearly	Little to no bubbling with dilute HCl
Hematite	Fe_2O_3	≅ knife	Brick red, iron ore opaque	None & uneven fracture	Dull	Brick red
Limonite	$Fe_2O_3(H_2O)_n$	harder than knife	Yellow, rust brown (ocre)	None	Dull	Yellow, earthy masses
Gypsum	$CaSO_4 \cdot 2H_2O$	< fingernail	Colorless to white	One	Pearly	fine, fibrous crystals

Figure 3.7—Continued.

Fewer than twenty minerals make up over 95 percent of continental and oceanic crust. These are called the **rock-forming minerals** because every rock contains more than one of these minerals. Figure 3.7 summarizes key properties of 15 of the rock-forming minerals. Key terms are defined below. The next two pages show color photos of these minerals. Right now, their composition is not particularly important to us. However, knowledge of mineral compositions will be important when we concern ourselves with such matters as the composition of a good soil.

What are the rock-forming minerals?

MINERAL SAMPLES

Field quality samples (pictured on the left) are common. Rarer, higher-quality display samples are pictured on the right. The standard paper clip is shown to indicate sample size.

Olivine

Pyroxene

Amphibole (hornblende)

Biotite (mica)

Muscovite (mica)

Potassium Feldspar (orthoclase)

Sodium Rich Plagioclase (feldspar)

Calcium Rich Plagioclase (feldspar)

Name	Composition	Hardness	Color	Cleavage	Luster	Other
Calcium rich Plagioclase (feldspar)	$CaAlSi_3O_8$	about knife hardness	Violet & blue iridescent, dark glassy	Yes, ≃ 90°	Greasy	Some iridescent, some like moss agate
Quartz	SiO_2	harder than knife	Whitish translucent—with some color	None	Greasy, glassy	Very common
Kaolinite	HAlSiO(OH)	very soft!	White, opaque	One perfect—not noticeable	None	Earthy smell
Calcite	$CaCO_3$	between fingernail & teeth	clear to slightly yellow-translucent	3 perfect rhomboid	Glassy	Bubbles with dilute HCl
Dolomite	$Ca,Mg(CO_3)_2$	between fingernail & teeth	White or gray	3 perfect rhomboid	Pearly	Little to no bubbling with dilute HCl
Hematite	Fe_2O_3	≃ knife	Brick red, iron ore opaque	None & uneven fracture	Dull	Brick red
Limonite	$Fe_2O_3(H_2O)_n$	harder than knife	Yellow, rust brown (ocre)	None	Dull	Yellow, earthy masses
Gypsum	$CaSO_4 \cdot 2H_2O$	$<$ fingernail	Colorless to white	One	Pearly	fine, fibrous crystals

Figure 3.7—Continued.

Fewer than twenty minerals make up over 95 percent of continental and oceanic crust. These are called the **rock-forming minerals** because every rock contains more than one of these minerals. Figure 3.7 summarizes key properties of 15 of the rock-forming minerals. Key terms are defined below. The next two pages show color photos of these minerals. Right now, their composition is not particularly important to us. However, knowledge of mineral compositions will be important when we concern ourselves with such matters as the composition of a good soil.

What are the rock-forming minerals?

MINERAL SAMPLES

Field quality samples (pictured on the left) are common. Rarer, higher-quality display samples are pictured on the right. The standard paper clip is shown to indicate sample size.

Olivine

Pyroxene

Amphibole (hornblende)

Biotite (mica)

Muscovite (mica)

Potassium Feldspar (orthoclase)

Sodium Rich Plagioclase (feldspar)

Calcium Rich Plagioclase (feldspar)

Quartz

Kaolinite

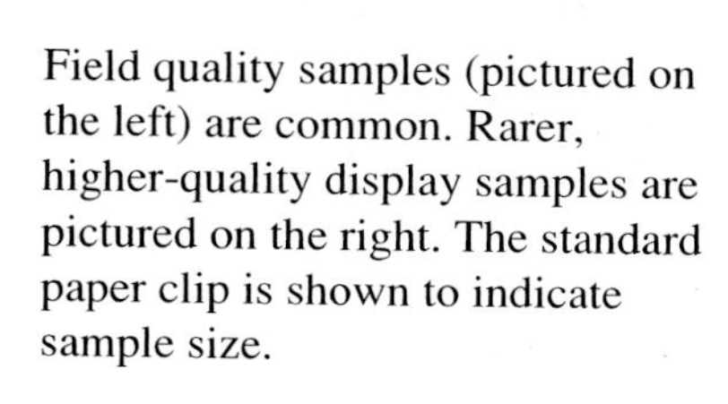

Field quality samples (pictured on the left) are common. Rarer, higher-quality display samples are pictured on the right. The standard paper clip is shown to indicate sample size.

Calcite

Dolomite

Hemitite

Limonite

Gypsum

Definitions

Hardness: The resistance of a mineral to being scratched.

Color: Although it is the most obvious physical property, it is commonly of limited use because many mineral specimens occur in a variety of colors, and different minerals may have similar colors.

Cleavage: A breaking or splitting that tends to be parallel to crystal faces and yields smooth, flat surfaces along certain directions. Minerals may have one, two, three or more directions of cleavage. The number and direction of cleavage surfaces, as well as the angles between them are constant for each mineral.

Fracture: Any break other than cleavage.

Luster: The appearance of the mineral surface in reflected light. Minerals can be divided into two major groups on the basis of their luster. One group has a metallic luster (looks like metal) and is opaque. The other group has a nonmetallic luster and may be either transparent or opaque. Nonmetallic lusters are given special names such as adamantine (like diamond), dull or earthy, glassy (like broken glass), greasy, pearly, resinous, silky, waxy, and iridescent (displaying colors like those of the rainbow).

Transparency: The degree to which a mineral will transmit light.

21 3.3 Rocks: The Solid Materials of the Earth's Crust

Rocks are made up of minerals. It is important to be able to identify the minerals in a rock sample if you wish to assess the uses for which the rock is suitable and its economic value.

? What is a rock? What are the three types of rock?

All rocks can be classified into one of three types, based on origin. The three types are igneous, sedimentary, and metamorphic.

a. Igneous Rock

Distinguish between magma and lava.

Igneous rock is formed by the solidification of hot fluid material. **Magma** refers to the molten material that exists beneath the earth's surface. The molten material that is extruded at the surface is called **lava.**

Igneous rocks are divided into two main classifications: **extrusive** and **intrusive. Extrusive** igneous rock is formed by the cooling and hardening of lava poured out onto the Earth's surface. If the lava cooled rapidly, the resulting rock may be filled with bubbles of gas that didn't have time to escape. If the lava cooled less rapidly, the gases probably escaped, resulting in a glassy material (obsidian) or in fine-grained rocks. The crystals in these are hard to see with the unaided eye.

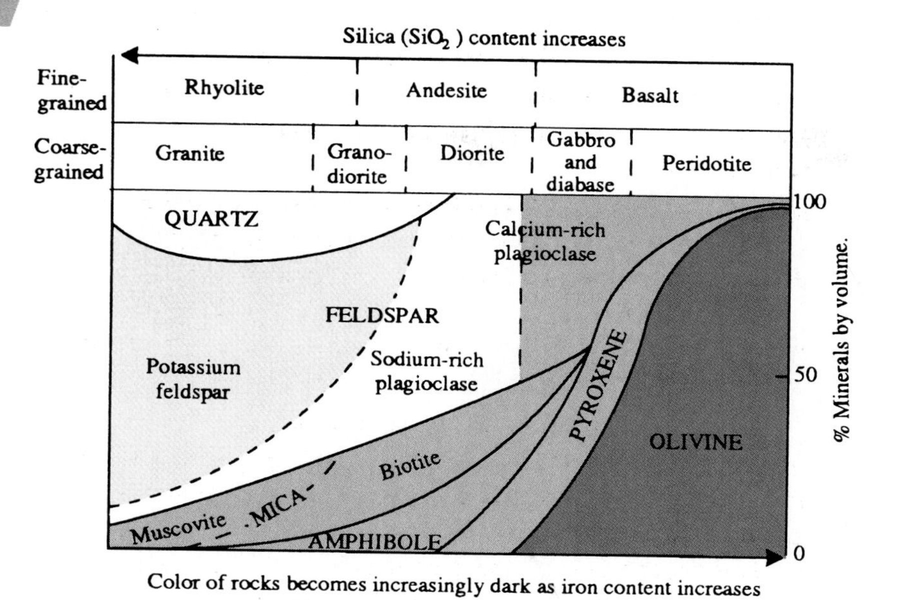

Figure 3.8 A scheme for classifying intrusive igneous rocks.

Size of Particle		Name of Loose Sediment	Name of Sedimentary Rock
Coarse		Gravel	Conglomerate
	– 2 mm		
Medium		Sand	Sandstone
	– $\frac{1}{16}$ mm		
Fine		mud: silt	Siltstone
		mud: clay	Shale

Figure 3.9 A scheme for classifying clastic sedimentary rock.

Intrusive igneous rock is formed by much slower cooling and solidification of magma beneath the Earth's surface. This allows time for crystals to grow to much larger sizes, which can be studied easily. These are referred to as **coarse-grained** rocks.

Figure 3.8 shows a scheme for classifying igneous rocks based on the amounts of silica and iron they contain. Notice that as the content of silica (the main ingredient of glass) increases, the color becomes lighter. Use Figure 3.8, the photos of the rock-forming minerals, and the photos of selected igneous rocks to help answer these questions.

1. Why is rhyolite light in color and basalt dark?
2. Why does granite have pink, white, and black crystals in it?
3. Why is diorite a white and black speckled rock?
4. Why is peridotite greenish?

The standard paper clip is shown to help size the samples.

EXTRUSIVE IGNEOUS ROCKS

Pumice

Obsidian

FINE-GRAINED IGNEOUS ROCKS

Rhyolite

Basalt

COARSE-GRAINED IGNEOUS ROCKS

Granite

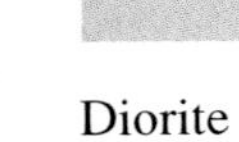

Diorite

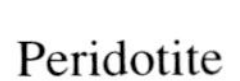

Peridotite

SELECTED SEDIMENTARY ROCKS

The standard paper clip is shown to indicate sample size.

Conglomerate

Sandstone

Shale

Limestone*

*Limestone: A clastic or chemical sedimentary rock.

SELECTED METAMORPHIC ROCKS

Slate

Schist

Gneiss

Quartzite

Marble

b. Sedimentary Rock

How are sedimentary rocks formed?

Sedimentary rock is formed by the erosion of all three major rock types. The eroded debris accumulates in basins, flood plains, lakes, and oceans. It becomes buried by additional sediment. This deep burial increases both temperature (up to 300° C) and pressure, compacting the sediment. Many sedimentary rocks have subangular to rounded grains and may contain fossils.

There are two major categories of sedimentary rocks depending on their origin. **Clastic** sedimentary rocks result from the accumulation of particles of broken rock and the skeletal remains of dead organisms. Over time, these materials become compacted and cemented together. Clastic sedimentary rock is classified by grain (particle) size, as shown in Figure 3.9.

Chemical sedimentary rock is formed by chemical precipitation from solution. Limestone is a common example.

c. Metamorphic Rock

How were metamorphic rocks formed?

Metamorphic rock is usually formed deep within Earth's crust by recrystallization of all types of preexisting rock due to high temperature, high pressure, or both. The minerals are changed chemically and rearranged in a more compact way. Some metamorphic rock is characterized by **foliation**—a parallel or nearly parallel structure caused by a parallel arrangement of platy minerals.

It is easiest to begin studying metamorphic rocks by looking at samples and reading the related descriptions. Examine Figure 3.10 which describes several of the most common metamorphic rocks. As you read the descriptions, examine the related photos. Then examine samples of the rocks themselves.

3.4 The Definition of an Ore

Elements in the Earth's crust.

Everything on and in the Earth is made up of about 90 elements. Various combinations of these elements make up all the materials we encounter. The percentages of the elements in Earth's crust are shown in Table 3.1. In this text, our primary interest is only in the **crust,** since that is what affects us directly and is what we use. Direct knowledge of the chemical nature of the Earth's interior is limited.

An examination of these figures reveals some startling facts. Only 10 elements make up over 98% of the Earth's crust (by weight). Nearly 75% of the crust is oxygen and silicon. Iron and aluminum are probably the only metals listed with which you are familiar. Gold, silver, copper, lead, zinc, nitrogen, phosphorus, sulfur, and chlorine aren't on the list. These elements must occur in very small quantities, yet many of them seem to be in ample supply. How is this possible?

Foliated metamorphic rock

- *slate:* fine-grained, with pronounced cleavage; formed from mudstone, a shale.
- *phyllite:* exceptionally lustrous rock in a higher stage of metamorphism than slate.
- *schist:* well-foliated, component platy minerals are clearly visible.
- *gneiss:* coarse-grained, commonly with marked layering but with imperfect cleavage.

Nonfoliated metamorphic rock

- *quartzite:* generally white, gray, tan or other light colors; often a recrystallized quartz sandstone with hardness of 7 and conchoidal fracture.
- *marble:* generally white and coarse crystalline (with sparkly crystal faces); a recrystallized limestone, made up of calcite and/or dolomite.
- *hornfels:* very hard rock, commonly studded with small garnet crystals and mica.
- *argillite:* fine grained, hardened mudstone showing no slatelike cleavage.

Figure 3.10 Identification and classifications of selected metamorphic rocks.

Table 3.1 Percent* (by Weight) of Elements in the Earth's Crust

oxygen	46.6%	sodium	2.8%
silicon	27.7%	potassium	2.6%
aluminum	8.0%	magnesium	2.1%
iron	5.8%	titanium	0.4%
calcium	3.6%	hydrogen	0.1%
		all others	0.8%

*Total slightly exceeds 100% due to rounding.

The answer lies in the abundance of those elements in scattered places. A question equivalent to "Who is buried in Grant's tomb?" is "Where do they mine copper?" The obvious answer is, of course, a copper mine! Why? Because a copper mine is a place where the amount of copper is far above normal. The average crustal abundance of copper is only 0.007%. This means, on the average, it would be necessary to mine a little over 7 tons of rock to recover only 1 pound of copper. Obviously, no one does this! Copper is mined only where the concentration of copper is high enough to be profitably removed.

Crustal abundance: The average percent concentration of a particular element or isotope in the Earth's crust.

A copper deposit of this concentration is called an ore. Thus, an **ore** is a natural mineral occurrence in sufficient concentration to be profitably used as a source for one or more elements. More simply, an ore is anything that can be mined at a profit. Though any natural mineral concentration might be a "mineral deposit," only one that can be

What is an ore?

removed at a profit is ore. Some mineral deposits that are classified as ores today weren't ores a few years ago, and vice versa. This is because the economics and technologies of recovery have changed.

How did copper become more concentrated at some locations than at others? Why was gold concentrated in California, Nevada, Colorado, Alaska and North Carolina, but not in Nebraska, Minnesota, or Alabama?

Obviously, mineral deposits are not evenly distributed around the country or the world. We will attempt to explain this in the next sections.

3.5 The Formation of Ore Deposits

How are ore deposits formed?

The plate tectonics theory maintains that the Earth's crust is constantly moving. The crust is the upper part of the plates, which move only a few (1 to perhaps 10) centimeters a year. As plates collide or move apart, deformation of the crust occurs. The crustal rocks are buckled, folded, cracked, and uplifted. Since some of the material below and in the crust is not solid, but flows as a highly viscous liquid, it is free to move into the cracks and crevices that develop in overlying or adjacent solid rock. The hot molten fluid, or magma, is under tremendous pressure. When it moves into cracks and cavities in the crust, some pressure is released and some of the heat is lost. When this happens, all sorts of things can occur.

Volatile: Evaporating rapidly; diffusing more or less freely in the atmosphere.

What does magma consist of?

As magma cools, the elements combine to form minerals. By far, the most abundant volatile part of the magma is water, which vaporizes when pressure is released. Other volatiles present are oxygen, nitrogen, carbon dioxide, hydrochloric acid, hydrofluoric acid, boron, and various gases of sulfur. It is strongly believed that the movement of these volatile parts is closely associated with the formation of many ore deposits. In addition, processes on or near the Earth's surface alter the chemical and physical environment that causes the elements in the crust to combine, recombine, and move in such a way that minerals become concentrated.

Name the four steps of the plate tectonics cycle.

The movement of the Earth's plates and changes in crustal features may be thought of as a four-step cycle:

1. Mid-ocean rifting or seafloor spreading.
2. Subduction at outer continental margins.
3. Mountain building where deep ocean crust collides with continental crust.
4. Weathering processes and minor crustal adjustments.

As weathering and gravitational processes wear down the surface, the Earth's interior is also stressed by convectional, rotational, and gravitational forces. New splits or rifts occur, all leading to continuation of the cycle on the Earth.

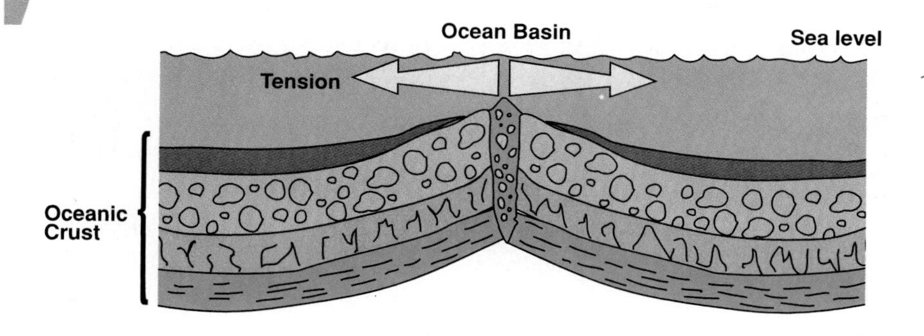

Figure 3.11 Mid-ocean rifting or seafloor spreading. (Richard Hutchinson)

3.6 Orebody Formation and Seafloor Spreading

The convection currents within the asthenosphere cause tremendous pressure on the plates. When these currents move in opposite directions, the opposing forces can cause plates to split or rift. As this occurs, molten material from below the plates moves into the void, and seafloor volcanoes erupt. Both new oceanic crust and some mineral deposits are created as the molten material solidifies. See Figure 3.11.

Orebody: a more or less solid mass of ore that is of different character than the adjoining rock. Orebodies are what exploration geologists look for.

Since the magma and lava associated with seafloor spreading originated below the dense ocean crust, its chemical makeup is different from the magma and lava found where plates collide. Hence, the ore deposits found at rift boundaries are of certain types. These include: chromite (chromium), magnetite (iron), nickel-copper sulfides, platinum group minerals, and copper-zinc sulfides that contain minute amounts of gold and silver.

3.7 Orebody Formation at Ocean Subduction Zones

When oceanic crust meets *oceanic* crust, one of the plates is younger and more dense than the other. It is subducted. When oceanic crust meets *continental* crust, the younger, more dense, oceanic crust is over-ridden by the older, less dense, continent. See Figure 3.13.

Since the magma and lava associated with subduction where oceanic plates collide is made up of partially molten former ocean crust material, their chemical makeup reflects this. The ore deposits found there include copper-zinc sulfides with gold and silver, certain iron-rich sedimentary rocks, and certain types of gold lodes.

Since the magma and lava associated with subduction at continental margins is a mixture of oceanic and continental materials, their chemical makeup reflects this. The ore deposits found along these continental margins are of certain types. These include copper-lead-zinc sulfides with silver and some gold.

Figure 3.12 Plume of hot, mineral-laden water spouts from mineralized chimney on the East Pacific Rise (see Plate Boundary map). The chimney and adjacent formations build up from dissolved minerals that precipitate around the hot jet as it mixes with the near-freezing waters at the ocean bottom. (Photographed from the deep-diving submarine, *Alvin,* by D. B. Foster, Woods Hole Oceanographic Institution.)

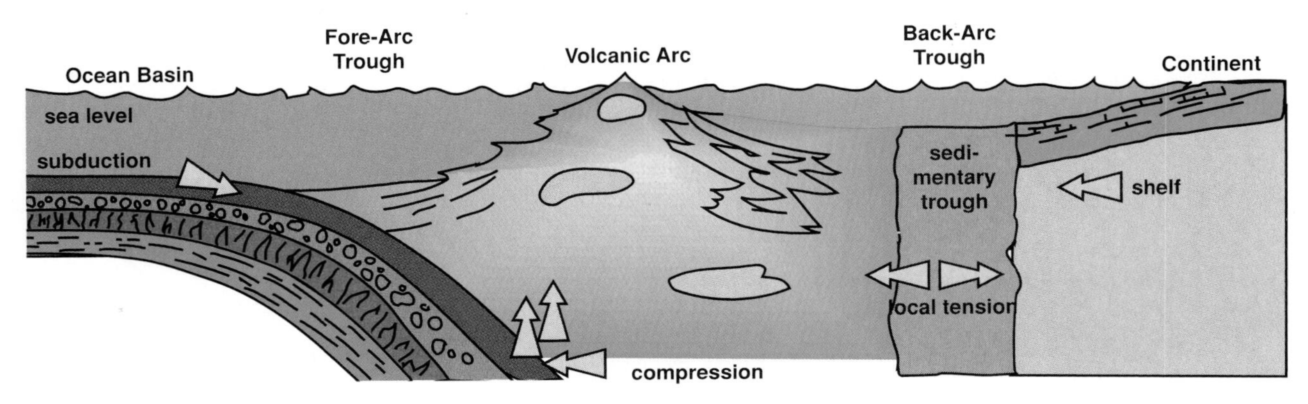

Figure 3.13 Subduction at continental margins.

3.8 Crustal Collision and Orebody Formation

As oceanic crust is subducted beneath continental crust, prolonged collisions can also generate important ore deposits. Here, major granitic intrusions cause uplift of continental edge mountain belts like those along the western edges of North and South America. In the process, 1) magma shoots up into cracks that are created, 2) some layers of rock may be forced over other layers, and 3) new sedimentary layers form in lowlands as the nearby high mountains weather away. See Figure 3.14.

The ore deposits associated with the crustal collisions of the type shown in Figure 3.14 reflect the nature of the collision and the

Figure 3.14 Mountain building where ocean crust collides with continental crust. (Richard Hutchinson)

composition of crustal materials. Hence gold and silver veins, along with lithium, nickel, and cesium are associated with region 1. Also, large porphyry, copper, and molybdenum deposits may form. Tin and tungsten deposits are found in region 2.

3.9 Weathering Processes and Minor Crustal Adjustments

The Earth's features constantly change. Wind, water, and gravity continually alter the surface. In addition, water, gravity, and pressure changes alter the crust below the surface. This is summarized in Figure 3.15.

As subduction wanes, 1) smaller amounts of magma will intrude into cracks and other openings that develop in the Earth's crust, 2) basalt can spill out onto the surface and flood large areas, 3 and 4) some magma will find its way to the surface to produce inland volcanic eruptions, 5) particles will erode from mountains and hills to form sediments in valleys and at the bottom of lakes and seas, 6) lakes and seas will evaporate and leave behind evaporite deposits, 7) soluble minerals will be removed in groundwater leaving behind laterite deposits, and 8) flowing water at the surface will produce placer deposits.

Finally, pressures from below cause a new split in the Earth's crust (see the right side of Figure 3.15), and the cycle repeats.

Laterite deposit: a red, porous deposit containing large amounts of aluminum and ferric (iron) hydroxides.

Explain why a new split begins a new cycle.

Figure 3.15 Weathering processes and minor crustal adjustments. (Richard Hutchinson)

 3.10 Mineral Concentration Processes

Minerals become concentrated in a variety of ways. A summary of several major processes follows.

a. Selective Crystallization from Solutions

How can minerals become concentrated in cooling magmas?

As magmatic and other hot solutions cool, minerals with higher crystallization temperatures come out of solution first. Often the minerals which crystallize first, such as chromite, are more dense than the solution itself. When this happens, the denser material sinks to the bottom. If these segregated mineral layers are useful to us, a valuable ore deposit has been created.

b. Immiscible Liquids

When shaken together, oil and water won't mix. They are said to be **immiscible.** Instead of mixing, they separate into two layers. Magma can separate and cause concentrations because of the immiscibility of some minerals within it.

c. Replacement Deposits

Why does replacement sometimes occur?

By nature, some minerals are chemically more reactive than others. When minerals of differing activity come in contact, replacement can occur. Replacement deposits result when one mineral takes for itself the space once occupied by another. For example, as solutions move in magmas, a deposit of lead might be replaced by zinc.

d. Deposition from Lake Water and Seawater

How do minerals become concentrated in lake and seawater?

All undistilled water contains ions of some dissolved chemical elements. The elements in the water come from the weathering (breakdown) of rocks. Streams transport these elements into lakes and seas. During dry periods, water in the lakes and seas evaporates. As the dissolved elements do not evaporate, the solutions become more and more concentrated. Eventually the elements may form solid crystals. Table salt and salts of potassium and boron are concentrated this way. See Figure 3.16.

a

Figure 3.16 Solar ponds in the Great Salt Lake, Utah. Water evaporates, leaving the salt. (Aerial photography: Ron Redfern, *The Making of a Continent:* Times Books, New York) The upper photo shows mechanical harvesting of salt. (Morton Salt/Jim Huizingh)

b

Figure 3.17 The Bingham Canyon Copper Mine is the Earth's biggest human-constructed excavation. (From Utah Copper Division, Kennecott Corporation, Don Greene, photographer.)

The sediments formed in shallow seas are an especially rich source of metals and salts. Two kinds of calcium sulfates, gypsum and anhydrite, were formed in this way. Today we use gypsum and anhydrite in making plaster. The largest iron concentrations in the world, called iron formations, were also once dissolved in shallow seas.

Manganese, copper, iron, cobalt, and other elements are concentrated in mineral form on the deep ocean floor. They originate in hot solutions that shoot out of cracks in the floor. The solutions are quickly cooled by ocean water, and mineral precipitates form.

e. Concentrations Caused by the Movement of Groundwater

How can minerals become concentrated by the movement of groundwater?

Mineral concentration may result from the movement of groundwater. This can happen in two different ways. **Secondary enrichment** occurs when a valuable substance is dissolved, carried downward or laterally, and redeposited in a concentrated state a short distance away from its original location. Secondary enrichment caused the formation of the large, enriched portion of the ore at the Utah Copper Mine at Bingham Canyon. This mine is the largest copper producer in the United States. It is shown in Figure 3.17.

Sometimes a residue of valuable substance is left behind when other material is dissolved and flows away. This is called **residual enrichment.** An example is bauxite, a mixture of various aluminum oxide minerals. Bauxite is the preferred source of aluminum.

f. Mechanical Concentration in Flowing Water

How can minerals be mechanically concentrated by flowing water?

Some concentration by flowing water is mechanical, or non-chemical. This occurs when the minerals in a mixture of sediments vary in density or hardness. The best known example is the formation of placer gold deposits.

The gold in primary deposits is subject to weathering and erosion, just like anything else. During weathering, rocks and ore minerals disintegrate and are carried into gullies, creeks, and rivers. Most metal-bearing minerals rapidly break up physically and chemically in this

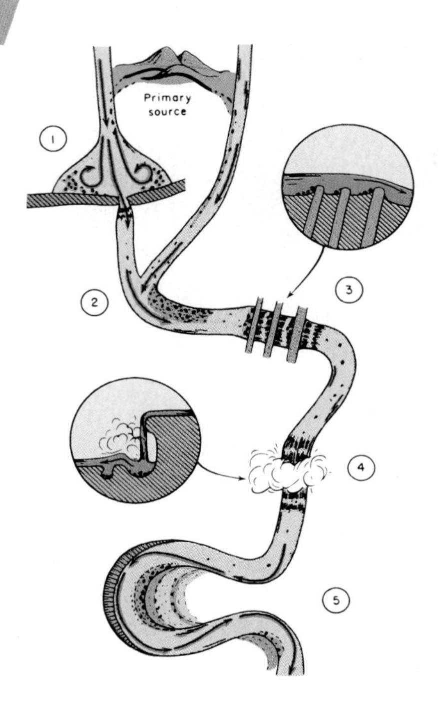

Figure 3.18 Diagram showing possible sites for placer accumulations along the course of a stream: (1) behind an obstruction that dams the stream; (2) downstream from a tributary mouth; (3) behind ridges formed by dipping resistant beds; (4) in plunge pools and pot holes; (5) in slack waters along inner shores of meander loops. (From *Our Mineral Resources*, by Charles M. Riley, New York: John Wiley & Sons, Inc.)

process. Some of their parts dissolve and float off in surface water. Gold, however, is extremely resistant to weathering. When freed from the enclosing rocks, gold is carried downstream as metallic particles.

Gold and coarse gravel will sink on the inside of curves in streams where the current moves more slowly, or where the stream gradient is reduced. Gold collects in sand and gravel bars but is about seven times more dense than sand or gravel. It quickly concentrates in the low points or pockets of a stream. Usually a few other very dense and resistant minerals accumulate with gold. Magnetite is the most common. Other minerals that may be present are platinum, cassiterite, monazite, ilmenite, chromite, and some gem stones.

A deposit of dense minerals concentrated mechanically is called a **placer** (pronounced "plasser"). It was a placer deposit that was discovered at Sutter's sawmill in 1848 and set off the great California gold rush. Figure 3.18 shows the most probable locations for placer deposits along a flowing stream.

Figure 3.19 illustrates one of the methods of working a placer deposit. A gold pan, rocker, and sluice box were used by prospectors. As shown, a portion of the stream is rerouted to flow over the box. Gravel from a possible placer deposit is dug up and shoveled into the sluice box. The rerouted, rapidly moving water carries away most of the gravel. The gold and other high-density minerals sink to the bottom and are held by riffles and possibly in the grooves of the canvas or other material that make up the bottom of the box. A sluice box makes it possible to process much more ore than can be worked with a gold pan in a given amount of time. For you would-be "gold finders," this method still works today! Astroturf works better than canvas for capturing gold flakes.

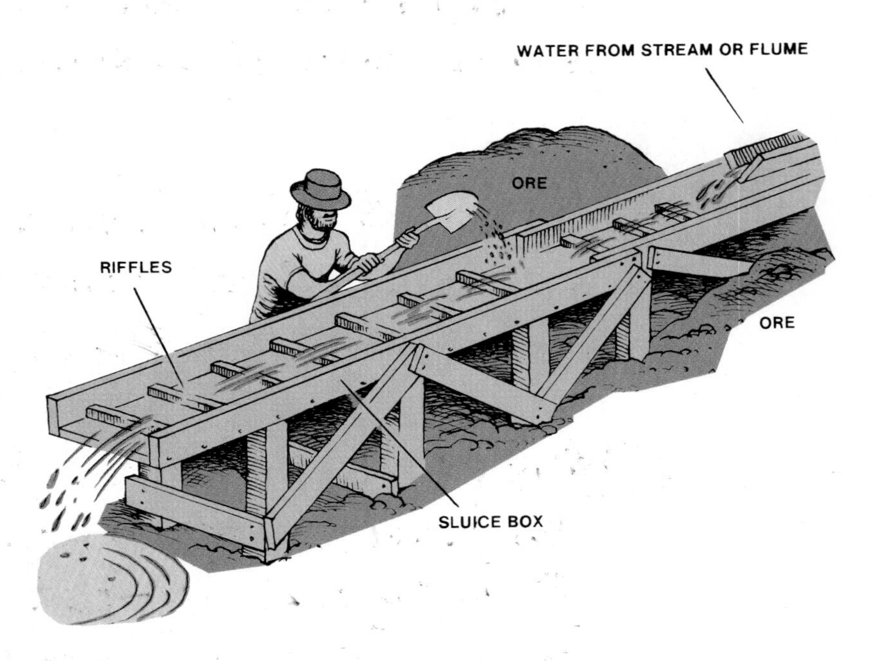

Figure 3.19 An early prospector working a sluice box. (Mineral Information Institute)

 3.11 Locating, Mining, and Milling Ore Deposits

Why did the exploration geologist say, "I'd rather be lucky than smart"?

How are ore deposits located and mined?

Prospecting and exploring for minerals involves using all the knowledge we have about the theory of ore formation. This knowledge, along with various technical tools and a good deal of luck, can lead to both great and small discoveries.

A geologist first studies scientific papers and other written documentation on the geology and past history of mining and exploration activities in an area. Satellite surveys are also examined. If the presence of ore seems likely, many exploration techniques can be used to assist in the discovery.

By studying reflected shock waves, geologists and geophysicists learn much about the arrangement of rock strata beneath Earth's surface. One of the most accurate exploration methods is the seismic reflection technique, which sends miniature shock waves down into the Earth. The waves hit the various rock layers and bounce back to the surface. At the surface they are recorded by a seismograph, an instrument like those used in detecting and measuring real earthquakes. The time it takes for the waves to travel down and back indicates how deep the formations are and also reveals other useful data. Information obtained from recordings is used to make maps that show the arrangement of rock layers in the subsurface.

The force of gravity varies from place to place, again depending partially on the density of the rocks underneath the surface. Sedimentary rocks are less dense than igneous or metamorphic rocks. By using a gravimeter, the pull of gravity at the surface is measured. The readings are plotted on a map.

Another test depends on the fact that some rocks contain more magnetite than others. The more magnetite a rock contains, the more magnetic it is. An instrument called a magnetometer is used to

Figure 3.20 An aerial electromagnetic survey in progress. Note the large transmitting "loop" and the receiving "bird" in the lower left corner. (Questar Surveys Limited, Mississauga, Ontario)

measure the force of magnetism at the surface of the Earth. A magnetic survey, either surface or airborne, gives a general idea of rock formations at depth. Many readings are taken over a large area in order to localize places that might be good prospects for other exploration techniques. This information is also plotted on maps. (See Figure 3.20.)

How are mineral deposits discovered?

All of this information, combined with previous knowledge about crustal composition and movements, sends the geologists to the field (the area they have investigated by above techniques). In the field, they gain additional information by analyzing: 1) the outcrops and soils derived from the underlying rocks; 2) the waters that flow through the area; and 3) the vegetation covering the area.

Collectively, the geological and geophysical data are used to determine the most likely places to drill for ore. Drilling is very expensive, but it is the only way to prove an orebody is present and to determine the character, grade, and size of the deposit.

Once a deposit has been discovered, it is a matter of years before the ore may be placed into production. Geologists and engineers have to determine which type of mining method to use. Many things have to be considered. Some deposits may be producing within ten years while others may take as long as 20 years. Table 3.2 shows the steps and period of time needed for **underground mining.**

Many things take place during the development and construction phase. If underground mining has been determined to be the most economic method, drilling and blasting take place. (See Figure 3.21.)

Name some mining techniques.

Ore deposits are extracted from the Earth in the most economical way. Open pit mines require the use of huge trucks, trains, or conveyors. For underground mines, small-tired trucks, trains, inclined conveyors or hoists will be needed. Each mining method is unique. For some deposits, such as salt bodies and other soluble minerals such as

Table 3.2 Scheduling Diagram for Open Pit Mining

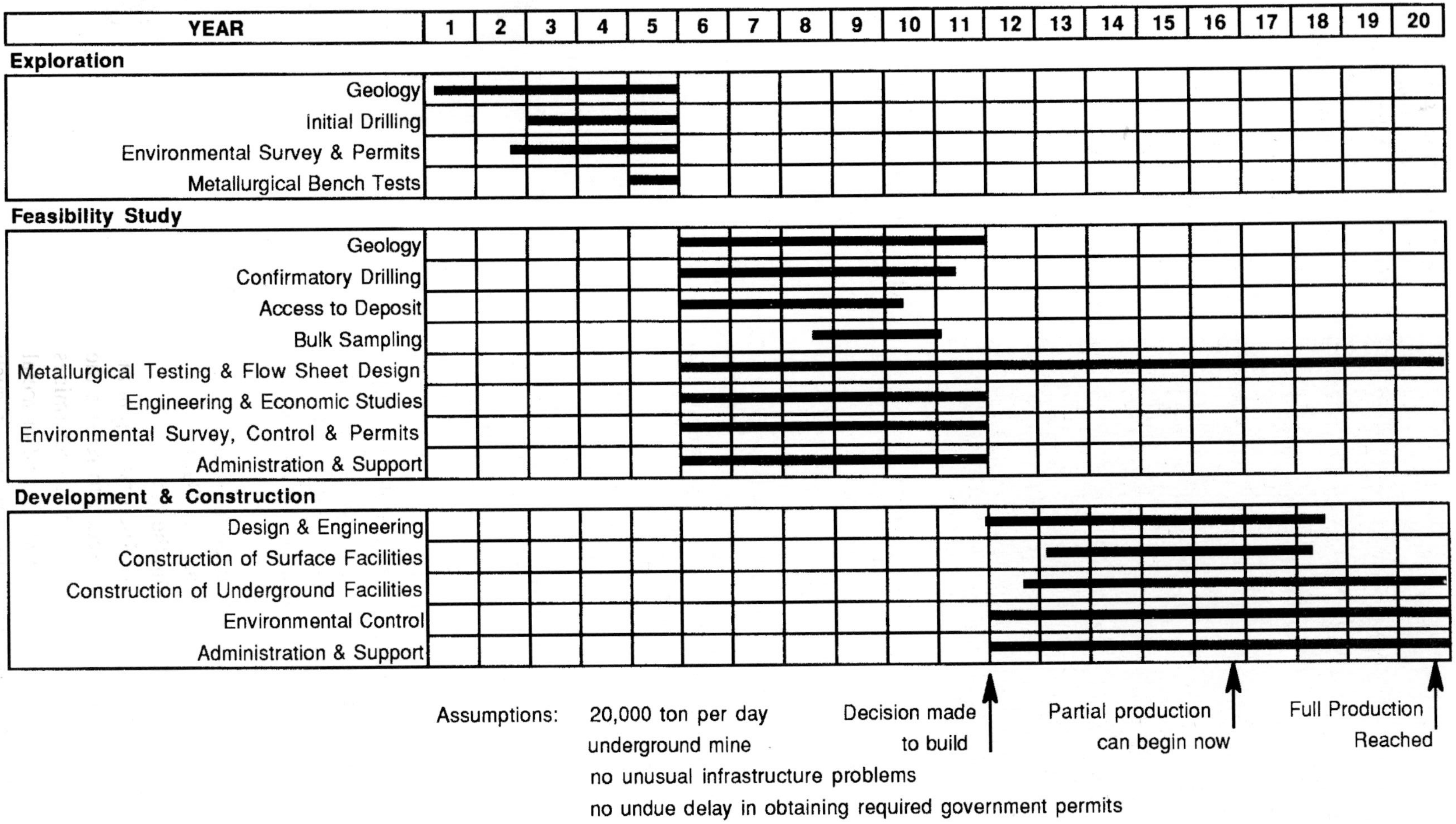

YEAR	1	2	3	4	5	6	7	8	9	10	11	12	13	14	15	16	17	18	19	20
Exploration																				
Geology																				
Initial Drilling																				
Environmental Survey & Permits																				
Metallurgical Bench Tests																				
Feasibility Study																				
Geology																				
Confirmatory Drilling																				
Access to Deposit																				
Bulk Sampling																				
Metallurgical Testing & Flow Sheet Design																				
Engineering & Economic Studies																				
Environmental Survey, Control & Permits																				
Administration & Support																				
Development & Construction																				
Design & Engineering																				
Construction of Surface Facilities																				
Construction of Underground Facilities																				
Environmental Control																				
Administration & Support																				

Decision made to build

Partial production can begin now

Full Production Reached

Assumptions: 20,000 ton per day underground mine
no unusual infrastructure problems
no undue delay in obtaining required government permits

Figure 3.21 Underground equipment at the Climax, Colorado Mine, Climax Molybdenum Company. Large equipment like this three-boom drill jumbo helps demonstrate the size of underground work areas in today's larger mines. The jumbo is used to drill blast holes into the rock which, when blasted with explosives, will create new mine areas for future production. (AMAX, Inc.)

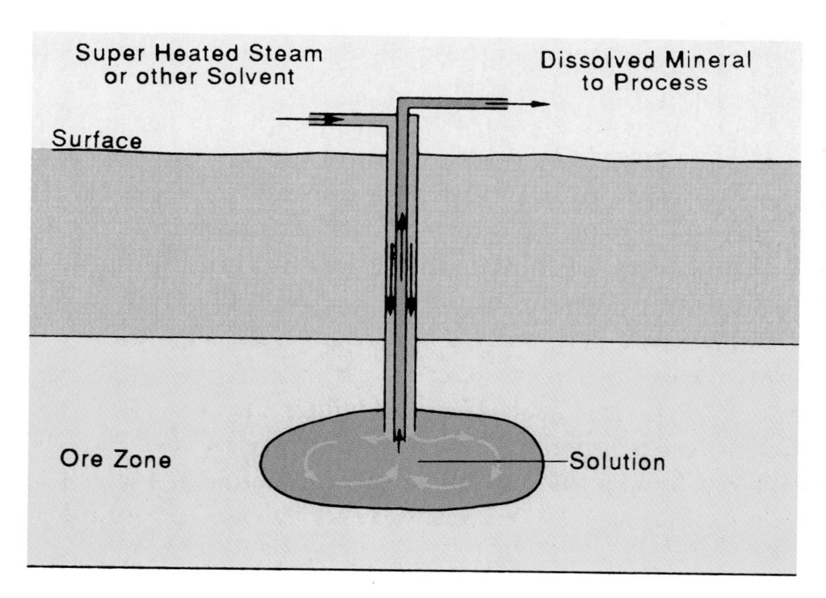

Figure 3.22 Solution mining (Frasch Process). (Brooks Minerals, Inc.)

sulfur, extraction may be by means of **solution mining.** Hot water is pumped down a drill hole into the mineral zone where the minerals are dissolved. The brines are pumped out of another drill hole. The brines carry the minerals, which are then recovered by evaporation. (See Figure 3.22.)

After mining, the next step is to concentrate the mineral. This involves separating the desired minerals from **gangue.** Gangue is the name for the nonvaluable minerals associated with the ore.

What is gangue?

After mining, the ore is transported to a mill. The first step in the milling process is to crush the ore as finely as needed to release the desired mineral. The crushing stages vary. The type of ore determines the steps that are required for separating the desired mineral or metal from the gangue. The particles are separated by physical means, such

?

What is milling?

Figure 3.23 Flotation machines in the milling process. (AMAX Inc.)

as washing, flotation, or magnetic attraction. Figure 3.23 shows flotation cells at a large mill.

Flotation involves agitating the ore in a vessel with a detergent or foaming agent. The more valuable mineral sticks to the bubbles of foam and floats off into a collecting trough, while the reject may remain in the vessel so that other minerals can be recovered.

Some minerals can be separated from their crushed ores with electromagnetic equipment. If an ore cannot be sufficiently concentrated by physical means, various chemical processes are used.

The residue that remains after the ore minerals have been separated from the gangue minerals is called **tailing.** The water used in the milling process transports the tailing to the disposal site. There the water is usually impounded and pumped back to the mill circuit for reuse. The tailing area can be reclaimed once the ore deposit has been mined.

?

What is smelting?

?

What is refining?

After the concentrate leaves the mill, it needs further separation. As an example, if the concentrate contains copper, lead, zinc, gold, or silver, the ore minerals will have to be separated. The concentrates are then transported to a smelter. **Smelting** is the fusing or melting of a concentrate to separate the metal or metals it contains from other elements, such as oxygen, iron, or sulfur. After smelting further refining is usually necessary. **Refining** is a general term for the process by which a metal is brought to a fine or a pure state. The metal may be used in its pure form (raw metal). More often than not it is combined with other materials to form an alloy. Figure 3.24 summarizes the steps of metal production.

If you live "the good life," you are involved with mining.

The refined metal is now ready to be put to its commercial uses. In addition, valuable by-products are recovered in the process of smelting and refining copper, lead, zinc, and many other ores.

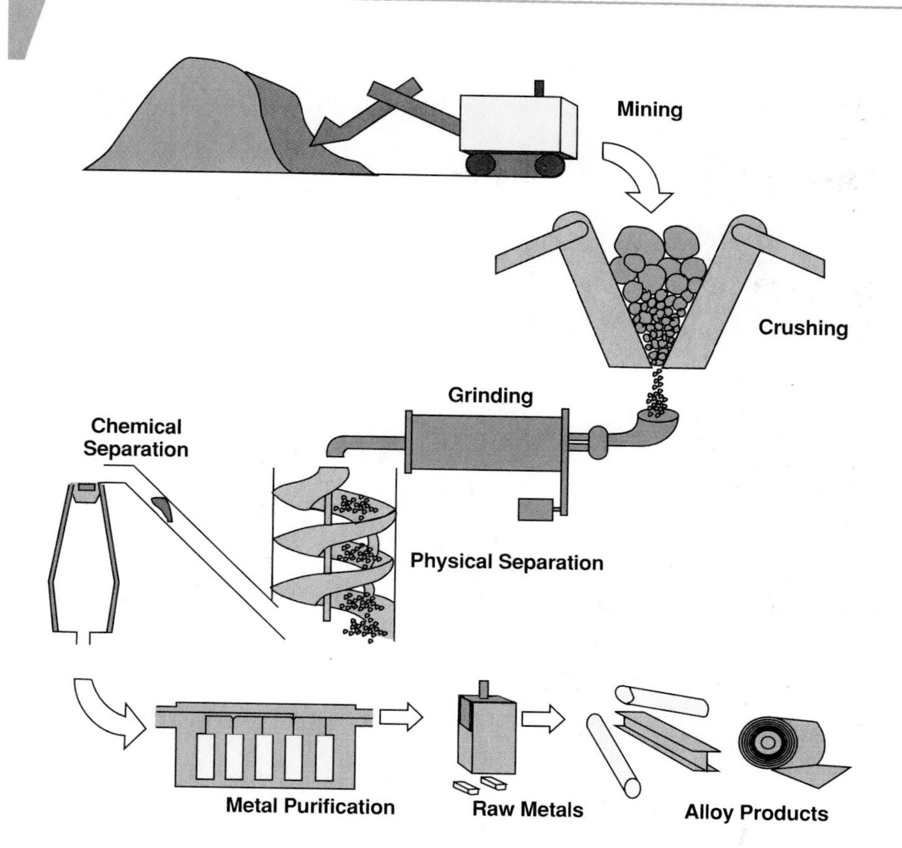

Figure 3.24 Steps in metal production. (Mineral Information Institute)

3.12 Alloys

Why are metals usually alloyed?

Metals are seldom used in their pure state. This is because the properties of metal mixtures (alloys) may be preferable to those of the pure metals. Dentists, for instance, may use alloys of gold, silver, platinum, and other metals in fillings and crowns. The mixtures can be melted, can retard heat conduction, and can bond to porcelain. None of the pure metals have all those properties. Although there are only about 75 metallic elements, there are thousands of different combinations of them, each with its own special properties.

A ductile metal can be stretched, drawn, or hammered thin without breaking.

An **alloy** is the solid that results when two or more metals are melted together to form a mixture and then allowed to cool. Alloys have properties of their own that often differ markedly from those of the elements from which they are made. For example, the melting point of an alloy may be higher or lower than the melting point of any of its constituents. Alloys are usually harder and stronger than the parent metals. Pure iron is quite soft and ductile in comparison with steel, though steel alloys are composed mainly of iron. Carbon is a common component of steel alloys. Alloys usually resist corrosion better than pure metals. Table 3.3 lists some alloy steels, together with their composition and uses.

As methods for producing some of the rarer metals are improved, and as the special demands of modern technology increase, metallurgical research will no doubt develop alloys to meet those demands. A great deal of

What? We're Out of Gas?

science at work

Oil and natural gas—no matter what your point of view about the pros and cons of using them in our homes and industries—remain two of the Earth's most valuable fuels. They rank high in terms of their contribution to overall energy system efficiency and energy quality. Discovering the geological repositories for these and other forms of long-stored solar energy is, according to David Hartley, "the greatest detective story" of all.

David, the president of Sacramento Energy, Inc., in Woodland, California, is an explorer with an important mission. His company investigates and maps underground rock structures, looking for new locations of oil and gas. This exploration involves many kinds of testing, measuring, and drilling, and David hires and works with the contractors who get these jobs done.

Before the 1920s, underground exploration was done by drilling for samples of resource and then drilling to extract the materials that were found. Today's tools for these searches are much improved; for instance, satellite data is now used to identify potential oil basins. Oil rigs are drilling deeper, and into rock once considered inpenetrable, as well as operating under all kinds of difficult environmental conditions. Rocks yield a bounty of information for modern prospectors like David; this analysis is called *lithology*. Measuring the electrical properties in rock strata indicates what type of rock is present. The fluid in the rock (fresh or salt water, natural gas, and oil) affects the rock's electrical and acoustic properties. Acoustical measurements are based on the velocity of sound conducted through the rock—for example, gas-filled rock conducts sound more slowly than fluid-filled rock, and solid rock conducts the fastest. Another indicator is resistivity, based on the rock's resistance to an electric current passed through it. To assess radioactivity, neutrons are fired at the rock and the bounce-back is measured. Seismic testing is also done, by measuring waves produced by explosion or vibration as they travel through the rock.

All these data are logged carefully, and together they give a picture of the underground area. Corrections are made for depth, based on values at sea level. The final product is a structure map that reveals a true treasure: an underground trap containing oil and/or gas.

David's office duties are pretty normal for a manager—he has his share of long days, phone calls, data management, and contract negotiations. But out in the field the work is more intense and exciting, with lots of suspense about what the tests will uncover. He lives at the site of the exploration, sometimes for several weeks, working day and night with contractors, mud engineers, and others involved in the project. There are many, many findings to be examined and reports to be completed.

David's training in the sciences of this work has been informal but rewarding. He spent much time watching and asking questions in the field with his father, an engineer for Standard Oil. That's where David began to learn about physics, chemistry, and engineering. He was only 17 when he decided he wanted to have his own business rather than go to college. Hard work and diligent study over the years has paid off, and he is confident of his abilities now. He is certain that there is still much oil and gas remaining to be found and used, and hopes to see continued exploration in promising locations.

Table 3.3 Examples of Carbon Steel Alloys*

% of Metal Alloyed with Iron (Fe)	Characteristics	Uses
Cr 1.0%	Strong, tough	Springs, wood-cutting tools
Cr 2.0–10.0% V 0.1–0.2%	Hard, fatigue resistant	Car axles, frames, connecting rods
Cr 0.2–1.5% Ni 1.0–3.5%	Strong, surface easily hardened	Piston rings and pins, ball bearings, gears
Cr 18.0% Ni 8.0%	Corrosion resistant	Surgical instruments, stainless cutlery, kitchenware
Mn 12.0–14.0%	Wear resistant	Grinding machines, jaws of rock crushers & power shovels
Mo in various percentages	Hard, high-heat resistant	Space vehicles, jet engines

*It should be noted again that the carbon (C) content of these carbon steel alloys differs. Some of them contain very little carbon (0.06%) while others have about 1% carbon.

research is being devoted to the study of alloys for use in high-temperature engines, space vehicles, nuclear power plants, and electronic applications. Examples of steel alloys with a carbon content from about 0.06 to 1.0 percent or more are listed in Table 3.3. The elements in the table are shown by their chemical symbols rather than by their full names. To acquaint you with each element's chemical symbol, it is shown in parentheses below:

Carbon (C)	Manganese (Mn)
Chromium (Cr)	Molybdenum (Mo)
Iron (Fe)	Vanadium (V)
Nickel (Ni)	

Steel alloys may differ from each other in the kinds of elements that are combined with iron. They also may differ in the proportions of elements present. The kinds and proportions of elements are combined to produce the characteristics needed for a specific steel use.

Some of the nonferrous (noniron) alloys are listed in Table 3.4. Note that many alloys contain large percentages of copper (Cu). To help you understand the combinations (or composition) of the nonferrous alloys listed, the element names are:

Silver (Ag)	Nickel (Ni)
Aluminum (Al)	Antimony (Sb)
Gold (Au)	Tin (Sn)
Bismuth (Bi)	Zinc (Zn)
Copper (Cu)	

3.13 The Importance of Minerals in Our Society

What are the two basic industries and why are they basic?

There are only two basic industries in modern societies: the mineral industry (extraction) and agriculture (harvesting). These industries are basic because

Table 3.4 Examples of Non-Ferrous Alloys

Alloy Name	Composition (Approximate)	Use
Red brass	Cu 85%, Zn 15%	Radiator cores, hardware
Yellow brass	Cu 67%, Zn 33%	Musical instruments, cartridges
Tin bronze	Cu 90%, Sn 10%	Valves, rods, door knobs
Aluminum bronze	Cu 90%, Al 10%	Gilt paint
White gold	Au 75%, Cu 3.5% Zn 5%, Ni 16.5%	Jewelry
Nickel silver	Ag 64%, Ni 18% Zn 18%	Silverware, plating, resistant wire
Pewter	Sn 85%, Cu 7% Bi 6%, Sb 2%	Metal dishes, artwork
Sterling silver	Ag 92.5%, Cu 7.5%	Silverware, dishes, jewelry, artwork

they provide the raw materials from which everything else comes. It is also true that we need ideas and labor to utilize our raw materials wisely. However, without raw materials modern society would cease to exist.

?
Why are minerals important in our society?

There is no need to get into a debate about which industry is more important. Neither can function without the other. Present-day farm machinery, fertilizers, fuels, and agricultural chemicals all have their origins in mineral resources. How to free agriculture from a portion of its heavy dependence on minerals and still feed the world is one of the great issues of our time. Figure 3.25 summarizes the importance of minerals to modern life-styles.

Table 3.5 lists many of the mineral resources our society depends on and some of the sources of those materials. Study the table carefully. It demonstrates our heavy reliance on mineral resources.

a. Construction and Building Materials

Name some building materials.

Besides cut stone, crushed stone, sand, and gravel, of which the world has enormous resources, the main building materials are limestone (used in cement), gypsum (used for plaster and in cement), and clay (used for tile and brick). Supplies of building materials are enormous. Considerations for their use are transportation costs, quarry location in environmentally acceptable areas, and costs of treatment and preparation. An overall shortage of these materials is not likely to occur, but local availability depends on the geology of a given area. Urban expansion into quarry areas may make them more expensive.

b. Fertilizer Materials

Growing plants draw the many chemical nutrients they need from the soil. Nature has its own way of recycling the necessary nutrients.

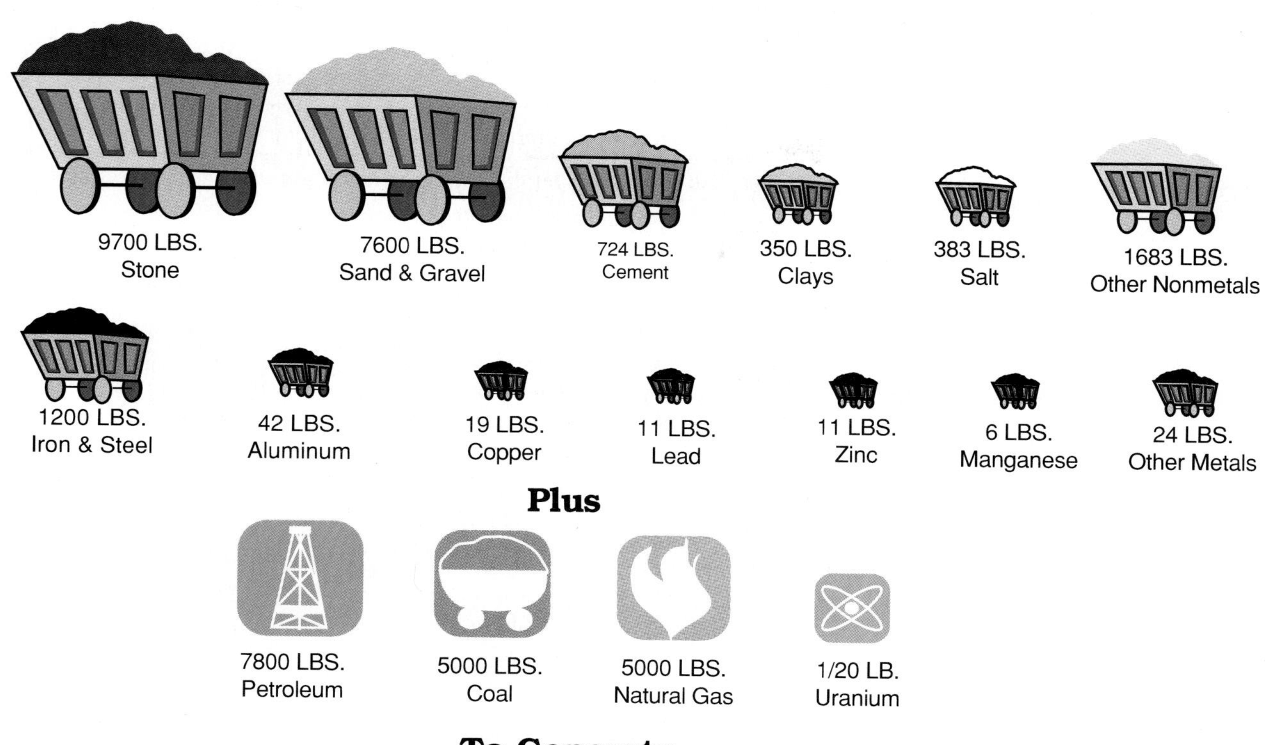

Figure 3.25 The importance of minerals in our society. About 40,000 pounds of new mineral materials are required annually for each U.S. citizen. (Mineral Information Institute)

When a plant dies and decays, rainwater washes the chemicals back into the soil. There they can be used again during the next growing season. Some are removed by ground water, but the loss is made up by chemical weathering of minerals in bedrock. We interfere with this cyclical process when we farm. This is because plant matter (corn, wheat, potatoes, etc.) is removed from the field and sold and consumed at some distant location. The soil becomes progressively depleted of nutrients that leave with the food. They must be replaced in the form of soluble fertilizers added to the soil.

What are the three essential fertilizer elements?

The three elements most needed in common fertilizer are nitrogen, phosphorus and potassium. An analysis of a fertilizer is often stated in terms of only these elements given in alphabetical order. For example, an 8-6-8 fertilizer contains, by weight, 8% nitrogen, 6% phosphorus pentoxide, P_2O_5, and 8% potassium oxide, K_2O.

Table 3.5 Economically Important Resources

Types of Resources	Sources and/or Examples	Resources
Fuels	Fossil fuel	coal, natural gas, oil
	nuclear fuel	uranium ore, thorium ore
Nonmetals	construction materials	sand and gravel, limestone, cement materials, gypsum, granite
	chemicals	coal, oil, natural gas, sulfur, salt, trona, sodium sulfate, compounds of boron
	fertilizers	phosphorite, potash, nitrates, air, natural gas
	refractories/fluxes	clay, magnesite
	abrasives	garnet, sandstone, industrial diamonds
	insulators	fiberglass (molten sand), rock wool (basaltic rock), polystyrene and urethane (petroleum), vermiculite (mica), perlite (volcanic ash), poly-isocyanurate (petroleum)
	plastics	petroleum
	pigments/fillers	clay, limestone, talc
	precious stones/gems	diamonds, amethyst, jade
Metals	iron	iron ore
	alloying	manganese, chromite, nickel, molybdenum, cobalt, vanadium
	base metals*	copper, lead, zinc, tin
	light weight	aluminum, magnesium, titanium
	precious	gold, silver, platinum
	rare earth minerals	bastnasite, monazite

* "Base metals" is a classification and not a use. It refers to certain metals of less monetary value per unit weight than the precious metals.

Figure 3.26 Your house comes from the ground. (Mineral Information Institute)

The **foundation** and **sidewalk** are probably concrete (limestone, clay, shale, gypsum, and aggregate mining) and the **driveway**—concrete or asphaltic concrete.

The **exterior walls** may be made of concrete block, brick (clay mining), stone (dimension stone mining), or aluminum siding (bauxite mining).

The **lumber** in the structure will be fastened with nails and screws (iron ore and zinc mining).

If the **roof** is covered with asphalt shingles, the granular surface of the shingles is from a variety of colored silicate minerals from mining; the body is fiberglass made from silica sand. The ashphalt comes from petroleum (oil well drilling), and is filled with finely ground limestone.

The **gutters** can be made of galvanized steel (iron and zinc mining), aluminum (bauxite mining), or plastic (petroleum).

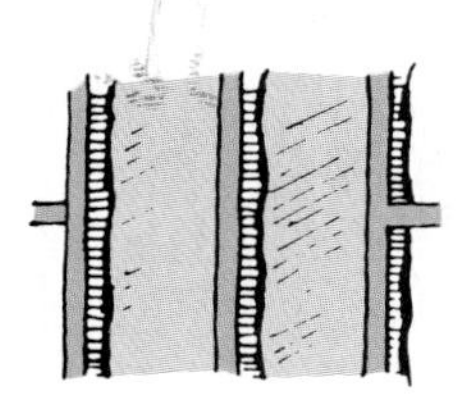

The **insulation** in the walls may be glass wool (silica, feldspar, and trona mining) or expanded vermiculite (vermiculite mining).

The **interior walls** are usually wallboard (gypsum mining).

Your **windows** are made of glass (trona, silica sand, limestone, and feldspar mining)

The **door knobs, locks,** and **hinges** are brass or steel (copper, zinc and iron mining).

Your **fireplace** is probably of brick or stone, lined with a steel box or you may have a wood/coal burning stove (steel—iron and other alloy metals). Your **furnace** and **air conditioner** and the **ducts** that bring the heat or cool air to your room are also metal (steel, copper, aluminum mining.)

If **paint** has been used (inside or outside), it is manufactured with mineral *fillers* and *pigments* that come from mining.

The **electrical wiring** is of copper or aluminum (copper or bauxite) protected by plastic wrapping (petroleum).

The **plumbing fixtures** may be made of brass (copper, zinc) or stainless steel (iron, nickel and chrome).

The **sanitary facilities** are made of porcelain (clay).

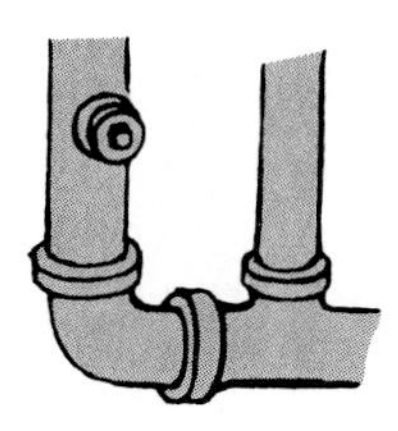

Your **water pipe** is made of iron or copper. Your **sewer piping** is made of clay or iron. Many pipes are plastic (from petroleum).

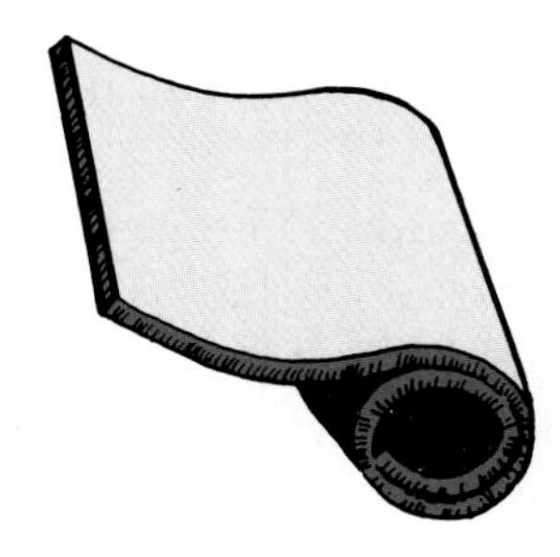

The **carpet** in your home is made from synthetic fibers (petroleum). The back is filled with limestone. If your carpet is made of wool, the back is still filled with limestone.

And finally, your **mortgage** or **rental contract** is written on paper made from wood or cloth fibers. The fibers are filled with clay to make the paper white.

Figure 3.27 How much phosphorus does this fertilizer contain? Potassium? Nitrogen?

(The phosphorus and potassium are usually not present as oxides, but are reported as oxides in accordance with the universal practice of the fertilizer industry.)

These elements are gathered from different sources. Nitrogen is recovered by chemical means from the atmosphere. Potassium is recovered from marine evaporite deposits as the soluble salt potassium chloride. Phosphorus is recovered as apatite from a special class of marine chemical sediments known as phosphorites or phosphate rock.

World supplies of the fertilizer minerals are large. They are probably sufficient for foreseeable needs. But there are difficulties associated with the distribution of fertilizers. They must be used in large amounts, and costs of treatment are high. Also, deposits of phosphorus and potassium compounds are geographically restricted. Phosphorus is found in parts of the United States, Canada, Morocco, South Africa, and the former USSR countries. Potassium is mined in the United States, Germany, the former USSR, and Israel. The cost of transport to other countries becomes important. This makes it difficult for poor countries to purchase all the fertilizer they need. To help resolve this problem, seeds sent to these countries may be coated with fertilizer.

In addition, calcium carbonate and sulfur must be added to soils to keep a balance between acidity and alkalinity favorable for maximum plant growth. Calcium carbonate is produced from the abundant limestone strata around the world. Sulfur is primarily obtained from salt domes, coal processing, gypsum, and as a by-product of oil and mineral refining. Supplies of sulfur are very large. Unfortunately for poor countries that need sulfur, the supplies are geographically restricted. Most comes from the Gulf Coast areas of Louisiana, Texas, and Mexico. Other large deposits are in Italy and Canada.

POTASH: the commercial name for a group of salts containing the element potassium. The most important type of potash is potassium chloride (KCl), which is mainly used to make fertilizer. Potash is also used in the manufacture of soaps and detergents, glass, ceramics, textiles, dyes, chemicals and drugs.

The mineral **sylvite** is the chief potash ore. Most potash ore is found in underground salt beds that formed when ancient seas evaporated. Potash also occurs in salt lakes.

The world's leading potash producers are the former USSR countries, Canada, Germany, and the United States. In spite of being a major producer, the U.S. needs more potash than it is capable of producing; therefore, two-thirds of the potash used in the United States is imported from Canada.

c. Metals/Alloys

Whether they are used in a relatively pure form or alloyed, metals are the materials from which we produce the tools and machines of modern civilization.

We can only mine and recover useful metals when concentrated deposits can be located. Just how much richer than ordinary rock the mineral deposit must be before it is an ore deposit depends a great deal on technology and economics. For example, iron must be concentrated five to ten times above its average crustal abundance. Copper requires a concentration of 80 to 100 times, zinc 300, and mercury an enormous 100,000 times. As mining and mineral processing becomes more efficient and less expensive, it is possible to work leaner and leaner ore. There is an economic and technological limit below which a particular element cannot be profitably extracted.

?

How might a prudent society use its minerals?

From this information we might conclude that a prudent society should use metals at rates directly related to the supplies available. In most cases we are doing just the opposite. The scarcer the metal, the faster we are using it up. This leads to some predictions that within your lifetime, demands for some of the scarcer metals such as mercury, silver, and gold will cease to be met. We will either have to develop ways of near-perfect recycling of scarce metals, or learn eventually to do without them, or substitute more abundant materials when we can.

Ceramics: materials made by firing clay or other inorganic nonmetallic minerals at a high temperature. Ceramics are highly resistant to heat and the action of chemicals.

d. Ceramic and Abrasive Materials

We sometimes forget how extensively we use ceramic materials (including glass) in our everyday lives. Some ceramics have properties that make them desirable substitutes for certain metals. We can anticipate that uses of ceramics will grow. Supplies of the essential raw materials—clays, feldspars, silica, and quartz are abundant and widespread. Clays have different properties, making them suitable for some uses and unsuitable for others.

Why are ceramics and abrasives important?

Abrasives also play a widespread and vital part in our lives. Their importance is commonly not appreciated. Modern industry requires machines that work accurately and efficiently at high speeds. This requires precision grinding, shaping, and polishing of the machine parts, and for this a wide variety of abrasives are needed, such as corundum, quartz, and diamond.

e. Chemical Materials

The most important sources of materials for the chemical industry are fossil materials—coal, oil, and gas. These are the raw materials needed for petrochemicals such as plastics, many drugs, pesticides, synthetic fibers, and countless other products. Many inorganic substances are needed also. The most important are sodium chloride (salt), sodium carbonate (trona), sodium sulfate, and minerals containing boron. Each of these is recovered by evaporation. Fortunately, the supplies of these chemical substances are very large.

f. Mineral Requirements of High Technology

High technology, born with World War II, continues to expand, adding new products and demanding new materials. Many of these are very precisely developed to provide specified properties. The list of products and materials grows constantly, using almost all of the naturally occurring elements in the periodic table. The list in Table 3.6 is not

SULFUR is a yellow, soft, nonmetallic element that has a variety of industrial uses. It makes up about 0.05 percent of Earth's crust (lithosphere). Resources of elemental sulfur occur in evaporite and volcanic deposits and sulfur associated with natural gas, petroleum, tar sands, and metal sulfides. The sulfur available in gypsum and anhydrite is almost limitless, and some 600 billion tons are contained in coal, oil shale, and shale rich in organic matter. Low-cost methods have not been developed to recover sulfur from these sources, however.

Nearly two-thirds of the elemental sulfur produced in the world on an annual basis is produced as a byproduct of petroleum refining and natural gas processing; therefore the quantity of sulfur supplied from these sources is dependent on the demand for fuels, not on the demand for sulfur.

All plants and animals need small amounts of sulfur to live. Most sulfur is converted to sulfuric acid and other compounds for manufacturing purposes. Few of these manufactured products themselves actually contain sulfur. Products that actually contain sulfur include fertilizers and some types of explosives, fungicides, insecticides, rubber, storage batteries, shampoos and chemicals used in developing photographic film.

Table 3.6 Mineral Requirements of High Technology*

Aerospace	Electronics	Energy
Use—structural components, electronic components, energy sources.	Uses—arc rectifiers, batteries, cable sheathing, capacitors, color TV, computers, conductors, contact materials, copper alloys, dielectric materials, electric conductors and connector alloys, evaporator filaments, ferrites, filters, fire retardants, insulating materials, lamps, light filaments, magnetic materials, optical uses, phosphors, plating, semiconductors, signals, solders, springs, thin film circuitry conductors, superconductors, transducers.	Uses—for fossil fuels, nuclear power, geothermal energy, solar energy, hydropower, bioconversion.
Mineral requirements—almost every element is required at some point in the fabrication and operation of aerospace vehicles. Of special concern are chromium, columbium**, cobalt, platinum group metals, tantalum, titanium, rare earth metals.	Mineral requirements—aluminum, antimony, beryllium, cobalt, columbium, copper, gallium, germanium, gold, indium, iron, lead, lithium, manganese, mercury, mica, molybdenum, nickel, platinum-group metals, quartz crystal, rare-earth metals, rhenium, selenium, silicon, silver, strontium, tantalum, tin, tungsten, vanadium, yttrium, zinc.	Mineral requirements—aluminum, antimony, asbestos, barite, bentonite, boron, cadmium, chromium, cobalt, columbium, concrete, copper, glass, indium, iron, lead, magnesium, manganese, mica, molybdenum, nickel, silicon, silver, thorium, tin, titanium, tungsten, uranium, vanadium, zinc, zirconium. In addition, many electronic components are required.

*From Minerals—Foundations of Society, by Ann Dorr, 2nd ed., © 1987, Alexandria, Virginia.
**Columbium is the term used by the mineral industry for the element niobium.

complete but it will give an idea of the wide range of minerals demanded in three fields: electronics, energy, and aerospace.

Economic and Political Issues

As the people in various areas of the world strive to improve their standard of living, they compete for a diminishing supply of resources. In addition, the use of resources leads to environmental problems. Many social and economic issues become intertwined with our dependence on minerals and agriculture.

3.14 Import/Export Issues

?

Why are imports an issue?

Mineral deposits are not evenly distributed around the globe because of the way geologic forces work. Some regions have a great variety of useful minerals, while others are almost barren. No country, however rich in minerals, has all the minerals it needs. Thus it must depend at least partially on imported materials.

Why must Europe, the U.S. and Japan import minerals?

Most of the world's great mineral users are in decline as producers. This is because they have been or were industrialized for a long period of time. Their industry was supported by a long history of mining. The European nations have already depleted their high-grade mineral reserves. They must now rely mostly on imports. The situation in the United States is similar, and Japan imports virtually all the minerals it uses.

Special Focus

Ceramic Engines

Of all the inventions made during the past 200 years, the two that probably have had the greatest impact on our lives are the incandescent light bulb and the internal combustion engine.

The light bulb ushered in electric power networks. These networks brought electricity to the homes of average people. This convenience has made it possible for us to have electric stoves, refrigerators, washing machines, clothes dryers, and all the other great "creature comforts" that can be plugged into the outlets of modern day homes.

The internal combustion engine made possible the automobile. The automobiles ushered in modern transportation systems with their associated networks of roads, interstate highways, international air travel, and a host of related applications such as gasoline powered lawnmowers and weeders.

The most surprising part of the whole story is the fact that these two devices are highly inefficient. The standard internal combustion engine is only about 30% efficient. Seventy percent of the energy locked in the fuel placed into the gas tank of a

Continued

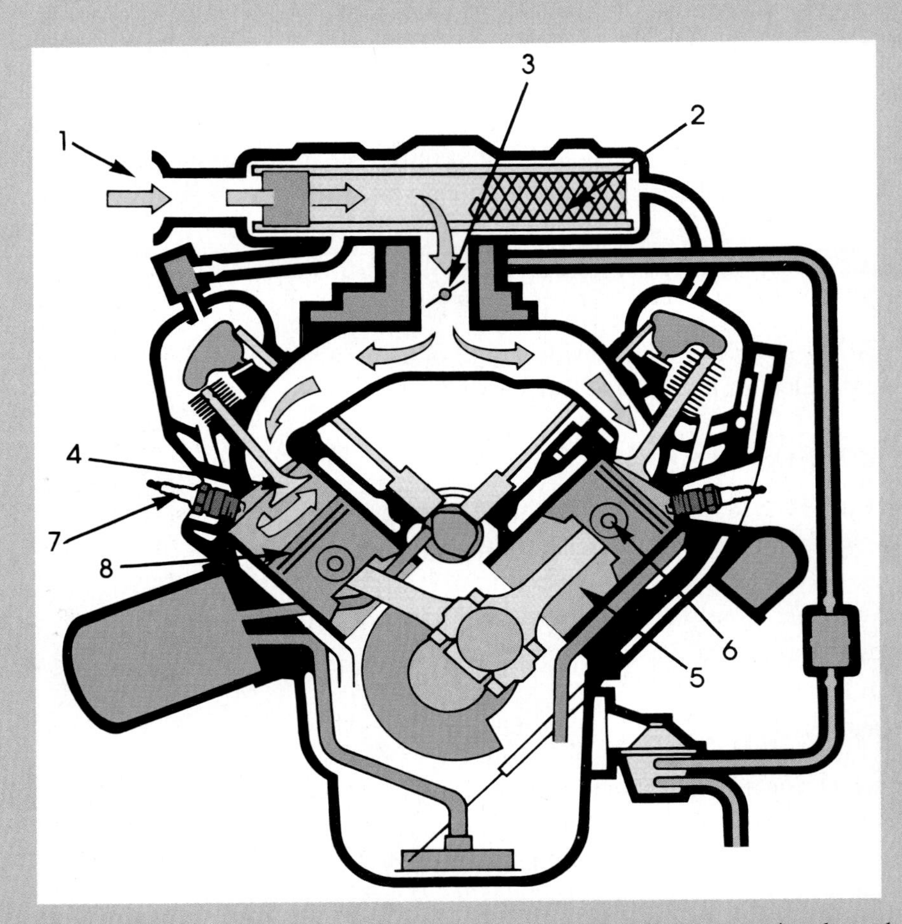

Figure 3.28 Cross section of a typical internal combustion engine. (1) The air enters engine through air intake; (2) the air filter stops airborne particulates (dirt, dust, grit); (3) clean air enters the carburetor; (4) then passes through the air intake to the valves; (5) continuing into the cylinders; (6) which house the pistons; (7) where combustion takes place between the pistons and spark plugs. The point of combustion is represented by (8). (Allied-Signal, Inc.)

typical automobile goes out with the exhausts as heat or is radiated into the atmosphere by the various parts of the cooling system. Why? The engine is made of steel, and most steel alloys cannot withstand temperatures much above 480° C (900° F). At higher temperatures they begin to weaken and show structural damage.

A promising solution to the internal combustion engine's inefficiency is the ceramically insulated adiabatic engine. An adiabatic engine is one that would run at a stable (nearly constant) temperature and would not lose significant amounts of heat to the air or to a liquid coolant. Ceramic parts would be critical in such an engine. Their ability to retain heat, thus providing insulation, allows them to function at high temperatures.

Ceramics are one of the most important classes of materials on which modern societies rely. Others are fibers, metals and plastics. Ceramics are of interest because of their resistance to the action of chemicals and their ability to withstand high temperatures. For these reasons, they have a wide variety of uses including bricks, dinnerware, and nose cones for rockets. Manufacturers make ceramic products from such minerals as clays, bauxite, feldspar, silica, and talc. In essence, the raw materials are sand and rock. When certain ceramic raw materials are heated, they become so hard and wear-resistant that only diamond tools will cut them. This resistance to corrosion and wear should result in engine components that last much longer.

Because ceramic engines can operate at temperatures twice that of conventional metal engines, they do not need a cooling system. Fuels are burned completely and efficiently. For these reasons, they can get up to 100% more miles per gallon than an all-metal engine. The ceramic intensive engine would still use some alloyed metal parts, but all parts that have to withstand high temperature would be ceramic.

The advanced adiabatic diesel (AAD) engine being developed by Adiabatics, Inc. in Columbus, Indiana, uses ceramics to insulate the combustion chamber. Among the ceramic parts are the piston tops, cylinder walls, cylinder heads, valves and exhaust ports.

Continued

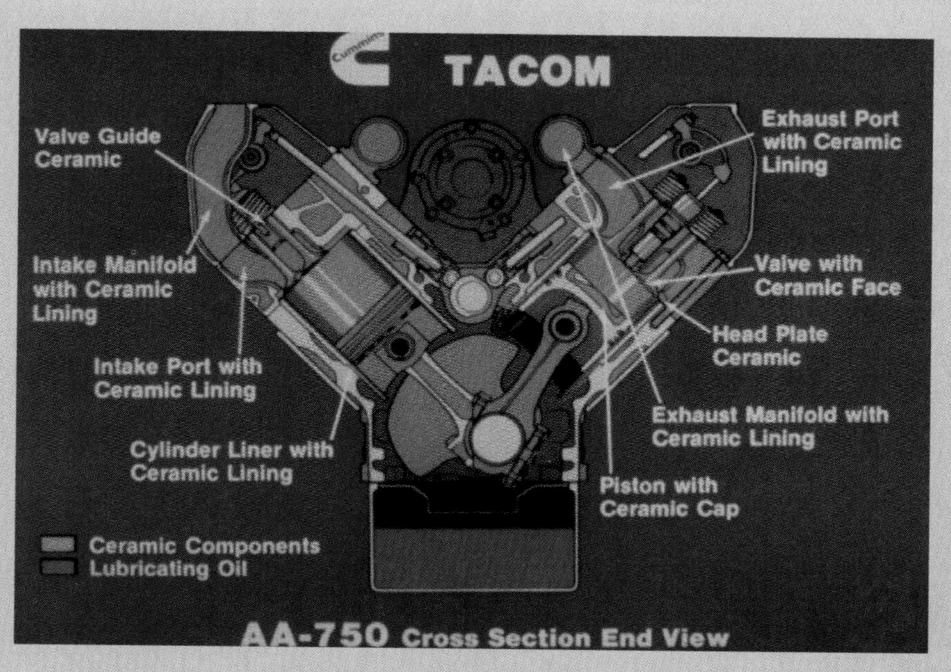

Figure 3.29 Schematic cross section of an experimental adiabatic engine showing ceramic parts in conjunction with other metal parts. (From U.S. Army Tank Automotive Command and Cummins Engine Company, Inc.)

All indications are that ceramic engines will perform as well as present-day automobile engines. See Table 3.7.

An advantage of ceramic parts is that they expand so little when heated that their shape remains essentially constant under a wide range of operating temperatures and conditions. This means that if the parts are correctly molded when they are initially formed, they will need little or no machining. Machining is required for most metal parts and adds significantly to their cost. Constant shape also means a tighter fit between moving parts. This leads to higher efficiency. Unfortunately, this advantage has yet to be realized. When close dimensional tolerance is required, ceramic parts must be ground (often with diamond abrasives), as opposed to machining or turning of most metals.

Table 3.7 Performance Comparison 3000-Pound Passenger Cars

Category	EPA Rating City/Highway (mpg)	Acceleration 0–60 mph (sec)
Baseline Metal Engine	37.7	15.2
AAD Ceramic Engine	78.8	13.9

Adiabatic ceramic engines should produce cleaner emissions. The higher operating temperatures will ensure complete combustion. This means that unburned hydrocarbons, particulates, and carbon monoxide will be greatly reduced. Nitrogen oxide production increases with increased combustion temperature. Smoother and faster combustion should reduce nitrogen oxide formation. The degree of change is unknown. However, exhaust gas recirculation should be adequate for nitrogen oxide control.

Unfortunately, several problems must be solved before adiabatic ceramic engines become widely used. One barrier to acceptance is the reputation of ceramics for brittleness. The parts have a tendency to

Continued

Figure 3.30 High-tech diesel-powered car utilizing an AAD ceramic engine. (Adiabatic, Inc.)

fracture or shatter under stress. Substantial progress is being made in several areas. These include improving the quality of ceramic powders, coating technologies, and establishing a ceramic design data base. The industry also is attempting to produce void-free parts. Small imperfections cause localized stress concentrations which cannot be tolerated by brittle ceramic parts. Researchers at Massachusetts Institute of Technology (MIT) are making great strides in solving this problem.

An additional requirement for the widespread market usage of high temperature ceramic engine components is the development of lubricants that are stable at high temperatures. It is relatively easy to undercool a ceramic engine and allow it to run hotter, but it cannot run without lubrication.

One of the brightest hopes for ceramic technology is that it may make the gas turbine more practical. This could someday lead to more efficient production of electric power.

Light-duty ceramic engine components are now being introduced on new cars sold in the United States. These components include exhaust port liners, valve train wear parts, and turbocharge rotors. Large increases in the use of ceramics are projected between 1995 and 2000. During this time, fuel prices are expected to rise and oil supplies tighten. If ceramic engine parts or engines can be demonstrated to save large amounts of fuel, and to show increased durability and lower emissions, they should be widely accepted.

Figure 3.31 Silicon nitride engine components under evaluation by several automotive companies. (Ceradyne, Inc.)

1987 NET IMPORTS BY THE UNITED STATES
Selected Nonfuel Minerals

MINERALS & METALS	PERCENT IMPORTED		MAJOR FOREIGN SOURCES
ARSENIC	XXXXXXXXXXXXXXXXXXX	100%	Sweden, Canada, Mexico
COLUMBIUM	XXXXXXXXXXXXXXXXXXX	100%	Brazil, Canada, Thailand, Nigeria
GRAPHITE (strategic)	XXXXXXXXXXXXXXXXXXX	100%	Mexico, China, Brazil, Madagascar
MANGANESE	XXXXXXXXXXXXXXXXXXX	100%	South Africa, France, Gabon, Brazil
MICA (sheet)	XXXXXXXXXXXXXXXXXXX	100%	India, Belgium, Japan, France, Brazil, Madagascar
STRONTIUM (celestite)	XXXXXXXXXXXXXXXXXXX	100%	Mexico, Spain, China
TITANIUM (rutile)	XXXXXXXXXXXXXXXXXXX	100%	Australia, Japan, India,
YTTRIUM	XXXXXXXXXXXXXXXXXXX	100%	Australia
BAUXITE & ALUMINA	XXXXXXXXXXXXXXXXXX	97%	Australia, Guinea, Jamaica, Surinam
TANTALUM	XXXXXXXXXXXXXXXXXX	92%	Thailand, Brazil, Australia, Canada, Malaysia
DIAMONDS (industrial)	XXXXXXXXXXXXXXXXX	89%	South Africa, United Kingdom, Ireland, Belgium, Luxembourg
FLUORSPAR	XXXXXXXXXXXXXXXXX	88%	South Africa, Mexico, Spain, Italy, China
PLATINUM-GROUP METALS	XXXXXXXXXXXXXXXXX	88%	South Africa, United Kingdom, U.S.S.R.
COLBALT	XXXXXXXXXXXXXXXXX	86%	Zaire, Zambia, Canada, Norway, Belgium Luxembourg, Finland
TUNGSTEN	XXXXXXXXXXXXXXXX	80%	China, Canada, Bolivia, Portugal, Republic of Korea
CHROMUIM	XXXXXXXXXXXXXXX	75%	South Africa, Zimbabwe, Turkey, Yugoslavia, U.S.S.R., Phillipines
NICKEL	XXXXXXXXXXXXXX	74%	Canada, Australia, Norway, Botswana, New Caldonia, Dominican Republic
TIN	XXXXXXXXXXXXXX	73%	Brazil, Thailand, Indonesia, Bolivia, Malaysia
POTASH	XXXXXXXXXXXXXX	72%	Canada, Israel, East Germany, U.S.S.R.
ZINC	XXXXXXXXXXXXX	69%	Canada, Mexico, Peru, Australia, Honduras, Spain
CADMIUM	XXXXXXXXXXXXX	66%	Canada, Mexico, Australia, West Germany, Belgium, Luxenbourg
BARITE	XXXXXXXXXXXX	63%	China, Morocco, India
SLIVER	XXXXXXXXXXX	57%	Canada, Mexico, United Kingdom, Peru
ASBESTOS	XXXXXXXXXX	51%	Canada, South Africa
FERROSILICON	XXXXXXXX	42%	Brazil, Canada, Norway, Venezuela
GYPSUM	XXXXXXX	37%	Canada, Mexico, Spain, Jamaica
IRON ORE	XXXXXX	28%	Canada, Brazil, Venezuela, Liberia
COPPER	XXXXX	25%	Canada, Chile, Peru, Zaire, Zambia, Mexico
ALUMINUM	XXXX	24%	Canada, Japan, Venezuela, Brazil
CEMENT	XXXX	20%	Canada, Mexcio,Spain, Norway, Bahamas
IRON & STEEL	XXXX	19%	E.E.C., Japan, Canada, Republic of Korea
LEAD	XXX	15%	Canada, Mexico, Peru, Australia, Honduras
SALT	XX	12%	Canada, Mexico, Bahamas, Chile, Spain
BERYLLIUM	XX	11%	Brazil, China, Switzerland, South Africa
TITANIUM (ilmenite)	X	8%	Japan, U.S.S.R., Australia, Canada
NITROGEN	X	7%	Canada, U.S.S.R., Trinidad & Tobago, Mexico
SULFUR	X	6%	Canada, Mexico

Note: Other imported minerals and metals not shown above, include: antimony barium, gold, mercury, selenium, pumice and volcanic cinder, and vanadium

Note: (E.E.C. = European Economic Community)
(West Germany = Federal Republic of Germany)
(East Germany = German Democratic Republic)
(South Africa = Republic of South Africa)
(U.S.S.R. = Union of Soviet Socialist Republics)

Figure 3.32 United States dependence on imports of selected minerals and metals. (Mineral Information Institute)

The United States' reliance on other countries for some selected minerals and metals is shown in Figure 3.32. The U. S. has deposits of many of the minerals and metals shown as largely imported. For reasons of cost and politics they are imported rather than produced domestically. The dependence of the United States on imports of various minerals from other countries will increase in the future.

To the developed world that must import large quantities of minerals, the challenges are to keep the avenues of commerce open and to trade equitably with fellow human beings. This needs to be done without taking advantage of Third World nations.

Why do Third World nations have such large mineral reserves?

The major mineral-producing countries include Brazil, Chile, Guinea, Malaysia, Mexico, Southern Africa, the former Soviet Union, Zaire, and Zambia. Also, many of the best reserves lie in Third World nations where exploration has been rather recent.

To the Third World, possession of mineral riches has been a mixed blessing. The mining and exporting of mineral wealth has brought in much-needed revenue. But in some cases, it has also brought devastated landscapes, dammed or polluted rivers, and the up-rooting or decimation of native people who were unlucky enough to live atop mineral deposits. Some poorer nations are so dependent on mineral exports that when prices fall, they increase production to pay their foreign debt. The result is that they are selling off their national mineral treasures at bargain prices.

Why has possession of mineral wealth been a mixed blessing to Third World nations?

3.15 Environmental Impact

Mining has an environmental impact because minerals are removed from the Earth by underground procedures or open pit excavations. The damage done depends on such factors as the ecological nature of the mining site, the quantity of material moved, the depth of the ore deposit, the chemical makeup of the ore and the surrounding rocks and soils, the mining method used, and the nature of the milling process. More and more often today, provisions for environmental protection and for land reclamation are included in original plans for mining and milling operations. Such provisions often are required by federal and state laws.

Mining can also add pollutants to the land or air. About 90% of metal ore ends up as tailing, which is most often placed in large piles or ponds near the mine. As the grade of mined ore decreases, the quantity of tailing increases. If not controlled, smelting can produce enormous quantities of air pollutants. Many countries have no controls over this source of pollution.

Globally the mining industry is one of the largest users of energy. Energy is needed at every stage of mining and processing.

Modern practices demonstrate that mining can be carried out in environmentally acceptable ways. Laws, rules, and regulations mandate that a) tailing be disposed of properly; b) the water used in mining, milling and refining be cleaned before discharge into streams; and c) mined land be reclaimed for other uses. The immediate costs may be high, but they may be less in the long run than those of restoring a badly damaged environment. For corporations to pay the costs and make a profit, the ultimate cost must be built into the price of the product.

?

How can the environmental impact of mining-related activities be reduced?

It must be remembered that laws and regulations mean little if enforcement is lax. Also, the environment and economy are not improved when cleanup laws are passed in a nation that imports cheaper minerals from another nation which has lower standards. This practice creates problems in both nations: Unemployment goes up in the first. The environment suffers in the other.

 3.16 Conservation

Why must we use minerals with care?

Because mineral resources are finite, present and future generations must use them with care. This is essential if the mineral requirements of modern society are to be met. It also is essential because of mining's impact on energy, on water resources, and on the environment. Wise mineral use involves a variety of strategies. These include:

a. Substitution

How does substitution work?

Some metals can be conserved by substituting others. Aluminum can often substitute for steel and copper. Copper has replaced other metals in our coins. During World War II, copper was needed for military purposes, and another metal was used for pennies. In some cases plastic pipe can take the place of metal pipe. The use of optical fibers made of glass in place of copper communications wire is another example. When it is economical, substitutes should be considered if supply of the substitute is adequate.

?

Why are substitutes not available for some minerals?

Some elements have unique properties that make a substitution impossible. Helium's ability to remain a liquid at temperatures below which other materials have solidified is an example. Another is mercury, which has a unique combination of high specific gravity, fluidity at normal temperatures, and electrical conductivity. Uranium and thorium are the only elements suitable for nuclear fission reactors.

b. Recycling

What is recycling?

Recycling is a conscious effort to conserve by slowing down the scattering of useful resources in the form of waste and scrap. Much of the metal that is now lost through dispersal and burial can be recovered. The only inevitable losses are those from oxidation and friction. Even they can be limited.

Why is recycling sensible?

How can economic factors influence our behavior?

As we learned in chapter 1, there is no "away" (law of conservation of mass). We don't really have any less gold, copper, or mercury today than before humans appeared on Earth. But we also learned that in the process of use, these and all other minerals become more scattered. We mine them where they are most concentrated, use them, and then throw them away at random (second law of thermodynamics). They become lost from an economic point of view. However, we can use our economics to slow this process down. We can make people economically responsible for their own pollution. When the reward for recycling an aluminum can rose above a penny a can in some states, the amount of aluminum recycled increased. It became worth the effort to save that can. In the economy of the future, it will be worth the effort to save almost everything from careless disposal. We must learn to design for recycling. This means that we must design out the potentially hazardous materials from manufacturing processes and the products created. A worn-out car **should** be returned for complete and easy recycling, not thrown away.

Figure 3.33 Recycling aluminum cans. (Adolph Coors Company)

c. Taxation

Partly to encourage conservation, but mainly to obtain additional revenues, many states impose a **severance tax** on some of the minerals that are extracted from their lands. The tax is paid on the nonrenewable natural resources removed from the earth because the value of the land is reduced greatly. The monies received are distributed to the local areas and counties for roads, schools, hospitals, and other public services.

What is a severance tax?

The justification for the severance tax is that since the minerals are located within the state, they in part belong to the state. Therefore, the people of the state should be compensated for that loss.

Part of the mining industry feels that severance and other taxes discriminate against them. Too high a severance tax can be a severe handicap to a mine. It can even prevent it from operating. The mining industry feels it is benefiting the community because it is a basic industry. The rest of the economy benefits from its success. When mining companies are successful, they increase employment and provide minerals to other industries for a moderate cost. These minerals can later be turned into products of higher value, thus increasing real wealth.

3.17 Wilderness

Some entire ecosystems, including their minerals, are legally protected from development. Large regions of the United States have been set aside by Congress as **wilderness areas.** This was done because of the

Why are wilderness areas established?

realization that ecosystems are valuable just as they are. No roads, exploration, or development activity are allowed. Most of these public wilderness lands are located in the western United States, including Alaska. See Figures 3.34 and 3.35. Wilderness designation protects many diverse landscapes: offshore islands, seashores, estuaries, rivers, lakes, forests, deserts, canyons, and mountains.

The Wilderness Act of 1964 established the National Wilderness Preservation System. It states: "A wilderness, in contrast with those areas where man and his own works dominate the landscape, is hereby recognized as an area where the Earth and its community of life are untrammeled by man, where man himself is a visitor who does not remain."

?

Why has setting land aside as wilderness become controversial?

The creation of the wilderness system has caused considerable controversy. Land designated as wilderness may contain an unknown wealth of minerals that are vital to our economy. In some cases, denying ourselves access to these minerals forces us to purchase them from foreign countries.

Some argue that the wilderness system preserves both valuable ecosystems and untapped ore deposits for future generations. Our descendants have some right to these minerals.

Others argue that the minerals can be removed without destruction of the environment. It is true that mining requires road building, land grading, waste disposal sites, and the digging of open pits and shafts. On the other hand, reclamation can restore much of the mined land to a natural state or even (from the human point of view) an improved state. Better forage for animals may be provided, or hardier species of plants grown. Environmental problems are global problems. So are problems related to the procurement of natural resources.

The mineral industry is correct in the argument that the United States runs a risk of having some of its imported mineral supplies cut off by unfriendly nations, while it locks up its own domestic supplies through wilderness or other restrictive designations. The Homestead Act of 1862 granted public land (not to exceed 160 acres to be developed as a farm) to any citizen or alien intending to become a citizen. All other public lands were to be used under the multiple use concept. Multiple use meant grazing, timbering, mining, recreation, fishing, and hunting.

National parks and monuments have been set aside because of their beauty and value as ecosystems. Other lands have been withdrawn from public use with such designations as Wild and Scenic Rivers, Wildlife Refuges, Conservation Areas, Wetlands, and so on. Controversy centers on how much public land should be set aside. It can also be argued that nothing is gained by the person who works to prevent the mining of copper or any other mineral in the U.S. for environmental reasons and then turns around and buys products made from minerals that were mined carelessly somewhere else.

Early mining techniques were primitive. So were the attitudes of many early miners. The landscape they left was often scarred. Technologies and attitudes have changed. Decisions which involve satisfying human wants must be tempered by a knowledge of the trade-offs which are likely to result.

Despite extensive exploration, well over 99% of the land surface of the U.S. has never been worked by miners and mining equipment. The total amount of land affected by mining is less than six million acres. Cities and urban areas use 77 million acres, and highways use 32 million acres. The greatest land use is the 1.2 billion acres used by agriculture.

Someone once said that mining is "the art of looking for Nature's needle in Nature's haystack." Since we must dig for minerals where they have been deposited, not where we would wish they were, land use controversies sometimes occur. For example, much untapped mineral potential exists in areas of great scenic beauty. The natural forces that create mountains and deserts also create mineral wealth. Thus, geologic placement of mineral and energy resources is scattered throughout the world.

Ore deposits are where you find them.

Notice in Figure 3.34 that *Coal Fields* and *Oil & Gas Fields* show some relationship to one another. A comparison of these to the *Mineralized Areas* map shows that in the Rocky Mountain region a variety of all the resources is available. Most of the metal producing areas are concentrated in the western states and Alaska, where the majority of public lands are found. According to the U.S. Bureau of Mines, some three-fourths of America's vast public lands—many in the most richly mineralized areas—are now off limits to mineral exploration, mining and oil drilling. It should also be noted that the map of *Alaskan Resources* is in scale with the maps of the lower 48 states. Make a copy of this figure. Cut out Alaska and lay it over a map of the contiguous 48 states. This will help you visualize just how big Alaska is.

3.18 Maintaining Industrial and Military Strength

?

What is a strategic mineral?

Strategic minerals are minerals which are essential to the functioning of our economy and military capabilities, which are not found or produced in the United States in sufficient quantities to meet such needs, and which are subject to import supply disruption. Stockpiling of strategic minerals began as a result of shortages during World War II. It is now authorized under the Strategic and Critical Materials Stockpiling Revision Act of 1979. This act sets stockpile goals based on military and essential civilian requirements for three years of a conventional war. Stockpile goals and policies have been altered several times. The demand for strategic minerals in the manufacture of a modern jet engine is illustrated in Figure 3.35.

There are two F100 engines on an F-15 fighter and one on an F-16 fighter. United States dependence on imports of minerals for these engines ranges between 5 and 100 percent (1987).

Figure 3.36 shows that temperature has a major effect on the demand for these elements.

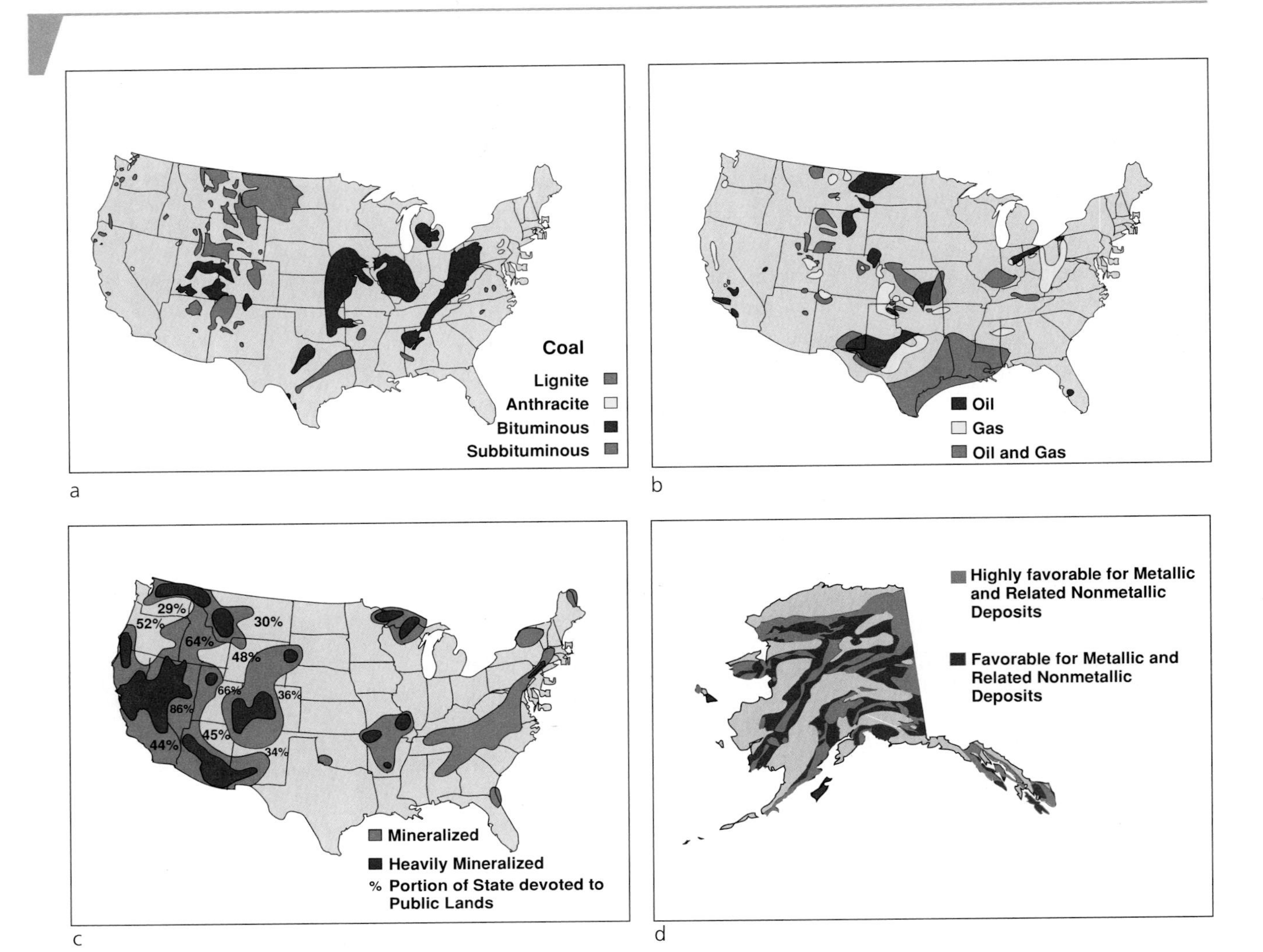

Figure 3.34 Resource Location Maps: A-*Coal Fields;* B-*Oil & Gas Fields;* C-*Mineralized Areas;* and D-*Alaskan Resources.* (Mineral Information Institute)

Metals Required for One F 100 Turbofan Jet Engine

Metal Imported	Pounds Required	Imported 1982	Imported 1992
Titanium	5479	35%	5%
Nickel	4597	73%	64%
Chromium	1537	91%	74%
Cobalt	886	93%	76%
Aluminum	715	94%	100%
Columbium	163	100%	100%
Tantalum	3	90%	87%

Figure 3.35 What does it take to build a jet engine? (Pratt & Whitney)

What factors determine strategic and critical mineral stockpile goals?

According to the United States Bureau of Mines, the four major factors that determine strategic and critical mineral stockpile goals are:

- critical need for the mineral during national defense mobilization,
- extent of domestic reserves and processing capacity,
- availability of acceptable substitutes,
- security of alternative sources of foreign supply.

At present, stockpiled minerals are far behind goals for many minerals and exceed goals for others. If all goals were met, the materials stockpiled would be valued at about $17 billion at current prices. The existing inventory is valued only at about $10 billion.

It has been proposed that a portion of the existing stockpile be sold to help reduce the national debt. Opponents argue that debt reduction is not the purpose for the stockpile.

Stockpiles can be used to influence prices on the world market. When world prices shoot up for a certain strategic mineral, we can threaten to release a significant portion of our stockpile at a much lower price and drive world prices down. But is this an ethical use of a program which was initially conceived as protection against wartime disruptions in trade? At a time of much international uncertainty, the stockpile provides some protection against disruptions of supply from politically unstable areas of the world.

There are many factors to consider when appraising our resource use. Since World War II, we have torn down many portions of our crucial industries, such as steel and mining production, and oil refining. The problem of materials supply is not merely a problem of supply of raw materials, but of usable materials.

On the other hand, advances in materials science are leading to the development of new types of plastics and ceramics. Many of these can replace metals.

Most Americans feel we must keep up our guard in case of aggression. If we can avoid using strategic mineral materials up by substituting nonstrategic ones where possible, part of our preparedness problem will be resolved.

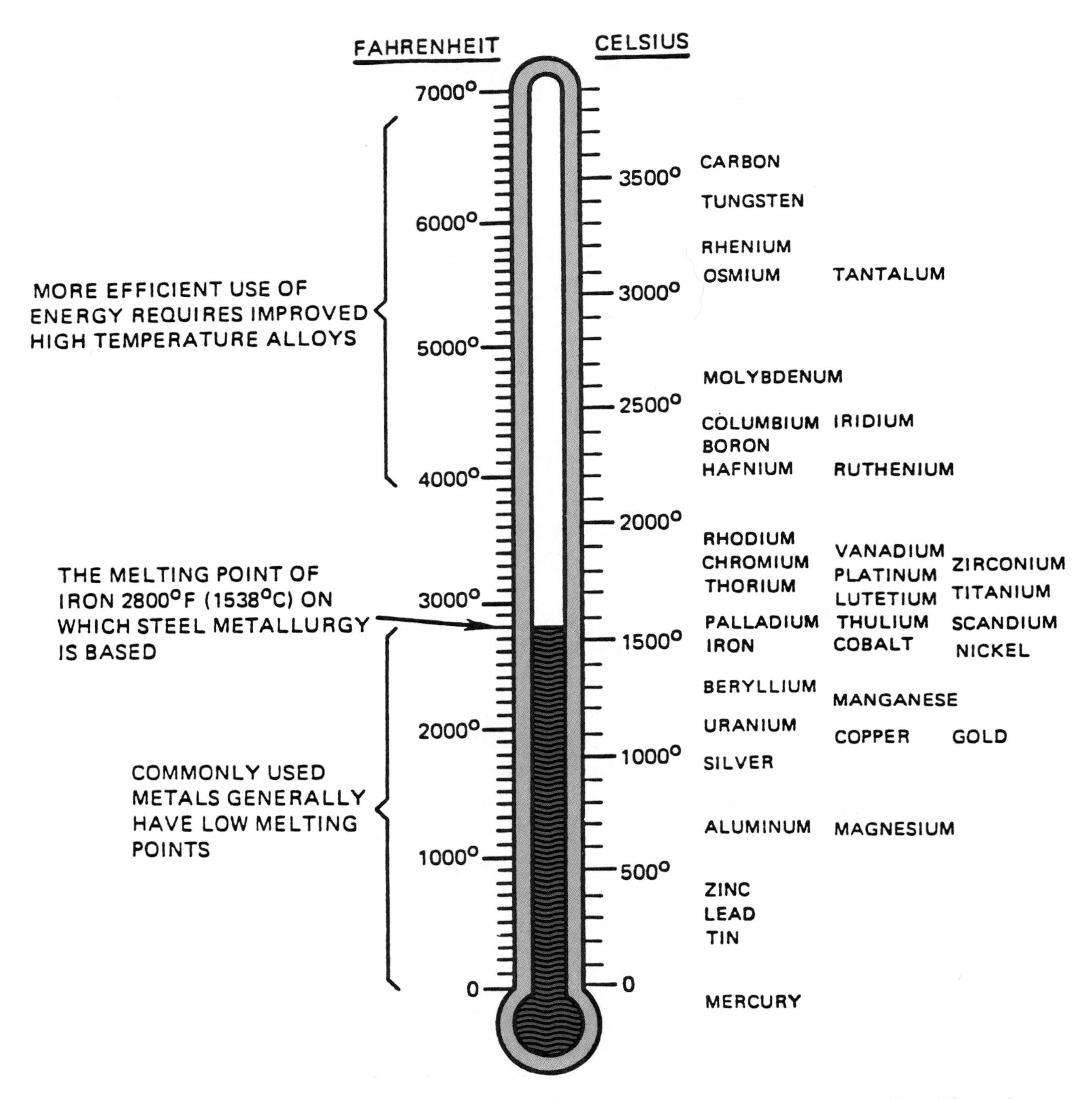

Figure 3.36 This chart shows all known elements with melting points above iron and major metals melting at lower temperatures. (USBM)

The United States Congress recognized the crucial role that minerals play in terms of national security, economic well-being, and global competitiveness when it passed the Mining and Minerals Policy Act of 1970. The Act declares it to be the continuing policy of the federal government, in the national interest, to foster and encourage private enterprise in the development of economically sound and stable domestic mining, minerals, metal and mineral reclamation industries. These goals were restated and reaffirmed in the National Materials and Minerals Policy, Research and Development Act of 1980.

Several factors have combined in the last several years to greatly weaken America's mineral industry. These include:

1. Loans to less developed countries by international financial institutions that enable those countries to keep producing certain minerals even though global demand for those minerals is down. This persistent overproduction contributes to falling world mineral prices, the closing of U.S. mines, and loss in domestic employment.
2. Both labor and management personnel in America's mineral industry receive substantially higher salaries and benefits than their foreign counterparts. This helps us live comfortably, but it makes it difficult to compete in the global marketplace.
3. Environmental and worker safety requirements are much more stringent in the United States mineral industry than they are in most other countries. This is what our people want, but again it costs money and makes it difficult for us to compete.
4. Millions of acres of public lands have been declared off limits to exploration and mining. Many of these acres are in the most richly mineralized areas of the United States. Severe restrictions on exploration and mining make it difficult for the industry to function.

Some of the major questions our society must answer are—Can we supply the raw materials to make the thousands of metal- and mineral-based products our technical society demands as well as make the new, advanced materials for high technology used in electronics, communications, and medicine? Can we, at the same time, hold hundreds of thousands of acres of unprospected and undeveloped wilderness off limits?

Some say the United States should be the source of ideas and information. Other countries can do the mining and manufacturing. What does it mean to our economic stability, balance-of-payments situations, and national security when we export our mining and processing industry overseas?

Are we really doing anything for the environment by locking up our own mineral wealth and then buying from suppliers that don't have environmental safeguards like ours? Protecting only a portion of the global ecosystem doesn't do the job.

One of the solutions to the environmental and resource scarcity dilemma involves the application of new and advanced technologies.

Superinsulation of homes and high-mileage cars are examples. However, if artificial intelligence, expert systems, remote sensing and automated process controls were adapted to the unique conditions and special requirements of the minerals industry, who knows what could be realized in competitiveness, worker health and safety and pollution control?

It seems that our challenge is to keep our industries strong and the environment clean. If we utilize our inventive genius, both goals should be possible.

Problems related to the use of mineral resources can be reduced by:

- Recycling mineral materials as often as we can.
- Redesigning products to reduce mineral requirements.
- Substituting more common materials for scarce minerals whenever possible.
- Using the best available technology to reduce both pollution and the health and safety problems related to mineral production.
- Reclaiming mined land and not buying minerals from countries that don't reclaim.

Summary

Minerals arise from the hot, molten substance called magma. As magma rises from the asthenosphere and solidifies, it forms a host of minerals at or below the Earth's surface.

Rocks, which are made up of minerals, are of three types. Igneous rock is formed by the solidification of magma. When any kind of rock erodes, settles, and becomes cemented in layers, the resulting new rock is called sedimentary rock. Metamorphic rock is rock that has been changed by high temperature and/or pressure.

Some minerals can be used by humans. Any mineral substance that can be mined at a profit is called an ore. Techniques have been developed for locating, mining, and milling these minerals. They eventually end up as the products of modern society. Obtaining these minerals involves a variety of issues we must deal with.

All indications are that the future of mineral supplies will be similar to the future of energy supplies. We will manage to get by, but present patterns will change. Some minerals will become more important. Other minerals will become less significant. Some substances, not used today, will assume major importance. One prediction can safely be made: Mining operations will get bigger, more materials will be used, and environmental impacts, for a time, will increase. How we choose to deal with these problems is one of the major issues of our time.

Mineral Resources

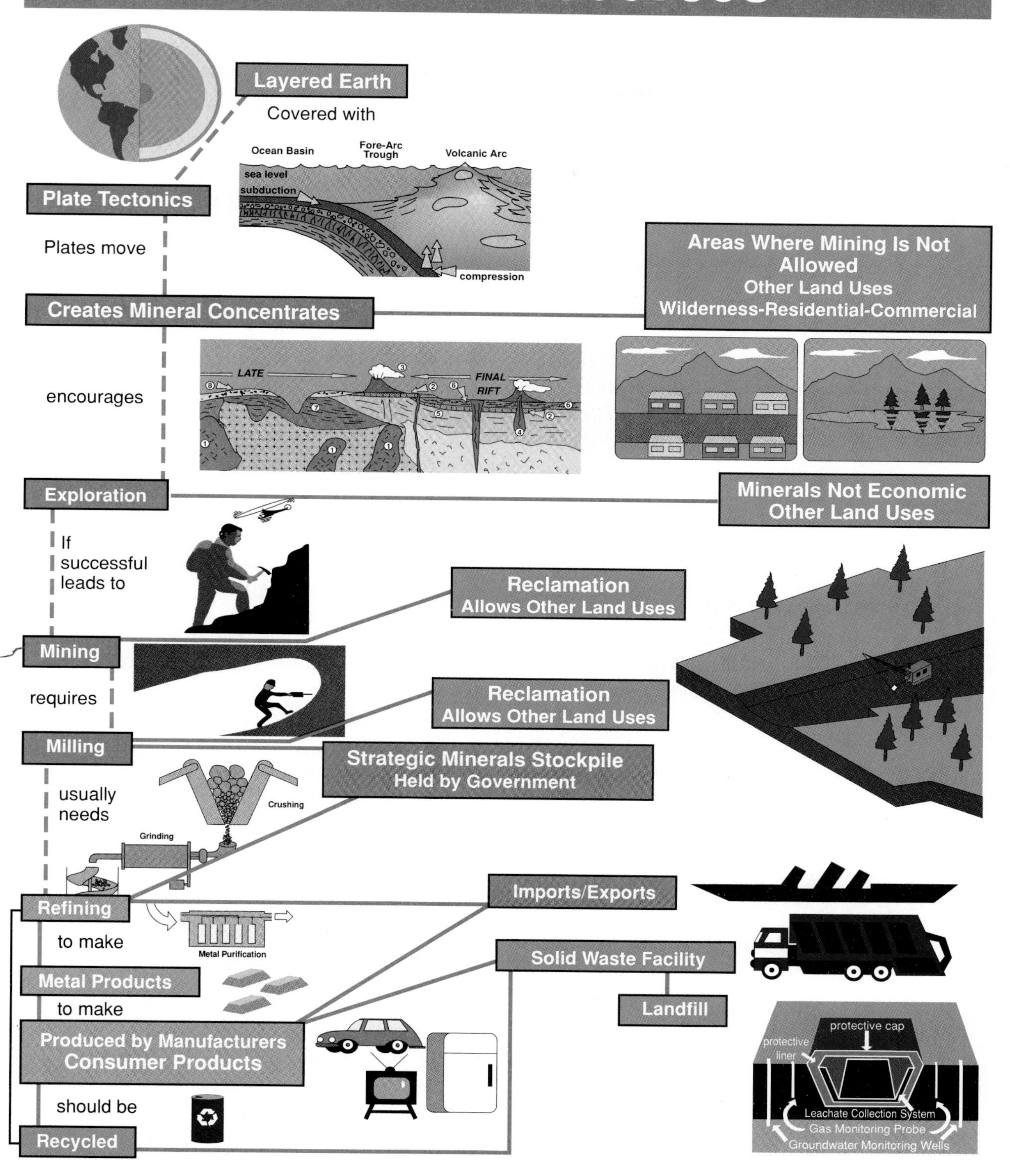

References

Adiabatics, Inc., 630 South Mapleton Avenue, Columbus, Indiana, 47201. Unpublished information provided to the author.

Annual Report of the Secretary of the Interior Under the Mining and Minerals Policy Act of 1970. *The Mineral Position of the United States—1987* (Washington, D.C.: U.S. Government Printing Office), 1988.

Cameron, Eugene N. *At the Crossroads: The Mineral Problems of the United States* (New York: John Wiley & Sons, Inc.), 1986.

Canby, Thomas Y. Reshaping our lives: advanced materials. *National Geographic,* 176:746, December 1989.

Cohen, Levin, et al. *Coming Full Circle: Successful Recycling Today* (New York: Environmental Defense Fund), 1988.

Craig, James R., David J. Vaughan, and Brian J. Skinner *Resources of the Earth,* (Englewood Cliffs, New Jersey: Prentice-Hall), 1988.

Dorr, Ann. *Minerals—Foundations of Society* 2nd ed. (Alexandria, Virginia: American Geological Institute), 1987.

Forrester, Tom. *The Minerals Revolution: Superconductors, New Materials, and the Japanese Challenge* (Cambridge, MA: MIT Press), 1988.

Gordon, Robert B., et al. *World Mineral Exploration: Trends and Issues* (Washington, DC: Resources for the Future), 1988.

Grable, Ron. Ceramic engine applications. *Motor Trend* November, 1988, p. 118.

Larson, Robert P. and Anant D. Vyas. The Outlook for Ceramics in Heat Engines, 1990—2010: Results of a Worldwide Delphi Survey. Society of Automotive Engineers *SAE Paper 880514,* March 3, 1988.

Leontief, Wassily, et al. *The Future of Nonfuel Minerals in the U.S. and World Economy: Input-Output Projections, 1980—2030* (Lexington, MA: Lexington Books), 1983.

Park, Charles F., Jr. *Earthbound: Minerals and Man's Future* (San Francisco: Freeman, Cooper and Company), 1981.

Press, Frank and Raymond Siever. *Earth,* 4th ed. (New York: W. H. Freeman & Company), 1986.

Tapp, B. A. and J. R. Watkins. *Energy and Mineral Resource Systems: An Introduction* (New York: Cambridge University Press), 1990.

U.S. Bureau of Mines. *Mineral Commodity Summaries* (Washington, DC: U.S. Government Printing Office), annual.

Young, John E. Mining the Earth Chapter 7 in *State of the World 1992* (New York: W. W. Norton & Co.), 1992

End of Chapter Questions ?

Set A

1. What is a mineral?
2. List five uses of minerals in our society.
3. Which two elements constitute 75% of the Earth's crust?
4. Why do crustal rocks buckle, fold, and crack?
5. How concentrated must a useful mineral in a rock be before the rock is considered an ore?
6. Where do the first and most dense minerals to crystallize from magma form ore deposits?
7. Explain how a million tons of magma can form deposits based on the immiscibility of the minerals in it.

8. What is the name of the deposit which remains when underground water dissolves away a non-valuable material, leaving behind the valuable mineral?
9. Suppose both rock salt and gold veins were exposed to frequent rain and washing. After a period of time has passed, which mineral would be found farthest from the original veins? Why?
10. When does mechanical concentration in flowing water occur? Give an example.
11. Why would gold be more likely to be found in a rapid flowing stream than in a slow one?
12. Why do gold flakes settle out of a stream at places where the stream curves and turns?
13. What kinds of devices are used to locate ore bodies?
14. What did the exploration geologist mean when he said "I'd rather be lucky than smart!"?
15. After an orebody has been located and claimed, what is the next step?
16. Define the following terms:
    a. ore
    b. gangue
    c. milling
    d. flotation
    e. tailing
    f. placer
    g. smelting
    h. refining
17. Ore is concentrated by separating useful mineral from the gangue. Where does this occur?
18. Describe three methods of physically separating the mineral from the gangue after the ore is crushed and ground.
19. In the milling process, describe two methods used to concentrate a mineral.
20. Name the process which brings a mineral concentrate to a fine or pure state.
21. Why are minerals important to us?
22. What are the two basic industries and why are they basic?
23. Name the three major elements used in inorganic fertilizers.
24. If fertilizer minerals are so abundant, why do some countries have difficulty obtaining them? How is this being resolved?
25. Why are imports an issue?
26. Why are substitutes not available for some minerals?
27. Explain why the use of substitutes for minerals considered to be in short supply can only extend the date of a shortage problem, rather than solve the problem.
28. Explain how an urban dump can become an "orebody."
29. Why is setting mineral-bearing land aside as wilderness controversial?

Set B

30. Which geologic features, containing a variety of metallic ores, do Colorado and California have that Iowa and Florida do not have?

31. Uranium ore bodies are produced by a limited supply of groundwater which leaches soluble uranium salts from a large area and deposits them in a small dry area. In which kind of deposit would the uranium ore be found?

32. Explain why the five locations in Figure 3.19 are all sites of possible placer accumulations.

33. How is agriculture affected by the mineral industry? Explain why these two industries are considered "basic" industries.

34. Why must an industrial country maintain trade relations with most countries in the world?

35. As a nation, what must we do to have a successful recycling program?

36. One knowledgeable geologist has stated, "Average rock will never be mined." Do you agree or disagree? Explain.

37. Express your opinion regarding state-imposed severance taxes on minerals. Give reasons to support your view.

38. Cassiterite, an important tin-containing mineral, has a specific gravity of about 7. How and why would you expect deposits of cassiterite to become concentrated?

39. The United States currently depends on foreign sources, especially South Africa, Zaire, Zimbabwe, Zambia, and Gabon, for more than 100% of its manganese (Mn), 75% of its chromium (Cr), 86% of its cobalt (Co), and 88% of its platinum (Pt). With these minerals in mind, list possible "ripple effects" of an embargo of those minerals on the U.S. economy.

40. Some people mistakenly believe that if one important mineral becomes very scarce or expensive, a substitute will inevitably appear. However, some substances, such as those listed below, have unique properties which are not easily imitated. See if you can match the substance with the exceptional property or use.

MINERAL	**PROPERTY/USE**
1. tin	**a.** anti-knock additive for gasoline
2. chromium	**b.** synthetic fertilizer
3. mercury	**c.** steelmaking
4. tetraethyl lead	**d.** sliding bearing
5. potash/phosphates	**e.** catalyst
6. platinum	**f.** amalgam
7. fluorspar	**g.** high-speed cutting tools

41. Sometimes the substitution of one material for another just increases the demand for the new one—which also may be in limited supply. Plastic is an example. Explain.

42. Explain how "outlawing planned obsolescence" can extend the life of a mineral.

43. Many responses dealing with the challenge of materials shortages rest on the assumption that more energy will be available to extract minerals from their lower grade ore. Using the second law of thermodynamics, explain why mining and refining lower grade ores is so energy-intensive.

A. J. Copley/Visuals Unlimited

Goal

To understand the basic properties of exponential growth. To relate that knowledge to world population issues.

Growth and Population

In order to understand the impact of population growth on your own life and on the future of the world, you must first know how populations are studied.

—John R. Weeks

Wheat on a Chessboard		
Square Number	**Grains on Square**	**Number of Grains on Board So Far**
(Number of Doublings)	**(Quantity Required to Double)**	**(Total Amount of Resource Used)**
1	1 (2^0)	1
2	2 (2^1)	3
3	4 (2^2)	7
4	8 (2^3)	15
5	16 (2^4)	31
6	32 (2^5)	63
7	64 (2^6)	127
|	|	|
|	|	|
|	|	|
64	2^{63}	$2^{64} - 1$

The Mathematics of Growth

Notice that the grains added to each square can be shown as exponents of 2, or 2^n. (n = number of the square).

There were once two kings in Babylon who enjoyed the game of chess. They played their games with gusto.

After one of their matches, the winner asked for an unusual prize. He handed the chess board to the loser and asked that it be returned to him with one grain of wheat on the first square, two grains on the second, four on the third, and so on. The grains were to double on each square until all sixty-four squares were filled.

The losing king was delighted at the seemingly modest request and quickly agreed to it. He was soon sorry he had. The situation he got himself into is illustrated in the following chart.

Square 64 represents 2^{63} grains of wheat. The total grains on the board would be one grain less than 2^{64} How much wheat is 2^{64} grains? It is about 500 times the annual harvest of wheat for the entire world in 1980. This amount is probably larger than all the wheat harvested in the history of the Earth! How did we get to this enormous number? We started with one grain of wheat and we doubled it a mere 63 times!

What are the main characteristics of exponential growth?

4.1 The Nature of Exponential Growth

Exponential growth like that on the chessboard is occurring around us in many situations. Exponential growth is a major factor in causing our energy/resource/environmental concerns. Therefore, we must make every effort to understand it. The chessboard problem illustrates the following properties of exponential growth:

Exponential growth starts slowly, but. . . .

Exponential growth plots as a "J" on ordinary graph paper

1. Exponential growth is marked by doubling. A few doublings can lead quickly to enormous numbers.
2. Exponential growth is deceptive because it starts out slowly, but it rapidly gets out of hand. (See Figure 4.1)

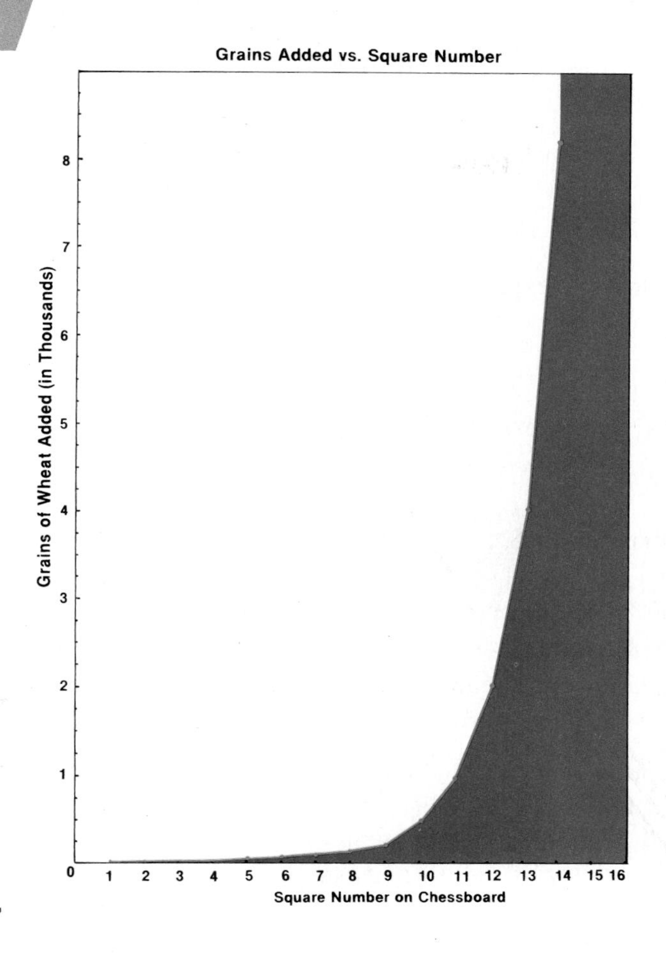

Figure 4.1 Plot of grains of wheat added vs. square number for the first 14 squares on a chessboard. Note that exponential growth plots as a "J" on ordinary graph paper.

3. The total growth in any one doubling is more than the total of all preceding growth.
   Analysis of your data and graphs in the exponential growth modeling lab will show additional characteristics of exponential growth:
4. Exponential growth occurs whenever the rate of growth (r), $\Delta N/\Delta t$, is directly proportional to ($\propto$) the number (N) present:

r = rate
N = number
t = time
Δ = change
ΔN = change in N
Δt = change in t
$\propto$ = is directly proportional to

$$\frac{\Delta N}{\Delta t} \propto N$$

Two quantities are directly proportional if their ratio is constant. As one increases, the other increases. Thus, when a population is doubled, if nothing else changes, it will also grow twice as fast.

5. A *quantity* exhibits exponential growth when it increases by a constant percentage of the whole in a constant time period (like a savings account bearing compound interest):

$$\frac{\Delta N}{N} \propto \Delta t$$

Exponential growth and doubling time.

6. It is useful to think of exponential growth in terms of **doubling time.**

$$\text{Doubling time (in years)} \simeq \frac{70}{\text{\% annual growth rate, r}}$$

$\simeq$ is a symbol meaning "is about equal to". If the annual growth rate is 10 per 1,000 persons (1% per year), then the population will double in 70 years. If r = 2%, the doubling time is 70/2 = 35 years; and so on.

Graphing exponential growth.

7. Plotted on semi-log paper, exponential growth is seen as a straight line.

Many real-world situations can be explained by scientific principles such as exponential growth. The application of principles from science and mathematics to the real world does not guarantee peace or happiness. It never has. It never will. However, the application of principles from science and mathematics can help us understand some of the problems we are facing in regard to population, food, pollution, and resource consumption. As the cartoon indicates, we must know how to count.

In this chapter we will examine the mathematics of exponential growth. Most people have never learned to count exponentially. However, many things around us are changing at exponential rates. A knowledge of exponential growth will help us understand them. We will first focus our mathematical knowledge on current population issues. This will offer new understanding as we examine food, energy supply, pollution, and resource management issues in later chapters.

"The greatest shortcoming of the human race is man's failure to understand the exponential function."
— Albert A. Bartlett,
Professor of Physics,
University of Colorado

4.2 The Limits of Exponential Growth

?

Why is exponential growth abnormal in finite systems?

Bacteria multiply by division (that sounds odd, doesn't it?) One bacterium divides and becomes 2, the two become 4, the 4 become 8, and so on. Assume that for a certain strain of bacteria the time for this division is one minute. This process is recognized as exponential growth

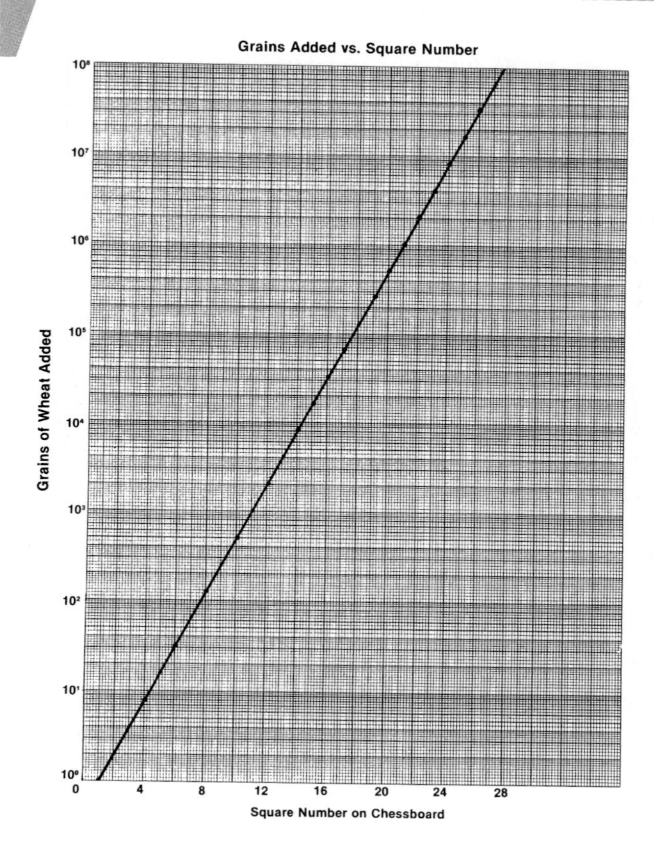

Figure 4.2 Plot of grains of wheat added vs. square number for the first 28 squares on a chessboard. Note that exponential growth plots as a straight line on semi-log paper.

Cartoon—Hagar "Stand up and be counted." (Reprinted with special permission of King Features Syndicate.)

with a doubling time of one minute. Suppose I put one bacterium in a bottle at 11:00 A.M. and observe that the bottle is full at noon. Here is a simple example of exponential growth in a finite environment. This is mathematically similar to the exponentially growing consumption of our finite nonrenewable resources. Keep this in mind as you consider three questions about bacteria:

1. At what time was the bottle half-full? Answer: 11:59 A.M.
2. If you were an average bacterium in the bottle, at what time would you first realize that you were running out of space? There

Figure 4.3 Cell division. The bacterium at the right has nearly finished dividing. (George Musil/Visuals Unlimited)

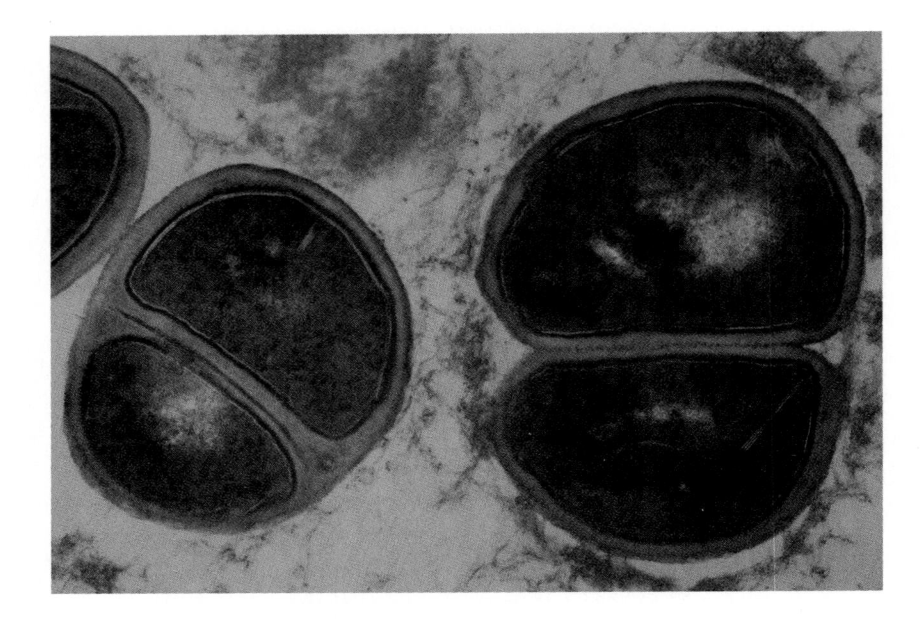

is no unique answer to this question, so consider: At 11:55 A.M., when the bottle is only 3% filled and 97% empty, would you be likely to perceive a problem?

Suppose that at 11:58 A.M. some farsighted bacteria realize they are running out of space in the bottle. Consequently, with a great expenditure of effort and funds, they launch a search for new bottles. They look offshore and in the Arctic, and at 11:59 A.M. they discover three new empty bottles. Great sighs of relief come from all the worried bacteria. This magnificent discovery is three times the number of bottles that had hitherto been known!

The discovery quadruples the total space resource known to the bacteria. Surely this will solve the problem so that the bacteria can be self-sufficient in space. The bacterial "Project Independence" must have achieved its goal.

3. How long can the bacterial growth continue in the quadrupled space resources? Answer: Two more doubling times (minutes)! The following table documents the last minutes in the bottles:

The Effect of the Discovery of New Bottles	
11:58 A.M.	Bottle No. 1 is one quarter full.
11:59 A.M.	Bottle No. 1 is half-full.
12:00 Noon	Bottle No. 1 is full.
12:01 P.M.	Bottles No. 1 and 2 are both full.
12:02 P.M.	Bottles No. 1, 2, 3, and 4 are all full.

The problem of exponentially increasing consumption.

Quadrupling the resource extends the life of the resource by only two doubling times. When consumption grows exponentially, enormous increases in resources are consumed in very short times!

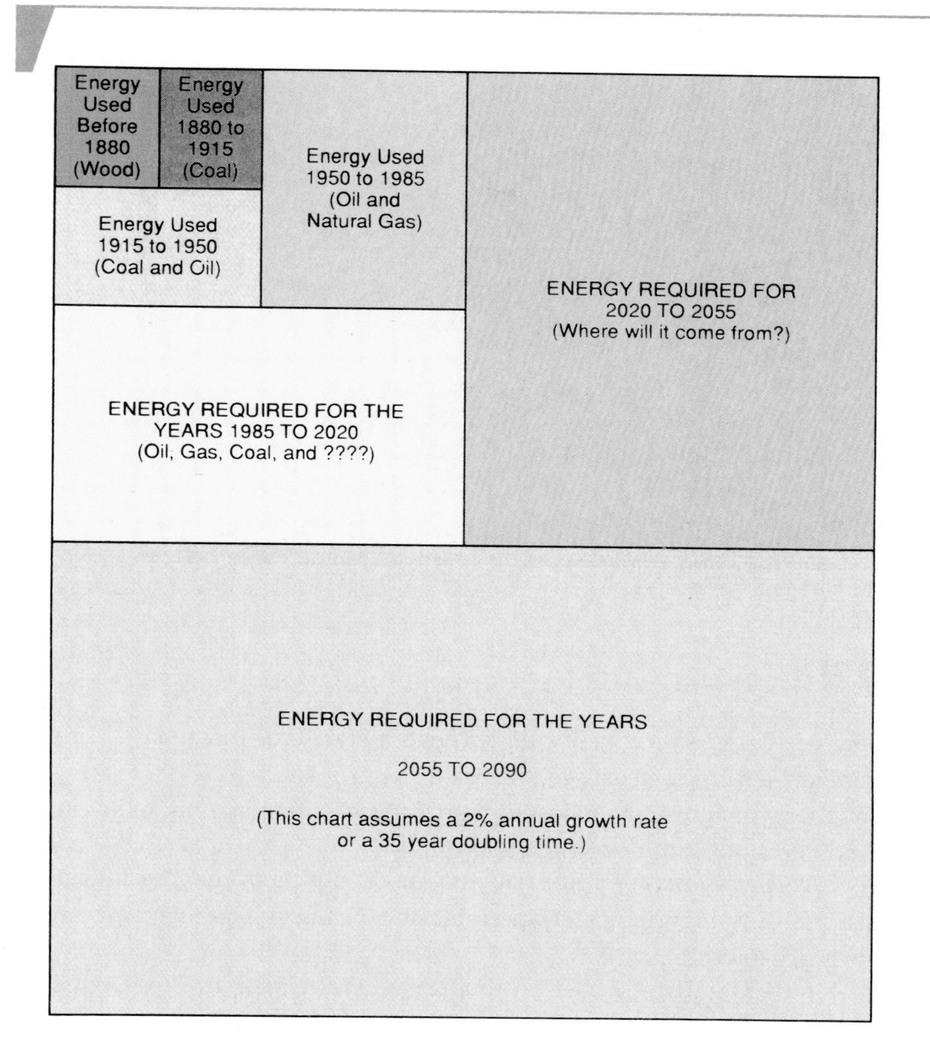

Figure 4.4 The energy history and possible energy future of the United States.

Like the bacteria, we are growing and using resources at an exponential rate. Figure 4.4 summarizes the energy history and possible energy future of the United States. The area of each rectangle represents the quantity of resources consumed or required during the thirty-five year period it represents. Although the percent annual growth rate has varied, the average for the last hundred or so years has been around 2 percent and many of our political leaders would like to "stabilize" the annual growth rate at about 2 percent. The chart makes use of the fact that the total growth in any doubling is slightly more than the total of all preceding growth. If x = all the energy used in the United States up until the year 2020, how much energy will be used in the 35 years between 2020 and 2055? In the 35 years after that?

Where will our future energy supplies come from? How do we plan for such growth? How long can this growth continue? These are serious questions that we will address as you work your way through this course.

Figure 4.5 Human population growth through time, 8000 B.C. to 2020 A.D. (Population Reference Bureau, Inc., 1875 Connecticut Avenue, N.W., Suite 520, Washington, D.C. 20009-5728.)

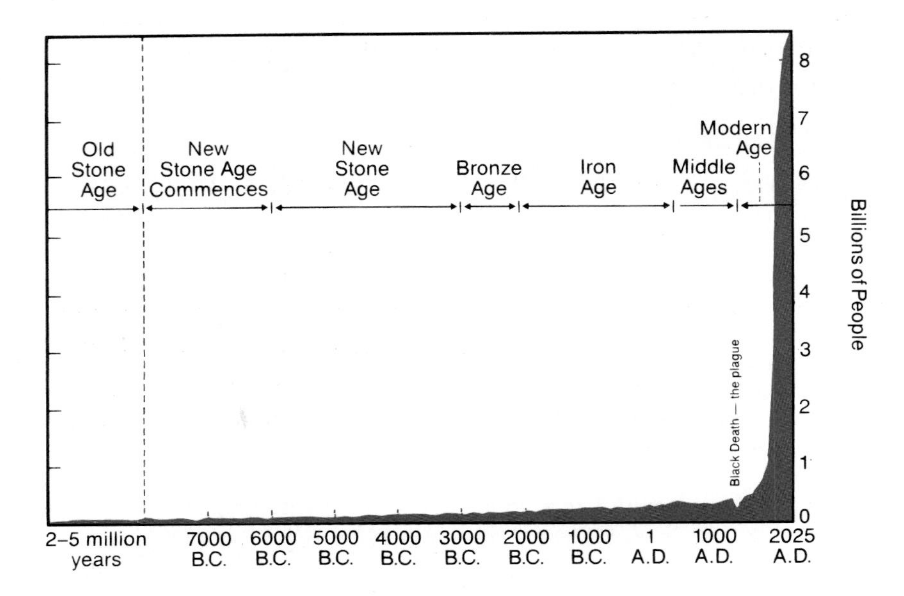

29 4.3 The Explosion of Human Population

One of the numbers increasing exponentially on Earth today is the number of people. Because population size is related to food availability, energy and resource consumption, industrial output, and pollution, it deserves our careful consideration.

World population size grew very slowly through most of human history. (See Figure 4.5.) This is because births and deaths were almost in balance.

In the 1600s things began to change. The standard of living significantly increased in Europe. Our understanding of diseases and their causes began to increase. Medical practices improved. For various religious, social, humane, and political reasons, people made major efforts to eliminate disease and premature death, but only minimal effort to understand and control births. Births consistently began to outnumber deaths. Since the birth rate was more than the death rate, population began to increase. At first, the natural increase was very small. By about 1850, the situation had changed greatly.

?

What caused the human population to increase exponentially during and after the 1600s?

Changes in population size have been recorded by **demographers.** (**Demography** is the study of human populations.) Demographers have a numerical equation expressing the rate at which all populations grow. Considering the world as a whole, the fundamental demographic equation is:

What is the fundamental demographic equation?

Population Growth Rate = Birth Rate – Death Rate

In Figures 4.6 and 4.7, the population growth rate is shown as "natural increase", the distance between birth rate and death rate in any one year. When we study the population in small regions, this equation must be modified to:

What factors determine the growth rate of a population?

?

Population Growth Rate = Rate of Increase – Rate of Decrease.

This is because people can move into a region (immigrate) or move out of a region (emigrate). The rate of increase equals the birth rate plus the immigration rate, and the rate of decrease equals the death rate plus the emigration rate.

We may choose to ignore the effects of immigration and emigration and write the equation as:

Rate of Natural Increase = Birth Rate – Death Rate

This is often done when immigration or emigration rates are small when compared to birth and death rates. This is the case in both Figures 4.6 and 4.7.

In studying population growth, demographers find it useful to divide the Earth into "developed" countries and "developing" countries. **Developed countries** are those that have industrialized and/or have a high standard of living. These include countries in North America, in Europe, and in the former Soviet Union; and Japan and Australia. **Developing countries** include those that have low standards of living. Most are agricultural nations that have little industry. In this category are India, the countries of East and Central Africa, and the People's Republic of China.

Distinguish between developed and developing countries.

The reason for this division is shown in Figures 4.6 and 4.7. In both regions, the death rate has fallen as medical practices, sanitation, and education have improved with time. However, in the developed world the birth rate also declined, though not as fast as the death rate, resulting in moderate population growth.

The present population growth rates for some developing regions are: Africa 3.0%, Western Asia 2.0%, Southeastern Asia 2.2%, Central America 2.5%

In the case of the developing world, the death rate has fallen much faster than the birth rate. This has resulted in rapidly growing populations and in growing poverty and starvation.

By the first half of this century, the annual growth rate reached 10 per 1000 persons (1% per year), which meant the world's population would double every 70 years. But the growth rate itself continued to grow until now it is approximately 17 per 1000 persons (1.7% per year, with a doubling time of 41 years).

Clearly, the addition of more and more people means less and less food, land, and resources for each person. The Earth is a finite system. Thus, exponential growth cannot continue forever.

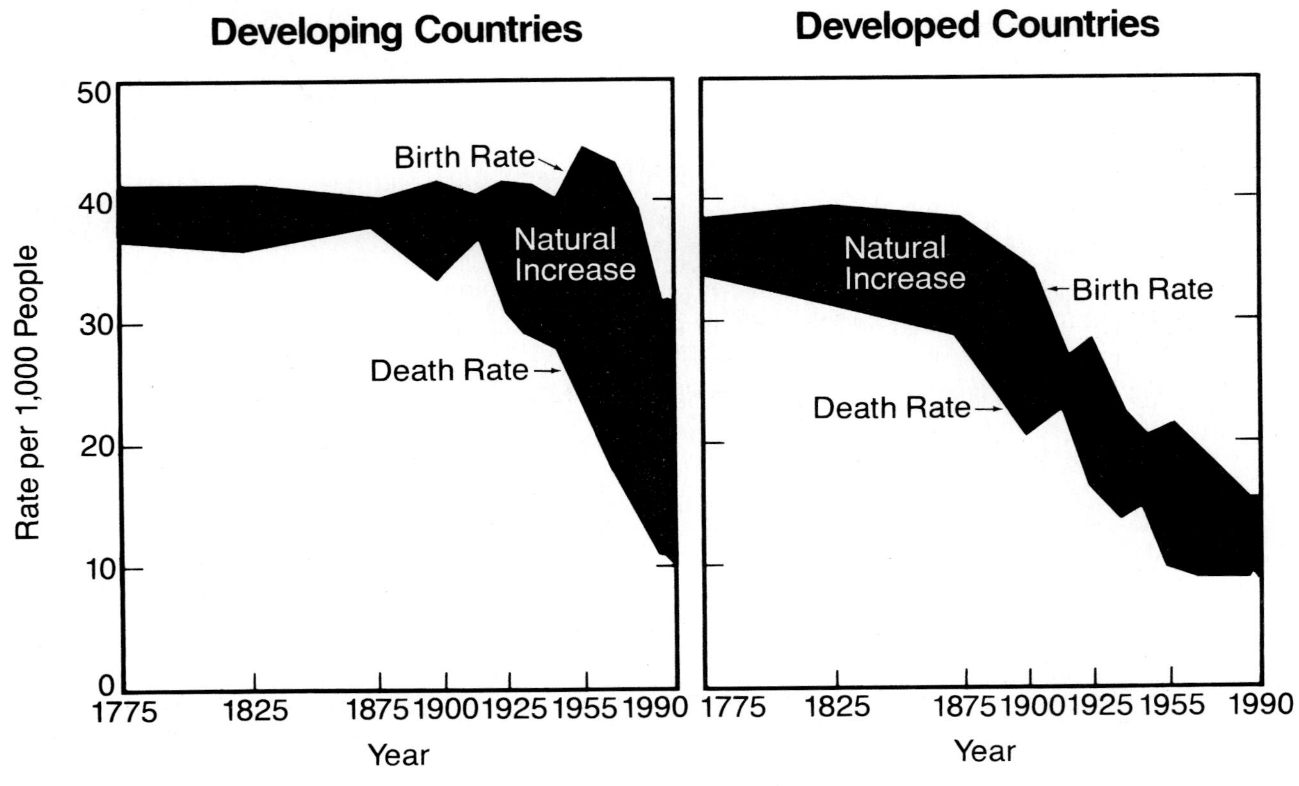

Figure 4.6 World birth and death rates in developing countries (1775–1990). (Population Reference Bureau, Inc.)
Figure 4.7 World birth and death rates: developed countries (1775–1990). (Population Reference Bureau, Inc.)

What is carrying capacity?

The present population growth rates for some of the developed regions are: East Asia 1.3%, USSR .80%, North America .80%, and Europe .20%.

The maximum population the Earth can sustain at some reasonable average living standard for its inhabitants is called the **carrying capacity.** The world human population today is over 5 billion. All indications are that it will exceed 6 billion by the year 2000.

Some experts feel the Earth's carrying capacity for humans is about 10–12 billion. Others feel it is less than that. Can we adequately provide for the minimal needs of six billion persons? Raising their standard of living to anything approaching ours may be impossible. Thus, the population problem is one that must receive our most serious consideration in the years ahead. If we do not control our population size, natural forces may do it for us.

> *Whatever God's will for man may be, surely it is not that population is best controlled by starvation, disease and nuclear holocaust.*
> — Clare Booth Luce

Information, Please . . .

science at work

In her job at the Los Angeles regional office of the U.S. Census Bureau, Nenet (pronounced "Nanette") Magpayo knows how valuable *information* is in our country's efforts to understand population—not just its numbers, but also its housing distribution, utility and transportation usage, education, and so forth. Each person or family Nenet interviews has been carefully selected to represent thousands of others throughout the country. She and other field representatives in 12 Regional Offices throughout the U.S. collect the data, and statisticians in a central office interpret the data and predict future patterns.

For instance, the Bureau's recent population growth estimate for California is that from 50 to 53 million people—15 percent of the U.S. population—will live there by the year 2020, depending on what happens to the state economically. Because of the information obtained by Nenet and other field representatives, we know much more about the ebb and flow of our nation's population, facts such as what proportion are immigrants and what proportion arrive by birth, and how many folks look for greener pastures in other states. Thanks to this data, the experts can estimate the resources we'll need.

After participating in the 1990 census, Nenet stayed on as a part-time employee of the Los Angeles office. Now, in addition to her survey work, she supervises other field representatives and recruits interviewers for the surveys. In the last few years she has gathered many different kinds of data, for other government agencies and some private organizations, as well as the Census Bureau. For the U.S. Bureau of Labor, she has asked questions about employment, and delved into people's spending habits for use in preparing the Consumer Price Index. She has talked to people about AIDS and other health issues for the NIH Center for Health Statistics, and interviewed crime victims for monthly Department of Justice studies.

Sometimes Nenet gathers data on individuals, sometimes on households, both in person and over the phone. The identity of everyone interviewed is, by law, kept confidential. But though she deals with cold, hard facts, Nenet's approach to interviewing is more personal. A survey of one household or individual may take as long as five hours, depending on the questions, and Nenet must be persistent but friendly—and polite, too—to put folks at ease. She has learned to be an excellent communicator.

Despite attending many meetings and handling thousands of letters to potential respondents, Nenet still helps other representatives prepare for interviews. She does a good deal of field work herself—about 40 follow-up cases a week—sometimes on weekends, when working people have more time to talk to her. Recording and organizing interview data is easier these days than in past years, because she has been trained to use a laptop computer with customized programs. The computer helps her record answers to questions and then summarizes the data, and she transmits the results over a modem. Nenet came to the United States from the Philippines, where she worked in a television station as a videotape engineer. Then she lived in Massachusetts, where she was a junior engineer, before moving to California. In addition to English and her native Tagalog, she speaks Spanish. Knowing several languages has been helpful to her Census Bureau work.

The next population and housing census will be in the year 2000, and Nenet will work on that one, too. The folks who join her in this work will be at least 18 years old, U.S. citizens, and have a high-school diploma or GED certificate. Nenet says it's a great job for those who enjoy talking to people, are self-starters, are detail-oriented, and who enjoy fast-paced, challenging work.

4.4 Analyzing Population Growth

a. Measuring and Analyzing Population Growth

Although we share the Earth with millions of different species of plants and animals, it is well to focus our study of populations on humans. This is because humans have a major impact on all other populations as well as their own. Much of what you will learn about human populations applies to all populations, however.

b. Picturing Population Growth

?

What is a population histogram and what information does it give?

What family size causes population growth to level off?

Population statistics are often shown as histograms, like those in Figure 4.8. Because of their shape, population histograms are sometimes referred to as population pyramids. A **population histogram** is a bar graph that divides a population up by age and sex. Each horizontal bar represents the percentage of the population that falls into a particular age/sex group. A relatively stable population would be represented by approximately equal percentages of the population in all age groups except for the very old.

Figure 4.8 consists of the population histograms for countries with rapid, slow and negative growth. From them we see that rapidly growing populations have huge percentages of very young people. If these young people have large families, the population will continue to expand rapidly.

c. Understanding Population Growth

As the proportion of young people decreases, the base of the pyramid shrinks. This is what has happened in the United States. The high proportion of people born in the 20 years after World War II presents problems and challenges.

Family size. Human population growth is not an automatic process. Many individual decisions contribute to both the birth rate and the death rate. Among them are decisions about when or whether to marry, and how large a family to have. Family size is one of the critical factors in the determination of population growth. If the "average" couple has three or more children, a population will grow rapidly. When the average drops to two or less children, the population begins to level off. If two-child families are the average, the children replace the parents and over the long term, population tends to stabilize.

?

What are some of the reasons that the population size continues to increase in the United States?

At present, population in the United States and the world will continue to grow for a number of years even if the overall preference is for the two-child family. This is illustrated on the graph of Figure 4.9 for the case of the United States.

The reason for the continued increase is because the birth rate is not the only factor involved in population growth. Death rate is of major importance. In addition, age at marriage, the proportion of

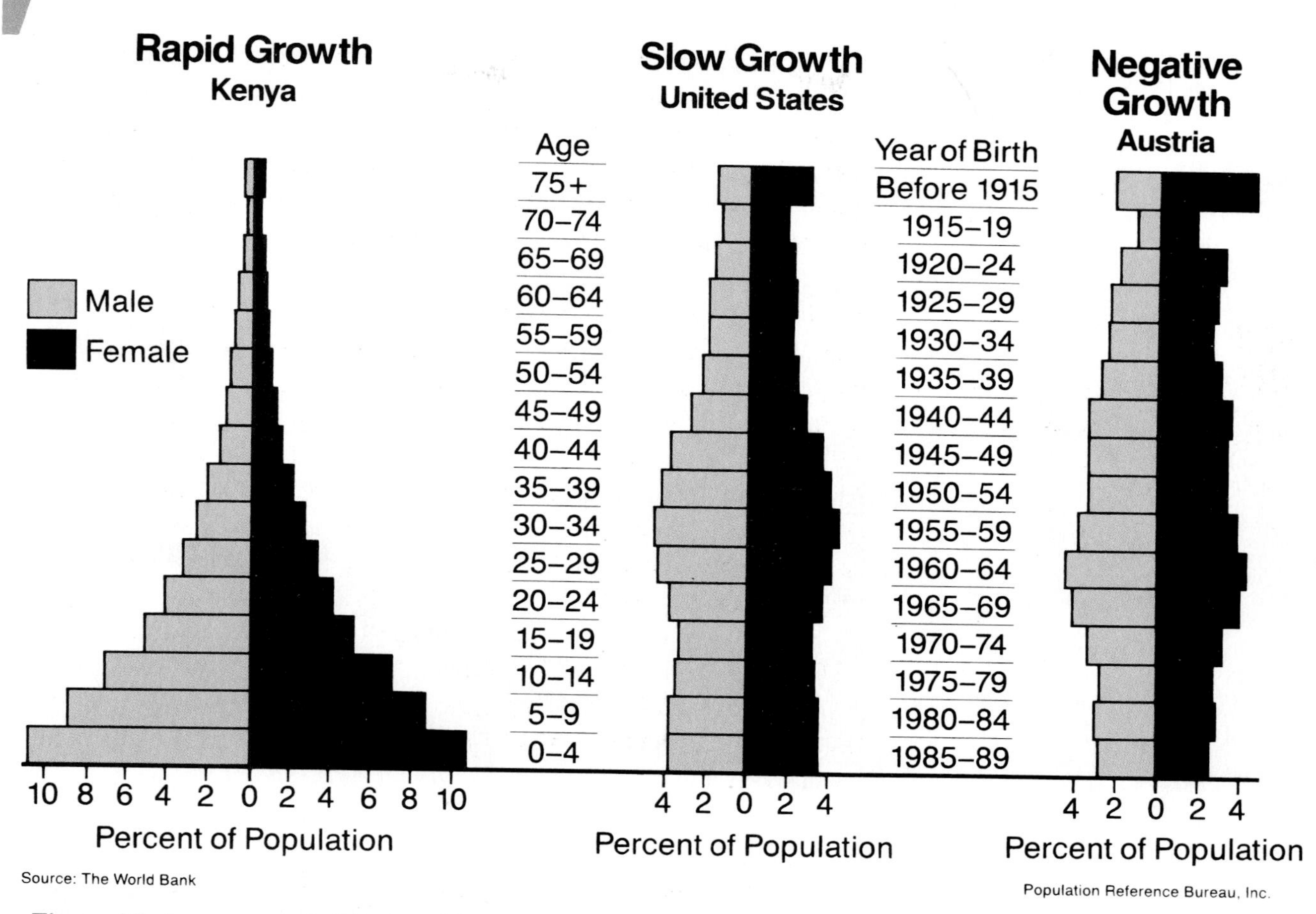

Figure 4.8 Age-sex population pyramids: rapid, slow, and negative models. (Population Reference Bureau, Inc.)

women who are of child-bearing age, and the rate of immigration are all contributing factors. The percentage of women of child-bearing age in the United States is relatively large.

Why does early marriage generally result in larger families?

Age at the time of marriage. Since women are generally capable of having babies between the ages of the early teens and the late forties, populations grow more slowly as the average age at first marriage increases. This is because most couples do not wish to have children until they are married. Thus, if a woman stays single until she is 25, she has on the average 19 years during which she may have children. If she were married at age 15, this span would have been 29 years. In addition, a woman who postpones having her first child is less likely to have a large family. She may become infertile, be divorced, or even die before having a second or third child. Postponement of marriage is a very effective way of lowering population growth.

The population histograms of Figure 4.8 illustrate why world population also will continue growing for several decades. It will continue even if the average preference around the world is suddenly for the two-child family. Replacement level reproduction (two-child families) must be maintained for about 50 to 70 years before a population

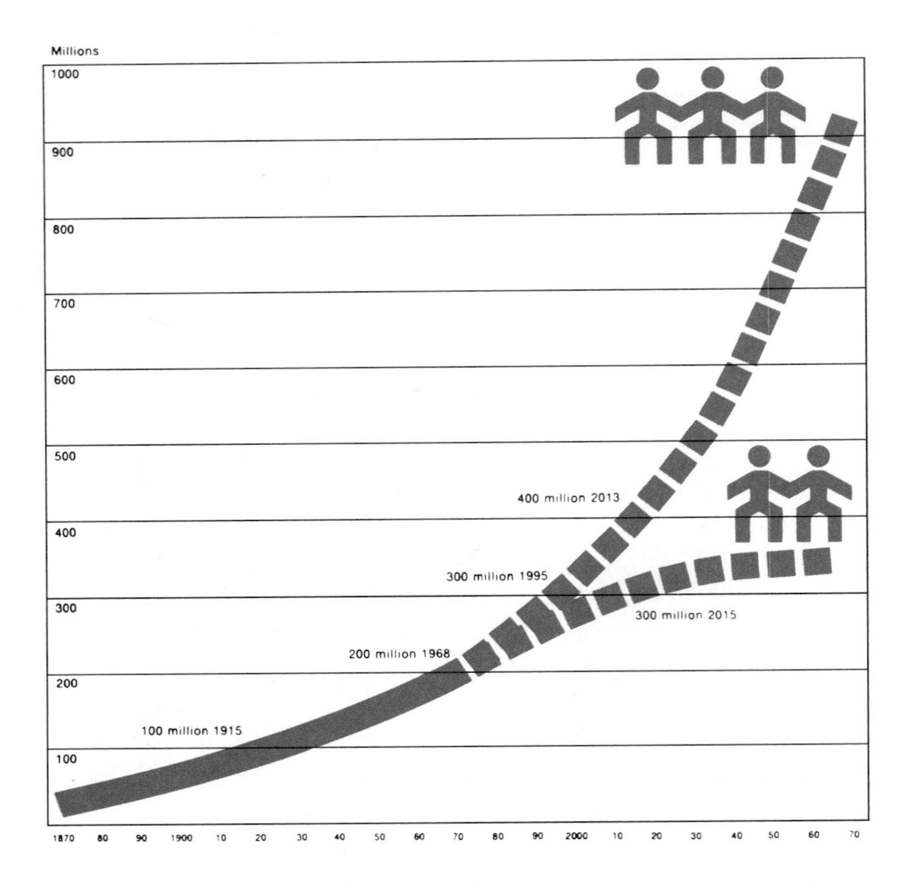

Figure 4.9 Projected U.S. population: 2- vs. 3-child family. (From The Report of the Commission on Population Growth and the American Future.)

Figure 4.10 Couples beginning their families in their late twenties and thirties generally have smaller families. (Jim Shaffer)

will stop growing. This is because several generations are alive at one time, and because growing populations have large proportions of young people.

Immigration. In addition, immigration into the United States, both legal and illegal, contributes to our population growth. The United States is one of only a few countries that do not have severe restrictions on immigration. In 1990, for example, more than 1,540,000 persons immigrated to the U.S. Our population also grew by more than 2,020,000, the number by which births exceeded deaths in that year.

4.5 Problems Related to Growth Reduction

?

What problems are encountered when human population growth is reduced?

Although the major problems related to population change are associated with population growth, problems also result when populations stop growing. As stated earlier for a population to stabilize, it must go through a transition period. As stabilization of the population begins, the base of the histogram shrinks. However, above the narrowed base exists a bulge. See Figure 4.8, middle and right histogram.

Several things happen as this bulge moves upward. The bulge represents a large age group followed by a smaller age group. When the large group gets to high school, the demand for large or more high school buildings, teachers, etc. goes up. However, the group behind them is small. As a result, elementary schools must close and their teachers are laid off. High schools are affected next, when the larger group goes to college and the smaller group enters high school.

List some problems that occur as a population stabilizes.

The biggest problem results when the larger, older group retires. Much of their retirement income will come from pensions and from social security deductions from the paychecks of the younger group. As you can see, the situation is difficult. If more money is withheld, less money remains for starting families and buying homes. Since the early years of marriage can be expensive, it is difficult for young people to put large amounts of money away for retirement. Probably the best solution is to have the older group retire at a later age. In this way, retirement funds are used for a shorter period of time. Retirement is not the only problem. The smaller group also represents smaller demand for the items industry makes—homes, cars, radios, etc. This means a smaller domestic market and production of consumer goods.

Another kind of problem appears when some countries stabilize their populations more than others do. Since it is the developed world that is stabilizing its populations first, the percentage of the world's people that first reaped the benefits of industrialization is shrinking. What are the implications of this on the course of human history? What happens when the present developed nations represent less than 10 percent of the world's people?

Figure 4.11 The shrinking West. (Copyright © June 22, 1987 U.S. News & World Report) *Note*: East and West Germany are now Germany, and the Soviet bloc is now the former Soviet bloc.

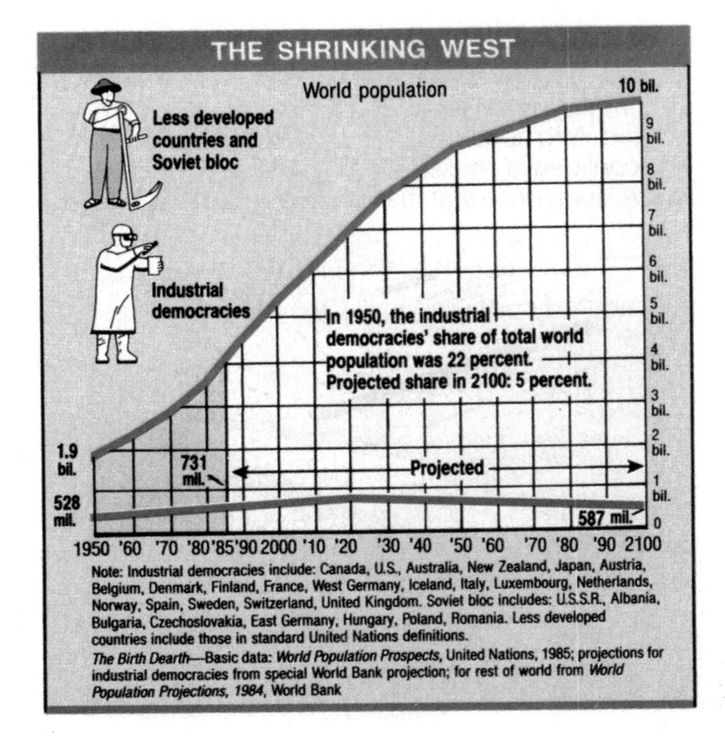

28 4.6 The Demographic Transition

?

What is the demographic transition?

The Japanese have the highest life expectancy—82 years for women and 76 years for men. On average, Japanese women are now giving birth to 1.53 children. Currently, one pensioner is supported by 6.5 workers. By the year 2010, there will be only two workers for every pensioner in Japan.

As you have seen, human populations grew in size very slowly before the 1600s. Because the difference between birth rates and death rates was small, there was little or no growth.

Then as medical care, sanitation, food production and knowledge about disease improved, the death rate among children dropped. Birth rates, however, remained relatively constant. This combination led to rapidly growing populations.

After a time, people realized that fewer of their children would die young. They didn't need to have six or more children to guarantee that one or two would survive to care for them in old age. Slowly, birth rates dropped. In many countries the result was population stabilization brought about by low birth and death rates. For example, in 1988 the birth rate in Denmark was 11.5 (per 1,000 population), and the death rate was also 11.5. In West Germany the figures were similar.

This series of changes is known as the **demographic transition.** It is summarized in Figure 4.12.

The exact cause of the demographic transition is not fully understood or agreed upon. Some scholars feel that the decline in birth rates is brought about by improved economic conditions associated with industrialization. Others argue that industrialization is not necessary. They think any combination of events that can bring about an improved standard of living will eventually result in population stabilization.

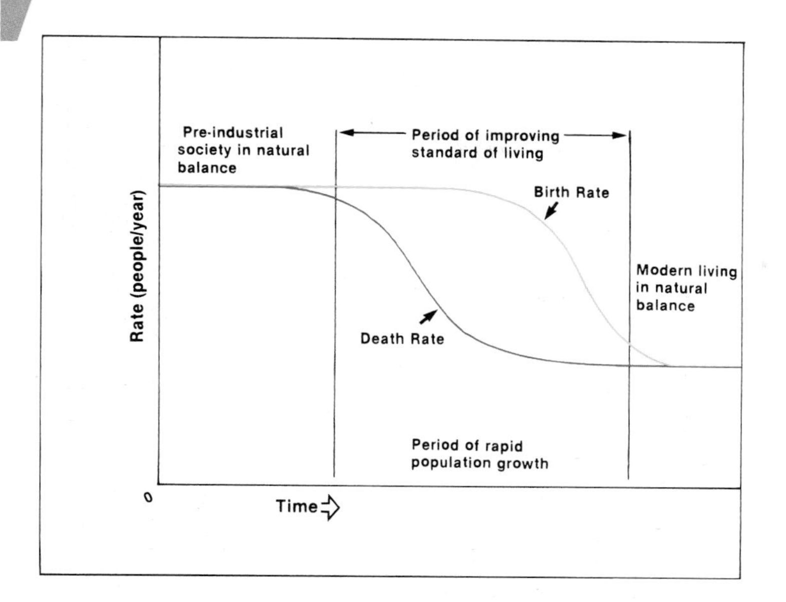

Figure 4.12 The idealized demographic transition.

Use Figure 4.12 to explain what the demographic transition is and why it should occur.

As a society makes the transition, the drop in birth rates is brought about by a shift in attitudes toward children. Before the transition, children are viewed as valuable labor and as insurance for care in old age. After the transition, children become an economic liability. They are desirable in terms of companionship, the family experience, general enjoyment of life, and the desire to have something of one's life continue. However, the financial costs and strain related to child rearing, coupled with career goals and the desire for independence and privacy, lead many couples to desire only small families or no children at all.

This attitude shift can be caused by social, political, or economic forces, individually or in combination. Often, for example, women will be better educated as economic conditions improve. They will also have more access to family planning services. As individual women can control the number of children they have, they can affect the population's birth rate. Men, too, may choose to father fewer children.

If a country can be helped to become modern, its birth rate is likely to fall. But is such help practical? Many developed nations built their industrial base by utilizing large quantities of cheap natural resources taken from poorer nations they dominated. Can China, India, Egypt or Mexico accomplish what Great Britain and Germany have done without access to large reserves of energy and mineral wealth? It appears their best hope is for the development of technologies leading to modern conveniences but using fewer resources. (More about that later.)

The drop in death rates and the rise in standard of living occurred during the same short time period for many of today's economic giants (U.S., Great Britain, France). Thus, their period of rapid population growth was relatively short. The situation in many developing countries is much different. After World War II, modern disease control

Figure 4.13 World population growth in developing and developed regions, 1750–2100. (Thomas W. Merrick, with PRB staff, World Population in Transition, Population Bulletin, Vol. 41, N. 2, [Washington D.C.: Population Reference Bureau, Inc., January 1988 reprint].)

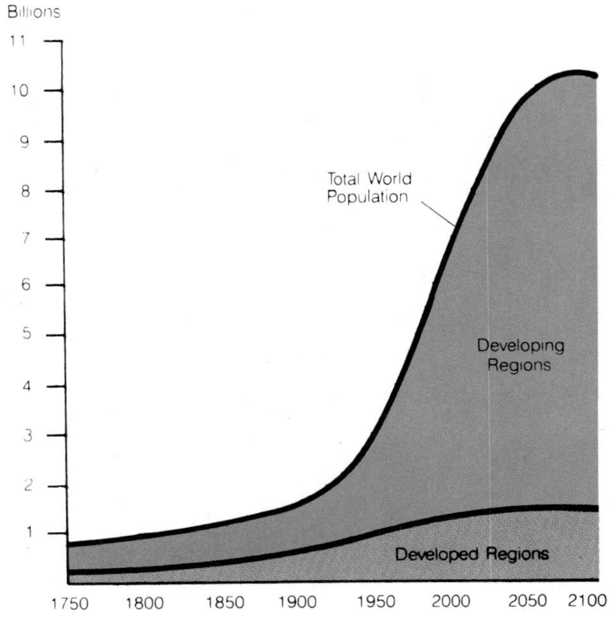

Wealth, rather than poverty, paves the road to a cleaner environment.

and sanitation practices were introduced to these countries. This resulted in a dramatic drop in infant mortality. Unfortunately, economic conditions did not always improve. The result has been a population explosion and stagnation in the middle of the demographic transition pattern.

If world population becomes too large, it may be desirable to go through a post-transition phase in which birth rates drop even lower than death rates. This way, the population can be reduced to some desired, optimum level.

4.7 World Population Trends

Why is population growing faster in developing regions than in developed regions?

The world's population passed the 5 billion mark in 1987. The present average growth rate is 1.7% with a doubling time of 41 years. Hidden in these figures is the fact that the developing countries are growing 2.1 percent per year, while the annual growth rate for the developed countries is only 0.6 percent. In the developing countries, a woman bears an average of five children. In the industrialized world, two children per woman is the norm.

Although the overall growth rate is declining, the world population in 2025 is expected to have increased another 3 billion since 1985. Long-range projections of world population size are guesses and based on a variety of assumptions. Long-range projections by the United Nations (U.N.) indicated that the world's population will almost double by the year 2100. According to the World Bank, population size will be about 10.4 billion in 2100. Ninety-five percent of the increase will be in the developing world. By the year 2100, the population of developing countries is expected to be 8.8 billion. The population of developed countries is projected to be 1.4 billion. One projection is shown in Figure 4.13.

Figure 4.14 (Jim Shaffer)

The United Nations projects stabilization of the world's population at 10.2 billion by 2100 if the average replacement level of 2.1 births per woman is reached by 2035. Demographers for The World Book Encyclopedia estimate that world population will not stabilize until it reaches 11.2 billion.

The reasons for the projected eventual stabilization of world population are many. They are part of complex human and economic factors. They appear to center around the following:

?

What factors may contribute to the stabilization of world population?

1. The declining importance of children as part of the family labor force.
2. The increased cost of raising and educating children.
3. The improved social status of women.
4. Rising educational attainment and improved employment patterns for women.
5. Increased urbanization.
6. Concern about natural resources and pollution.

Countries that have had official population-planning policies in effect for some time show gradual decreases in fertility rates. Birth rates are declining along with the economic benefits of having several children.

Present trends seem to indicate that world-wide human and economic interactions will complete the demographic transition on a worldwide scale. The status of women around the world, as indicated by education attainment and employment opportunities, is also on the increase.

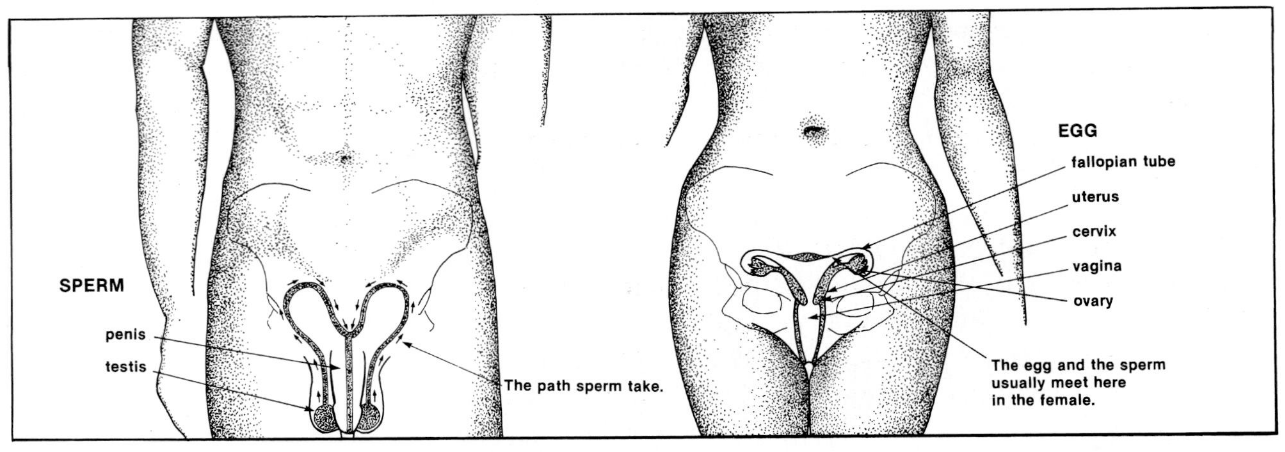

Figure 4.15 The sperm and the egg. (Adapted from Me in the Future. Copyright © 1977 by Biological Sciences Curriculum Study [BSCS].)

Controlling Growth

There are two accepted approaches to controlling human population: *economic development* and **family planning.** As you have just seen, economic development raises the standard of living and alters the economic importance of children and the social status of women.

Family planning helps people have the number of children they want when they want them. Family planning strategies are the topic of the next section.

4.8 Family Planning

?

What is family planning? On what is it based?

Family planning is the process by which couples discuss and determine the number and spacing of their children. It is based on:

1. The desire of people to practice birth control.
2. The availability of birth control information.
3. The availability of a wide variety of birth control methods.

What is fertilization/conception?

Birth control allows a couple to decide if and when they want the woman to become pregnant. It includes many methods of interrupting the production, movement, or joining of eggs and sperm cells. In doing so, they prevent conception, the formation of a fertilized egg.

Egg production happens in a female's ovaries. Once a month, an egg moves from an ovary through a fallopian tube, where it may be fertilized by a sperm cell. The sperm cell has traveled to the fallopian tube from the uterus, which is just above the vagina. During sexual intercourse, sperm cells and fluid are released into the vagina from an opening in the male's penis. As the penis is hard, or erect, during intercourse, sperm can be released into the upper part of the vagina, where they are most likely to swim far enough to reach an egg and fertilize it. Sperm cells are formed originally in the male's testicles and move through tubes into the penis.

If a fertilized egg is formed in the fallopian tube, it must then move into the uterus and attach to the uterine lining before developing further. Pregnancy begins when the fertilized egg attaches to the uterus. Some methods of birth control prevent that attachment from happening.

When does pregnancy begin?

The following is a brief description of the most common methods of birth control.

?

What are some of the major birth control methods? How effective are they?

a. No Intercourse, or Total Abstinence

Total abstinence is the most effective method of birth control. It is 100% effective provided the abstinence is total. This is the "just say no" technique. It is highly recommended for unmarried couples. Society as a whole believes that intercourse should be practiced within the bonds of marriage. This is partly because children born to unwed parents are much less likely to receive the emotional and financial support necessary for a happy and productive upbringing. In addition, many people believe that intercourse outside of marriage is morally wrong. Finally, it is dangerous because of sexually transmitted diseases (STDs). Diseases like AIDS may be acquired from blood transfusions or contaminated needles; but a drug-free person whose only sexual partner is not infected with any STD is unlikely to become infected.

What is total abstinence? How effective is it? Why is it highly recommended for unmarried couples?

b. Vasectomy

To keep from fathering children, a man can have an operation, called a vasectomy or male sterilization. The tubes that carry sperm to the penis from the testicles are cut (a piece is removed from each tube) so that sperm cannot get through. The man's ability to have intercourse is not affected, but he is permanently sterile. A vasectomy is usually done in a doctor's office. After the surgery, any sperm already in the tubes can still cause pregnancy, and so there is a time lag between the surgery and the man's becoming sterile.

Vasectomy.

c. Condoms

The penis can be covered during intercourse. This cover prevents sperm from entering the female. The covers are called "rubbers," or condoms. They catch sperm so they don't get into the female organs.

Condoms.

If used properly, condoms can be quite effective. They do on occasion break or slip off during intercourse. Effectiveness is increased if condoms are used along with spermicides. Condoms and abstinence are the only birth control methods that also offer some protection against *sexually transmitted diseases* (STDs).

d. Tubal Ligation

If a woman desires no more children, she can receive a tubal ligation. This involves cutting or tying the fallopian tubes. As this is surgery inside the abdominal wall, tubal ligations usually require hospitalization; so, they are more expensive than vasectomies. Women often have this done after the delivery of what they want to be their last baby.

Tubal ligation.

Tubal ligations are almost 100% effective. In rare cases, sperm may accidentally reach an egg.

e. Rhythm Method

Rhythm method.

The rhythm method involves the timing of intercourse to avoid a woman's time of greatest fertility. Hence, she has intercourse only when eggs are not released. An egg is usually released about two weeks before the beginning of the menstrual period. However, the ovulation cycle varies greatly. To determine her "infertile" times, a woman must take her temperature (oral or rectal) each morning before any physical activity. In this way, the fertility cycle can be estimated.

Unfortunately, some women's cycles are quite irregular. Also body temperatures can vary due to tension, infection, lack of sleep, or prior physical activity. For these reasons, the rhythm method has a low reliability rate (70–75%). Under the best conditions it requires diligent record keeping and strong self-restraint. However, abstinence and the rhythm method are the only birth control methods permitted by some religions.

f. Diaphragms and Cervical Caps

Diaphragms and cervical caps.

Fertilization can be prevented if the entrance to the uterus is blocked or covered during intercourse. If the entrance to the uterus is covered, sperm cannot get to the tube where the egg is located. A diaphragm is such a barrier. It is a soft rubber cup with a flexible rim around the edge.

Diaphragms can be quite effective provided a woman is properly fitted for one by her doctor. Hence, diaphragms are not sold over the counter. They can be inserted several hours before intercourse and should be left in place at least 6 to 8 hours after intercourse. For high effectiveness, they must be used with a spermicide.

The cervical cap is a birth control device which is much like the diaphragm. It fits over the entrance to the uterus which is called the cervix. It is called a barrier contraceptive because it prevents sperm from entering the uterus. The device, which looks like a large rubber thimble, is less than half the size of a diaphragm. It can be worn at least twice as long as a diaphragm. Like the diaphragm, it is used in conjunction with spermicidal jelly. A woman must be properly fitted for the cervical cap by her doctor.

g. Spermicides

Spermicides.

Spermicides are chemical substances placed in the vagina before intercourse for the purpose of blocking or killing sperm. Spermicides come in the form of foams, creams, jellies and suppositories. They do not harm vaginal tissue.

Spermicides are not highly effective when used alone. Their effectiveness increases when used with a diaphragm or condom.

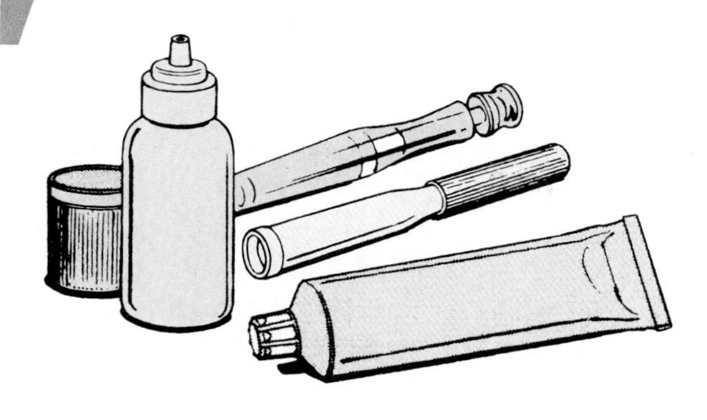

Figure 4.16 Spermicides and spermicide applicators. (Adapted from Me in the Future. Copyright © 1977 by Biological Sciences Curriculum Study [BSCS].)

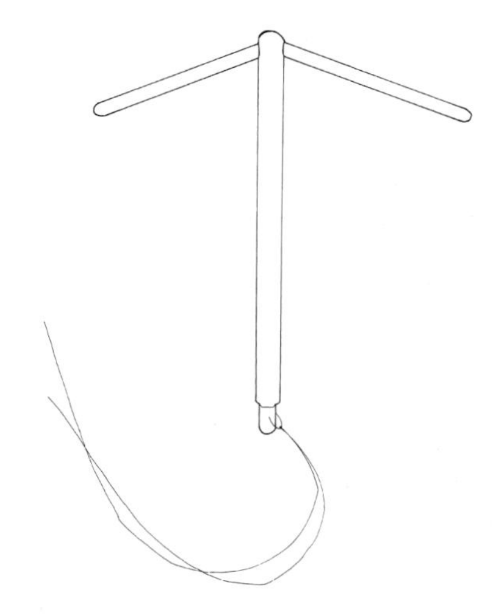

Figure 4.17 Intrauterine device.

h. Intrauterine Devices (IUDs)

Intrauterine devices.

An intrauterine device (IUD) is a small metallic or plastic object placed inside a woman's uterus to prevent pregnancy. IUDs require a physical examination and proper fitting by a doctor. They are most effective after a woman has had her first child.

It is thought that IUDs work by altering the lining of the uterus. This prevents implantation, or the attachment of the fertilized egg to the lining.

IUDs are highly effective. However, they can have serious side effects. Their use should be carefully thought out, and based on reliable information and discussion with medical personnel.

i. Birth Control Pills

Birth control pills.

Pills can be taken to prevent pregnancy. These pills prevent the egg from leaving the ovary. If the egg never leaves, fertilization cannot occur.

Birth control pills are highly effective if used correctly. However, it must be remembered that they are powerful drugs. They can cause serious problems in some women. They offer no protection from STDs. To obtain maximum protection and minimize risks, a woman must see her doctor for both an examination and a prescription.

Figure 4.18 Birth control pills and pill dispenser. (Adapted from Me in the Future. Copyright © 1977 by Biological Sciences Curriculum Study [BSCS].)

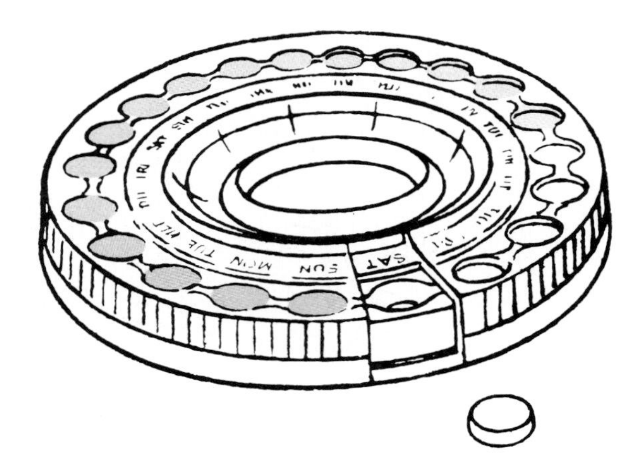

Figure 4.19 A family planning clinic in Asia. (E. F. Anderson/Visuals Unlimited)

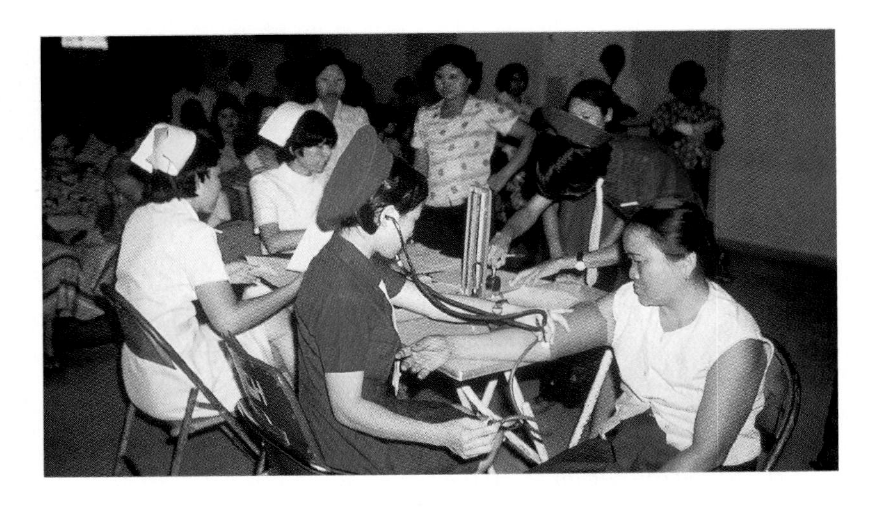

j. Implants

Implants.

Women can obtain five years of reliable birth control by having six rubbery, matchstick-size capsules inserted just beneath the skin of the upper arm. The capsules are filled with a powdered synthetic sex hormone. This hormone slowly leaks through the wall of the capsule and prevents the ovaries from releasing an egg. Insertion and removal of the capsules requires minor surgery. The implants offer no protection against STDs.

k. Injections

Injections.

Depo-provera is the trade name of a powerful drug that can be injected into the woman for contraception. It acts by preventing ovulation. The effect of the injection lasts for at least three months. It is more convenient than taking the pill every day, and it is as effective as the implant or a tubal ligation. Injections offer no protection against STDs.

Strong international family-planning programs coupled with economic development aid from the developed nations seems to be the best combination for achieving a stabilized world population below the 10 billion figure. This approach, combined with true equality for women, may lead to a community of nations that act more harmoniously than the way we do today. At least more people should have children for the right reasons.

Table 4.1 Summary of Birth Control Methods.

Method	How It Works	Effectiveness
1. Abstinence—no intercourse	Male and female do not have intercourse.	100%
2. Vasectomy	Tubes in male cut so sperm cannot pass through.	100% after 30 days (tubes may grow back together, but rarely).
3. Tubal ligation—cutting the tubes	Tubes in female cut, so eggs cannot enter uterus.	100%, (sperm may reach accidentally, but rarely).
4. Condoms	Penis covered during intercourse. Sperm cannot enter female.	High, approximately 90%. Effectiveness increased when used with spermicide.
5. Implants/Injections	Prevent release of eggs from ovary.	Nearly 100%
6. Pills	Prevent release of eggs from ovary.	Nearly 100% if taken properly.
7. IUDs	Stops embryo from sticking to uterus.	High, not 100%
8. Diaphragm	Blocks uterus opening.	Medium
9. Spermicides	Kill sperm before they can reach egg.	Lower
10. Rhythm Method	Intercourse only when eggs are not released.	Lower (80%)

Problems related to population growth can be reduced by:

Individually

1. Abstain from sexual relations until marriage, and only have as many children as one can financially afford and properly take are of.
2. Plan early for retirement so that family/society is not left with the problem of costly elder care.

Collectively (Nations/Society)

1. Make birth control information & devices available to those that desire this service.
2. Expand educational and employment opportunities for women. This increases interest in family planning.
3. Where religious preferences discourage the use of artificial contraception, provide education in natural birth-control methods.
4. Increase funding for research and development of new methods of birth control that are easier to use, more reliable, and more acceptable in some cultures than current methods.
5. Raise the standard of living (in an ecological way) in poorer nations. Speed up the demographic transition.

Special Focus

To Have or Have Not? The Question of Children

All across the U.S., married couples who have put off having children to get head starts on careers or to gain good financial footings are reaching decision time. Now in their 30s, many can't afford to wait much longer to start families.

Typical are Michael and Deirdre Searles, both in their early 30s. He is vice president of an oil-drilling and exploration firm; she is communications director for a large computer company. How is this San Antonio couple dealing with the important question of parenthood? Deirdre provides a glimpse.

—San Antonio

For professional couples in their 30s, such as Michael and myself, the decision on whether to have children is a pressing and difficult one. In many ways, it is the first irrevocable life decision that we've had to make.

The passage of time, rather than clarifying our feelings, has tended to make the issues more complex. As the biological clock winds down, we are being forced to confront our feelings toward parenthood and come to grips with how having children will affect our careers, lifestyle and marriage.

Why is this decision more difficult for us in our 30s than it would have been in our 20s? First, I feel we wouldn't have been making a rational choice if we had decided in our 20s whether or not to have children. At that time, having gone to college and found jobs, we might have borne children as our "next logical step" rather than making a well-reasoned choice.

In our 20s, we had a far more idealistic view of the world. We would not have really thought about the cost of college in 2020 or the physical drain of going three months without a good night's sleep when an infant comes home from the hospital. By our early 30s, we had ample opportunity to observe in other families the less enchanting aspects of parenthood.

Over the years, our careers have also made the decision more difficult. In our 20s, our major goal was gaining the financial security we felt was necessary before having children. As time passed, our careers gained importance to the point where the jobs that were to be the financial vehicle to enable us to afford parenthood actually became obstacles.

Both of us have challenging jobs that require travel, overtime and a lot of emotional involvement.

If we have children, we question whether we will be able to maintain the delicate balancing act necessary to provide time with the children, keep a healthy marriage and not neglect our careers. Even if we can manage to handle all of these things, will we enjoy our lives? Or, as we see in many families, will we just exist on a never-ending treadmill of demands with no time to enjoy ourselves?

Many, including some of our friends, would say that we are selfish. To an extent that is true. On the other hand, we have known people who have had children for extremely selfish reasons. At least if we have children, we know it will not be for such reasons as insurance against our old age, a hedge against regretting it if we didn't have them, to prove that we are responsible, functioning adults or to find extensions of our own egos.

And yet, we know that you really can't analyze what it feels like to have pudgy little arms grab you and give you a hug or project the joy in watching a 3-year-old rip open Christmas packages. There are the twinges you feel when the young child of a friend, all scrubbed and ready for bed, comes to you for a good-night kiss. Or the fleeting feelings of envy on seeing parents and their laughing children at a beach or an amusement park. We can't hope to comprehend the emotions involved in watching the baby you raise go off to college, get married, or forbid, go to war. Can we deprive ourselves of these experiences and really be complete people?

And so we sit, firmly ambivalent at the moment. In the typical American way, we want it all—challenging jobs, well-adjusted children, and a good marriage. We are mature enough to realize that wanting something doesn't always result in having it. Maybe we're not wise enough to determine what's truly worth having.

If we don't decide, time will make the decision for us, and that is something neither of us wants. So we'll decide. Maybe not today or next month, but soon. We only hope it will be a decision without remorse.

From: *U.S. News & World Report, March 22, 1981*, page 81.

Summary

The Earth and its resources are finite. Exponential growth in a finite system is abnormal and cannot continue unchecked. Failure to understand this fact and *live* accordingly can lead to human tragedy. This is because both population size and quality of life are tied to exponential growth. Exponential growth is hard to deal with because it creeps up on you. It starts slowly, but it can generate huge numbers very quickly. It can produce human populations we cannot feed. It can lead to demands for resources we cannot fill.

We must understand how populations grow, what good nutrition involves, and the demands populations place on natural resources. We must understand that the growth rate is equal to the birth rate *minus* the death rate. Lowering the death rate was a desirable accomplishment. However, doing nothing about the birth rate can cause huge population increases. Failure to understand this has caused fantastic human suffering. This problem continues to worsen.

Population histograms, growth rate versus time graphs for developed and developing countries, analysis of family size, and the concept of age at marriage all help us understand population issues. Both rapid population growth and rapid growth reduction lead to serious problems.

The demographic transition explains why many modern populations stabilize. There are some indications that human population may stabilize around the 10–12 billion figure.

Family planning is the process by which couples discuss and determine the number and spacing of their children. Many couples desire to maintain some control over the occurrence and size of their family. The reliability of the various birth control techniques varies a great deal.

Questions of birth, life, and intimacy are important questions. They are serious questions we all face. The ways we answer them have a significant impact on how successful most of us will be in life. They play an important role in what happiness we experience. Choose wisely.

References

Bartlett, Albert A. The exponential function. *The Physics Teacher,* October, November, and December issues, 1976.

Brown, Lester R., and Jodi Jacobson. *Our Demographically Divided World* (Washington, D.C.: Worldwatch Institute), 1986.

Carlson, Allan. Depopulation Bomb: The Withering of the Western World. *Washington Post,* pp. C1, C2, April 13, 1986, .

Donaldson, Peter J., and Amy Ong Tsui. The International Family Planning Movement. *Population Bulletin,* Vol. 43, No. 3 Washington D.C.: Population Reference Bureau, 1990.

Dychtwald, Ken. Age Wave: The Challenges and Opportunities of an Aging America (New York: Jeremy Tarcher), 1989.

Ehrlich, Paul R., and Anne H. Ehrlich. *The Population Explosion* (New York: Simon and Schuster), 1990.

Fornos, Werner. *Gaining People, Losing Ground: A Blueprint For Stabilizing World Population* (Washington, D.C.: Population Institute), 1987.

Keyfitz, Nathan. The Growing Human Population. *Scientific American,* pp. 118–126, September, 1989.

Merrick, Thomas W. et al. World Population in Transition. *Population Bulletin,* Vol. 41, No. 2 (Washington, D.C.: Population Reference Bureau), 1986.

Population Reference Bureau. *World Population: Fundamentals of Growth* (Washington D.C.: Population Reference Bureau), 1990.

Population Reference Bureau. *World Population Data Sheet* (Washington D.C.: Population Reference Bureau), Annual.

Saunders, John. *Basic Demographic Measures: A Practical Guide for Users* (Lanham, MD.: University Press of America), 1988.

United Nations. *Demographic Yearbook* (New York: United Nations), Annual.

Wattenberg, Ben J. *The Birth Dearth* (New York: Pharos Books), 1987.

End of Chapter Questions

Set A

1. What is exponential growth? Answer in one sentence.
2. It is easy to contrast exponential growth with arithmetic (additive) growth. Make two graphs for this purpose. Start each growth with a population of 2 at time zero. Use any time scale you wish. For the exponential graph, multiply the original population by 2 for each unit of time. For the arithmetic graph, add 2 for each unit of time. How are the two graphs different?
3. If energy consumption increases 2% a year for the next 35 years, how much energy will the United States consume? Assume 2% to be the average annual growth rate since the U.S. became a nation.
4. What caused world population to start growing exponentially in the early 1600s?
5. Populations cannot continue to grow at exponential rates forever. Why?
6. How does a National Aeronautics and Space Administration (NASA) photo of the whole Earth from space help us understand the problems brought about by exponential growth?
7. Use Figures 4.8 and 4.9 to explain why the population of the U.S. will continue to grow for some time even if the average preference is for the two-child family.
8. Explain why a girl who is married at age 18 is likely to have a larger family than a woman who is married for the first time at age 25.
9. What problems are encountered when human population growth is reduced?
10. What is the demographic transition?
11. Why is population growing faster in developing regions than in developed regions?
12. What factors may contribute to the stabilization of world population?
13. What is family planning?

14. When does a female become pregnant?
15. Why is total abstinence highly recommended for unmarried couples?
16. Name some of the more common birth control methods and indicate their average reliability.

Set B

17. What major changes could curb the exponential growth of human population yet still allow for improvements in our medical care?
18. Refer to Figure 4.4. Speculate on the energy sources that will power the United States from the year 2013 to 2047. Record and defend your reasoning.
19. Refer to Figure 4.5 to answer the following.
    - **a.** Estimate the number of years it took the human population of Planet Earth to grow to one billion.
    - **b.** According to the graph, how long will it take to add another five billion?
    - **c.** What does the answer to (b) tell you about the rate of growth in the later stages of an exponential growth curve?
    - **d.** It is obvious that exponential growth in a finite system cannot continue indefinitely.

      What things can happen to bring the growth of the human population down if the carrying capacity of Planet Earth is exceeded?
20. Which of the following do you think grew more or less exponentially between the end of World War II and the 1970s?
    - **a.** U.S. population
    - **b.** U.S. electric energy production
    - **c.** Auto air pollution emissions
    - **d.** Miles of state highways
    - **e.** Growth of horsepower
    - **f.** Airline miles flown
    - **g.** U.S. water use
    - **h.** U.S. expenditures for research and development (R & D)
    - **i.** Number of scientific journals in print
    - **j.** U.S. advertising expenditures
21. Explain, in words, the unique properties of the phenomenon of exponential growth.
22. In real life, what factors tend to limit the population size of various organisms?
23. Do you agree with the following statement? "Since humankind can control its environment (i.e., produce its own food, dispose of its own waste, control the populations of other organisms, etc.), the problems associated with exponential growth do not apply to the human population." Explain.
24. In what way is the growth of the human population most similar to money in the bank earning compound interest?

25. Figure 4.4 represents graphically the past and future energy growth of the United States for a 2% growth rate in energy consumption. How would Figure 4.4 have to be changed to show an annual growth in energy consumption equal to 1%?
26. If all U.S. couples decided to have only two children, our population would still continue to grow for a time. Why?
27. How should we in the developed world face the fact that we are fast becoming a small percentage of the total world population?
28. Will the forces associated with the demographic transition lead to the stabilization of world population, or will the forces of nature bring this about?
29. Is it in the interest of developed nations to help the developing nations raise the standard of living of their people? Why, or why not?
30. Why is family planning such a controversial issue?

End of Chapter Problems

1. If the annual population growth rate is 5%, what is the doubling time? (Hint—doubling time = 70/growth rate × 100%.)
2. If the doubling time is 7 years, what is the % annual growth rate?
3. If you invest $5,000.00 in a business venture that guarantees 11% annual interest, how long will it take your investment to grow to $10,000.00?
4. A developing baby's cells double about 50 times in the prebirth process. If this is true, how many cells make up a new baby?
5. A bank advertises doubling your investment money in 12.3 years. What percent simple interest will it be paying?
6. A city growing at a 15% rate will have twice its population in how many years?
7. At the present time, it is estimated that it will take 97 years for the human population of the North American continent to double. What is the percent annual growth rate?
8. The population of Latin America is growing at 2.5 percent per year. At this rate, how long will it take for the population of Latin America to double?
9. Use Figure 4.8 to explain why many Americans born in the 1950s may face financial problems when they reach retirement age.
10. The population of South America is growing 1.9 percent each year. At this rate, how long will it take the population of South America to double?
11. If the doubling time for the population of Europe is 350 years, how fast is the European population growing?
12. Use the fundamental demographic equation to explain the demographic transition.

Jim Shaffer

Goal

To understand the fundamentals of food production, and relate them to modern agricultural practices and the world food situation.

Food, Agriculture, and Population Interactions

Give a man a fish and you feed him for a day. Teach a man to fish and you feed him for a lifetime.

—Ancient Chinese Proverb

Figure 5.1 Farmers protest in America's heartland. (Jim Shaffer)

Soil: Linking the Nonliving to the Living

Though we use many minerals directly, some come to use indirectly. They are mixed with organic matter to become soil, or they dissolve in water. Minerals from soil and water are taken up by plants and combined with the products of photosynthesis. In this way, the nonliving world is linked to the living.

The abundant good soil and climate in the United States has made it possible for our farmers to feed our own population and export many foods as well. Many other countries also are successful in agriculture. New varieties of wheat and rice bring record harvests in some regions of the world. American farmers are so successful, in fact, that we have problems with a food surplus.

Some nations of the world have an excess of food while people in other nations starve. Can these two facts be related to help solve a problem?

Halfway around the world, thousands die of starvation as deserts expand, and arable land and forests shrink. Clearly, something is wrong. The system isn't working.

In this chapter we will focus on food production, agricultural practices, and the world food situation. From this analysis, it is hoped the outline of a plan of action will emerge.

5.1 Soil Formation and Characteristics

Soil is what supports life. Without good soil, there isn't enough plant growth to feed many animals or people. The key to healthy living is a healthy ecosystem, and one key to a healthy ecosystem is good soil.

Weathering.

When Earth was formed, there was no soil. But as time passed, the action of wind, rain, ice, water flow, and gravitational forces all served to break down rock into smaller and smaller particles. This breakdown process is called *weathering*. Primitive plants grew in the early products of weathering, and soil formation began. The expanding roots of the

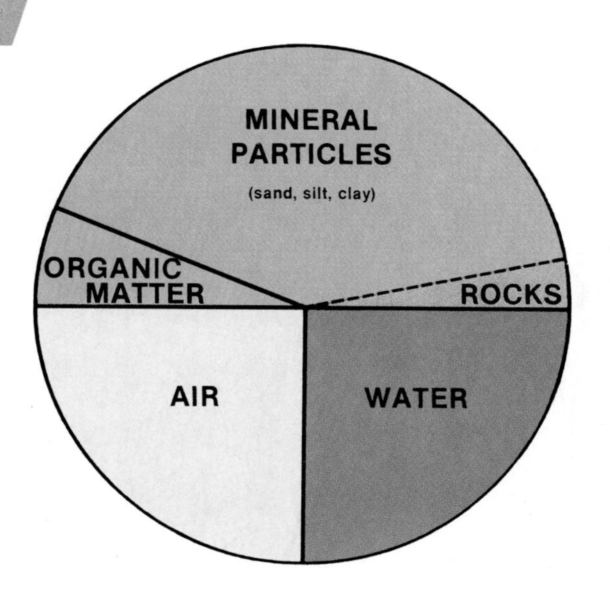

Figure 5.2 Composition (by volume) of a typical loamy soil. The proportions vary somewhat with soil type and environmental conditions.

growing plants also contributed to the process. They helped weather rocks, and when they died, they added material to the soil.

What is soil?

Soil is a mixture of minerals, organic matter, water, and air. It has a definite structure and composition, and forms on the surface of the land. Figure 5.2 shows the average composition of a typical soil. There is a relationship between the composition of soil and the nutritional needs of plants. The elements plants need for healthy growth originate in the mineral particles. Decomposers break down the organic matter and free the nitrates (NO_3^{-1}), phosphates (PO_4^{-3}), and sulfates (SO_4^{-2}) that plants require.

How rapidly soil forms depends on the "parent" material in the region, and on the climate and surface features. If the parent material is hard rock, formation may take hundreds of years. If the parent material is shale, sandstone, volcanic ash, or some other softer material, formation may require only 20 to 30 years under warm, moist conditions.

The upper layer of fertile soil.

The upper layer of a typical fertile soil is teeming with life. Bacteria, fungi, molds, ants, earthworms, centipedes, spiders, and a host of other creatures live here. They burrow, dig, and act as decomposers of organic matter. See Figure 5.3. As they go through their life processes, they free up soil nutrients, maintain soil **porosity** (space for air and water), and hold solid particles together.

The mineral particles in soil are classified in three main categories based on particle size. The larger (coarse) particles are **sand,** somewhat finer particles rare **silt,** and the extremely fine particles are **clay.** The relative amounts of sand, silt, and clay in a given soil sample make up its **texture.** Figure 5.4 shows how soil texture is classified.

What is soil texture?

What do soil textures indicate?

A soil's texture determines how much water it can hold and how rapidly water will percolate through it. A sandy soil can absorb a lot of water. However, these soils also drain very quickly, and so they retain almost no water. At the other extreme are clay soils. Clay particles are so small and packed so close together that water

Figure 5.3 A soil ecosystem. (From United States Department of Agriculture (USDA), Soil Conservation Service [SCS].)

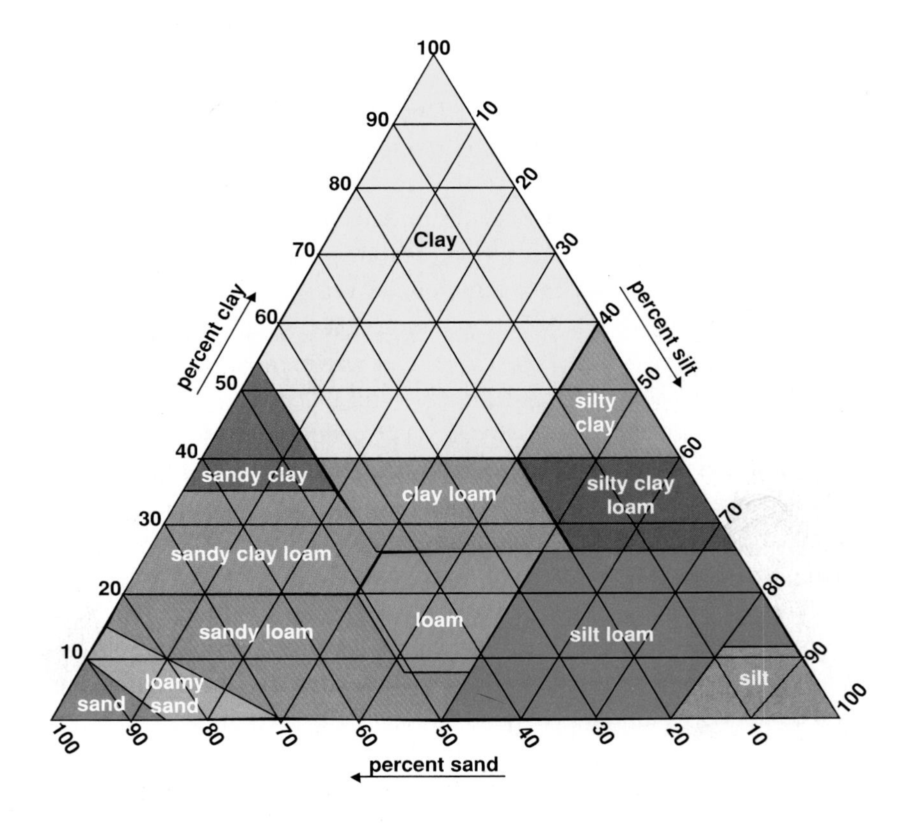

Figure 5.4 Classification of soil textures. (From USDA *Soil Survey Manual*.)

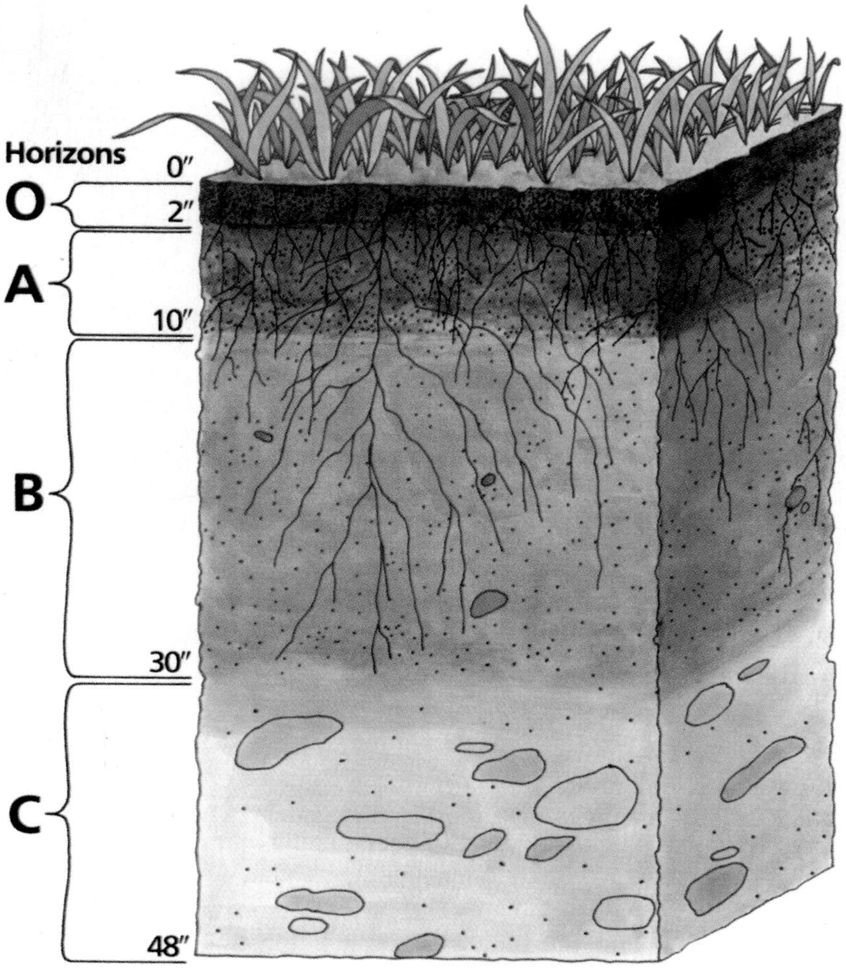

Figure 5.5 A soil profile. (From USDA, SCS.)

can hardly penetrate. These soils are poorly aerated and do not drain well. Plant roots have trouble penetrating them.

From Figure 5.4, we see that a **loam** soil has about equal amounts of sand and silt, but very little clay. The loams are the best soils for growing crops. Porosity is sufficient to allow air circulation and good water drainage, but enough water is retained for good plant growth.

The suitability of a soil for agricultural production depends on both its texture and its structure. The most productive soils have a crumbly structure, developed when small particles are held together by organic materials. Such soils are well aerated and have a large capacity for retaining water.

?

What are the characteristics of a good soil?

5.2 Soil Profiles

If you take a close look at a road cut through a hill covered with vegetation, you may see soil layers having different colors and compositions. These layers make up the **soil profile.** (See Figure 5.5.) A soil profile is the succession of distinctive soil layers, called **horizons,** from the surface down to the unchanged parent material beneath it.

What is a soil profile?

Figure 5.6 Soils in the United States can be divided into two major groups that are separated by a line along which annual rainfall is about 63.5 cm. (25 in.).

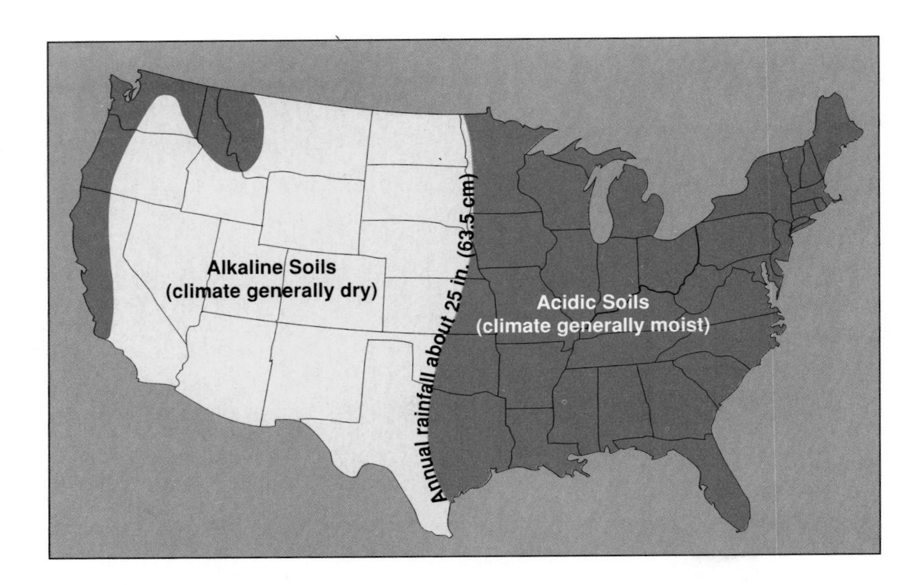

The top layer, the O-horizon, consists of organic matter such as fallen leaves, dead grasses, and partially decomposed organisms.

The A-horizon is the topsoil. It is usually grayish or blackish because of the humus it contains. **Humus** is the highly decomposed plant and animal residue that is part of the soil. The mixture of organic and inorganic nutrients makes this layer valuable economically, because it supports agricultural crops. In this layer the living and nonliving link together to produce the food that supports all life on Earth. The A-horizon, or topsoil, may be anywhere from one inch to two feet in thickness. Eight inches is about average. Because of its texture, a good topsoil will hold adequate moisture and allow air to circulate. The A-horizon is also known as the "zone of **leaching**" because nutrients are leached out (carried away) as water percolates through it from the surface.

The B-horizon, or subsoil, although poor in organic content, is a zone of accumulation. It contains part of what has been leached from A.

The C-horizon is part of the profile, but it is not part of the soil itself. It is part of the parent material from which the soil in the region originated. The C-horizon has no distinct lower limit.

5.3 Climate and Soil Groups

Parent materials differ widely, and strongly influence the makeup of soils, especially during the soil's early development. However, over long periods of time, the influence of climate is even greater. Under similar climate conditions, differing soils will become surprisingly alike.

Describe the three principal soil groups.

Climate conditions have produced three major soil groups that differ in the minerals present in their A and B horizons. Two of the three major soil groups are found in the United States. The soil makeup is the result of leaching by rainwater. (See Figure 5.6.)

Figure 5.7 Soil erosion. (From USDA, SCS, Ron Nichols.)

In the drier western regions, the soils contain soluble minerals, especially calcium. These **alkaline soils** are normally not very fertile. This is a result of mineralogy, texture, and climate. The dry climate does not permit a rich population of organisms in the soil.

In moister regions, rainwater has leached away the more soluble materials. The resulting soil has an abundance of aluminum and iron. Calcium carbonate is absent. These more fertile grounds are called **acidic soils.**

A third soil type, **oxisol,** is found in very wet regions. This is the deep red soil of the tropics and is found in much of Central and South America. So much water has passed through these soils that all but the most insoluble materials are gone. These soils may support vegetation in places, but almost all the nutrients are held in the plants themselves. Clearing and tilling for crops causes the humus to oxidize (breakdown) quickly in the wet, warm climate, instead of accumulating to give a rich, black soil. For this reason, most oxisols can be used for only a few growing seasons before they become barren and have to be abandoned. The clearing of tropical rain forests for agricultural use, for example, is almost useless.

From this summary of soil groupings, we see that rich topsoil is the key to food production.

5.4 Soil Erosion

Soil classification and land use.

Soil groups and profiles tell us how best to use the land. Is it best for pasture, cropland, forests, rangeland, or wildlife habitat? Soil analysis can give us the answer. Incorrect use, along with poor management practices, can damage or destroy hundreds of millions of acres of land. History has shown how humans unknowingly misused land. Topsoil that provided a base for food was lost.

Soil erosion.

Soil erosion is the process by which soil particles are carried away by wind and water. It is often human-caused and destructive (Figure 5.7).

Human activities such as wood gathering, overgrazing, poor farming practices, and clearing for construction contributed to erosion. When plants are removed or damaged, their roots no longer hold the soil in place, and wind and rain can more easily reach the surface. Erosion often results. Because soil formation is such a slow process, we should regard topsoil as a nonrenewable resource. This attitude would cause all of us to support soil conservation programs actively. With humans occupying virtually every habitable portion of the Earth, we must learn to become stewards of the land.

5.5 Soil Conservation

Major progress is being made in soil conservation efforts in the United States and other countries. The Soil Conservation Service (an agency of the U.S. Department of Agriculture) was formed after the Dust Bowl drought of the 1930s. This federal agency provides technical assistance and cost-sharing to landowners who apply conservation practices. Local conservation districts also help farmers and ranchers apply soil and water conservation measures on a voluntary basis.

?

What practices conserve soil?

A variety of conservation practices have proven effective in combatting soil erosion. These include:

a. Conservation Tillage

What is conservation tillage?

Conservation **tillage** refers to any of several methods of crop production that minimize cultivation and leave crop residues on the surface throughout the year.

Holding cultivation to a minimum helps maintain soil structure, reduce compaction, and prevent plowpans (plow-caused paths followed by water). Leaving crop residue on the surface reduces erosion, conserves moisture, and improves root development and soil aeration. It also increases water infiltration and improves ease of cultivation.

Of all methods of conservation tillage, **no-till** is the most effective in reducing erosion and providing food or cover for wildlife. All crop residue is left on the surface. In many areas, farmers using no-till plant the crop and apply fertilizer, herbicides, and other chemicals in one trip across the field.

b. Cover and Green Manure Crops

What are cover and green manure crops?

With this strategy, grasses or legumes are planted in a cropping system to reduce erosion, to add organic matter to the soil, to fix nitrogen, and to produce forage (food for horses and cattle) or hay. These crops hold soil and moisture as they grow. Green plants that are plowed under for the purpose of soil building are called green manure.

c. Strip Cropping

What is strip cropping?

In strip cropping, strips of a row crop are alternated with soil-conserving strips of small grain or a cover crop, such as grass or a grass-legume mixture. The soil-conserving strips trap soil that erodes from the row crop strips.

Figure 5.8 No-till corn in Iowa. (From USDA, SCS, Gene Alexander.)

Figure 5.9 Strip cropping. (From USDA, SCS.)

d. Grass Waterways

What are grass waterways?

As storm water runoff flows downhill, it tends to form streams and gullies. To prevent gullying, a grass waterway can be planted to carry storm runoff slowly off the field. The waterway's depth and width are based on size of the drainage area, topography, amount and distribution of rainfall, and other factors.

e. Terraces

A terrace, or step, reduces erosion on sloping cropland by intercepting runoff and shortening the slope. With narrow-base terraces, the slopes are not cropped but are planted with permanent vegetation.

Figure 5.10 Grass waterways. (From USDA, SCS, Erwin Cole.)

Figure 5.11 Terraces. (From USDA, SCS, Tim McCabe.)

f. Field Windbreaks

Windbreaks.

A field windbreak is a strip of large plants planted in or adjacent to a field to reduce wind erosion, trap blowing snow, conserve moisture, and protect crops, orchards, and livestock from wind. Nearly all field windbreaks consist of trees or shrubs, or both, but there are exceptions. For example, giant reed is planted to control erosion in southwest citrus orchards; it also provides nesting cover for birds.

g. Field Borders

Field borders.

A field border is a strip of perennial vegetation. Usually it is established to control erosion, protect field edges used as turn areas or travel lanes for farm machinery, or reduce competition from adjacent woodland.

Figure 5.12 A windbreak of herbaceous species, shrubs, and trees controls wind erosion and adds diversity to habitat. (From USDA, SCS, Gene Alexander.)

Special measures for wise management of rangeland, pastureland, woodland, and ponds also exist. Let us hope that a combination of knowledge, wise economic incentives, and meaningful legislation will all lead to good soil management.

Food and Ecosystems

An ecosystem is a marvelous thing. Energy flows through and powers the system. Chemicals are continually recycled. The balance that exists is wonderful. However, ecosystems can be disturbed and damaged. A lack of understanding of how they work can result in actions that destroy the delicate inner workings.

Farms and pastures are ecosystems. They also are linked, by air and water, to the ecosystems around them.

Uncontrolled growth of one population can destroy an ecosystem's balance. For example, the exponential increase in human population is taxing the ability of our biosphere to provide the food and other needs of all its people.

If you eat, you're involved with agriculture.

5.6 Plant Nutrition

Before we examine the food crisis, let's look at the essentials of food production. As we explained in chapter 1, a food chain has three main levels: producers, consumers, and decomposers. Producers make their own food. Consumers rely on what the producers make. Decomposers are special types of consumers that break down plant and animal refuse into simpler chemicals that plants and animals can use. Hence, decomposers are necessary for the recycling of minerals. They also help maintain soil structure and aeration.

Nutrition: The intake of food for promoting growth and maintaining body tissue.

Figure 5.13 Harvesting corn.
(Photo courtesy of Deere & Company, Moline, Illinois)

?
What items make up a plant's nutritional needs?

A plant's nutritional needs are the following:

1. sunlight
2. carbon dioxide (CO_2)
3. water (H_2O)
4. minerals (soil nutrients)
5. oxygen (O_2)

In the photosynthesis (energy-trapping) process, plants combine carbon dioxide and water to form organic compounds from which they make their body parts (stems, leaves, etc.) and obtain their energy. Oxygen is a product of photosynthesis. Both plants and animals use oxygen during respiration. In the respiration (energy-releasing) process, organic materials are broken down as oxygen is consumed. Carbon dioxide and heat are given off. Heat is necessary to maintain an acceptable body temperature in which chemical (metabolic) reactions can occur.

The importance of minerals for plant growth.

Minerals are essential for the growth of healthy plants. The necessary minerals must contain 13 different elements. Nitrogen, potassium, and calcium are required in relatively large quantities. The remaining ten nutrients—phosphorus, magnesium, sulfur, manganese, boron, iron, zinc, copper, molybdenum, and chlorine—are needed in lesser amounts. For some of them, only a trace is needed.

The minerals a plant needs must be absorbed from the soil. The nutrition of plants is thus dependent on the ability of the soil to store essential elements and to make them available in a form that can be used by plants. If a soil is poor in some minerals, this ability can be enhanced by application of manure and synthetic fertilizers. In nature, this replacement occurs more slowly, as rock weathers and organic matter is decomposed.

Since soil contains enough calcium for plant growth, the three elements that may have to be supplied with fertilizer are nitrogen, phosphorus, and potassium.

31 5.7 Animal Nutrition

What items make up an animal's nutritional needs?

The nutritional needs of animals are:

1. water (H_2O)
2. oxygen (O_2)
3. minerals (elements)
4. vitamins
5. food (nutrients)
   a. proteins
   b. carbohydrates
   c. fats (lipids)

Animals obtain their food either directly or indirectly from green plants. They obtain their energy and get materials for body parts by first breaking down the energy-rich products of photosynthesis into simpler, less energetic molecules. Many of these less energetic molecules become the **nutrients** that the animal absorbs for the building of its own body parts.

What is metabolism? What is nutrition?

The chemical reactions that take place in an organism as food is utilized are referred to as **metabolism. Nutrition** is the uptake of materials necessary for metabolism.

Function of water.

Water regulates the body temperature, transports nutrients, carries waste, and participates in metabolic reactions. The adult (human) body is 65 percent water by weight.

Oxygen for respiration.

Oxygen is required for respiration, which is the breakdown of food by organisms to release nutrients, energy, carbon dioxide, and water. Both animals and plants carry on respiration.

Minerals.

Essential mineral elements are involved in the functions of nerves and muscles, the formation of bones and teeth, the activation of enzymes (organic catalysts), and in the case of iron, the transport of oxygen. Minerals are so widely distributed in nature that dietary deficiencies are unlikely. However, changes in the balance among them may have important consequences for health.

Proteins.

Proteins in food are broken down by the body into amino acids. The amino acids are then reassembled into body proteins. Some serve to give structure to the organs of the cell. Others act as enzymes, antibodies, hormones, and metabolically active compounds.

Figure 5.14 (Jim Shaffer)

Figure 5.15 Summary of nutritional needs.

NUTRITIONAL NEEDS

Plants:	Animals:
1. sunlight	1. water (H_2O)
2. carbon dioxide (CO_2)	2. oxygen (O_2)
3. water (H_2O)	3. minerals (elements)
4. oxygen (O_2)	4. vitamins
5. minerals (soil nutrients)	5. food (nutrients) a. proteins b. carbohydrates c. fats (lipids)

Carbohydrates.

The breakdown of carbohydrates provides our body's main source of energy. Adequate carbohydrate intake prevents the breakdown of protein for energy needs. This "protein sparing" is important because protein is best used for body-building functions.

Fats.

Fats help in maintaining cell membrane structure and function. They also serve as building blocks for some hormones, provide a concentrated source of energy, carry certain vitamins, and provide insulation and protection for important organs and body structures.

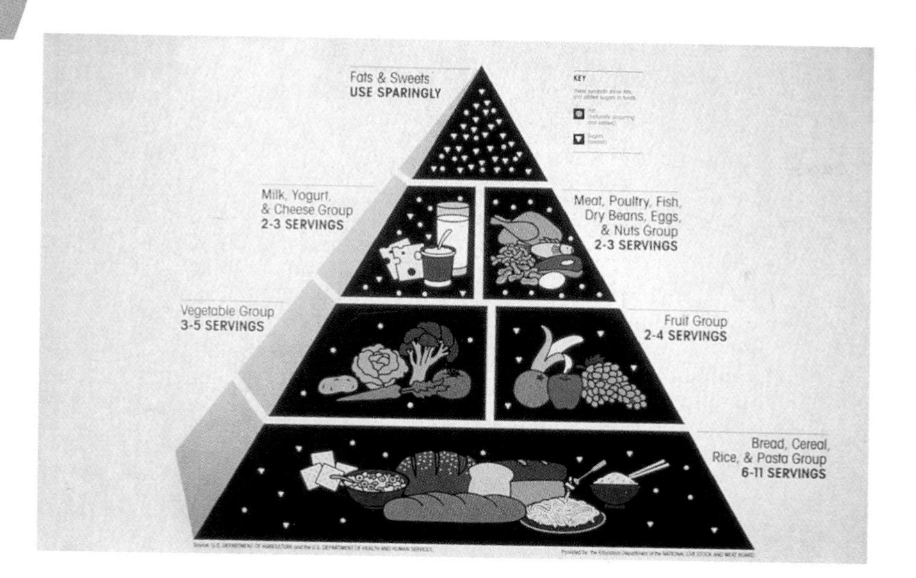

Figure 5.16 The food guide pyramid. (USDA)

Proper nutrition is essential for the growing of lush, healthy plants and animals. We need sufficient amounts of fats, proteins, and carbohydrates. If we eat excessive amounts, they are converted to body fat.

Vitamins are organic molecules that are needed in small quantities in the diet of higher animals to perform specific biological functions. For example, vitamin K is important in blood clotting. Vitamins and enzymes often work in combination.

Vitamins.

5.8 Nutrition Guidelines

What is good nutrition for humans? There is no simple answer to this question. Nutrition is a complex subject, and there are many points of view regarding what people should eat.

The U.S. Department of Agriculture developed the "Food Guide Pyramid" to help people make daily food choices for better health. The pyramid is shown as Figure 5.16. Eating as the pyramid suggests will enable you to fulfill your nutritional requirements.

?

How does your daily diet compare to the Food Guide Pyramid?

The food guide pyramid helps you choose what and how much to eat from the five food groups shown in the three lower sections of the pyramid. The number of servings that are right for you depends on how many calories you need. This depends on your age, sex, size, and your daily activities. You should strive to maintain a healthy weight.

How many servings do you need each day?

From the pyramid it can bee seen that a person should:

List some general rules for having good nutrition.

- go easy on fats, oils, and sweets.
- eat a variety of foods.
- choose a diet with plenty of vegetables, fruits, and grain products.
- use table salt and other sodium only in moderation (they are not even on the chart).
- eat meat, poultry, fish, and eggs in moderation.

Food for Thought

"Eat your vegetables!" how many times have you heard your folks say that? Michele Brown says it, too, but not just to kids who are bored with their dinner. Michele says it to young people who have a special need to know about nutrition—mothers and fathers who are raising or getting ready to raise children. As a community health program representative, Michele works in the Expanded Food and Nutrition Education (EFNEP) Program, sponsored by the University of California Cooperative Extension Service. In this program, low-income parents and parents-to-be learn how to eat better to feel better, to save money, and to give their children a jump-start in life. Even before a baby is born, its health is affected by what the mother eats. Also, kids who start out making smart choices about food are learning an important skill that will stay with them as they grow up.

Michele works mostly with groups, which meet at high schools, family shelters, and other convenient places. Michele talks to teenage mothers and fathers, women recovering from substance abuse, and other homemakers who need some extra help understanding how to give their families nutritious food on a low budget. Many people find out about the EFNEP groups through their food-stamp issuing agency or emergency food bank.

We all know what we like to eat and what we don't like, but many of us don't stop to think about the *science* of the food we're eating—about metabolism and how our bodies utilize protein and carbohydrates. To catch the interest of the people in her groups and teach them about these facts, Michele starts with simple concepts. For instance, in explaining the dangers of saturated fats, she starts by showing the difference between a liquid oil and a solid fat at room temperature, and then uses molecular models to demonstrate the difference between the two structures. It doesn't take long before her students are asking questions; then Michele can instruct them about the major food groups, how to retain the vitamins in food when cooking it, what low-cost foods to keep on hand, and the special nutritional needs of babies and young children.

She teaches about eating behaviors, too, and the consequences of consuming too much or too little of particular foods. One technique is to challenge people to list everything they have eaten during the last 24 hours. She encourages them to remember their cues for eating, such as genuine hunger, boredom, anger, and so on.

Michele's days usually begin early and sometimes end late; she has to set up group sessions whenever people's busy lives allow them to attend. Most days she is out in the field, in Oakland, Hayward, and other cities. She also reports on her work to government agencies.

Of course, Michele knows alot about the chemical basis of nutrition, and says it's important for people in her field to keep up with modern developments. She does that by taking classes and reading as much as possible about health issues, cooking techniques, child development, and related subjects. Through her work she also has acquired skills in dealing with people. As she talks with her clients, who come from many backgrounds and face a wide variety of social difficulties, she is glad for her own well-rounded interests and her ability to listen and communicate. When she can help folks deal with their daily lives, they are more open to her lessons about food and eating.

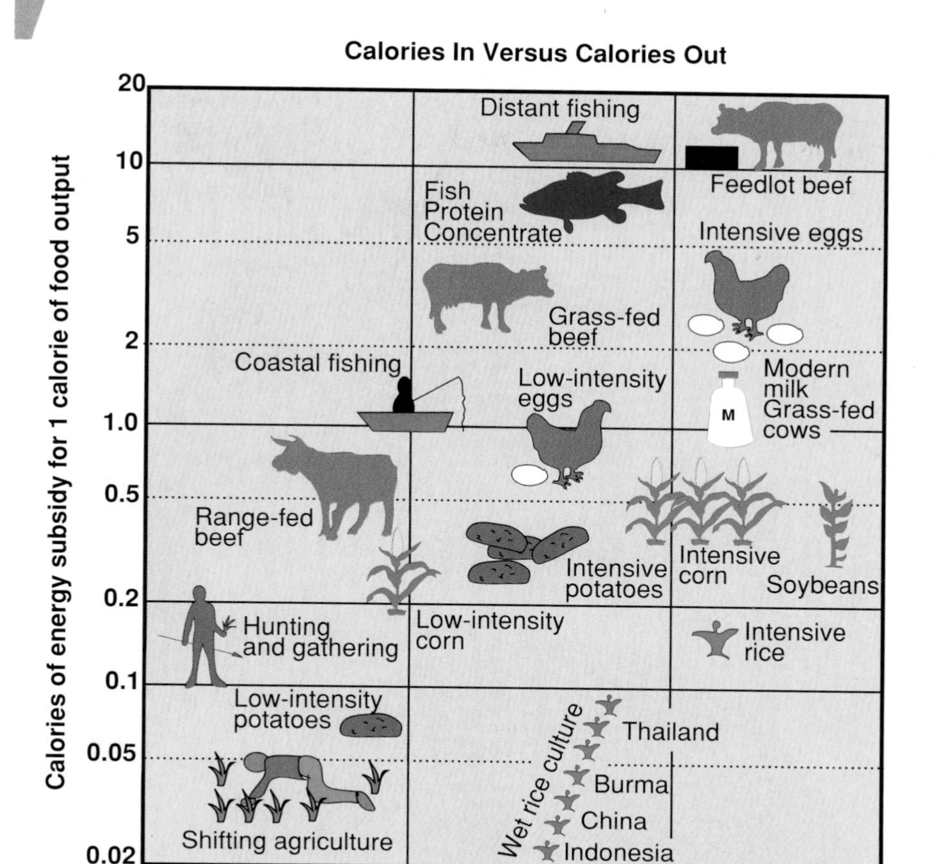

Figure 5.17 Energy subsidies for various food crops. (Adapted from *Energy: Sources, Use, and Role in Human Affairs* by Carole E. Steinhart and John S. Steinhart, © 1974 by Wadsworth, Inc., Belmont, California 94002. Reprinted by permission of the authors.)

Each of the food groups provides some, but not all, of the nutrients you need. Foods in one group can't replace those in another. No one group is more important than another—for good health, you need them all.

The labels on the processed foods you buy, used with the food guide pyramid, should help you plan healthful meals.

Also, young people should not drink alcoholic beverages. Older people who choose to drink should only drink in moderation. Pregnant women should never drink.

5.9 Food and Resources

How productive are American farmers?

The agricultural system used throughout most of the United States produces a very high yield of product per farmer. The average American farmer produces enough food and fiber to fulfill the needs of 128 people (94.3 in the U.S. and 33.7 abroad). This production is made possible by using energy and mineral resources that provide the "muscle" to get the job done. Because of this, our industrialized food system uses several times as much energy to produce, process, retail, and prepare food as the food itself contains.

Why does it take so much energy to produce feedlot beef?

Figure 5.17 shows the energy yields for various food types. Note that about ten calories of energy are used to produce each calorie from feedlot beef. On the other hand, range-fed beef provides two calories of output for one calories of input. This information is useful in a world where energy supplies are becoming more expensive.

Figure 5.18a Energy use by the food & fiber sector of the U. S. economy. (Council for Agricultural Science & Technology)

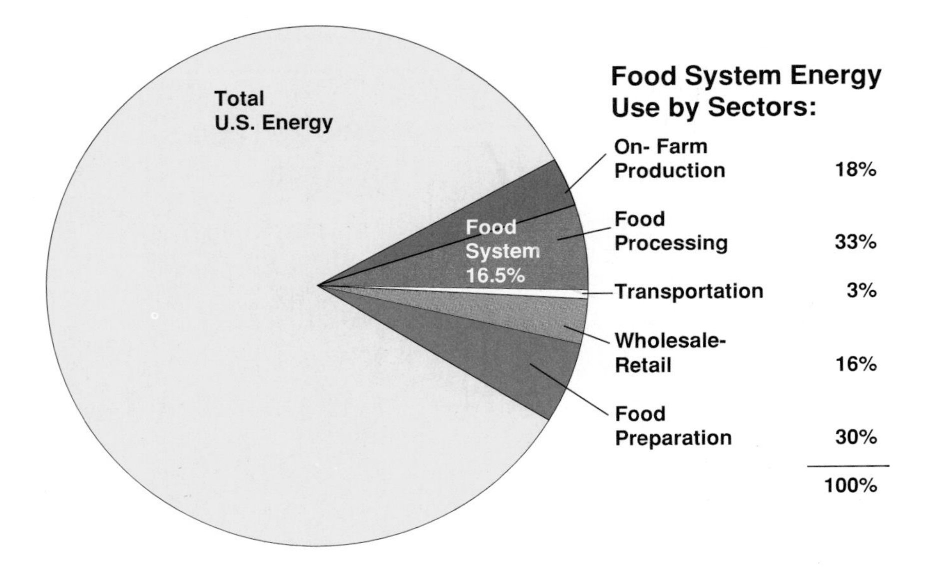

Figure 5.18b Food system energy use in the U.S. by category. (Council for Agricultural Science & Technology)

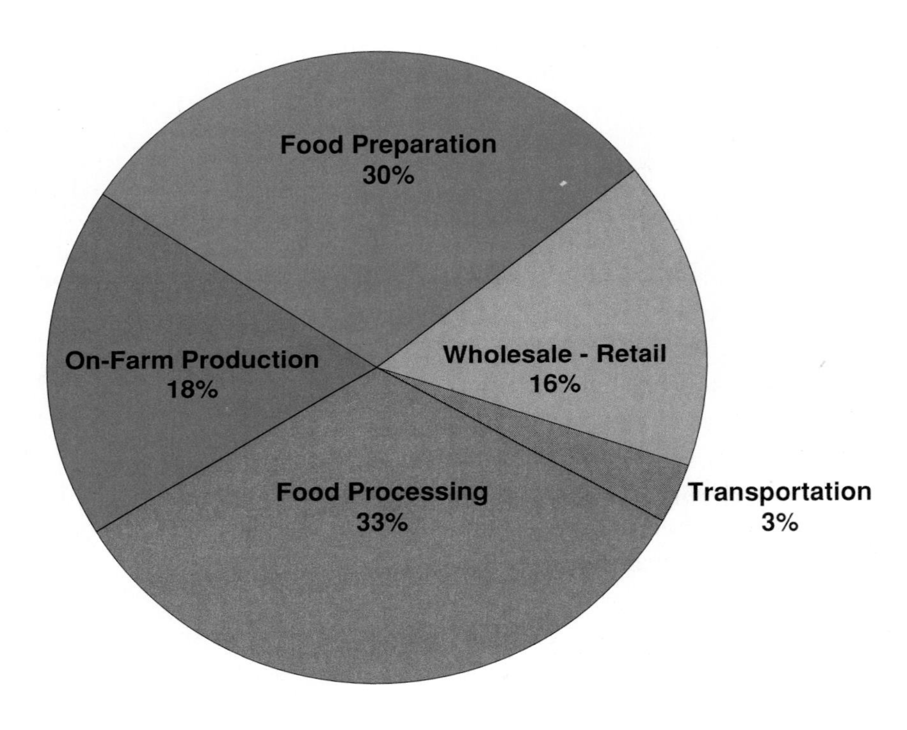

?

Why does it require so much energy to provide food?

The food and fiber sector of our economy uses about 16.5% of the total energy consumed in the United States each year. See Figure 5.18a.

We can make the best use of energy when we know how it is used. Figure 5.18b summarizes food-related energy consumption in the United States for a recent year. We see that on-farm production used only 18% of the total. This includes field work, transportation, irrigation, crop drying, and activities related to the raising of livestock, dairy cattle, and poultry. The food processing industry used 33% of the total. This includes pre-cooking and packaging of frozen, canned, and dehydrated foods. The marketing process (transportation-wholesale-retail) used slightly more energy than was required to

Special Focus

Nitrogen in Fertilizer Production

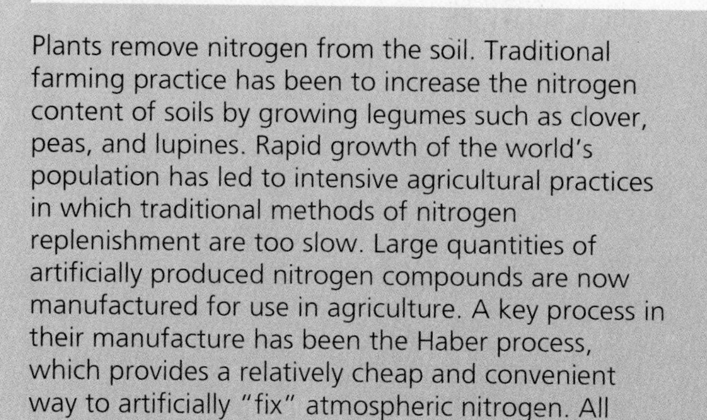

Plants remove nitrogen from the soil. Traditional farming practice has been to increase the nitrogen content of soils by growing legumes such as clover, peas, and lupines. Rapid growth of the world's population has led to intensive agricultural practices in which traditional methods of nitrogen replenishment are too slow. Large quantities of artificially produced nitrogen compounds are now manufactured for use in agriculture. A key process in their manufacture has been the Haber process, which provides a relatively cheap and convenient way to artificially "fix" atmospheric nitrogen. All modern nitrogen fertilizers are derived from ammonia. The most common of these are:

- Liquid ammonica (NH_3) which is applied directly to the soil. Low transport costs are associated with the use of ammonia because of its high nitrogen content.
- Ammonium sulfate, which is produced by reaction of ammonia with sulfuric acid.

$$2NH_3(g) + H_2SO_4(1) \longrightarrow (NH_4)_2SO_4(s)$$

- Ammonium nitrate, which is produced by reacting ammonia with concentrated nitric acid.

$$NH_3(g) + \underbrace{H^+(aq) + NO_3(aq)}_{\text{from nitric acid}} \longrightarrow NH_4NO_3(s)$$

- Urea (NH_2CONH_2), which is produced by reaction between ammonia and carbon dioxide at 140° C and 100 atmospheres pressure.

$$2NH_3(g) + CO_2(g) \longrightarrow NH_2CONH_2(s) + H_2O(1)$$

(From *Elements of Chemistry: Earth, Air, Fire, and Water,* Vol. 1, Chemistry for Australian Secondary Schools, Australian Academy of Science, pp. 422–423.)

produce the food. Households and restaurants consumed 30% of the total. Refrigeration, including freezing, was the most important single use. Cooking was a close second.

From all of this we can see that the greatest energy saving can probably be obtained not at the farm, but in the processing, distribution, and marketing end of the food system. Nonetheless, much energy can be saved in agriculture, because it is such a huge enterprise.

A major energy input to agriculture is in the form of chemicals. The production of **fertilizers** and farm chemicals, such as pesticides, herbicides, and repellents, requires extensive use of fossil fuel energy.

Farm fertilizers.

Intensive agriculture depends heavily on adding nitrogen fertilizer to soil. Most nitrogen fertilizer is synthesized by the industrial Haber process, in which atmospheric nitrogen reacts with hydrogen to form ammonia (NH_3). The ammonia can be applied directly to soil, or it can be used as a raw material for the manufacture of urea, nitrates, or other nitrogen compounds. The hydrogen required by the haber process is generally extracted from natural gas. Thus, through industrial nitrogen fixation, fossil fuels directly enter the nutrient cycle. (See the boxed section above.)

Crop drying and irrigation are other important uses of energy in modern agriculture. In the Midwest, corn is the main crop to be dried in order to minimize field losses, for efficiency at harvest, and for grain preservation. The energy required to pump the water used in irrigation systems is considerable.

Why are many crops dried?

Figure 5.19 This solar grain drying system includes a modified 3,500 bushel aeration bin. Air is drawn under the black collector plate, heated, and then pulled down through the grain by a ½ horsepower fan. (Center for Rural Affairs. Walthill, Nebraska)

What does the future hold? Our fast-deteriorating supply of oil may signal major changes in American agriculture. We must begin to plan now for a shift away from oil and natural gas. If we shift to a coal/nuclear energy base, increased reliance upon electricity will be mandatory.

What might American agriculture be like if we shifted to simpler technologies?

If we shift to sustainable agricultural systems, the following scenario may apply: Wind power will make a strong comeback in rural areas. Increasing amounts of sterilized human excreta will be returned to the soil as nutrients and will reduce the demand for chemical fertilizers. Direct solar power will play an important role in heating buildings and drying grain. On-the-spot bioconversion of agricultural wastes will produce enough fuel to allow many farms to fill their own energy needs. Finally, overpackaging and other wasteful practices will be eliminated.

Sustainable agricultural systems will be defined more fully later.

5.10 Food and Hunger

After food is eaten, the carbohydrates are converted to sugars, the proteins are converted to amino acids, and the fat is converted to small lipid fragments. These nutrients can be used both as building blocks for the body's needs and as a source of calories for immediate energy demands. In addition, our foods provide the vitamins and minerals necessary for our digestive and food utilization processes.

What is meant by undernourishment?

On average, Americans consume 3,450 Calories of food per person each day.

For millions of people around the world, a gap exists in the nutrition cycle. They are **undernourished;** that is, they are not obtaining enough total energy (food Calories). United Nations agencies define an adequate intake as being approximately 3,000 Calories per day for an adult man and 2,200 Calories per day for an adult women.

Figure 5.20 shows world food Distribution by region. Clearly, the distribution is not even.

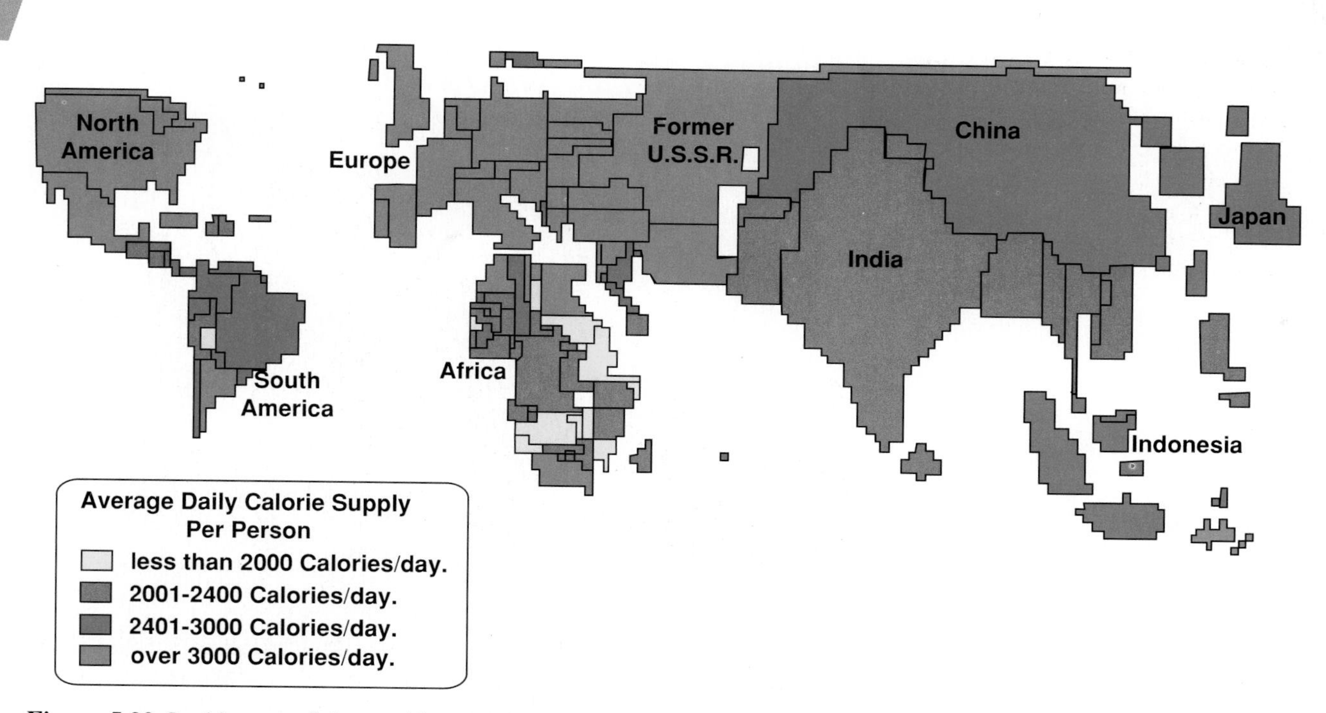

Figure 5.20 In this map of the world, each country's size is proportional to its population. Thus, China dominates the map with its more than one billion people. Greenland is just a small dot in the North Atlantic. (From *Population: An Introduction to Concepts and Issues*, 4th ed., by John R. Weeks. Copyright © 1989 by Wadsworth, Inc., Belmont, CA 94002. Reprinted by permission of the publisher.) Calorie data from the United Nations Food and Agriculture Organization (FAO), AGROSTAT.

Starvation involves more than calorie intake alone. The nutritional requirements of people (and animals) includes proteins, vitamins, and minerals. When these are in short supply, serious problems result. **Malnutrition** is the state of poor health in which an individual's diet lacks one or more essential vitamins and nutrients, especially proteins.

What is malnutrition?

Our protein intake is as important as our calorie intake. Protein requirements vary. Babies, pregnant women, and breastfeeding women need much more protein than children and adults. Young adults need more than the elderly. As a rule of thumb, we may say that an adult human being requires about one gram of protein per kilogram of body weight per day (about 60 grams/day/adult.)

How much protein does the average adult need?

In countries where meat and other animals products are eaten, obtaining enough protein is usually no problem. On the average, Americans consume about twice as much protein as their bodies actually need. In countries where the population lives largely on a vegetable diet, the high protein requirement of a rapidly growing child are difficult to meet. About one-half of the infant deaths around the world are due to protein deficiency.

Most of the effects of malnutrition can be remedied by correcting the protein intake, but some cannot. Brain development begins in the early embryo and is complete at an early age (under two years) Malnutrition during this period may be the cause of mental retardation that cannot be remedied by later corrective measures.

How can malnutrition be corrected?

Figure 5.21 Severely malnourished Ethiopian child. (UNICEF/Roger Lemoyne)

In 1992, 10.5% of all Americans received stamps to help buy food. (U.S. Food and Nutrition Service.)

Malnutrition is not limited to the poor nations of the world. In countries such as the United States, diets are often high in calories, saturated fats, salt, and sugars, but low in fruits and vegetables, and distorted toward heavily processed foods. This contributes to a high incidence of obesity, diabetes, tooth decay, hypertension, intestinal cancer, and heart disease. There may be marginal deficiencies of certain minerals and B vitamins. Some poor people in the United States simply do not get enough food.

Is there enough food to feed all people on Earth?

How extensive is world hunger? According to the United Nations World Food Council:

- Global food production is adequate to feed all people on Earth.
- Overall indications suggest that a new world order is taking shape in which cooperation, rather than confrontation, will prevail.
- Over 550 million people (about 10% of the human population) are threatened with starvation.
- In the developing world, 188 million children are malnourished.
- Millions of people subsist on diets below the 1,000 Calories a day needed for staying alive. Adults require a minimum of 1,600 Calories each day if they are to suffer no health impairment.
- **Famine** haunts millions of people in some developing regions. In Africa more than 25 million are threatened by famine and require emergency food relief. Starvation and death caused by

How many Calories/day are needed just to stay alive? How many Calories/day/adult are needed to suffer no health impairment?

Famine: A food shortage widespread enough to cause malnutrition and the starvation of many members of a human population.

Figure 5.22 Operation Lifeline in the Sudan. 188 million children in the developing world are malnourished. 13 million children under the age of 5 die every year of causes related to hunger. (UNICEF/Jeremy Hartley)

famine are still occurring in a number of countries. Most of these countries are in eastern and southern Africa.

- Civil strife and war are tied to the plight of most famine victims.
- Severe drought affects almost all countries in southern Africa.

5.11 Food Chains and the Second Law of Thermodynamics

?

Why is it more efficient to eat lower on a food chain?

Feeding in an ecosystem is a sequence of energy transfers in the form of food from one organism to another. At each step, energy is transformed. There is always some loss of usefulness, primarily in the form of heat. As food moves from producer to consumers and to decomposers, more and more energy is lost. The most *efficient* food chain is the *shortest* (but not necessarily the most desirable) food chain, because the fewest transfers occur. This means that if humans ate "low on the food chain," that is, if we all became vegetarians or near-vegetarians, the world could feed more people. See Figure 5.23. The same amount of plant material feeds four times as many people in China and India as it does in the United States and France. It should be pointed out again that it is more difficult to obtain proper proteins when one does not eat meat. Vegetarian diets, to deliver adequate amounts of protein, must include a variety of plant food combinations to deliver all of the amino acids that the body cannot make. It has also been pointed out that the world has adequate food for everyone now living.

Because of inefficient conversion, the average steer can convert 16 pounds of gain and soy to only one pound of meat on our plates. The other 15 pounds is inaccessible to us. It is used by the animal, either to produce energy or to make some part of its own body we do not eat. Or, it is "lost" in the form of manure. In the steer's defense,

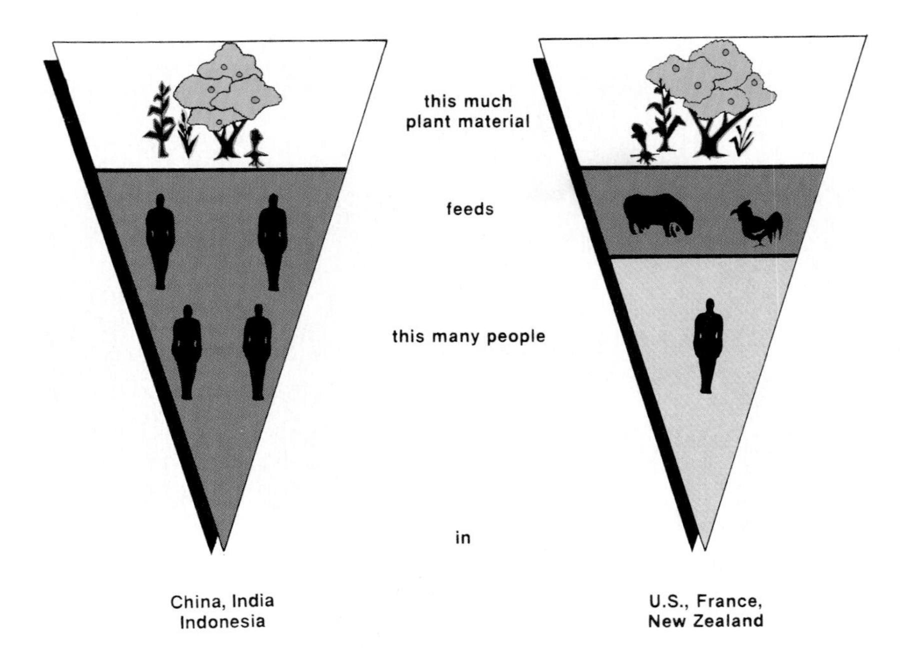

Figure 5.23 Vegetarian vs. cafeteria diet.

we can argue that it ate grass and hay which humans cannot eat directly. In fact, the justification for animals in agriculture is their ability to transform products of little or no value into nutritious human food. However, in the United States, beef cattle commonly also eat large quantities of corn, soybeans, and wheat bran that could be utilized in other ways.

The conversion ratios for our most common farm animals are shown in Figure 5.24.

   5.12 Earth's Carrying Capacity

What is carrying capacity?

Carrying capacity is the maximum number of a given organism that a given ecosystem can support. When we refer to Earth's carrying capacity, we're generally referring to the capacity for people. Of course, no single number can be given as the carrying capacity. The number of people the Earth can support is inversely related to the standard of living. As the standard of living goes up, the carrying capacity goes down. Also, the type of diet is important. The Earth can support many more vegetarians than meat-eaters.

In the Solar Input lab, you calculated that the Earth can support about 20 billion people who eat like Americans. This number is useful, but it must be put in perspective. First, the number assumes that sufficient energy and/or strategies will be continually available to produce the food Americans enjoy. Secondly, it assumes a worldwide efficient food distribution network. Thirdly, it assumes there will be no major changes in climate.

What do others estimate the carrying capacity to be? The Committee on Resources and Man of the National Academy of Sciences—National Research Council concluded that it is unlikely that food

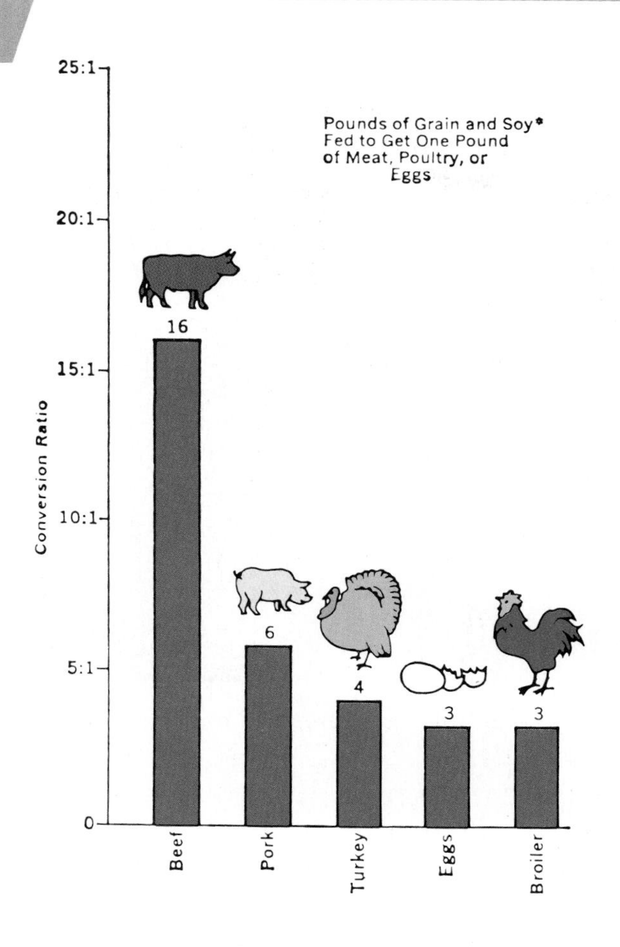

Figure 5.24 Pounds of grain and soy* fed to get one pound of meat, poultry or eggs. (*Soy constitutes only 12% of steer feed and 20–25% of poultry.) (From USDA, Economic Research Service, Beltsville, Maryland. Graph from *Diet for a Small Planet* by Frances Moore Lappe, New York: Ballantine Books, Inc.)

Figure 5.25 There is some point beyond which we cannot adequately support everyone. (Bill Garner)

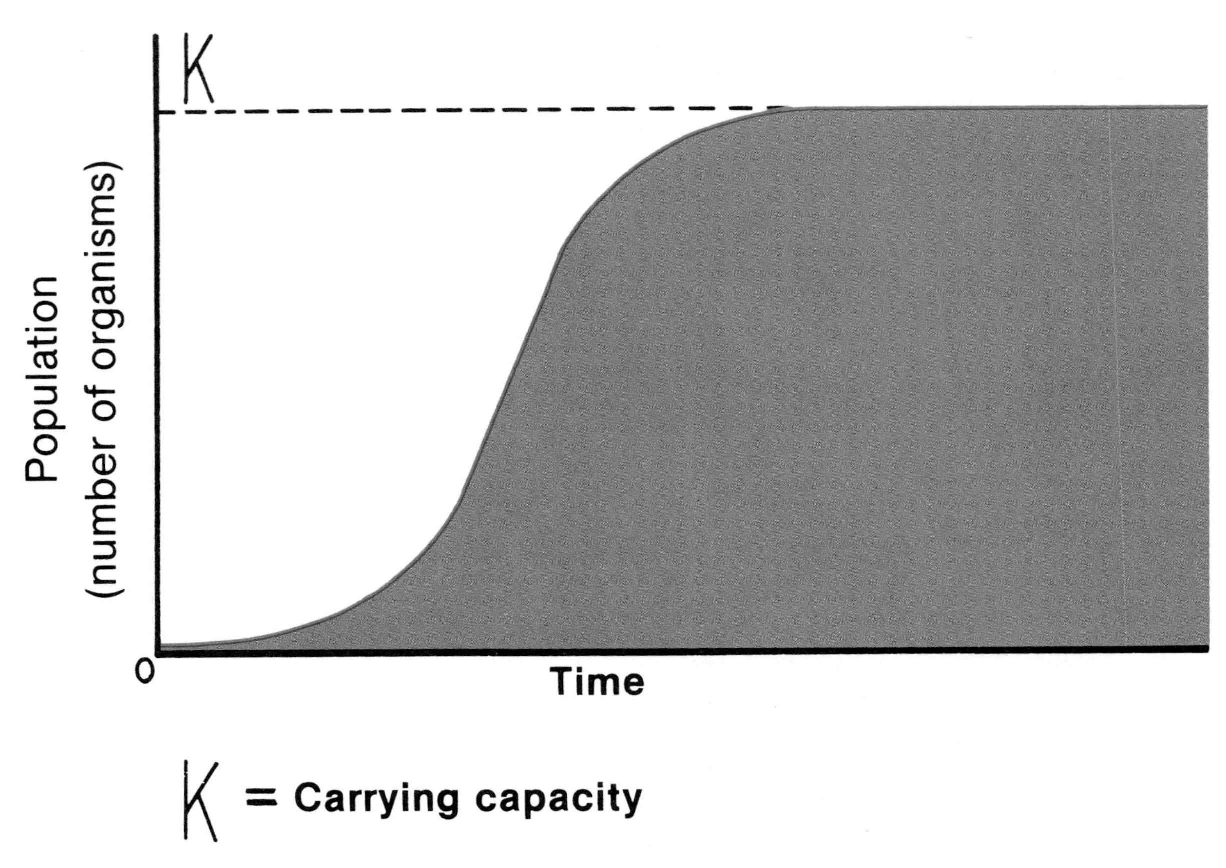

Figure 5.26 Idealized approach to carrying capacity.

The present world population exceeds 5.5 billion.

production will ever grow to more than nine times current production levels. Given that limitation, Earth's carrying capacity is about 30 billion people, *most of whom will be near starvation*. At the present growth rate, the human population could reach 30 billion by the year 2075. Even if the population levels off at about 10 billion by 2050, we will need intensive management of resources to have any comfort and individual choice. For all people to have enough food, and for environmental quality to be maintained, the population should remain well below 10 billion.

Our hope is that human population growth will continue to slow and that we will stabilize at or below the carrying capacity. The idealized approach to carrying capacity is shown in Figure 5.26.

Population Interactions

Competing for available food.

Up to this point, we have implied that humans are the only organisms eating products of agriculture. Clearly, that is not the case. Other organisms compete for the food available in the ecosphere. Quite often they are so successful that they greatly reduce the amount of food available to people.

We have all seen some loss of food to other organisms. Food left too long in the refrigerator spoils and must be thrown away. The

Figure 5.27 Aphids. (H. Hungerford)

spoilage of the food is the result of its breakdown by bacteria, fungi, and other decomposers. These cannot be seen at first, but they often grow to visible size. For example, the mold on bread is a kind of fungus. Flour and cereals left on the shelf for long periods can support large populations of weevils and meal worms, specially in dry climates. Improperly canned foods can host bacterial strains fatal to human beings. Have you learned never to open and consume the contents of a can when the ends bulge? The bulging is evidence of the production of gas inside the can. The gas is made by bacteria living and growing within the can.

Food spoilage.

Spoilage is less of a problem in the United States than in many other parts of the world because of the food-processing and refining techniques that require using energy. Refrigeration and freezing retard bacterial growth. The use of preservatives extends the shelf life of products ranging from soda crackers to instant pudding.

Insects consume food supply.

Bacteria, fungi, and other microorganisms are not our only competitors for food. Among the most widespread and serious threats to the human food supply are insects. A scientist at the Smithsonian Museum of Natural History estimates there are 30 million species of insects in the world. Furthermore, "in poundage, insects collectively outweigh the human race by a ratio of 12 to 1" (U.S. News and World Report, June 14, 1982, page 44).

Most city dwellers assume that ridding crops of insect pests is a simple matter of using "bug killers" in the fields. They may worry about the hazards to human health that insecticides represent, but few understand why the use of chemicals to control agricultural pests should be less than totally effective. Understanding why requires a look at some of the fundamental principles of biology. Let's look at those principle and then return to the question of the loss of food crops to insects.

5.13 Evolution

Theory of evolution.

The word **evolution** means change. In biology, evolution refers to the changes in plants and animals that have occurred since life began, and that are continuing today. In some cases, evolution has taken millions of years. Scientists have been able to observe changes in some organisms over relatively short periods of time, however.

What does the theory of evolution say?

A classic example of rapid evolution is the story of the "peppered moths" in England. Before the Industrial Revolution, most of the tree bark was light-colored, and so were most of the moths that lived on the bark. As the number of factories grew and large quantities of black smoke were released into the air, the trees became dark—discolored by industrial pollution. Curiously enough, a change occurred in the new moth populations as well. Most of the moths in the population were dark, like the trees. Only a few were light-colored like their ancestors.

How did this happen? No, the moths did not become discolored by the soot. The answer lies in predation. Experiments with real moths and predator birds have confirmed an evolutionary explanation. Birds eat the moths from the trees. Light moths on dark bark are clearly visible and are more likely to be eaten than dark moths on dark bark. Dark moths are camouflaged on darkened trees. This provided a protection that was previously an advantage to the light moths when the trees were light-colored.

Where did the new dark moths come from?

Where did the new dark moths come from? They came about through normal reproductive processes. What we must remember is that *not all* members of the original population were light-colored. All populations are **variable,** that is, individual members of a population are different from each other in some obvious and not-so-obvious ways. In the original moth population, a few individuals were dark-colored. As long as the tree bark was light, dark-colored moths were at a serious disadvantage. They showed up and were likely to be eaten by predators. The numbers of dark-colored moths in the population tended to remain small.

But *when the environment changed,* patterns of predation changed. Now light-colored moths were more subject to predation, while dark ones were far more likely to survive and reproduce. The proportions within the population changed dramatically within only a few generations. The offspring of dark-colored moths—carrying the genes necessary to produce dark body color—survived, reproduced,

Figure 5.28 Dark and light forms of the peppered moth on a tree covered with light-colored lichens (right) and on a tree blackened by soot (left). Which moth in each photo is most likely to be eaten by predators? (From *Biological Science: An Ecological Approach*, BSCS Green Version, 6th ed. 1987.)

and passed their genetic information on to the next generation. Evolutionary change had occurred so rapidly that English scientists were able to observe and document the change.

Genes contain the biological code that controls heredity.

 5.14 Natural Selection

Change in organisms is often easy to observe. There is little doubt that many populations exhibit the same changes as the moths of England, although over longer periods of time. Many changes in species are the result of the process called **natural selection.** Natural selection means just what the words say. Natural forces at work in the environment tend to select individuals of one form or another. Individuals

What is natural selection?

Figure 5.29 Natural selection. These predators are about to capture their prey. The deer shown was separated, and hence selected from the herd because of a physical disability. The disability may have been its inability to fight off a disease, deformed teeth, or oversized (overweight) horns.

possessing some characteristic that increases their chances of survival and reproduction are said to have a **selective advantage.** When conditions in the environment change, that advantage may be lost. Another "variant" in the population may become more likely to survive and reproduce. The survival of one form over another leads to changes in the proportions of certain genes in the population. The processes of natural selection go on continuously.

5.15 Extinction

What causes natural selection to occur?

The agent of natural selection is not always predation, as in the peppered moth story. Individual members of a population of fish may be more or less tolerant to certain chemicals in the water. Some may withstand a wider range of temperatures than others. As long as the water is fairly clean and the temperature variation not too large, all may survive equally well. But if polluting chemicals are introduced or thermal dumping from a power plant raises temperatures, the population may be subject to new selective forces. The tolerant fish will survive, while the less tolerant will die out. The proportion of certain genes in the next generation will be greater than it was previously. And, if the fish carrying this genetic makeup continue to enjoy a selective advantage, they will continue to survive and reproduce in greater numbers than those fish carrying a different set of genes. The fish population may not be visibly different from what it was before, but it will certainly be physiologically different.

Of course, there are limits to the genetic variability found in any population of organisms. In the fish population just described, we would expect the range of tolerance to have definite upper limits. If the chemical composition of the water changed too much or if temperature extremes became too great, we might expect all the fish to die. Such is sometimes the case. The total loss of a species worldwide is called **extinction.**

What is extinction? Extinction is forever.

Focus on Solutions

Throughout the ages, unknown thousands of species of plants, animals and insects have appeared on this planet, remained awhile, then vanished. All of the species of plants, animals and insects now alive are but a small percentage of those that have been here since the dawn of life.

If this is so, then why try to save an **endangered species?** An endangered species is merely becoming extinct, and extinction is a natural process of evolution.

What is an endangered species?

5.16 Why Save Endangered Species?

?

Why save endangered species?

What is man without the beasts? If all the beasts were gone,
man would die from great loneliness of spirit.
For whatever happens to the beasts, soon happens to man.
All things are connected.
—Chief Seattle, Suquamish Indian Tribe

While extinction is more or less the rule in nature, if we look at the rate, or the number of species disappearing in any given time period, we can see that we have a problem. Take the mammals, for example. In the seventeenth century, seven species became extinct; in the eighteenth century, eleven species disappeared; in the nineteenth century, 27 species were lost; and thus far in this century, 71 species of mammals have been eliminated from the planet.

Endangered species: Any species which is in danger of becoming extinct throughout all or a significant portion of its range.

Spineless Hedgehog Cactus (Marv Poulson)

Thrift (Copyright © 1994 Wendy Shattil/Bob Rozinski)

Threatened species: Any species which is likely to become an endangered species within the foreseeable future.

Why the drastic increase in the rate of extinction? The answer is directly linked to human population increase and the greatly expanded areas of human activity. The present high rate of extinction is caused by humans and is not a natural process.

And still we need to answer the question, why save an endangered species? The question is simple enough, and we might think there is a single direct answer. However, when we begin to look for that answer, we find that the question becomes more and more complex.

Endangered species are indicators or warning signals of something amiss in the environment. What is happening to the animals may happen to us. For instance, the decline of the peregrine falcon and other birds of prey in the 1960s warned scientists of the deadly nature of the pesticide DDT.

There are a variety of reasons for saving endangered species, including:

All life has a right to exist.

1. *All* life has a right to exist. Most societies teach that it is immoral to kill other human beings, and general acceptance of this belief is fundamental to *our* survival on Earth. However, the creatures with which we share the planet also have a right to exist. They are genetic marvels that took millions of years to adapt and fill their current niches. Who are we to eliminate them?

Bald Eagle (Copyright © 1994 Wendy Shattil/Bob Rozinski)

Stellar Sea Lions (Robert L. Pitman)

Whooping Crane (Copyright © 1994 Wendy Shattil/Bob Rozinski)

Loggerhead Sea Turtle (Robert L. Pitman)

2. The variety in nature adds enjoyment and meaning to life. Most of us enjoy a trip to the forest, the mountains, or the lake. Part of that enjoyment comes from seeing a wild animal, or intricate flower, or strange insects. We delight at the crazy antics of penguins at the zoo, or the beauty of a butterfly. We owe it to all future generations to pass on the variety that was given to us.

Variety in nature adds enjoyment and meaning to life.

3. Variety adds to the diversity of ecosystems, and diversity means stability of our life-support system. Thus ecosystems provide tremendous economic services to us. They moderate climate, cleanse air and water, recycle waste, protect crops from pests, replenish soils, cycle nutrients, pollinate plants, supply our food, and maintain a genetic library. Diversity insures their survival. The stability of the biosphere is life insurance, both for us and for our children.

Variety adds to the diversity of ecosystems. Diversity means life insurance to our biosphere.

River Otter (Copyright © 1994 Wendy Shattil/Bob Rozinski)

Black-footed Ferret (Dean Biggins [USFWS])

Humpback Chub (Roger Hammon [USFWS])

Humpback Whale (Thomas Jefferson/Intersea Research)

Every organism contains genetic information that may some day be valuable to us or to other species.

4. Every different organism is a genetic marvel that may someday be valuable to us or other species. Many plants and animals have proven to be useful in agriculture, science and the production of medicines. About 1,400 plants in tropical forests are believed to offer cures for cancer; in fact, a drug made from the periwinkle plant found in tropical forests is now used to treat childhood leukemia and Hodgkin's disease. One out of four pharmaceuticals used by western chemists comes from a tropical plant. We should retain as many species as possible for future generations as we cannot predict which species will later prove valuable.

   The entire enterprise of high-yield agriculture, upon which the future of civilization is utterly dependent, rests on having an adequate supply of varying genetic combinations to be used in artificial selection. Commercial grains must be constantly modified to resist attack by disease or insects. It is diversity that makes that modification possible.

5.17 Natural Selection, Pests, and the Food Supply

Now let us return to the question: Why is it so difficult to control losses of food crops to other organisms, especially insect pests? Why are insecticides a poor solution to the problem?

Why isn't the pest problem solved with insecticides?

Insects are widespread, diverse, and numerous. They reproduce rapidly. There is tremendous genetic variability within a single species. There is even greater variability across species. Variability is the raw material of natural selection. When one genetic form is at a disadvantage, another is at an advantage.

In 1981, California farmers were plagued by hordes of gnat-sized flies that carried a virus. As the virus infected plants, millions of dollars worth of melons, lettuce, and squashes were lost.

How can such losses be prevented? Suppose a farmer sprays a field of squash with an insecticide known to be effective in killing flies. At first, the spraying works. Most of the flies are susceptible to the spray and are killed by it. But a few flies have a genetic resistance to the chemical. They survive and reproduce, passing their genetic advantage on to most of their offspring. At first, the population is small. In fact, it may go unnoticed for years. The farmer may decide the problem is solved. But eventually, a large new population of flies appears. This time most member are resistant to the pesticide that was so effective only a few years earlier. Now a new spray must be found. The selective process starts all over again.

?

How is evolution involved in farming?

Using the principles of diversity.

Farmers cannot win the battle against natural selection. However, there are strategies that reduce the loss of valuable crops to insects. It is possible to employ the principles of diversity that protect natural ecosystems. In a monoculture, like the field of squash, only one plant species is present. One insect population can destroy the entire crop and all is lost. If, instead, a farmer plants some squash, some beans, and some spinach, only the squash would be lost. Part of the crop could be saved.

Figure 5.30 An imported stingless wasp attacks a cereal leaf beetle larva by inserting wasp eggs into its body. After hatching, wasp larvae will kill the beetle, a potentially costly pest of small grains. (USDA, Animal and Plant Health Inspection Service)

Figure 5.31 A stingless wasp attacks a Mexican bean beetle larva by inserting wasp eggs. Developing wasp larvae feed on the beetle until all that's left is a "mummy" (an empty shell). As farmers increase the use of natural predators and other forms of integrated pest management, they reduce the application of potentially harmful pesticides. (USDA, Animal and Plant Health Inspection Service)

Modern methods of pest control, called **interated pest management,** offer alternatives to the use of chemical pesticides. This is especially important when pesticides threaten human health or destroy the predators that naturally keep insect populations in check. Biologists have been able to breed sterile males of some insect species. Releasing them to mate with wild females retards the reproductive rate of the insect population. We can also raise and release "good" insects that kill "bad" insects. See Figures 5.30 and 5.31.

Using biological pest control.

Crop rotation, the use of pest-resistant crop strains, and deliberate infections of insect populations with naturally occurring parasites are all being tried.

Crop rotation helps maintain soil quality and disrupts the life cycles of insects.

Will the time ever come when we lose no food to other organism? Probably not. Perhaps the most we can hope for is reducing our losses, yet allowing some of our competitors to survive.

?

What is organic farming/sustainable agriculture?

5.18 Organic Farming

In the past, pesticides were used extensively in agriculture. Farmers assumed they should try to kill off the insects and other pests that compete with us for food crops. Now many modern farmers are rethinking their methods of operation. This rethinking was brought about by the increased costs of energy, artificial fertilizers, and pesticides, and the realization that regular applications of herbicides and pesticides often did nothing but build stronger pests, degrade the living portion of the topsoil, and cover the soil and crops with unwanted chemicals.

These realizations have led to growth in organic farming. **Organic farming** is a method of raising crops and livestock naturally; only organic fertilizers are used. These come from **compost,** legumes, animal manure, green manure, and sound soil conservation practices. Natural pest control involving crop rotation, the use of plants that are more pest resistant, and the use of beneficial insects that kill insect pests, can eliminate (or at least greatly reduce) the need for synthetic chemicals. This approach prevents the loss of humus and lessens the reduction in soil productivity associated with the use of human-made chemicals for agricultural purposes.

When farmers switch over to the organic techniques, their production usually drops a little. This loss is offset by the lower costs of the organic materials. Some organic farmers do better financially. In any case, they can often charge higher prices for their produce.

In the long run, organic methods should be superior, because soil fertility is maintained. A significant switch to organic farming could result in less food available for export. (At the present time, we can't sell all the food we have that is available for export. The American food surplus of the late 1980s and early 1990s has been an economic hardship to our farmers.)

?

If there is enough food, why are people starving? What can be done to solve this problem?

5.19 Solving the Food Problem

If you want to live in Camelot, you've got to build Camelot;
and you have to build it using the hand you've been dealt.
—J. W. Christensen

Enough food is grown today to feed the world's people. The technology exists to raise, harvest, and distribute it. Unfortunately, accomplishing the task is almost beyond us. The necessary transfer of capital would be massive. The technology is complex. The political implications are immense. The following is a list of the most frequently mentioned approaches to solving the problem. The ultimate solution will most certainly involve a combination of all these ideas.

Why must population control be part of any solution?

a. Population Control

All the other approaches to the food crisis will be futile if population growth is not brought under control. Without population control, we would have to double food production on a global scale in 42 years just to maintain our present condition. It makes little sense for people who have variety and equality in their diets to sacrifice that variety if population growth continues and people continue to starve anyway.

Population control is not a simple issue. Some feel that population control proposals are a racist plot by the rich countries to keep developing nations weak and powerless. Many religions forbid artificial methods of birth control. In some cases, people have not been taught how to practice birth control.

b. New Farmlands

Have you ever looked out from an airplane, seen huge areas of bare ground, and wondered about the potential of all that land for farming? At present, only 11% of the world's total land surface, or about 3.5 billion acres, is under cultivation. However, the best land is already being farmed. Many of the remaining areas—deserts, arctic regions, tropical rain forests, and mountains—are not suitable for growing crops. It may be possible to more than double the area of the world's croplands. However, this would not double the yield. The cost of preparing and maintaining the new lands, as well as the negative impact on our planet's diversity, would be immense.

What about making new farmlands?

c. Biotechnology/Better Yields

By manipulating genes—the biological code that controls heredity—scientists are endowing plants and animals with new traits, such as disease resistance or larger size. Though many scientific and social obstacles must be overcome, genetic engineering promises to bring about another revolution in food production. Biotechnology is also making it possible to produce larger amounts of substances that are made naturally only in very small amounts, such as bovine-growth hormone (BGH). BGH is already in use for increasing productivity as much as 40% in dairy cows. The Department of Agriculture is also working on ways to differentiate between sperm that will produce males and sperm that will produce females. As an extra bull in a dairy is just another mouth to feed cows could be artificially inseminated to produce only heifers.

The global seed bank network must be maintained and expanded. New strains of wheat, rice, and other crops can produce higher yields on the same parcel of land—provided these crops receive adequate moisture, fertilizer, and energy. The law of conservation of mass maintains you can't get something for nothing. Food is no exception. The "Green Revolution" was made possible with a tremendous expenditure of energy in the form of fertilizer and equipment operation.

What must be done to improve crop yields?

The Green Revolution of the 1960s was a period when farmers achieved higher production through hybridizing and crossbreeding.

d. Eating Less Meat

The world could feed more people if we all became vegetarians. Most people in the developing world have no other choice. Nutritionist Jean Mayer noted that "the same amount of food that is feeding 210 million Americans would feed 1.5 billion Chinese on an average

Should you become a vegetarian?

Special Focus

Seedbanks and Insectaries

Between 1950 and 1990, world grain production increased by almost 300%, while the population increased by about 200% (Barr, 1981). While the grain production per person increased steadily until 1984, it has dropped since then. A combination of population growth and rising income levels is responsible. Though it may not be possible to restore the pre-1984 pattern, even if population growth is controlled, some opportunities for expanding food production are possible.

The gain in food production was much greater for developed countries than for developing countries. One thing that made this possible was improved varieties of corps.

Most people do not realize that the pre-1984 gain in food production was bought at a heavy price. We must understand how it was achieved if we are to correct some of the risks we are taking. With corrective action, we can continue to produce food for the masses and do it in a more ecologically acceptable manner.

Large expanses of land are now being farmed in climatically marginal land. In addition, farmers are relying on new high-yield hybrids that are more vulnerable to inclement weather, diseases, and insect pests than traditional native varieties. The seeds often lack the hereditary material, called germplasm, necessary to resist pests or to fight environmental stress such as drought.

The total reliance on hybrids is of particular concern. Agricultural technology makes it most profitable to plant thousands of acres in a a single crop. The result is that genetic diversity of crop varieties is decreasing. For example, in 1970 five specific inbred lines constituted part of the parentage of about 70% of the seed corn used in the United States. Approximately 40% of the hard red winter wheat acreage was planted to two varieties and related derivatives. Most Northern-grown soybeans had two varieties as common ancestors (National Academy of Sciences, 1972).

History tells us that this type of farming is very risky. The potato famine in Ireland in the 1840s is one example. Only a few varieties of potatoes were planted. When a fungus began to spread among the plants, there was nothing to stop it. The result was that two million Irish died of hunger and disease. An additional two million emigrated. The most spectacular and widely publicized example of

Continued

Figure 5.32 Combining wheat. (H. Oscar/Visuals Unlimited)

genetic vulnerability in the U.S. was the Southern corn leaf blight epidemic of 1970. Most of the corn crop was of one variety and was wiped out by a fungus.

A similar incident occurred in 1980 when the peanut crop, consisting of two varieties, was almost entirely destroyed by drought and disease. In both of these recent cases, seed companies quickly introduced resistant seeds, and recovery was rapid. Without this capability, our farmers could experience a disaster such as occurred in Ireland.

These examples from the past provide the key that should enable us to foresee potential disaster and forestall its occurrence. As humans expand their presence over all portions of the globe, we are eliminating complex ecosystems and the genetic material that made them stable. We must preserve the genetic material in two ways:

1. Large expanses of various ecosystems must be preserved in the form of wilderness, parks, and monuments. These serve as living banks from which we can withdraw genetic materials when the need arises;
2. We must collect, preserve and maintain the **germplasm** of naturally growing native plants and strains of food crops in genetic **seed banks** in different areas.

Significant progress is now being made in collecting and preserving germplasm. The International Board for Plant Genetic Resources (IBPGR) was established in 1974 to create and coordinate a worldwide network of germplasm resource conservation centers. The IBPGR receives funds from the World Bank, The Food and Agriculture Organization of the United nations (FAO), and the United Nations Development Program.

Figure 5.33 Southern corn leaf blight. (USDA)

Membership of the Board consists of these three sponsors, as well as 14 donor governments, three regional development funds; the European Economic Community; The Ford, Rockefeller, and Kellogg Foundations; the International Development Research Center (Ottawa, Canada); and two representatives from each of five major developing regions.

The most significant result of the Board's work has been its stimulation of genetic resources activities in many nations. Many international, regional, and national agricultural research centers have responded. Some 60 research institutions serve as the repositories for the world's base collections of seed of the principal food crops. In addition, the IBPGR has aided in the establishment of storage and information management systems and has helped to develop training programs to provide personnel for genetic resources work.

In 1978, the National Plant Genetic Resources Board (NPGRB) was established by the United States Secretary of Agriculture. This United States group cooperates closely with the IBPGR.

The U.S. national plant germplasm system. All germplasm collected through the USDA's Research Service (USDA/ARS) becomes the property of the U.S. National Plant Germplasm System (NPGS), which provides samples to plant scientists upon request. The NPGS currently maintains more than 400,000 kinds of germplasm, to which some 7,000 to 15,000 foreign and domestic additions are made annually.

Continued

Figure 5.34 Some of the ear and kernel types in the U.S. Department of Agriculture collection of corn germplasm from Yugoslavia, Guatemala, the former Soviet Union, and Turkey. (Raymond Clark, North Central Regional Plant Introduction Station, Ames, Iowa)

The NPGS is a diffuse network of federal, state, and private institutions, agencies, and research stations that work cooperatively to acquire, maintain, and improve germplasm; conduct research on the preservation of genetic diversity and on methods of preserving viability through improved storage procedures; and monitor genetic vulnerability. The NPGS includes seven key elements:

1. *The National Plant Germplasm Committee*
   This committee coordinates research and service efforts of the federal, state, and industrial units engaged in introducing, preserving, evaluating, and enhancing plant germplasm. It also fosters relationships with international plant germplasm programs.
2. *Crop Advisory Committees*
   These committees are national groups of specialists from the public and private sectors. They provide analyses, data, and advice about the activities necessary for effective acquisition, maintenance evaluation, and use of genetic resources.
3. *The USDA/ARS Plant Genetics and Germplasm Institute*
   This Institute is part of the Beltsville Agriculture Research Center in Maryland. They catalog all incoming germplasm; coordinate plant explorations, conduct studies to determine the geographical and ecological distribution of significant genetic diversity in crop species; maintain a computerized data base to register new germplasm, maintain an inventory, monitor viability of collections, process seed requests, and provide information on plant characteristics. The Institute serves as an isolation facility where disease or prohibited introductions from other countries are grown under quarantine to produce disease-free stocks for distribution, and houses some 100,000 samples of various crop grains.
4. *The National Seed Storage Laboratory (NSSL)*
   The laboratory at Fort Collins, Colorado, is the nation's only long-term storage facility for seeds. It stores a base collection of seed-propagated plant germplasm. Samples in the base collection are intended for long-term storage, and are regrown as infrequently as possible (to reduce genetic change that may be encountered during seed production), but often enough to prevent germplasm loss through deterioration and loss of viability of some portions of the seed.
5. *The Regional Plant Introduction Stations*
   Four stations have a national responsibility of maintaining germplasm of specific crops. These stations are located in Ames, Iowa; Pullman, Washington; Geneva, New York; and Experiment, Georgia.

Continued

Figure 5.35 Trays of seed samples in metal cans being removed from a cold storage room for testing the germination. After the test, the samples will be returned to storage in reusable, heat-sealed, foil-laminated bags. Accessions that are critically low in germination will be planted to increase the seed. (USDA/ARS)

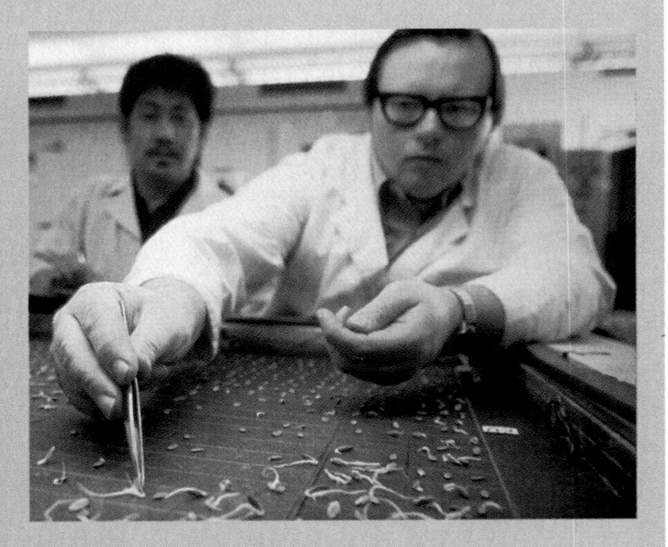

Figure 5.36 Gradual changes in surface temperature across a "thermogradient plate" enable researchers to find the temperatures most favorable for rapid germination of various seeds. A wetted germination blotter is spread over the surface. Here cucumber seeds are being tested. Seeds closer to the warmer corner of the plate have germinated faster than those near the cooler portion. (USDA/ARS)

6. *The State/Federal Interregional Potato Introduction Station*
   Located in Sturgeon Bay, Wisconsin, this station maintains and upgrades potato germplasm, develops new potato varieties, and conducts research on improved methods of preserving potato germplasm.

7. *The National Clonal Germplasm Repositories*
   A system of repositories is now being developed. The primary purpose is to maintain and distribute germplasm to plant breeders and other researchers in the United States. Other countries in need of special genetic materials will have access to the repositories. Much of the material has come from countries other than the United States.

Continued

Figure 5.37 Variability in fruit types in a portion of the USDA collection of cucumber germplasm. Countries represented include Japan, India, Iran, and Turkey. (North Central Regional Plant Introduction Station, Ames, Iowa)

Figure 5.38 Head and kernel types from a portion of the USDA collection of sunflower germplasm from the former Soviet Union and the United States. (North Central Regional Plan Introduction Station, Ames, Iowa)

Future needs. The future will require plants and animals that can survive a variety of climatic changes, diseases, and insects. A storehouse of genetic material is our best hope for developing plants and animals that can survive. However, the process of natural selection will enable harmful organisms to evolve and make the new varieties ineffective if we are not constantly alert. Hence, our commitment to the future must be sufficient and ongoing. We must enable researchers to draw on the numerous plant and animal varieties that are now quickly diminishing. We owe no less to ourselves and future generations.

Insectaries. An **insectary** is a place where beneficial insects are raised for the purpose of using them to control certain plant and insect pests. This is called **biological pest control.**

The use of predatory insects to fight pests is considered to be a safe biological solution to an age-old problem. However, exotic insect species must be strictly quarantined before they are made available for general release.This ensures that no close relatives of the pest species will be attacked by biological control agents.

There are approximately 25 government-funded insectaries in the United States. They are operated by the Federal Government, through the Department of Agriculture, and by various state governments. In addition, numerous commercial insectaries are in operation. This number is rising as more and more chemicals are withdrawn from agricultural use.

Figure 5.39 Two varieties of cabbage illustrating a difference in susceptibility to bacterial black rot. The variety in the row on the left, typical of commercially available cabbages, is susceptible. The leaf tips die, turn brown, and roll downward. Eventually the heads rot off. The variety in the row on the right is highly resistant. It is derived from an old Japanese variety known as Early Fuji. Early Fuji is no longer available commercially and exists only as stored inventory in one or two seed banks in Japan. It remains the most valuable source of black rot resistance known today. (Paul H. Williams, University of Wisconsin)

Figure 5.40 The unquenchable appetite. (Cartoon by Gene Bassett, Winner of Editorial Category Award in the 1974 Population Cartoon Contest. Credit: Scripps-Howard Newspapers.)

Chinese diet." But don't the developed nations have the right to eat better if they control the size of their populations?

One thing to consider is that a vegetarian diet is not necessarily low quality, and can even be more healthful than a high-meat diet. People who eat little red meat and little fat are less likely to have circulatory disorders and to be overweight than people who eat large amounts of red meat and fat.

e. New Food

Creating new foods.

It may be possible to manufacture synthetic food from crude oil. Algae could be converted into something edible. However, people have a tendency to reject potential foods that do not taste good to them. Further, the energy cost of some of the new foods may be higher than we can pay.

At one time, farming the oceans seemed promising. Unfortunately, pollution and overfishing have resulted in a world catch that has actually declined for the last two decades.

f. Land Ownership

Increasing land ownership.

People seem to work harder when they own the land that they farm. Unfortunately, vast areas in Asia and Latin America are controlled by absentee landlords. The sharecroppers that actually work the fields have little incentive to better the land. Changing this situation is very difficult, usually requiring a revolution. The rich minority resist giving up their lands. Can nonviolent means be found to bring about land reform?

g. Sustainable Agriculture

Sustainable agriculture.

Sustainable agriculture is a method of growing crops and raising livestock based on maximizing soil, water, and energy conservation, as well as using organic farming and biological pest control. If properly done, farm fields/pasture lands should continue indefinitely in their present form and, in some cases, improve. New technologies emphasizing solar power can enable developed countries to maintain high yields and still reduce the consumption of conventional fuels. Poorer nations can increase yields, improve soils, and continue their

Figure 5.41 U. S. Marines were sent to Somalia in December 1992 in the hope of creating conditions of stability, so that thousands of starving people could receive food that had been sent to them. (Peter Turnley/Black Star)

labor-intensive methods. To them, high labor intensity is important because it enables large numbers of people to do meaningful work.

As a general rule, sustainable agriculture promotes the raising of a variety of crops, conserves both soil and water, builds new topsoil, reduces water pollution, and increases biodiversity.

h. Famine Relief

Famine relief efforts.

When famine strikes, a series of negative events occur. People begin to wander, social structures collapse, bands of lawless individuals roam, sanitation systems fail, and diseases spread. Under these conditions it is difficult to establish order, handle emergencies and solve the famine problem. It may also be true that more people are dying from civil wars and political conflicts than from natural disasters such as drought, floods, and plant diseases.

A coordinated effort, possibly through the United Nations, could begin to solve the problems. The solution might work as follows:

1. **Establish a world grain reserve.** If a world grain reserve were established, grain could be quickly delivered to regions hit by famine.
2. **Build infrastructure in poorer nations.** Food often doesn't reach starving people. Roads are bad or nonexistent, and vehicles don't work. Military units from richer nations could help with distribution. The process would be much more efficient if major roads and communications networks through poorer regions were established.
3. **Assist people in settlement.** People should be kept with their families in their local areas. When they wander in search of food, social structures break down. Thus, first-aid and feeding stations must be set up where the people live. Relief workers must be able

to bring food supplies through battle lines in famine-affected areas. Food should not be used as a weapon. There must be an international agreement that starvation will not be used as an instrument to wage foreign or civil war, and that any group using this strategy will be cut off from the international community of nations.

4. **Improved agricultural and population planning.** Countries that are vulnerable to famine can be helped with strategies of sustainable agriculture and population planning. The United Nations and other agencies could provide assistance to those who desire it.

i. Global Cooperation

Do nations have to cooperate?

Until the peoples of the "have-not" nations are convinced that their children will survive to live a meaningful life, they will probably continue having large families and deepening the food crisis. Surviving children are the parents' only hope for care in their old age. But how do you enable their children to live longer? How do you guarantee care for the elderly? This probably can't be accomplished without some redistribution of wealth, either within a country or between countries. China did it, but with a violent revolution. Can redistribution take place without a revolution? Some say it can.

However global cooperation occurs, it must involve more than just giving food away. As the ancient Chinese proverb says: "Give a man a fish and you feed him for a day; teach a man to fish and you feed him for a lifetime." This does not, however, imply that we should attempt to westernize the world. Each culture is different. Each ecosystem is different. Solutions must be found that recognize the uniqueness of each people and their land.

At present we have enough food, and we have the means to deliver it to those that are starving. What we lack is the ability to communicate with others who have different beliefs, attitudes, and world views. We need skill in conflict resolution, and must pledge to keep working at improving it.

World food problems can be reduced by:

- population control efforts that recognize the beliefs and customs in rapid-growth nations
- advances in biotechnology
- improvements in the nutritional habits of all people
- land reform that enables farmers to work their own land
- expansion of sustainable agriculture
- a coordinated famine-relief program
- global cooperation

Summary

Soil links the nonliving to the living. Good soil is essential to raising healthy crops and can be maintained using a variety of conservation strategies.

Proper nutrition requires a varied diet that emphasizes grains and bread. World hunger has been reduced, but hunger remains one of our major global problems.

Modern agriculture relies on a large and steady supply of energy and mineral resources. These substitute for labor, land, rain, and climate. The drain on resources may force us to examine some new strategies for producing and marketing food.

The stability of our environment depends on diversity. We must protect that diversity if we are to survive.

Microorganisms and insects destroy large quantities of food each year. Natural selection makes it difficult to combat this problem. The use of herbicides and insecticides only works for a time. Farmers can use other ecological strategies to reduce crop losses—rotation, pest-resistant crop strains, and the release of both sterile male insects and "good" predator insects. They work best when they are part of long-term planning. They have limited effectiveness when emergencies occur. However, long-term planning is something on which quality living depends.

References

Andrewartha, H. G. and L. C. Birch. *The Ecological Web: More on the Distribution and Abundance of Animals* (Chicago: University of Chicago Press), 1986.

Brown, Lester R. *The Changing World Food Prospect: The Nineties and Beyond* (Washington, DC: Worldwatch institute), 1988.

Brown, Lester R. and John E. Young. Feeding the world in the nineties. *State of the World* (Washington, DC: Worldwatch Institute), 1990.

Brown, Lester R. and others. *State of the World* (New York: Norton), 1994.

Conway, Gordon, R. and Edward B. Barbier. *After the Green Revolution: Sustainable Agriculture for Development* (London: Earthscan), 1990.

Council for Agricultural Science and Technology. *Plant Germplasm Preservation and Utilization in U.S. Agriculture,* Report No. 106 (CAST, 137 Lynn Avenue, Ames Iowa 50010-7120), November 1985.

Crosson, Pierre R. and Norman J. Rosenberg. Strategies for agriculture. *Scientific American* pp. 128–135, September 1989.

Durning, Alan Thein and Holly B. Brough. Reforming the livestock economy. *State of the World* (New York: W. W. Norton & Co.), 1992.

The Ecologist, vol. 21, no. 2. 1991—Issue devoted to world hunger.

Hendry, Peter. Food and Population: beyond five billion. *Population Bulletin* Vol. 43, No. 2. Washington, DC: Population Reference Bureau, 1988.

Huntley, D. B. Beeler, A. Johnson, D. Littlejohns, and J. Tanner. *Seeds for a Hungry World* (Ottawa: Canadian Seed Trade Association), 1984.

League of Women Voters. U.S. Farm Policy: Who Benefits? Who Pays? Who Decides? (Washington, DC: League of Women Voters), 1990.

Molnar, Joseph J. and Henry Kinnugan, ed. *Biotechnology and the New Agricultural Revolution* (Boulder, Col.: Westview Press), 1988.

National Academy of Sciences. *Alternative Agriculture* (Washington, D.C.: National Academy Press), 1989.

Oram, Peter A. Moving toward sustainability: building the agroecological framework. *Environment* Vol. 30, No. 9, November 1988.

United Nations Food and Agriculture Organization. *The State of Food and Agriculture* (Rome: United Nations), Annual.

United Nations World Food Council. *The Global State of Hunger and Malnutrition* (Rome: United Nation), Annual.

Wilson, Edward O. Threats to Biodiversity. *Scientific American* pp. 108–116, September 1989.

End of Chapter Questions

1. What is soil?
2. Sketch a soil profile and describe each of the horizons.
3. Name the three soil groups and explain how each got to be what it is today.
4. Name seven soil conservation practices.
5. What items make up a plant's nutritional needs? Why is each item needed?
6. What items make up an animal's nutritional needs? Why is each item needed?
7. Use the food guide pyramid to plan one day of healthy meals. Defend your choices.
8. Why does it require so much energy to put the food we enjoy on our tables?
9. Compare the food you can receive with what you must invest to get:
   a. Iowa-grown corn,
   b. Nebraska soybeans,
   c. rice in China,
   d. "hand-grown" potatoes,
   e. beef.
10. Compare the percentage of energy that goes into the original production of food with the energy it takes to get it from the farm to your table.
11. "There is no such thing as free lunch" is especially true as it relates to the food industry. Choose a food item on your most recent school lunch menu and list in sequence all of the energy inputs required, from growing it or (raising it) to finally getting it to your school. Place an "L" next to those steps which probably represent large energy input, an "M" next to those which show moderate energy input, and an "S" next to those which represent relatively small energy input.
12. A reduction in energy use for food production could bring about many changes in resource use, lifestyle, conservation patterns, and labor intensity. List an example of each of these changes.
13. What is the difference between undernourishment and malnutrition?

14. Brain development depends partly on protein in the diet. Why would providing an inadequate protein diet from age 2 to 10 probably result only in mental retardation?
15. How do fossil fuels enter into the process of fertilizing crops?
16. Approximately how many people in the world die from hunger each year?
17. Why is it more efficient to eat lower on the food chain?
18. Americans eat large quantities of beef. The conversion efficiency of plant material to beef is low. Is there any way to justify this kind of diet?
19. If our only basic reason for eating were to stay alive, which protein source(s) would be most efficient for our use?
20. Discuss your ethical responsibility to become (or not to become) a vegetarian for the sake of those starving throughout the world.
21. Explanations of cause and effect are very important in science. They must be stated very carefully. Identify at least two problems with the following statement: "The moths in England turned dark because of the soot of nearby factories."
22. In real life, what factors tend to limit the population size of various organisms?
23. Sketch the idealized approach to carrying capacity graph and explain why it is the ideal approach.
24. Explain how the process of natural selection could lead to the extinction of a species *in the absence of any human intervention.*
25. One of the difficulties with the use of antibiotics in the treatment of disease is that antibiotics that worked a decade ago against a particular disease are no longer effective against the same disease. Give an evolutionary explanation for how that might occur.
26. How might attitudes and technology that exist in our present society cause the number of rattleless rattlesnakes to increase? Explain using principles of natural selection.
27. Explain how human activities can bring about the extinction of species.
28. Extinction is a natural process. It occurs all the time, whether human beings do anything or not, so why should people be concerned about "endangered species" and the extinctions that result from human activity?
29. Why is it so difficult to fight insect pests?
30. Name some modern pest control strategies.
31. What is organic farming?
32. How are research scientists endowing plants and animals with new traits?
33. By how much can the cloned bovine-growth hormone boost milk production?

34. If dairy farmers can differentiate between the sperm for male and female reproduction, they will most likely artificially inseminate cows and produce only ___________________ .

35. What is an insectary?

36. List some of the most frequently mentioned solutions to the world's food problems. Can you suggest other solutions?

37. Which of the nine proposed solutions to the food problem do you think are the most effective? Why?

38. Do you agree with the following statement? Since humankind can control its environment (i.e., produce its own food, dispose of its own waste, control the populations of other organisms, etc.), the problems associated with exponential growth do not apply to the human population. Explain.

39. If you were a national or international leader, how would you solve the hunger problem? Support your answer with facts.

40. What can the average person do to reduce hunger . . . locally . . . globally?

41. When does it become acceptable for our nation (or a group of nations) to send troops into another nation for humanitarian (basic human rights) reasons? Do nations belong to governments or do they belong to people?

Goal

To understand the energy sources relied on by modern societies.

Energy Today

To chart a course through the cross currents of varying points of view and opinion, one must understand the fundamental facts about where our energy comes from, how we use it and how efficient these uses are.

—Energy: The Critical Choices Ahead (U.S. Department of Commerce)

Energy For Our Planet

In chapter 2, we introduced you to the idea of energy flow. Energy is not simply burned up like a pile of wood or coal. It is transformed from one form of energy to another—for example, from the chemical energy in coal, to heat energy. By controlling what transformations take place, we can use energy to do desired tasks for us. What does change as energy flows through various transformations is its quality. With each conversion from one form to another energy becomes more difficult to convert to mechanical energy (the second law of thermodynamics). In this chapter, the flow of energy through our society will be examined in some detail.

Why do modern societies require large amounts of energy?

Modern societies require huge amounts of energy. If we are to continue to live in the "manner to which we have become accustomed," we must understand where our energy comes from and how we use it. If we desire to change our energy use patterns in an intelligent way, we must understand this also. Living the good life in the future may not require as much energy as it has in the past. However, an orderly future won't just happen. It must be carefully planned.

Energy use is increasing rapidly in countries outside the United States. Their uses of energy, like ours, affect world resources and pollution. In considering energy patterns in the United States, you need to see them as part of a worldwide system.

What energy sources does the United States rely on at the present time?

6.1 Where We Get Our Energy

You can see in Figure 6.1 that most of the energy consumed in the United States comes from the fossil fuels: oil, natural gas, and coal. On a worldwide scale, the percentages are similar (Figure 6.2).

6.2 How We Use Our Energy

Figure 6.3 shows how Americans use energy. Note that the uses are divided into three main use sectors or areas. The residential and commercial sector includes houses, apartments, office buildings, stores, and shopping malls. The industrial sector includes manufacturing plants, paper mills, oil refineries, chemical & fertilizer plants, steel mills, and auto assembly plants, as well as agriculture, mining, and construction. The transportation sector includes all light-duty vehicles, freight trucks, air transport, boats/ships, and trains.

From Figure 6.3, we see that energy is divided fairly equally among the three sectors. Well over half the energy used in residential and commercial buildings goes for space heating and cooling. The second highest use is for water heating, followed closely by lighting. The largest industrial energy consumers are the manufacturers of chemicals, rubber, and plastics. As one might expect, light-duty vehicles (mostly automobiles) consume two-thirds of all fuels that are used for transportation.

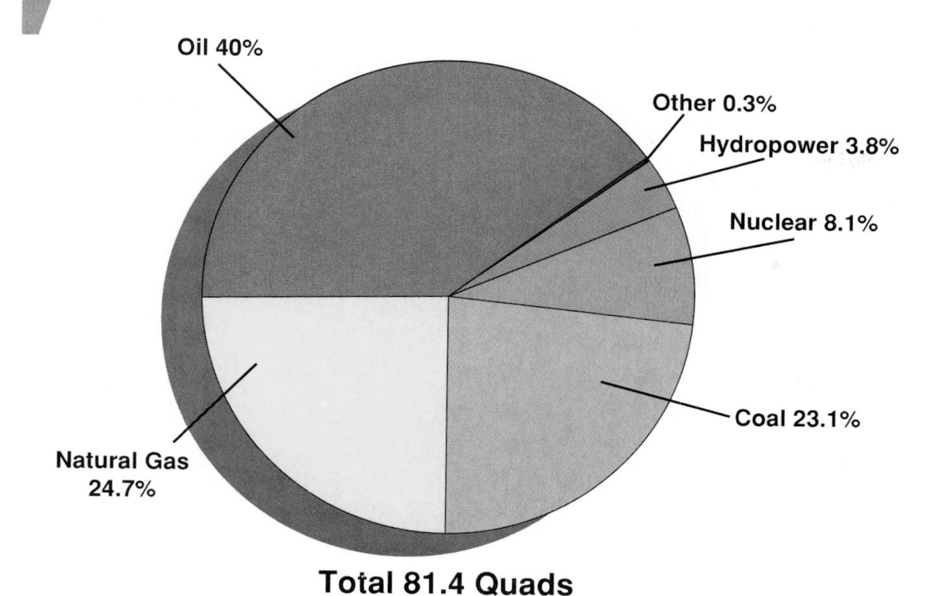

Figure 6.1 U.S. consumption of commercial* energy in 1991. (From U.S. Department of Energy. Energy Information Administration.)

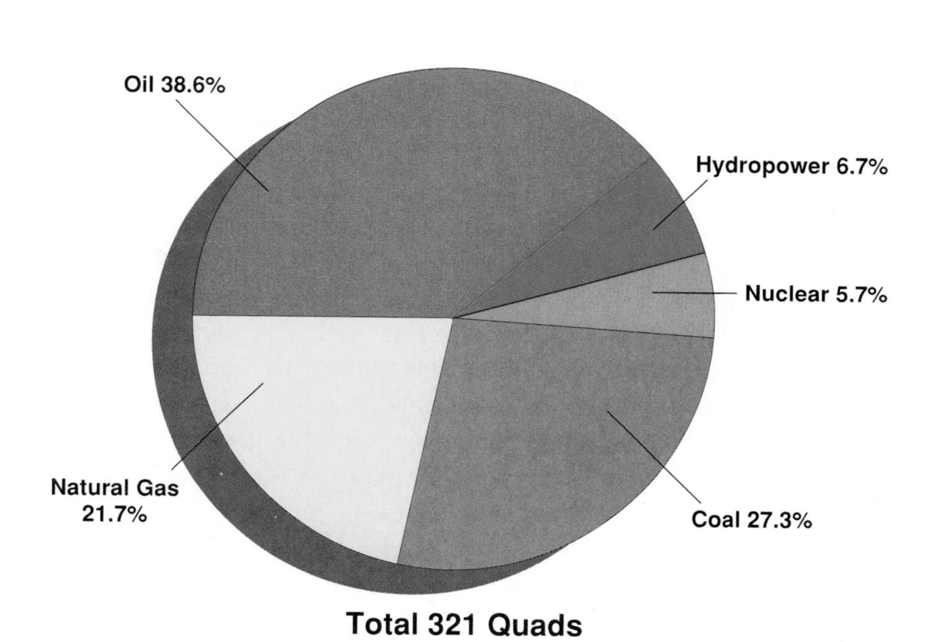

Figure 6.2 World consumption of commercial† energy in 1990. (Source: BP Statistical Review of World Energy.)

*Commercial energy does not include energy from wood, waste, geothermal, wind, photovoltaic, and solar thermal energy, except for small amounts used by electric utilities to generate electricity for distribution.

†Commercial energy means commercially traded sources only. Not included are sources such as wood, peat and animal waste which, though important in many countries, are unreliably documented in terms of consumption data.

U.S. transportation is almost entirely oil-dependent, obtaining more than 97% of its energy from petroleum. This is because liquid fuels, such as gasoline, are easy to transport, store, and use in our vehicles.

As energy use is examined, the focus should be on efficiency. Are we using our energy wisely?

Name the three main energy use sectors.

Figure 6.3 U.S. energy end-use consumption by sector in 1990. Total consumption = 64.2 Quads. Not shown are electrical generation and distribution losses = 20.9 Quads. (Source: U.S. Department of Energy. Energy Information Administration.)

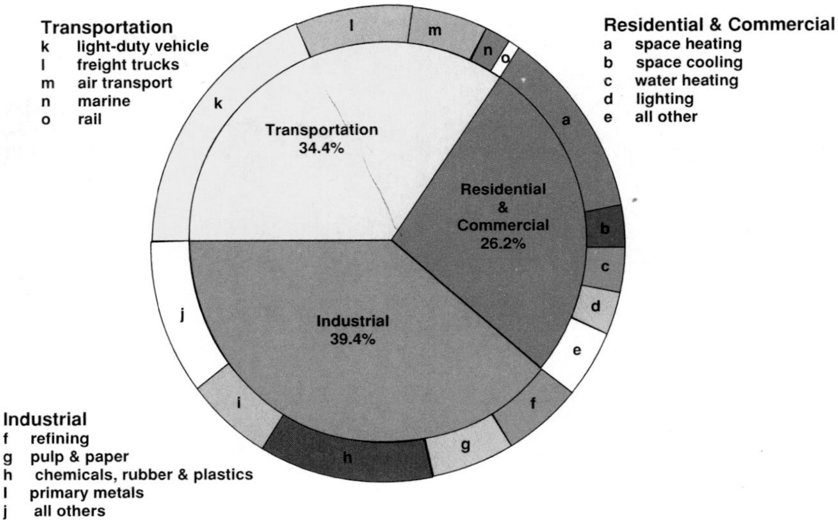

Transportation
k light-duty vehicle
l freight trucks
m air transport
n marine
o rail

Residential & Commercial
a space heating
b space cooling
c water heating
d lighting
e all other

Transportation 34.4%
Residential & Commercial 26.2%
Industrial 39.4%

Industrial
f refining
g pulp & paper
h chemicals, rubber & plastics
I primary metals
j all others

6.3 An Energy History

A renewable resource can be used continuously without using it up.

At the beginning of human life, our ancestors relied on renewable sources of energy. The first humans lived on solar energy stored in food and other plant parts. They ate fruits, vegetables, and animals (which ate plants and other animals). They burned wood from fallen trees. Even when people learned to broaden their energy base, using the winds to move ships and flowing water to drive their machines, early human civilization was still solar powered.

?

What major energy transitions has the United States already made?

Even though the energy stored in fossil fuels was discovered early in human history, the fossil fuel age really began in England after 1700 with the Industrial Revolution. During that period, coal was used extensively for heating buildings and smelting iron. As the coal near the surface was used up and mines were dug deeper, problems with flooding arose. In response to the demand for power to pump water out of the mines, the steam engine was invented. These steam engines consumed even more coal. The use of the steam engine led to the discovery of a host of other industrial applications.

Wood as primary fuel.

Wood alone accounted for about 90% of U.S. energy consumption in 1850 (see Figure 6.4). The average consumption in the frontier American home (mostly for heating) was 17.4 cords per year. (A cord of wood is a 4 ft. by 4 ft. by 8 ft. stack.) This wood was used inefficiently, as it burned in fireplaces that allowed much heat to escape. Its total energy content is 2–4 times the average amount of energy used to heat a home today. But, in those times, wood was the only useful source of heat.

Most of the wood (140 million cords in 1850) was used for heating homes. Wood also was an important source of energy for the country's young industry and transportation system. Trains and steamboats burned 7 to 8 million cords of wood annually. Almost 2 million cords were turned into charcoal for smelting iron. This consumption of charcoal, amounting to about 750,000 tons, is now almost matched by the consumption of charcoal in outdoor barbecue grills.

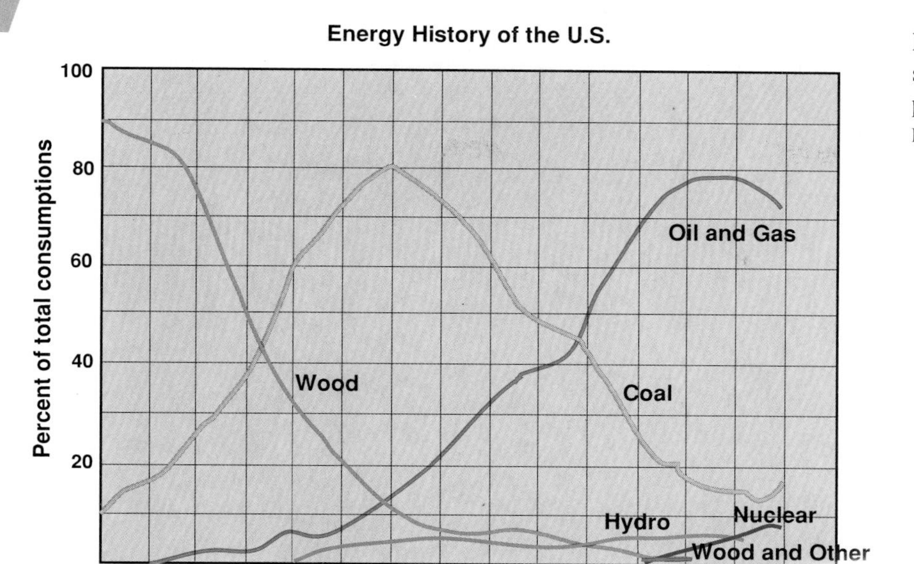

Figure 6.4 The United States has shifted to different fuel use patterns. (From U.S. Department of Energy.)

Depletion of forests in Europe caused dependence on coal to come earlier there than in the United States. Americans continued to rely for many years on renewable resources—wind, wood, and water.

The U.S. conversion to coal began at the end of the 1800s. Forests near cities had been cut down, and it became necessary to transport logs from far away. Wood, when burned, produces about 6.5 million Joules per pound. Coal has more than twice that energy density—13.0 million Joules per pound. If you have to transport energy, you want to carry as much per pound as you can. Thus, coal replaced wood. By 1910, coal accounted for over three-quarters of the total energy used. Railroad transport made coal a good source of energy.

Why did we switch from wood to coal?

In the 1840s coal began to replace wood on river boats.

The use of petroleum products (oil and natural gas) began to grow during the 1920s. Petroleum is easier to use and cleaner than coal. It was also easier and cheaper to transport by pipeline. At the end of World War II, the petroleum age arrived.

Why did we switch from coal to petroleum and natural gas?

It now appears that the dominance of petroleum products may also be drawing to a close. In 1991, they dropped to less than 65% of the total.

Is a transition to a new dominant source beginning? The 1991 data are unclear. We see two small surges. Nuclear energy's contribution has grown from less than 1% in 1970 to about 8%. Some see in this growth the beginning of a nuclear age. Also, coal is showing a revival. It contributed 17% of the total in 1975, but 23% in 1991.

It would be foolish to predict the future of either coal or nuclear energy right now. What happens will depend on the outcome of a complicated and interrelated set of environmental, economic, and political considerations. We will pursue questions regarding energy for the future in chapter 9.

The United States voluntarily went through two energy transitions. We are now going through a third, but this transition is not by choice.

Figure 6.5 Energy projections made in 1975 of the ERDA-49 Program. (From the ERDA-49 Program, U.S. Energy Research and Development Administration.)

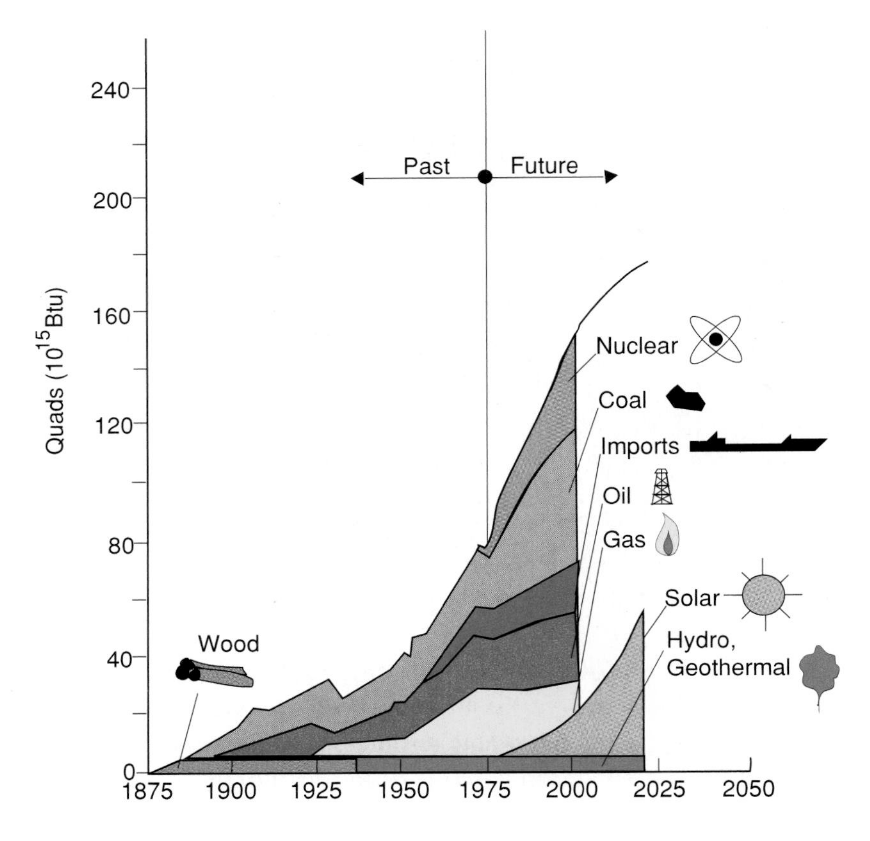

6.4 Increasing Demand for Energy

Energy history of the United States.

Figure 6.5 is another way of showing the energy history and possible energy future of the United States. It shows our increasing demand for energy. We not only are beginning to use some new and more environmentally acceptable energy sources, we may also choose to develop these new sources on a grand scale.

Figure 6.5 reflects the U.S. economy as it was seen in 1975. The effect of the depression of the 1930s is clearly seen, as are the economic recessions in the 1950s and in the middle 1970s. In 1976, energy consumption began to rise again. At that time, sharp rises in energy use were predicted.

Why might our future demands for energy not grow as rapidly as they have in the past?

The projection in Figure 6.6, made in 1992, is more cautious than that in 6.5. It reflects a greater awareness of some of the physical and political limitations the United States must face as we plan for our future. Why such a lowering of our energy expectations? We will examine this question in the chapters to follow.

Now that we have looked at some projections, let's look at actual U. S. energy production from 1949 to 1991. Figure 6.7 shows United States production of energy by source. We see that domestic energy production has grown very little since 1970.

Who consumes the most energy in the world?

Figure 6.8 shows energy consumption for the world as a whole. (This data is for "commercial" energy; wood, cow dung, etc. are not included.) The demand for energy on a global scale is increasing. The

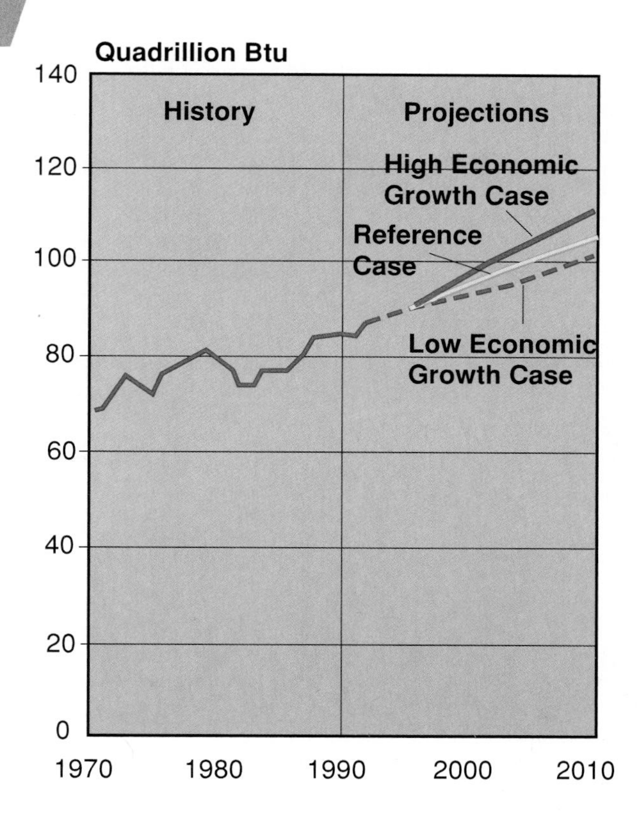

Figure 6.6 Total U.S. energy consumption projected to 2010 with a range of uncertainty. Projections made in 1992. (From USDOE, EIA, *Annual Energy Outlook 1992*.).

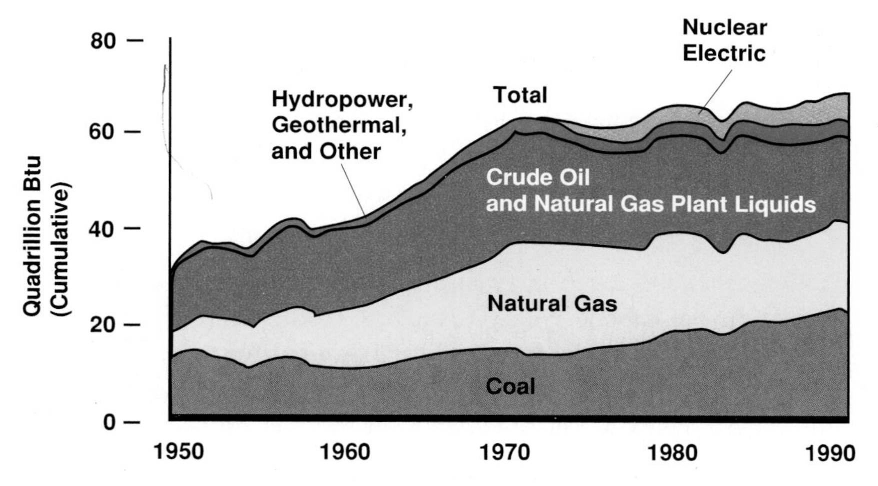

Figure 6.7 United States production of energy by source, 1949–1991. (From USDOE, EIA, *Annual Energy Review* 1991, June, 1992.)

standard of living is growing throughout much of the world. The challenge is to provide a comfortable life to all Earth's people and at the same time maintain a clean environment.

Fossil Fuels

Current sources of energy are dominated by **fossil fuels.** These fuels—oil, gas, and coal—were formed millions of years ago by the compression of plant and animal matter buried in mud and sand.

? Why are oil and gas desirable fuels?

Figure 6.8 World energy consumption. (Source BP Statistical Review of World Energy.)

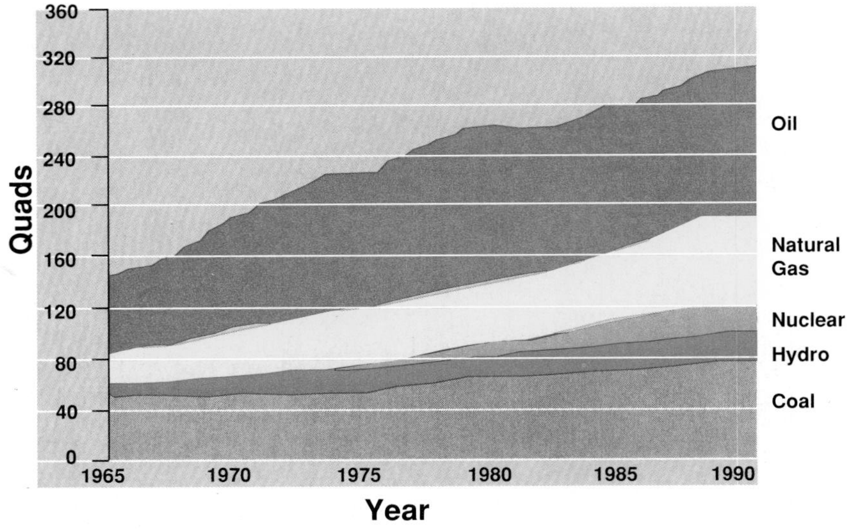

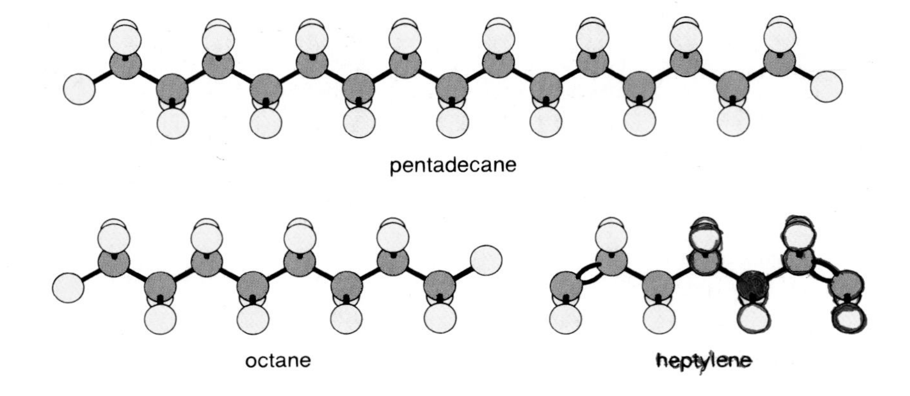

Figure 6.9 Chemical models of petroleum molecules. The yellow spheres represent hydrogen, the blue spheres represent carbon, and the black connectors represent chemical bonds. (Enterprise for Education)

6.5 Oil

Oil as an energy source.

Crude oil is consumed in great quantities because of the widespread use of the automobile. Since it is a liquid, oil is more usable than the other forms of primary energy. Oil is fairly easily stored, transported, and consumed. For these reasons, oil is the leading source of energy in the United States. If our reserves of oil were not shrinking, oil would probably maintain that dominance for a long time.

Petroleum consists chiefly of flammable carbon and hydrogen compounds that occur naturally in liquid, gaseous, and solid form.

Crude oil is a product of the decay of **organic** (carbon-containing) matter, both plant and animal. The hydrogen and carbon atoms **(hydrocarbons)** in today's petroleum are derived from the remains of prehistoric plants and animals. In a similar way, tiny amounts of petroleum are being formed today. Most **petroleum** exists in the Earth in one of two forms, liquid or vapor. The liquid is called **crude oil.** The vapor is known as **natural gas.** Petroleum also exists as a solid in deposits like the Athabasca tar sands of Alberta, Canada, and the oil shale beds of Colorado, Wyoming, Utah, and elsewhere in the world. Figure 6.9 contains a chemical representation of some of the hundreds of petroleum molecules.

Figure 6.10 Off-shore rig. (© 1992 ARCO Photography Collection, Los Angeles, CA.)

Although scientists report finding traces of hydrocarbons in rocks that are more than a billion years old, they feel that most petroleum was formed less than 500 million years ago. Some formed as recently as 10 million years ago.

How is oil formed?

Most scientists believe that oil was formed from the remains of countless tiny creatures and plants that lived in the sea, or washed into it with mud and silt from streams. This material settled to the bottom of the ancient seas and piled up, layer atop layer.

Compressed by the tremendous weight gathering above them, these deeply buried layers of mud, silt, and sand were gradually formed into layers of sedimentary rock. The rocks included sandstones, shales, limestones, dolomites, and other types. Rock formation was further aided by heat, coming both from pressure and from interior parts of the Earth.

Over millions of years, the organic matter was transformed. Billions of bits of decayed plant and animal matter, held captive by the mud and silt, were changed to petroleum by heat, and compression. The actions of bacteria, chemicals and radioactive materials also contributed. As ages passed, the sea withdrew, and the Earth's crust heaved and buckled, creating structures which trapped the oil and gas.

Layers of sediment in which petroleum was formed are referred to as **source beds.** After its formation, petroleum migrated from these source beds into layers of **porous** and **permeable** rock. These are the **reservoirs** sought by today's petroleum geologists.

Figure 6.11 The geologist.
(Courtesy of Exxon Corporation.)

How did oil and gas become trapped underground?

Just how petroleum moved from these source beds to reservoirs is not fully known. One line of thinking is that because oil and gas are less dense than water, they tended to rise to the top of the ancient seawater that filled the porous spaces when the sedimentary formations were laid down. They seeped upward and outward through porous and permeable layers until stopped by dense **impermeable** rocks.

When further movement was halted, oil and gas collected or were "trapped" between impermeable layers. Gas, the lightest, rose to the upper parts of the traps. Oil remained beneath the gas. Seawater, the most dense, sank to the lowest parts.

Most scientists agree that many of the trapped oil and gas concentrations resulted from uplifts and movements of rock strata layers. Originally, the sea floors were nearly horizontal. Over millions of years, the continental plates moved (see chapter 1), and horizontal layers were shifted, bent, and broken. Ancient sea bottoms often became dry land areas. These movements sometimes rearranged permeable and impermeable rock layers so that further movement of oil was stopped.

Only rarely are concentrations of oil found near the Earth's surface. Most are thousands of feet deep. Exploratory techniques to locate rock formations in which oil or gas might have formed or been trapped are very complex and expensive. Only drilling can prove the presence of oil or gas, outline the field, and determine potential amounts.

What do geologists look for as they explore for new oil deposits?

Today these traps are the object of a search for oil throughout the world. In advising companies about where to begin exploratory drilling, **geologists** and geophysicists usually look for three things. First, they look for source beds of shales or limestones which originally contained an abundance of organic remains. Next, they seek the porous and permeable sandstones or limestones which later became reservoir beds. Finally, they look for a trap which sealed off the reservoir beds and held the oil and gas in place.

How were "traps" formed?

Two basic types of trap are most important to petroleum geologists: structural and stratigraphic. The **attitude** of rocks—whether they are folded, fractured, or displaced—is called their geologic structure. Therefore, the **structural trap** for oil or gas is the result of folding, faulting, or other deformation.

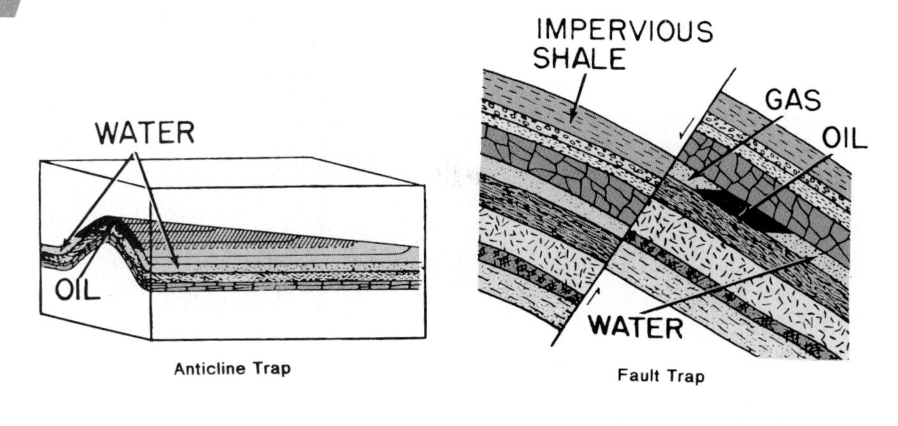

Figure 6.12 *a*. Anticline trap, *b*. Fault trap, *c*. Salt dome trap, *d*. Stratigraphic trap.*

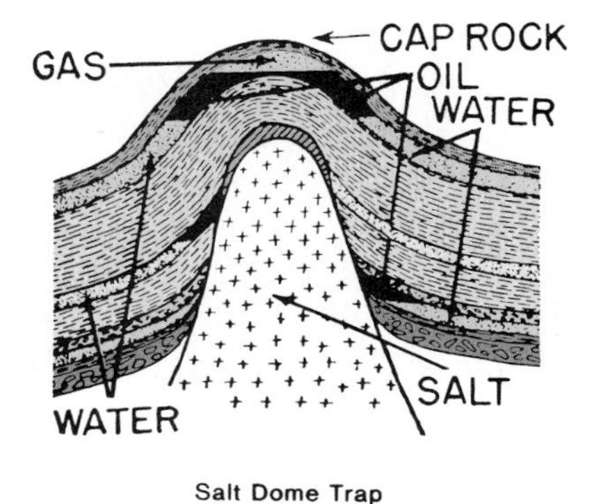

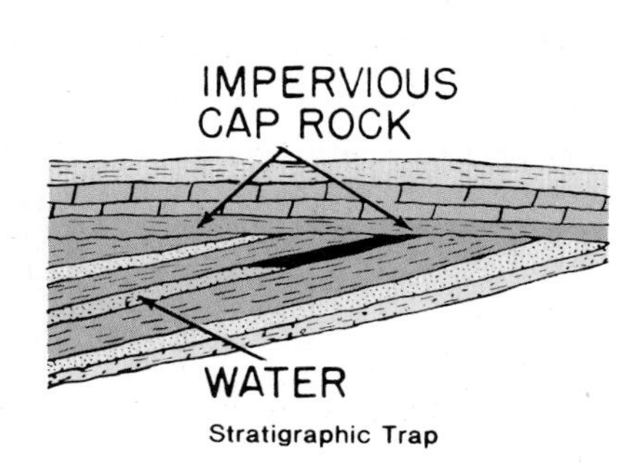

*Figures 6.12a–d are from *Primer of Oil and Gas Production*, 3rd ed., (American Petroleum Institute), 1971.

Anticline as structural trap.

As a result of folding, oil may be trapped in the crest of an **anticline** or upward bulge of rock layers. The oil lies in tiny spaces between grains in porous rock, but is trapped by impermeable rock layers. (See Figure 6.12a.)

Fault as structural trap.

Faulting can create structural traps. A **fault** is a break in the Earth's crust along which movement has occurred. This movement may result in a permeable rock layer being offset by a nonporous and impermeable layer. The oil moving along a permeable layer is "dammed" or blocked by the impermeable rock. (See Figure 6.12b.)

The salt dome trap.

Another type of structural trap is called a **salt dome** trap. Salt dome traps are found along the Gulf Coasts of Texas and Louisiana, and in the western Colorado-eastern Utah area. This type of structure results from the upward surge of a great mass of salt far below the Earth's surface. When a salt dome rises through an oil-bearing layer, oil may be trapped. (See Figure 6.12c.)

The stratigraphic trap.

One of the hardest places to find oil is in a **stratigraphic trap.** Here, the porous layers bearing oil taper off under nonporous layers (**strata**) of rock. The stratigraphic trap is formed by the thinning out (sometimes called pinch-out) of porous and permeable sandstone between two layers of impermeable shale. This creates an "envelope" where oil and gas may accumulate. This type of trap may have formed from buried beaches and sandbars. The famous East Texas field is a "strat" trap. (See Figure 6.12d.)

Figure 6.13 A modern drilling rig.
(American Petroleum Institute)

By searching for the source beds, reservoirs, and traps, geologists can greatly increase the likelihood of finding oil. But, in the final analysis, only the drill holes find oil. It takes a combination of the latest in Earth science technology and sound economic evaluation to explore for hydrocarbons profitably. Many traps are geologic successes, but economic failures.

What products result when oil is burned?

As we've already implied, oil consists of a mixture of liquid hydrocarbons of varying composition. During burning, the hydrogen and carbon in a hydrocarbon each combine with oxygen, forming water and carbon dioxide. The burning of oil to obtain energy may be represented by this equation:

$$\text{oil} + \text{oxygen } (O_2) \longrightarrow CO_2 + H_2O + \text{heat energy} + \text{wastes}$$

The wastes usually consist of unburned hydrocarbons, carbon monoxide, nitrogen oxides, and some sulfur gases.

The use of refining techniques to make oil-related products.

Refined petroleum is used for more than simply making gasoline for automobiles. **Refining** crude oil yields a host of products. Figure 6.14 shows what an "average" barrel of oil is used for. Many of our lubricants, plastics, and pharmaceuticals have their origin in crude oil.

Figure 6.15 illustrates how the petroleum industry underlies much of the U.S. economy.

6.6 Natural Gas

Why is gas such a desirable fuel?

Oil and gas originated together, and are searched for together. At first, natural gas was an unwanted by-product of the search for oil. It was considered of little value. For a long time, only the gas associated with oil was produced. Part of the production was utilized locally, and the rest was simply flared to the atmosphere. But after World War II, the

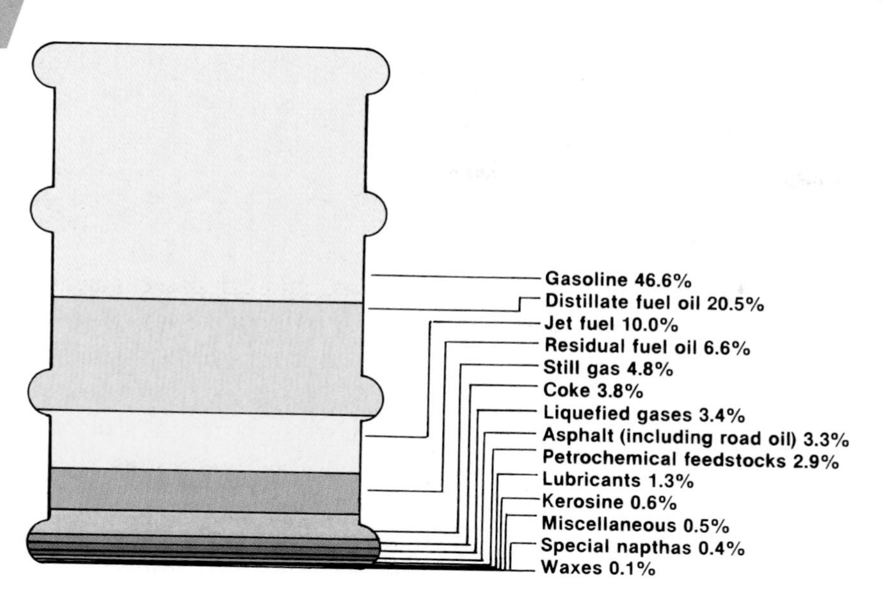

Figure 6.14 Average annual yields from a barrel of crude oil. (One barrel of oil contains 42 gallons.) (Source of percentage yield, USDOE. Gallons per barrel computed by American Petroleum Institute.)

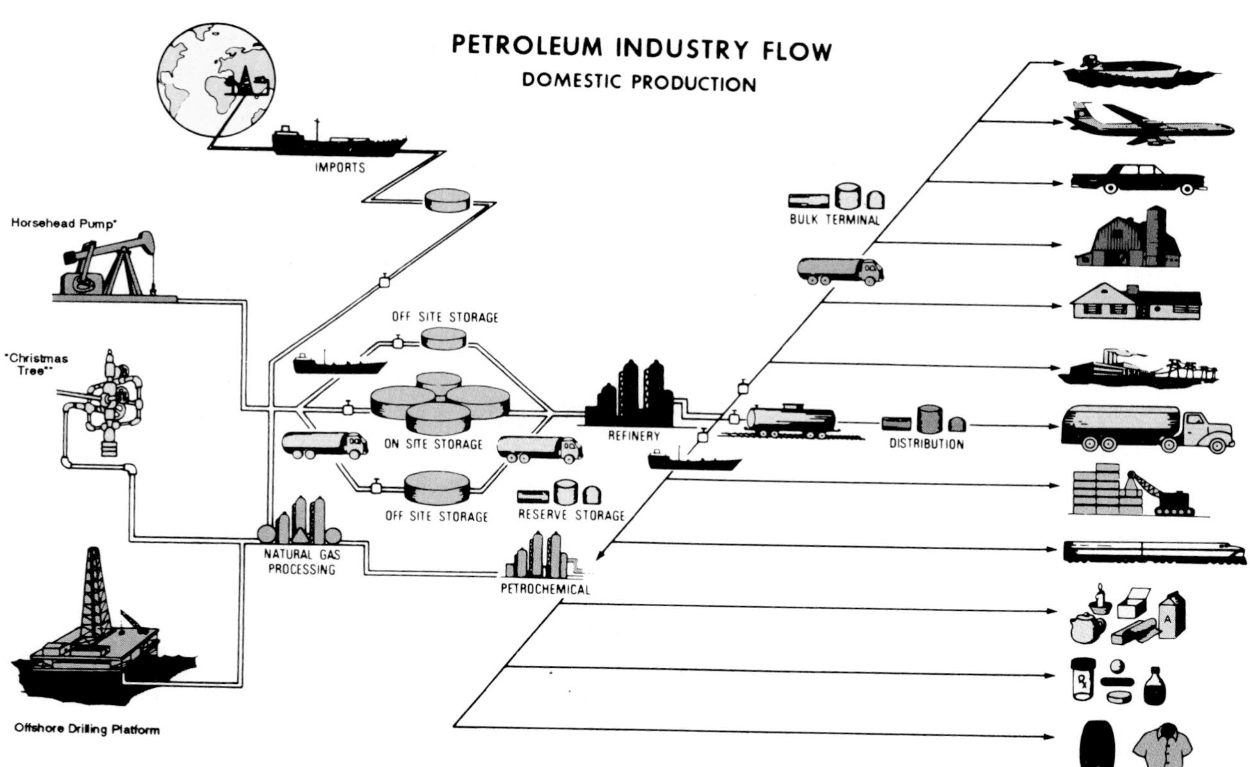

Figure 6.15 The broad base of the petroleum industry. (From U.S. Bureau of Mines, Department of Interior.)

true value of natural gas as a primary source of energy was recognized. There were strong efforts to develop widespread markets. Because of its excellent fuel qualities and the low price charged for it, gas began to be used at a rapidly increasing rate. By 1958, gas had displaced coal as the nation's second-most-important source of energy. Gas is a much cleaner fuel than coal or oil. It burns almost completely, and produces practically no harmful by-products.

The basic equation for the burning of natural gas is the same as that for oil. The only difference is that the hydrocarbon molecules that make up natural gas are smaller. Almost no wastes are formed, although some nitrogen oxides and some SO_2 are produced.

$$\text{natural gas} + \text{oxygen} \longrightarrow CO_2 + H_2O + \text{heat}$$

Natural gas as a fuel.

Natural gas is primarily a fuel resource, although gaseous hydrocarbon compounds such as ethane, propane, and butane are also used for petrochemical feedstocks. More U. S. homes are heated with natural gas than with any other fuel.

The industrial sector is the largest consumer of natural gas. Natural gas is used for raw material processing, food preparation, petrochemical feedstocks, refinery fuel, and many other uses.

6.7 Coal

Coal as a fuel.

Coal is now the third-ranking source of energy in the United States. It was once number one. Coal was replaced by oil and gas for the following reasons:

1. It is less useful than oil and natural gas. Being a solid, it cannot be moved, stored, or utilized as easily.
2. Coal does not burn as cleanly and completely as oil or gas.
3. Coal is often removed from the ground in large quantities by strip mining, which has a visible effect on the land surface. While post-mining reclamation is now required in most states, many old sites remain as scars on the countryside. Nature has gradually restored some of the old areas, but others are on steep slopes where erosion interferes with restoration. Or, early mining methods sometimes removed so much soil that nothing can grow there.
4. It is found in deposits which contain varying amounts of sulfur. When sulfur is burned, such as in striking a wooden match, it produces a smelly odor. Although it is expensive to remove sulfur from coal, low-sulfur coals are readily scrubbed and burn with little sulfur-related pollution.

Fly ash: Nonflammable impurities in burning coal that are carried away by the draft.
Bottom ash: The inorganic residue that remains after incineration.

The chemical equation for the burning of coal is:

$$\text{coal (C)} + \text{oxygen } (O_2) \longrightarrow CO_2 + \text{heat} + \text{waste}$$

Why is there a renewed interest in coal?

?

The wastes consist of sulfur dioxide, nitrogen oxides, carbon monoxide, soot, fly ash, and bottom ash.

Despite drawbacks, coal has experienced a revival as an energy source. This is because of declining U. S. crude oil reserves and production while energy demands continue to grow. Coal reserves are large and well mapped out. We have the equipment to get at them.

Figure 6.16 A lump of coal. (National Coal Association)

Coal can be loaded into trucks and transported safely, but oil and gas must be moved in tanks or pipelines and protected from flames.

The United States has an estimated two trillion tons of coal resources. About one-half trillion tons can be mined economically by current technology. The coal in our shallower reserves can meet our short-term needs, and reduce U.S. dependence on foreign petroleum supplies. The remaining 1.5 trillion tons are too deep, in seams too thin, too wet, or too mixed with rock to be recovered by today's mining methods. Current production of coal is about one billion tons yearly. At this rate, one-half trillion tons would last 500 years.

Electricity and coal.

The main reason coal can so readily be used in our economy is that most of our electrical generating plants are already set up to run on coal. Electricity is a highly desired form of energy.

a. The Origin of Coal

How was coal formed?

Coal occurs in strata (miners call them seams) along with other sedimentary rocks, mostly shale and sandstone. A look through a magnifying glass at a piece of coal reveals bits of fossilized wood, bark, leaves, roots, and other parts of land plants. This shows that coal is fossilized plant matter.

Coal is an organic substance, being made up primarily of carbon. It also contains varying amounts of hydrogen, oxygen, nitrogen, and sulfur. Coal is composed of the fossilized remains of land plants that flourished millions of years ago.

The places where coal accumulated were ancient swamps and marshes in equatorial regions. Only under these conditions is plant matter likely to become coal. On dry land, dead plant matter (composed chiefly of carbon, hydrogen, and oxygen) rots away. This is because bacteria use atmospheric oxygen to form carbon dioxide and water from dead material. Under stagnant or nearly stagnant water, little oxygen is present. The plant matter is attacked by **anaerobic** (without air) bacteria, which partly decompose the matter by splitting off oxygen and hydrogen. These two elements escape, combined in various gases. Carbon gradually becomes concentrated in the remains. The bacteria themselves are destroyed before they can finish the decay. Acids liberated from the dead plants kill the bacteria. This could not happen in a stream, because flowing water would bring in new oxygen and dilute the acids.

With the destruction of bacteria, the plant matter has been converted to peat. **Peat** is brownish-black organic material that looks very much like decayed wood. Dried peat will burn and produce heat. Because peat still contains some water, it is very smoky when burned. Here is a chemical equation which represents the formation of peat from plant material:

$$\underset{\text{plant cellulose}}{6\,C_6H_{10}O_5} \xrightarrow{\text{anaerobic bacteria}} \underset{\text{carbon dioxide}}{7\,CO_2} + \underset{\text{marsh gas}}{3\,CH_4} + \underset{\text{water}}{14\,H_2O} + \underset{\text{peat}}{C_{26}H_{20}O_2}$$

What are the four types of coal and what are their uses?

As peat is buried beneath more plant matter, and beneath accumulating sand, silt, or clay, both temperature and pressure increase. This brings about a series of continuing changes. The peat is compressed, and water is squeezed out. Gases such as methane (CH_4) escape, leaving an ever-increasing proportion of carbon. The peat is converted first into **lignite,** then into **subbituminous coal,** and finally into **bituminous coal.** These coals are sedimentary rocks. A still later phase, **anthracite,** is a metamorphic rock.

As anthracite generally occurs in folded strata, we infer that it has undergone a further loss of volatiles and a concentration of carbon. This is the result of the pressure and heat that accompany folding. Because of its low content of volatiles, anthracite is hard to ignite. But once alight, it burns with almost no smoke. This quality makes it the most desirable of all coals for space heating. In contrast, lignite ignites so easily that it is dangerously subject to spontaneous combustion. It burns smokily. The four types of coal are summarized in Figure 6.17.

The heat density (or energy content) of coal helps to determine its quality and usefulness as a fuel. The higher the proportion of carbon to moisture in a coal, the more heat density it has. Lignite ranks lowest among the coals. Anthracite ranks highest. (The use of lignite in coal gasification processes may generate a new demand for it. This is discussed in Chapter 9.)

Subbituminous coal is used primarily for producing steam. The principal uses of bituminous coal are for electric power generation and for smelting steel. "Metallurgical grade" is the classification given several varieties of bituminous coal that are required for blast

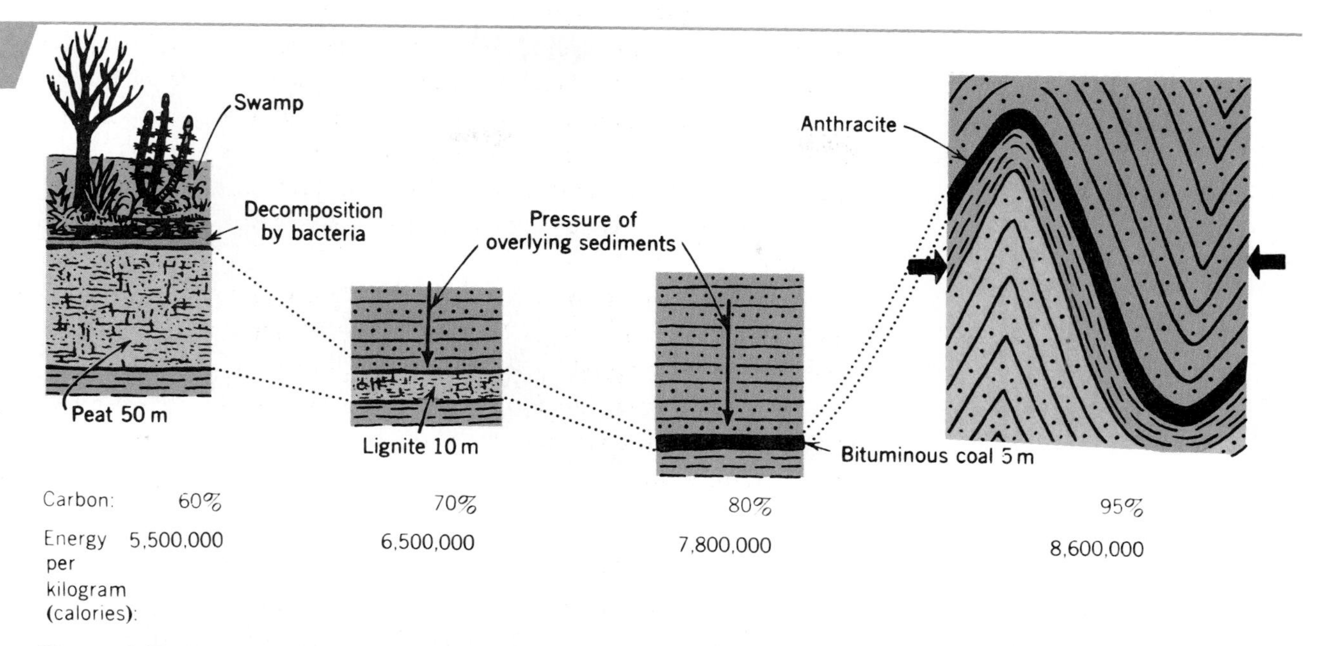

Figure 6.17 Accumulating plant matter is converted into coal by decomposition, pressure and heat. By the time a layer has been changed from peat to bituminous coal, it has decreased to one-tenth of its original thickness. During the same time, the heat density has risen continually. (From *Physical Geology,* 2nd ed., by R. F. Flint and B. J. Skinner, copyright © 1977, John Wiley & Sons, Inc. Reprinted by permission of John Wiley & Sons, Inc.)

furnaces. It is called "coking coal." (Coke is bituminous coal from which the volatile parts have been driven off by heat so that the fixed carbon and ash are fused together.) Coking coal burns with a long yellow flame, creating an intense heat.

b. The Location of Coal Deposits

Proven coal deposits exist on every continent, even on Antarctica. This can only be explained by continental drift. Coal formed in swampy equatorial regions but was "rafted" by the moving lithosphere to other areas.

As the map in Figure 6.19 shows, coal has been found in most of the United States. In fact, nearly one-eighth of the country lies over coal beds. For discussion it is convenient to divide the coal fields of the U.S. into eastern and western regions.

Eastern coals occur generally in connected seams up to twelve feet thick. They run throughout 2,000 to 3,000 feet of stratified clay, sandstone, or limestone. The eastern coal fields are mostly high-grade deposits.

Western deposits are usually isolated from each other and are less predictable. They are usually less extensive than eastern deposits. Most are also thicker and closer to the surface.

Coal seams vary considerably in thickness, from a few inches to more than 100 feet. The average thickness of bituminous coal seams in the United States is 5.4 feet. Most of the coal mined in this country

Figure 6.18 Advances in technology have enabled the electric arc furnace to replace the less-efficient blast furnace and basic oxygen furnace in steel making. In most cases, the electricity for operating these furnaces is generated at coal-fired power plants. (Barry McGee/Sidbeck Dosco—Canada)

is from beds varying in thickness from 3 to 10 feet. Many of the seams strip mined in the west are more than 80 feet thick and very close to the surface.

Table 6.1 summarizes many important contrasts between eastern and western coal. We will return to some of these items in later chapters.

c. Mining Methods

Underground mining.

In the beginning, most coal was obtained by mining underground. Underground mining methods are shown in Figure 6.20. Generally, a series of large underground rooms are cut into the coal seam, and **pillars** (columns) of coal are left standing to help support the roof. Once a particular area is mined out, the pillars are systematically removed and the roof allowed to fall.

In the past, underground miners recovered no more than about 50% of the coal present. The work was hard, unpleasant, and dangerous. Today underground mining has been modernized by huge automatic coal-cutting and loading machines (see Figure 6.20). This modernization has improved mine safety, along with increasing coal production (by 10 to 20 times) and coal seam recovery (to about 60%).

What is continuous mining?

Figure 6.20 shows a **continuous mining machine** at work. This machine can cut the coal loose and load it in one operation. Two men operating it can mine coal at the rate of about 12 tons a minute. That's a

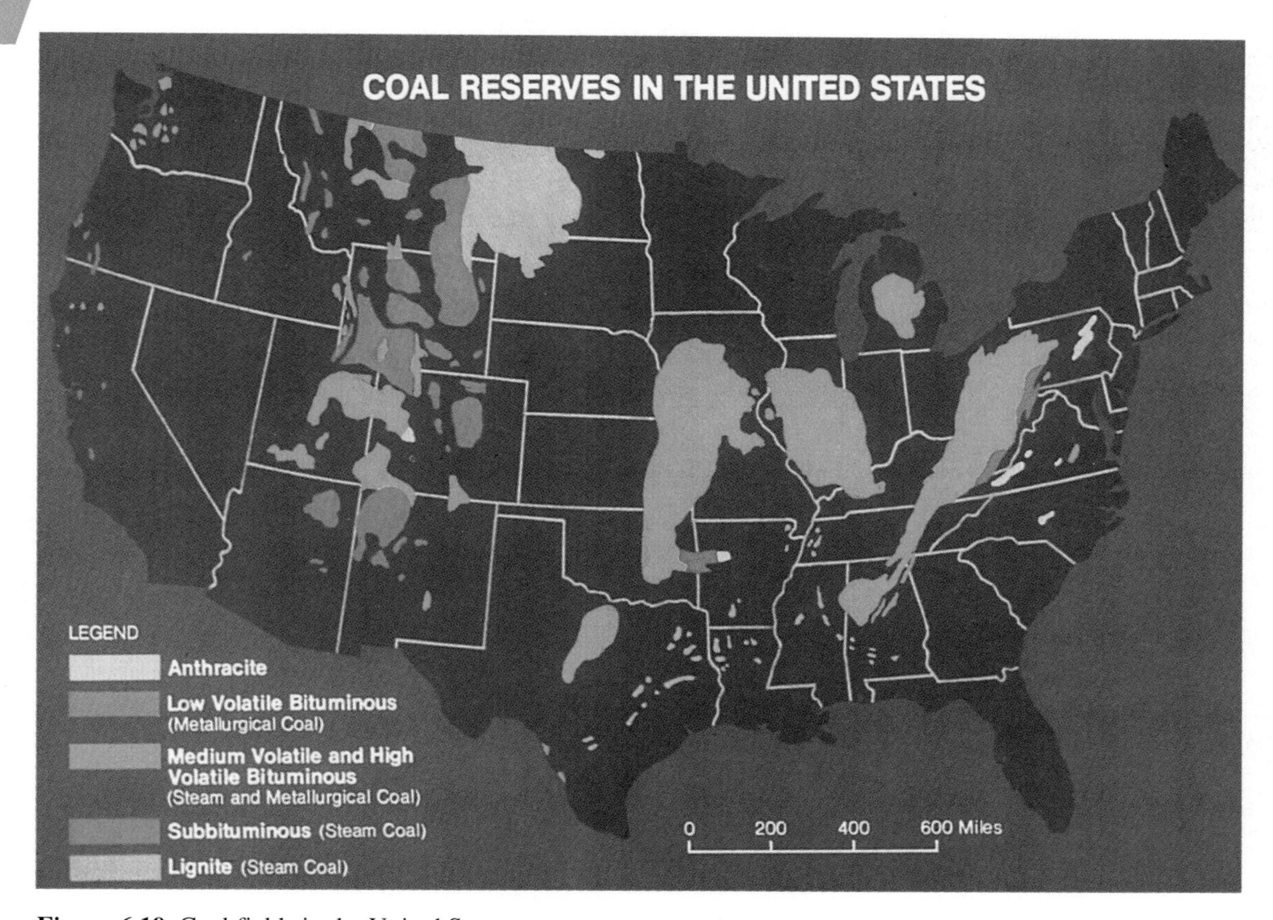

Figure 6.19 Coal fields in the United States. (From National Coal Association.)

lot of coal compared to the days of "Big John," the pick-and-shovel miner. The continuous mining machine is like a gigantic coal eating monster. It chews coal from the mine face, gathers it in its claws, feeds it onto a moving belt, and dumps the coal at its rear end.

Another underground mining method gaining popularity in the United States is **longwall mining** (illustrated in Figure 6.20). In this system, coal is mined by a cutter (shears) which is pulled back and forth across a mine face 300 to 800 feet long. The loosened coal drops onto a conveyor belt that lies along the bottom of the face. As the mining machine cuts its way into the seam, hydraulic jacks automatically push steel roof supports forward toward the receding face. This creates a space in which workers and machines can operate without being endangered by falling roof material. When the coal is removed from a section, its roof is allowed to fall.

The use of longwall mining.

Using longwall techniques, miners can recover up to 90% of a coal seam. There is no need to leave pillars supporting the roof. Another benefit is that roof subsidence (sinking) occurs more uniformly with longwall operations than over room-and-pillar systems. Shortwall mining, a modification of longwall mining, is used to mine odd, irregular sections of a coal seam.

Table 6.1 A Comparison of Eastern and Western Coal.

Item	Eastern	Western
U.S. Percentage	60%	40%
Types	Bituminous, anthracite	Subbituminous, bituminous, lignite
Sulfur level	high-to-low	low-to-medium
Depth	Average–200′ deep	shallow
Mining methods*	Underground: room and pillar, longwall, continuous	Surface: strip, open pit
Average $ value (1992)	$38.43/ton	$21.26/ton
Recovery	50%–70%	90%
Water supply	Enough water for both people and coal processing	Low supply of water for both people and coal processing
Reclamation challenges	Wet; water pollution (acid mine leaching), spoil banks, and subsidence	Dry; lack of water for slurries, gasification, and reclamation
Labor	Unionized	Mostly non-union
Safety	Problems	Few problems
Human impact of mining	Low; many mining towns to absorb population growth if coal production increases.	High; few mining towns (usually small), making an infux of people very hard to accommodate.

*Some eastern coal is surface mined, and some western coal is mined underground.

Surface mining.

About 60% of the coal produced annually in the United States is recovered by **surface mining.** If coal lies less than 200 feet beneath the surface and the seam is thick enough, it may be mined by removing the overlying surface rock (called **overburden**) with draglines, shovels, or wheels. (Figure 6.21). Power shovels then dig the coal and load it onto huge trucks (Figure 6.22). The trucks carry the coal to a nearby processing plant where it is separated from impurities, crushed, sorted into various sizes, and washed. Then it may be trucked or loaded onto railroad cars for shipping.

How is surface mining done?

Surface mining, referred to as *strip mining* or *open pit mining,* greatly reduces the danger to miners, and permits recovery of 90% or more of the coal in the ground. Less than 10% of all coal in the United States is close enough to the surface to be reached by strip mining. Because much of the shallow, strippable coal occurs in rich farming areas, farming and farmland may be disturbed. However, now the land is restored after mining is completed. Both mining and reclamation can go on at the same time. Planned in advance, the cost is moderate. Reclaimed land may even look better than before the surface was disturbed (Figure 6.23).

Electrical Energy

Coal continues to be the largest and most important source of energy for generating electricity. Because of environmental concerns, other

Types of Underground-Mining Equipment

The type of equipment that an underground mine requires depends on the method of mining it uses. Mechanized mines use three main methods: (1) the conventional method, (2) continuous mining, and (3) longwall mining. Each of the three methods calls for a different type of equipment.

WORLD BOOK illustrations by Robert Addison

Conventional-Mining Equipment. The conventional method of mining involves a series of steps, three of which require special machinery. First, a cutting machine, *left*, cuts a deep slit along the base of the coal *face* (coal exposed on the surface of a mine wall). Another machine, *center*, drills holes into the face. Miners load the holes with explosives and then set the explosives off. The undercutting along the bottom of the face causes the shattered coal to fall to the floor. A loading machine, *right*, gathers the coal onto a conveyor belt.

Continuous-Mining Equipment eliminates the need for separate steps in mining a face. A continuous-mining machine, *right*, gouges out the coal and loads it onto a shuttle car in one operation.

Longwall-Mining Equipment. Longwall mining differs from the other methods of underground mining in its system of roof support. The other methods are used only in room-and-pillar mines, where pillars of coal are left to support the mine roof. In the longwall method, movable steel props support the roof over one long coal face. The miners move a cutting machine back and forth across the face, shearing off coal. The coal falls onto a conveyor. As the miners advance the cutter into the bed, the roof supports are moved forward. The roof behind the miners is allowed to fall.

Figure 6.20 Types of mining equipment and methods. (From The World Book Encyclopedia. Copyright © 1993, World Book, Inc. Reproduced with permission.)

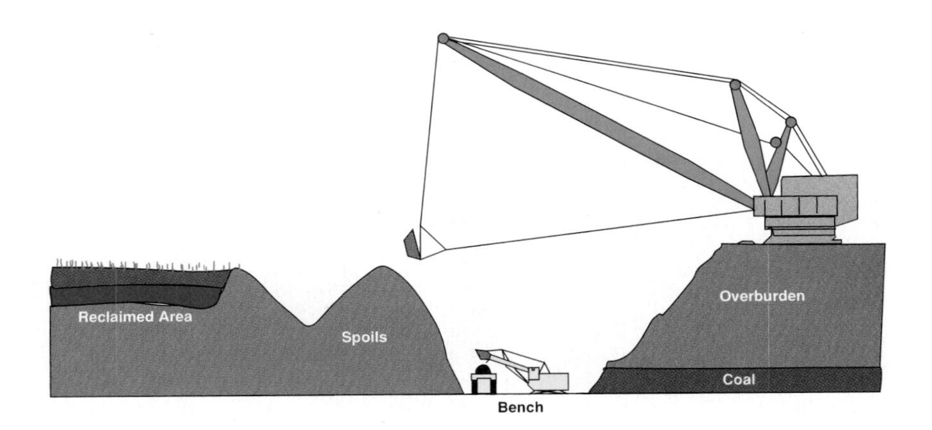

Figure 6.21 The strip mining of coal.

Figure 6.22 This huge truck is typical of those used in modern surface mines. (Courtesy Caterpillar, Inc.)

energy sources are also being used. The two major alternative sources are nuclear energy and hydropower, or energy from water. Scientists are continually trying to perfect new and more desirable methods for producing electric power.

6.8 Hydropower

The potential energy of dammed water is utilized as an energy source in certain regions of our country where there are both rivers and hills or mountains. **Hydropower** is used almost entirely for generating electricity. Of the total amount of primary (beginning) energy utilized in the United States in 1991, hydropower represented about 4.0%.

Figure 6.23 Mining operation surrounded by reclaimed farmland. (From The National Coal Association, Absaloka Mine in Montana.)

Figure 6.24 Aerial view of Shasta Dam. (U.S. Bureau of Reclamation)

The basic equation for the utilization of hydropower might be represented as follows:

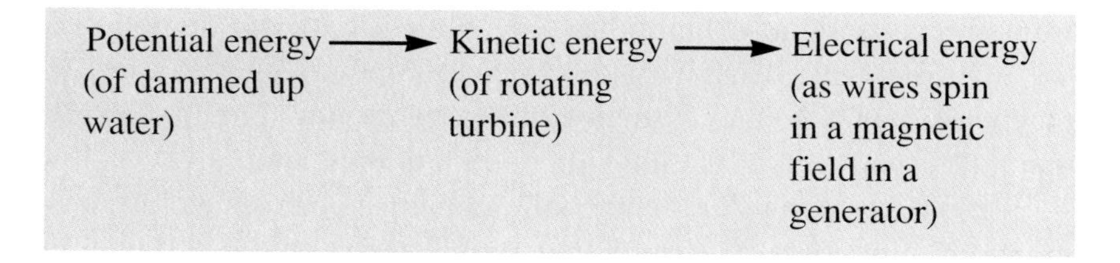

Trace the parts of this equation through the cutaway view of a hydroelectric powerplant (Figure 6.25).

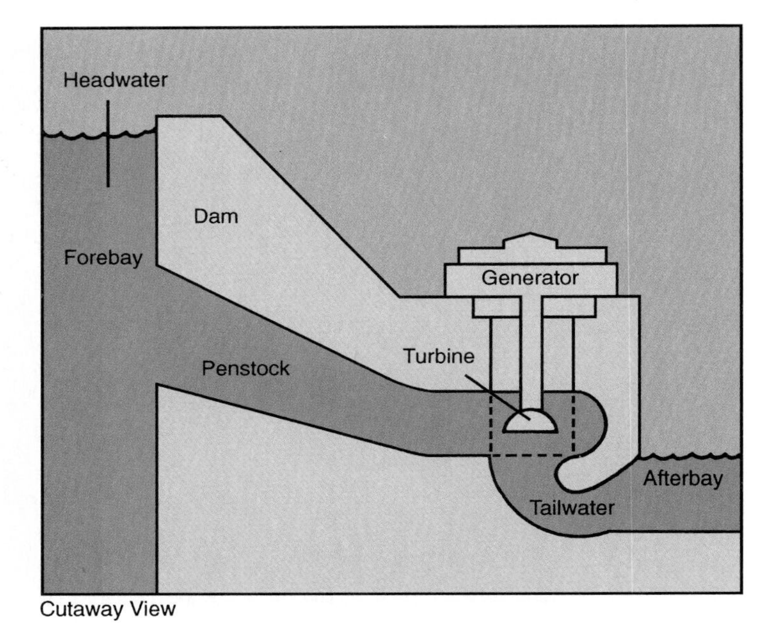

Figure 6.25 Cutaway view of a hydroelectric power plant. (U.S. Bureau of Reclamation)

Why is the use of hydropower not expected to greatly increase the amount of energy available?

In spite of the relative low cost and cleanliness of hydropower, its role is not expected to increase in the years ahead. Few large hydroelectric sites remain that can be developed and effectively utilized. The Southwest has the elevation changes necessary for good sites, but lacks the water. The Eastern portion of the United States has the water but not the elevation changes. In the Northwest hydropower has been developed almost to its capacity.

How is electric energy produced?

 6.9 Generating Electricity

Electrical energy is very popular because it is easily transformed into motion, heat, or light. All we have to do is flip a switch. With that, a motor starts, heat is available, or a light goes on. At our command, with another switch or knob, a radio plays, or a television set brings us news and pictures from around the globe. What is electricity? How is it produced?

Electric **current** consists of electrons moving in an organized way in a wire. Electrons are already in the wires. However, they will not move in an organized way without a source of power. One power source is a battery. Another is an electric power plant.

Almost all the electricity we use is generated at an electric power plant. From there, power lines bring the electricity to our homes. Figure 6.26 shows the basic parts of an electric power plant. Typically, they consist of a boiler, a **turbine,** and a **generator.** The paragraphs that follow will explain the function of each of these units.

A galvanometer is a meter that detects both the presence of electric current and the direction of current flow.

Electric power generation is built around an event called **electromagnetic induction.** Michael Faraday, an English physicist, found in 1831 that if a copper wire was moved in a **magnetic field,** electrons in the wire would move. He used a galvanometer to detect the movement. If the wire was made a part of a complete **circuit,** electricity

Figure 6.26 The basics of electric power generation. (Public Service Company of Colorado)

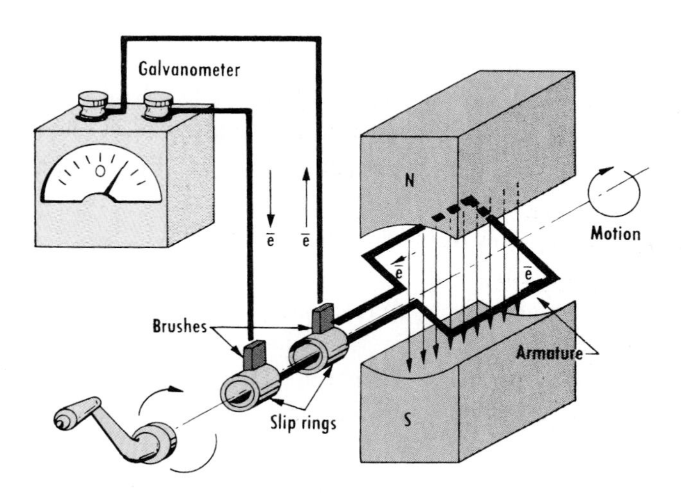

Figure 6.27 The rotation of the coil between the poles of the magnet induces alternating current. (From *Modern Science 3*, by Blanc, Fischler and Gardner. Copyright © 1983 by Holt, Rinehart & Winston, Inc.)

would flow through the circuit. To produce electricity, it is necessary to continually change the magnetic field. The easiest way to do this is to rotate a coil of wire between the poles of a strong magnet. The basic principles involved are illustrated in Figure 6.27.

The rotating coil is called an **armature.** As it spins around, current flows back and forth in the coil; this is called alternating current (AC). One coil moving through a magnetic field produces very little current. Thousands of coils spinning rapidly in a powerful magnetic field can produce enough electricity to satisfy the needs of a small town. In a power plant, it is the electric **generator** that contains the coils of wire and the powerful magnet.

Unfortunately, the coils do not spin easily. It takes energy to drive electrons through an electric circuit. The conservation of energy law dictates that we cannot get something for nothing. Therefore, to power an electric circuit, the coils must be forced to rotate. To do this, the generator is connected to a **turbine.** The turbine consists of a series of

Figure 6.28 Turbine blades. (USDOE)

thousands of blades that are carefully directed and shaped to transfer the force of moving steam or water to a central shaft. As the shaft spins, the armature coils spin and electric current flows. Figure 6.28 shows the blades of a typical turbine.

Electric power plants differ primarily in how they are designed to turn the turbine. Most of them direct high pressure steam onto turbine blades. The steam is produced in a steam generator. This is usually heated by burning coal, but some power plants burn oil or natural gas. Others obtain their heat from nuclear reactors. Hydroelectric plants use the pressure of water behind a dam to turn turbines.

Electric power plants are large-scale operations. A 1,000 megawatt coal-fired plant may burn 10,000 tons of coal a day to provide the needs of millions of people. The coal is often brought to these plants by a unit-train. A **unit-train** may consist of one hundred 100-ton cars. They often move nonstop from mine to power plant. At the power plant, they are usually unloaded automatically. The train moves slowly forward as the cars are mechanically rotated and dumped. When empty, the train returns directly to the mine.

At the plant, the coal is carried by conveyor to a crusher and a silo. It is fed by gravity into a pulverizer, where it is continually hammered into particles as fine as flour. The pulverized coal is then blown into the boiler where steam is produced.

For steam to rush through the turbine, the pressure must be high at the incoming end and low at the exit. Steam leaves the boiler at very high pressure and is blown onto the turbine blades. At the exit end of the

Figure 6.29 A typical coal-fired electric power generating plant. This plant is located on the Mississippi River in Minnesota. (Northern States Power Company.)

turbine, the steam comes in contact with cool pipes from the **cooling towers.** The steam quickly condenses back to water, and the pressure drops dramatically. The water in the cool pipes absorbs the released heat and is warmed. This warmed water goes to the radiator unit of the cooling tower. Here sprinklers spray the water onto tile baffles. The baffles provide a huge surface area for the warm water to flow over. As heat and steam rise in the tower, cooler air flows into the bottom of the tower and past the spray of water. This causes some of the water to evaporate and cool the lower region. Most of the water is cooled, collects at the bottom of the cooling tower, and is returned to the low-pressure end of the turbine. The cycle then repeats. (See Figure 6.30.)

Electricity is typically generated at approximately 20,000 **volts.** Before being transmitted to consumers, it flows to the power **transformer,** where the voltage is increased or stepped up. A transformer is a highly efficient electrical device used to either increase (step up) or decrease (step down) voltages.

Voltage is related to the driving force behind the current. It is often compared to the concept of pressure.

All wires offer some **resistance** to the flow of electric current. This resistance results in the heating of the wire. The more current in the wire, the greater the heating. Unfortunately, if these wires are the **power transmission** wires, energy is being lost to space in the form of heat. To cut down on this energy loss, electrical energy must be transmitted at the lowest current possible. To step down the current, the transformer steps up the voltage. Transmission voltages may be as high as 760,000 volts.

Resistance to current flow depends on the kind of wire (copper, aluminum) and the diameter of the wire. The larger the diameter, the lower the resistance.

High-voltage transmission lines carry electric power over many miles. It eventually ends up at a local substation. The transformer at the substation then steps the voltage down again (12,000 volts is

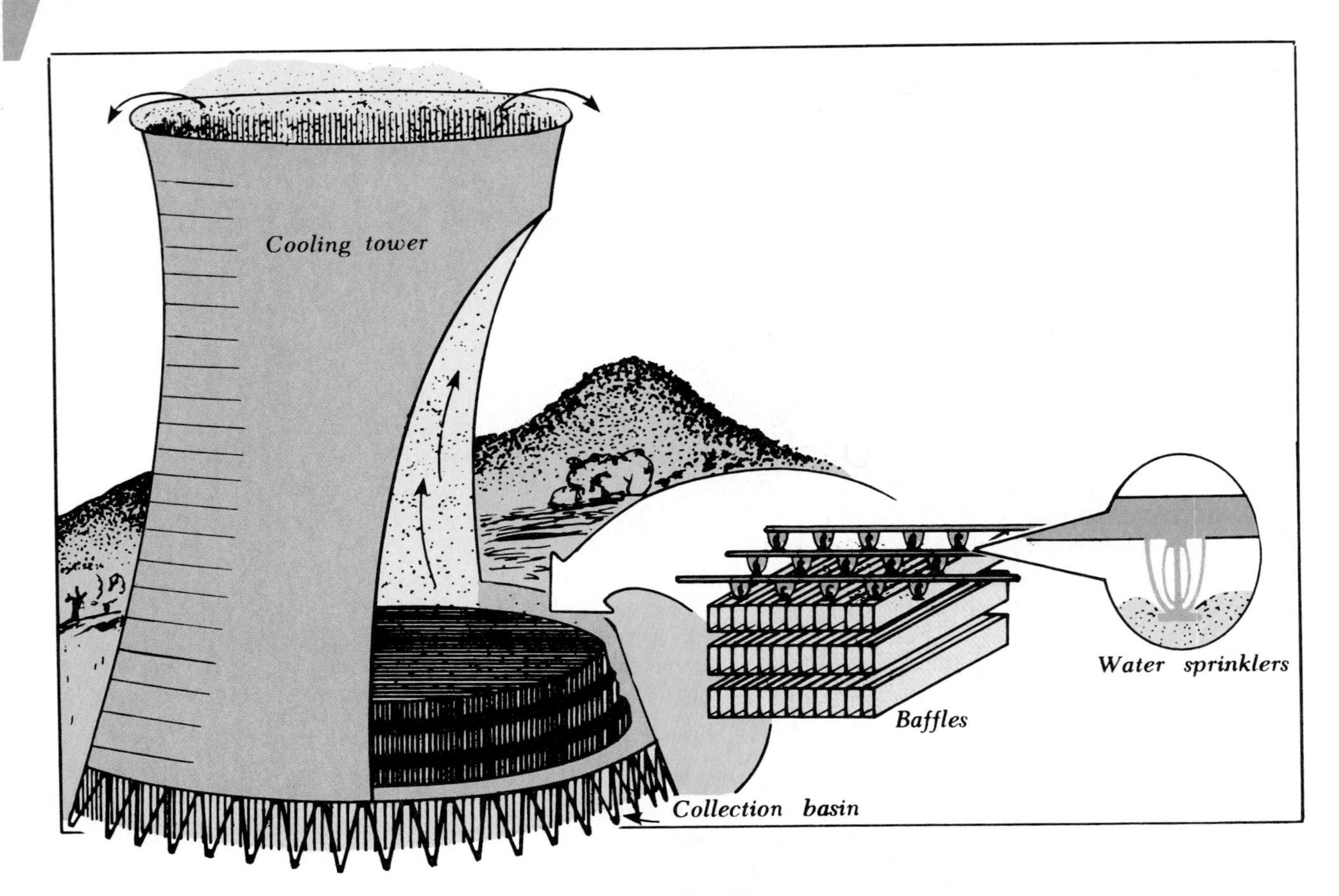

Figure 6.30 Cooling tower operation.

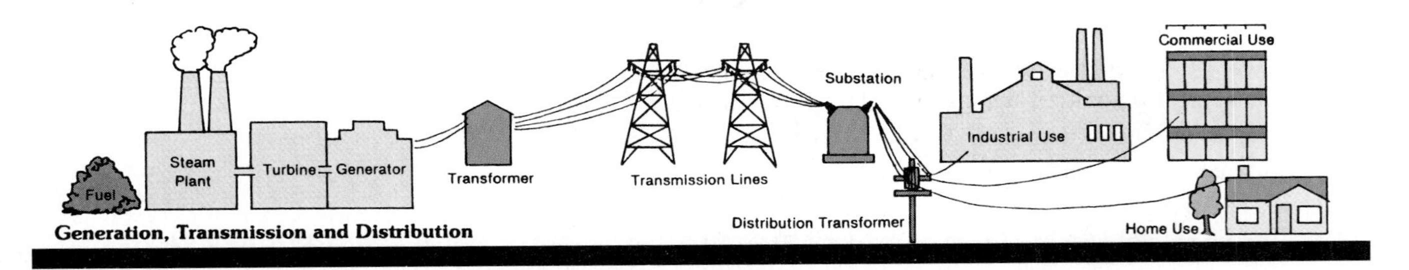

Figure 6.31 Generation, transmission, and distribution of electricity. (National Energy Foundation)

common). As the voltage is stepped down, the electric current increases to the current that the consumer wants. Current flows from the local substation through a network of lines attached to power poles. However, before the lines go to homes and buildings, they first pass through the smaller step-down **transformer** that is fastened high up on the power pole. Neighborhood underground distribution systems

Figure 6.32 A high-voltage (500kv) transmission tower under construction. (Northern States Power Company)

are growing in popularity. They are seldom touched by earth-moving equipment and cannot be damaged by storms (falling trees, ice overloads, etc.).

From these transformers, 240- and 120-volt lines extend to homes and smaller commercial buildings. Electrical devices that heat, such as electric stoves and clothes dryers, require more current and a higher voltage (220–240 volts). Most other appliances are built to operate at 110–220 volts.

Before passing into a building, the lines pass through the **watt·hour meter,** which monitors and records electrical energy usage. The lines then enter the circuit breaker box, where all the circuits in a building originate.

Electricity is a unique form of energy in that it cannot be stored, except for the relatively small amounts stored in batteries (or pump-filled reservoirs). It must be used immediately on generation. Thus,

The watt hour is a unit of electrical energy. The watt hour meter records the amount of electrical energy used in the building.

What is one of the unique properties of electrical energy?

Figure 6.33 Utility pole transformer. (Public Service Company of Colorado)

Figure 6.34 A home watt hour meter. (Public Service Company of Colorado)

electricity must be produced on demand. The demand is signaled by someone turning on an additional air conditioner or TV, for instance. The signal is sent at nearly the speed of light, and it must be met just as swiftly.

The load is related to the demand for electrical energy.

If all air conditioners, motors, and refrigerators required a constant power **load,** meeting it would not be too difficult. However, the demand fluctuates hourly, daily, weekly, and seasonally. In a city like New York or Chicago, for instance, the loads build up quickly on weekday mornings as elevators run up and down in tall buildings, and the subways take their rush hour loads to work. The weekend load is much lower.

Figure 6.35 shows a typical weekly load curve. It reaches a minimum a few hours after midnight, and builds to a peak in the early afternoon. The midweek peaks are higher than those of the weekend. To

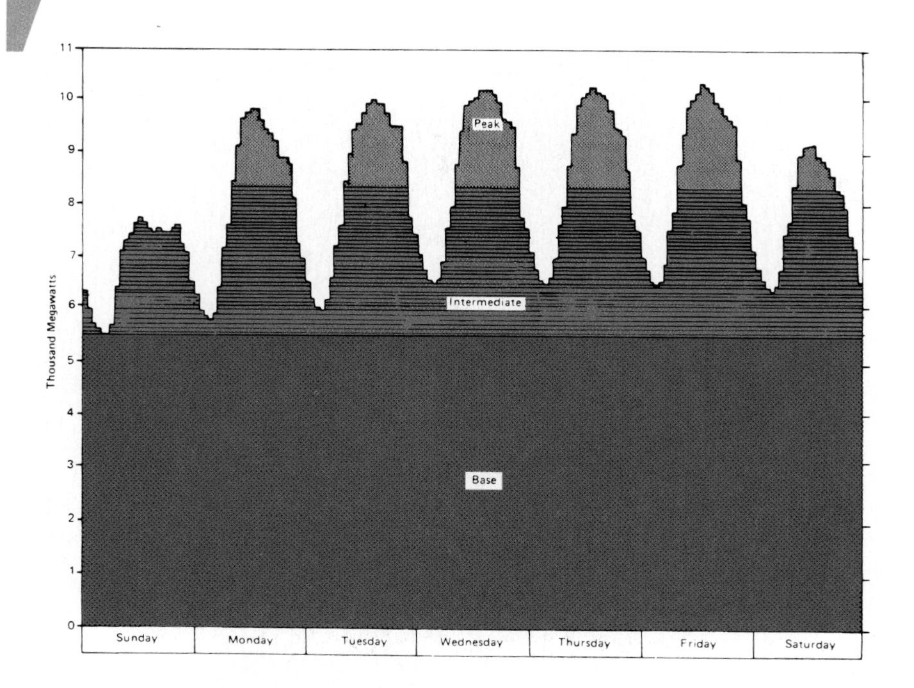

Figure 6.35 Electric power weekly load curve. (From The 1970 Power Supply Part I, Federal Power Commission Washington, D.C., 1970.)

respond to these changing customer needs, a utility system must have a variety of generators to turn on and off.

The different types of loads can be summarized under four headings: baseload, intermediate load, peak load, and reserve. The baseload is that part of the load that doesn't change. This demand is met by the large fossil fuel-fired or nuclear generators. These are usually 500–1000 megawatt (mW) generators, designed to run continuously. If shut down, they need at least 24 hours to restart. Baseload generators are usually the most efficient generators and produce the least expensive electricity.

Explain the meanings of baseload, intermediate load, peak load, and reserve.

The intermediate load does fluctuate somewhat, and therefore generators that can be varied in power output are needed. Oil- or gas-fired steam turbine units (some of them as large as 500 mW) are useful for this purpose. They are relatively easy to control and can operate at less than full power output without a great loss of efficiency. They can typically be shut down and restarted in four to six hours.

The least efficient generators are those used to meet the peak load demand. This part of the load varies from day to day and even hour to hour. Peak load generators must be turned on and off in minutes, instead of hours. Diesel-powered motor-generator sets or gas turbines are most often used for this purpose. These engines burn expensive fuel and are considerably less efficient than the larger systems (25% vs. 35 or 40%). Thus, the electricity they produce is expensive.

Hydroelectric power is being used more and more to meet peak load demand. The big turbines are allowed to turn (since they do not use expensive fuel), but are connected to the generators only when needed. They serve, therefore, as "spinning reserve."

Figure 6.36 Giant turbine-generators at a large nuclear power plant. (U.S. Council for Energy Awareness)

Reserve capacity.

The fourth type of generator capacity is reserve. As it is impossible to predict exactly what the maximum load during a year will be, a utility must have more than enough generation capacity to meet the predicted peak load. Reserve capacity is also needed to take over when other generators break down or during routine shutdown of other equipment. United States utilities try to maintain a 20% to 25% reserve capacity. This is, of course, the most expensive electricity because the costly pieces of equipment sit idle much of the time.

Brownouts and blackout.

What happens in an emergency, such as the failure of a generator? The eventual response has to be repair or replacement. The load, however, must be reduced immediately. This can be accomplished by either a "brownout," in which the voltage is deliberately lowered, or by a "blackout," in which all or part of the load is turned off.

Of course, most utility systems now share power with others in a power pool. Problems with one generator are then compensated for by all the other generators in the pool. The enormous amounts of energy stored in the hundreds of spinning rotors of the pool can take care of a considerable emergency.

The "blackout" in New York in July 1977, however, shows that even a pool can be overloaded. (See Figure 6.37.) In that instance, the New York utility, Consolidated Edison, was already buying a lot of

Figure 6.37 The New York City blackout, July 13–14, 1977. Note the automobile headlights and that some buildings had auxiliary power. (New York Daily News Photo)

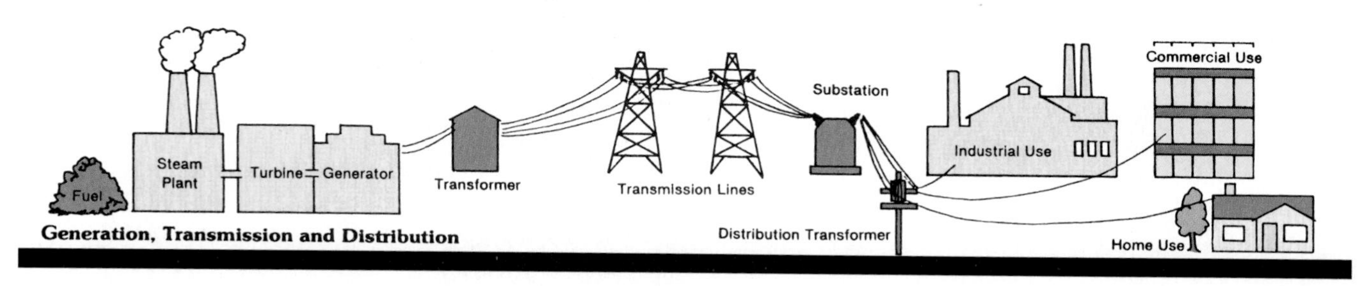

Figure 6.38 Generation, transmission, and distribution of electricity. (National Energy Foundation)

power from the regional pool because one of the large Indian Point nuclear generators was shut down for repair. When a lightning storm knocked out one of the transmission lines bringing in power, and later knocked out the other Indian Point generator, the remaining "tie lines" bringing in power were overloaded and in danger of burning up. The whole system then had to be shut down.

6.10 Transmission and Distribution

You have read about the details of electrical generation. Now consider briefly the rest of the system: transmission, distribution, and end use. The entire system is summarized in Figure 6.38.

Electric power is produced at voltages in the range of 2,000 to 30,000 volts. It is then stepped up for transmission to greater than 200,000 volts in most places, and to voltages as high as 765,000 in the newest lines.

The reason for the growth in ultrahigh voltage (UHV) transmission lines (with voltages in excess of 530,000 volts) is financial cost. Since the resistance loss in a transmission line depends on the current in the line, it pays to make voltage (V) as large as possible in order to keep current (I) as small as possible. (A 765,000-volt line can carry as much power as five 340,000-volt lines or thirty 138,000-volt lines *).

Why is electrical power transmitted at high voltage and low current? Why develop UHV transmission lines?

No Coal? Cool

science at work

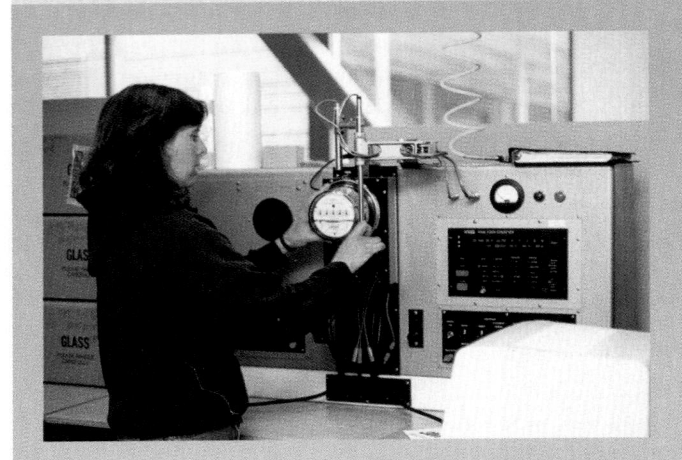

"It's all a matter of training" says Sue Coakley. She knows women can have a career in any field they're interested in, as long as they get the knowledge and training they need. Sue is a meter service technician at the City of Alameda/Bureau of Electricity, and she's part of a very special team. The island community of Alameda, California, lies just east of San Francisco. Alameda's 80,000 people have a broad cultural mix, and the city is proud of its diversity. Its sources of electricity are diverse, too—and none of them are coal. During 1992, the Bureau of Electricity obtained 100 percent of its electric power from geothermal and hydroelectric sources, and combustion turbines that run on natural gas.

Alameda gets some of its electricity through the federal government's Western Area Power Administration, but about 80 percent is provided by the Northern California Power Agency (NCPA). The NCPA consists of 14 customer-owned utilities. The NCPA's geothermal power plants, with a capacity of 232,000 kilowatts, are run by steam from adjoining wells, delivered via a computerized system. Lately there has been a reduction in the steam produced by the project's wells, and a second water retention dam has been constructed. Water from condensation and rain has been injected to extend the life of the steam reservoir. There are now a total of 69 steam-production wells and 6 water-injection wells. The NCPA's combustion turbine project generates power during peak electrical demand periods as well as backup power for the other NCPA sources. Natural gas—because it's cheap and kind to the environment—produces the steam to run the turbines.

But let's get back to what Sue Coakley does. In addition to turning electric service on and off at the meter, Sue keeps a close eye on those meters, which measure electricity usage in Alameda's homes and businesses. When the service at a particular address changes, she pulls the meter out, checks it for proper voltage and wiring, and arranges for a line worker to service the meter if necessary. In the field or in the shop, she tests and calibrates the meters with a device that uses electric current to measure the meters' accuracy. "Most meters are quite accurate," Sue says with a smile in her voice, "regardless of what their users think!"

Working outdoors is probably her favorite part of the job, Sue says. She likes the feeling of competence her work gives her. She's glad she paid attention to her math and science instructors in high school—especially math—because that's where she learned many basic principles she uses every day. Starting out as a meter reader, she worked her way up to the higher-level position she now holds, and acquired additional training in AC and DC circuitry at a community college.

Sue has some personal contact with her customers, too, advising them about conserving their electricity. When they understand how much electricity each of their appliances uses, people pay more attention to how they use electricity throughout their home or business, and try harder to conserve. For instance, using a comforter on a waterbed helps hold in the mattress's heat, and turning a fax machine off at night means it uses power only during the work day. Every little bit helps.

The 765,000-volt lines need only 200 feet of right of way, compared with 750 feet for five 340,000-volt lines. Land prices, construction costs, and material costs all argue for the ultrahigh voltages.

*The explanation for this is beyond the mathematical scope of this course.

Other technological improvements in transmission are also likely. Lines may be cooled to lower their resistance. The ultimate in this would be "superconducting" transmission lines. These lines will probably need to be cooled with liquid nitrogen and constructed of rare materials. The technical problems are thus imposing, and superconducting lines will be used (if at all) only to carry huge amounts of power (greater than 10,000 mW) short distances; for example, from an offshore nuclear park to New York City. (This would be a very controversial proposal.) At the moment, our knowledge related to superconductivity is changing rapidly. It is a field of scientific research that is receiving much emphasis.

Direct current (DC) lines may also be used more in the future. The invention of the transformer made alternating current (AC) the early choice for transmission and distribution. However, recent advances in the technology of electronic techniques for increasing and decreasing DC voltages and converting them to AC have returned DC transmission to favor.

Direct current (DC) lines.

Electric power is a prime example of a capital-intensive, highly centralized form of energy production. Generators, power plants, and utility systems are all getting larger and larger. The whole country is tied together in a massive power pool (although in practice, power pools function on a regional basis). This centralization and interdependence provides a backup of power in case individual systems fail. On the other hand, blackouts may have widespread consequences. Distrust of such centralization has helped lead to the proposal of an "appropriate technology" alternative (many small, consumer-sized energy production units). We will discuss this alternative later.

6.11 Thermal Pollution

As was explained in Section 6.9, for the turbine at an electric power generating plant to spin, the low-pressure end of the turbine must be kept relatively cool. This is accomplished by cooling the water in the cooling loop. The process for keeping this water cool can lead to **thermal pollution**—the addition to air or water of abnormal amounts of heat, resulting in environmental changes.

Thermal pollution defined.

In the past, electric power plants often dumped the heated water from the cooling loop into a nearby body of water. Figure 6.39 shows an infrared photo of such an operation.

Because this heat dumping usually has an adverse effect on the aquatic environment, most states have laws that prohibit power plants from returning hot water directly to nearby bodies of water. In fact, most states have laws that prohibit increasing water temperature by more than 2.8 Celsius degrees (5 Fahrenheit degrees) at the point where water is discharged into a river, lake or bay.

Figure 6.39 An infrared photo of the thermal plume from a power plant located on Lake Michigan. The plume extends approximately 1,500 meters (4,900 feet) offshore. The photo was taken during relatively calm waters. (From Professor T. Green, Marine Studies Center, University of Wisconsin–Madison.)

These laws were enacted to prevent a variety of problems. The water taken into the plant contains fish and smaller organisms. These are killed by heat as the water is pumped through the pipe that cools the condenser. The result is a reduced food supply for larger organisms. The warm discharged water also holds less dissolved oxygen than cold water can. Lack of adequate oxygen may cause organisms to die. At the same time, the increased temperature increases the metabolic rate, and hence the need for oxygen, by both microorganisms and fish. The result is often a large fish kill due to suffocation.

List some of the negative impacts of thermal pollution.

Thermal pollution often leads to changes in species composition. Desirable algae may be replaced by undesirable blue-green algae. Desirable fish populations, such as trout, may diminish. On occasion, some desirable fish populations such as bass and catfish have benefited.

Cooling ponds.

To prevent such negative impacts, many utilities have special artificial lakes, called **cooling ponds.** Warm water from the condenser is pumped into these ponds. Evaporation of the water and transfer of

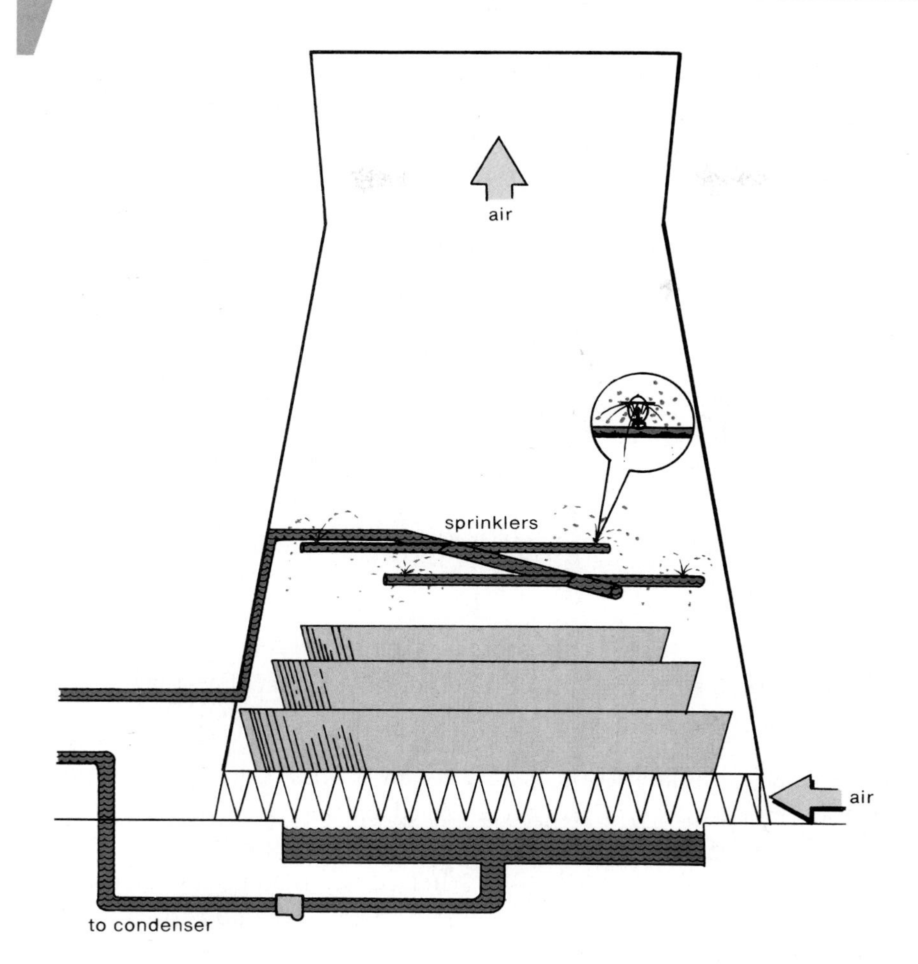

Figure 6.40 Cooling tower design. The dumping of waste heat.

heat to the outside air result in cooling. Cool water is drawn from the deepest point of the pond and returned to the cooling loop. To be effective, cooling ponds must be large.

Cooling towers.

Modern electric power plants use **cooling towers** to remove heat from the condenser and dump it into the air. Cooling towers are typically giant hollow cylinders about 500 feet high. These cylinders are pinched in near the top. They are supported on legs that allow air to flow under the tower. Like many other power plant structures, the towers are made of thick concrete containing steel reinforcement bars.

About 500 feet up inside the cooling tower there are several layers of special tiles called baffles. The baffles provide a huge surface area for the cooling water to trickle over. Water that was warmed in the condenser is returned to the cooling tower and sprayed onto the baffles. As the water trickles down the baffles, it loses heat. The large surface area of the baffles causes the heat to be quickly transferred into the air.

Since hot air rises, the warmed air moves up through the cooling tower. Cooler air flows under the tower—replacing the heated air. As this process continues, a natural breeze begins to blow up through the baffles and out of the cooling water. On a cool day, a huge cloud of steam can be seen rising from a cooling tower.

Most of the cooling water does not evaporate. It is cooled to about 24 degrees C (75 degrees F) and collected at the bottom of the cooling tower. Some of this water may be returned to a nearby river, but most is used again in the cooling loop. (It is important to remember that in a nuclear power plant, none of this water ever comes in contact with the reactor core, so the water carries no radioactive materials.)

Dry cooling towers.

Dry cooling towers have been designed for use in arid regions, where water is scarce and expensive. These towers cool the water from the condenser but do not evaporate large quantities of water. Unfortunately, they are more expensive both to build and to operate.

Cooling towers are being constructed at most new power plants despite their high cost. The waste heat dumped into the atmosphere doesn't seem to have noticeable negative impact on the local environment.

It is hoped that in the future, it will be possible to capture and use the waste heat from power plants. This heat could be used for heating homes, growing crops in greenhouses, or for fish farming near the power plants. These uses only cool the water slightly. Unfortunately, the water must still be cooled further for efficient use at the power plant.

Summary

Americans use primarily the energy stored in oil and gas molecules to operate their society. These fuels are easily adapted to a variety of tasks—moving vehicles, heating homes, and running machines. Unfortunately, domestic reserves of oil and gas are running low. Because of this, there is a continuing interest in coal, especially for electric power generation. Coal is mined underground with a variety of mining techniques. Where it is located near the surface, it is strip mined. The heat from burning coal can be used to boil water and make steam. The steam then forces a turbine to rotate. If the rotating turbine is attached to a generator, electric power is produced. This is because a coil of wire in the generator is forced to move across a magnetic field. Electricity can also be generated using the energy stored in water held behind a dam.

References

British Petroleum Company. *BP Statistical Review of World Energy* (London: The British Petroleum Co.), 1991.

Fowler, John M. *Energy and the Environment,* 2nd ed. (New York: McGraw-Hill), 1984.

Shell Oil Company. *Oil* (Houston, Texas: Shell Oil), 1992.

United Nations. *Yearbook of World Energy Statistics* (New York: United Nations), Annual.

U.S. Bureau of Reclamation. *Hydropower: Water at Work* (Washington, DC: U.S. Government Printing Office), 1991.

U.S. Department of Energy *Annual Energy Outlook 1992: With Projections to 2010* (Washington, DC: U.S. Government Printing Office), 1992.

U.S. Department of Energy. *Annual Energy Review* (Washington, DC: U.S. Government Printing Office), Annual.

U.S. Department of Energy. *National Energy Strategy: Powerful Ideas for America* (Washington, DC: U.S. Government Printing Office), 1991.

World Book Encyclopedia. *Coal* (Chicago: World Book), 1992.

End of Chapter Questions ?

Set A

1. What energy sources does the United States rely on at the present time?

2. What major energy transitions has the United States already made?

3. Why might future demands for energy in the United States not grow as rapidly as they have in the past?

4. Why are oil and gas desirable fuels?

5. Petroleum is most often formed in the sedimentary beds deposited in ancient ____________ , whereas coal originated in ancient ____________ .

6. Name four different types of oil and gas traps.

7. The chances of discovering a high-profit oil trap are ____________ . (Choose one: high, low.)

8. What waste products are formed when oil is burned?

9. List five common products made from petroleum.

10. In what ways is it better to use natural gas as a fuel, rather than oil?

11. Where is natural gas usually found?

12. Why is there a renewed interest in coal?

13. Coal is mostly ____________ .

14. What waste products are produced when coal is burned?

15. Since coal combustion poses environmental dangers, why is the United States returning to coal as a significant source of energy?

16. Why can coal be used so readily in our economy?

17. List and distinguish among the four different kinds of coal.

18. Describe a major use for each kind of coal you just listed.

19. What determines the usefulness of coal as a fuel? Which kind of coal ranks highest as a fuel?

20. List the ways in which modern underground mining has improved.

21. How is longwall mining superior to room-and-pillar mining?

22. How has the significance of hydroelectric power changed in the United States since 1950?

23. Explain why the electric utility companies would like to have a constant electrical power demand.

Set B

24. U.S. demand for oil has fallen to the lowest level since 1971. Give two or three reasons which might help explain the decline in the demand for petroleum.

25. Some experts have predicted that the United States' demand for oil (and for total energy from all sources) will pick up again. In your opinion, what might be the major reason for the predicted upturn in consumption? Are there other possibilities?

26. As the developed countries face the transition to the "post-petroleum era," it might be helpful to reflect on the past transitions illustrated in Figure 6.4. In what ways might the next transition be different from those pictured?

27. Reexamine Figure 6.1. Which two fossil fuels has our society been using to satisfy the lion's share (about 66%) of our energy needs? Yet those two fuels represent only about 8% of our total coal, oil, and gas reserves. (Coal represents about 92%.) In your opinion, is there a danger associated with this kind of dependency? Explain.

28. Suppose you have been placed in charge of media relations for a large western utility company. Write a press release to be aired on the "Noon-Day News," announcing that a brownout is imminent. In your paragraph, explain the reason(s) for the problem, what may happen if the problem is ignored by the community, and how a blackout can be averted.

Goal

To examine the depletion pattern for nonrenewable resources. To examine how resource lifetimes are determined.

Nonrenewable Resource Depletion

It's there. I tell you, it's there.
All we've got to do is go find it.

—Michel Halbouty
Texas oil wildcatter, 1984

In the 1950's, we discovered about 50 barrels of oil for every barrel invested in drilling and pumping. Today, the figure is only five to one. In other words it will generally become uneconomical to search for any oil for energy in the United States.

—Carrying Capacity, Inc.
Washington, D.C. 1986

Figure 7.1 Heavy freeway traffic.
(National Renewable Energy Laboratory)

Diminishing Reserves of Energy

Disagreement over oil supply.

The central focus in discussions of the energy crisis has always been the eventual exhaustion of fossil fuel resources, with the major concern being oil. It is the most popular fuel, and the one most difficult to replace. As the two beginning quotations show, it is difficult to find agreement on the seriousness of the anticipated oil shortage, or on when it will occur.

Disagreement like this is frustrating to scientists, and more so to the public. Whom should we believe? It is hard to take serious action when there is no general agreement as to who or what the problem is.

There is little disagreement, however, about the *facts* of energy use. As in most controversies of this type, when the "experts" disagree, the confusion is over the definition of the issues and in the handling of the uncertainties involved. Behind the statements quoted above lie different definitions of resources, different assumptions about the growth of consumption, and different assumptions about resource economics. All of these areas—geology, technology, economics, and consumer response—must be taken into account.

We will use this chapter to clarify these issues. We will distinguish between such terms as "reserve" and "resource." This will help you avoid confusion. It will help you keep your eye on the heart of the supply-and-demand problem.

We will also provide current "best guesses" about how much of our depletable (**nonrenewable**) fuel resources remain. Then we will consider some projected rates of use of these fuels, and the implications of these projections on resource lifetimes. At the same time we will draw upon and add to your knowledge of exponential growth.

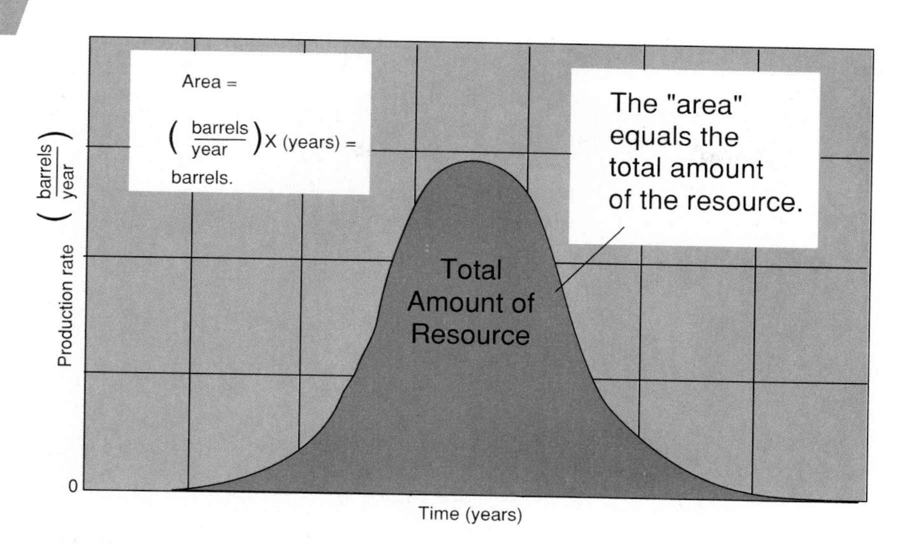

Figure 7.2 The full production cycle of a nonrenewable resource.

40 7.1 Depletion of a Nonrenewable Resources

What is a resource depletion curve?

None of our nonrenewable resources is removed from the ground at a constant rate. Instead, removal usually goes through a production cycle that starts slowly, rises to a peak, and then slowly diminishes as a resource is exhausted. A typical production cycle, called a **resource depletion curve,** is illustrated in Figure 7.2.

The history of crude oil is a typical production cycle. When crude oil was first discovered, its rate of consumption was very low. It had some uses as a lubricant and as a fuel for lamps. But as the years went by, people became more familiar with crude oil and how to separate it into gasoline, kerosene, jet fuel, etc. Its use expanded. Automobiles were invented, using gasoline as their source of power. Mass production made automobile transportation possible for millions of people. Demand for gasoline rose exponentially, thereby causing exponential growth of oil production. Then came the diesel locomotive, the airplane, trucks, asphalt, the motorcycle and minibike, heating oil, and the oil-fired electric power generation plant. Demand and production continued at an exponential rate.

The Earth and its resources are finite, and oil is a nonrenewable resource. Thus, the production rate will eventually peak and then decrease exponentially. As crude oil gets harder to find, more dry holes will be drilled. Even wells that do produce will be deeper and located in more remote regions. Making a profit will become more difficult. Some companies will be forced to leave the oil business. Economical substitutes for the products that come from crude oil will be developed. The demand for crude oil will drop.

A resource depletion curve represents the complete production cycle of a resource in a given region.

What does the area under a resource depletion curve represent?

A resource depletion curve represents the complete production cycle of a resource for a given region. A curve like this has a useful property: if you draw a vertical line through any given time on the horizontal axis, the area under the curve to the left of the vertical line represents the quantity of the resource that has been extracted from that region. *Make sure you understand this before you proceed.* This is an important concept.

Figure 7.3 The relationship between resources and reserves.

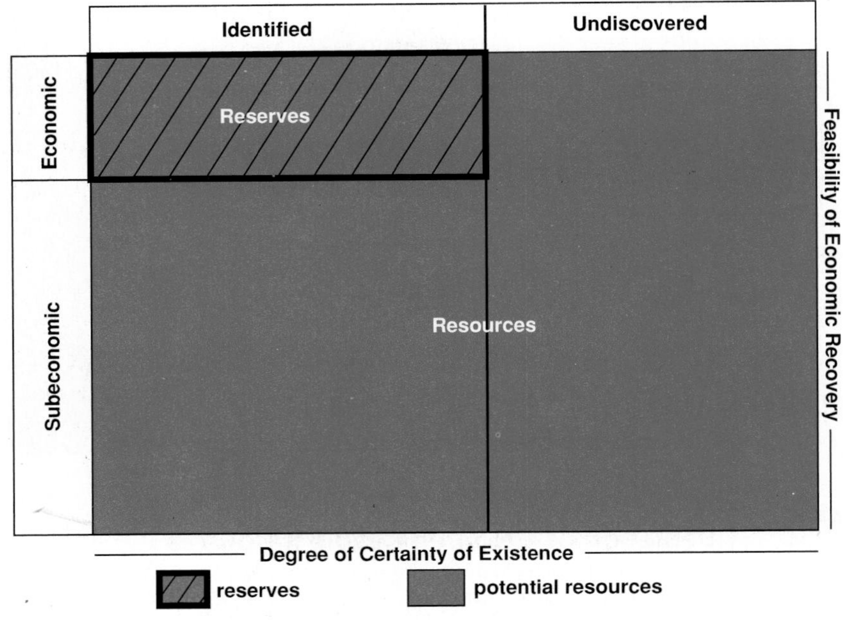

?

What is the difference between resource and reserves?

7.2 Resources and Reserves

The terms **resources** and **reserves** are used when we discuss how much of some material exists. The terms are often misused as synonyms. They do not mean the same thing.

Resources are amounts of materials which are known or assumed to exist, and for which extraction is economically feasible now or in the future with potential technology. Reserves are known amounts of a material that can be extracted profitably with existing technology under present economic conditions. So, reserves are part of resources. The general relationship between resources and reserves is shown in Figure 7.3.

It can be seen from Figure 7.3 that resources are much larger than reserves. They are also much more speculative. They can be assumed to exist but have not yet been discovered. Extracting them may or may not be profitable. It is important to understand that total resource estimates are always highly questionable. There is no way to know when, or even if, resources will be discovered or whether they actually exist.

Reserves represent deposits that have been studied enough for the amount and grade of the material to be estimated. Reserves can be mined under present economic conditions using the technology available. Even in a well-known deposit, reserve estimates change from year to year. Material is extracted, thereby reducing the reserves. At the same time, further detailed exploration of the deposit may add measurable quantities of reserves. New technologies or changes in economic conditions may shift known deposits from the resource to the reserve category.

Although reserve estimates are essential to short-range planning, they rarely give a good long-term picture. Resource estimates, when used with caution, are a better tool for probing the future.

7.3 Techniques for Estimating Resources

Estimating the size of our energy and mineral resources is a complex task. It involves a combination of data gathering and processing techniques, as well as guesses based on historical trends. The process is as much an art as a science.

Once estimates have been made, there is the problem of interpreting their meaning. Opinions vary concerning the amount of any given resource that can be economically extracted. Thus we find a wide variety of figures stating what our reserves are. Unless the estimation of reserves is one's occupation, the best one can do is first determine who is making and paying for the estimates. Then one must ask: For what purpose are they making the estimates? What techniques are they using? How are they defining their terms? By what rules are they playing? How reliable have their estimates been in the past?

We will not explain all the techniques used for estimating our reserves of nonrenewable energy resources. However, we will briefly describe three methods of estimating the ultimate amounts of recoverable crude oil and natural gas in a specified region. These techniques may be used individually. However, their greatest usefulness is achieved when they are used jointly, and their separate results are compared. The three methods are described in the following paragraphs.

a. Estimation Based on Geological Analogy

The **geological analogy** technique is the least accurate method for estimating resources. However, it is practically the only method available that can be used prior to the exploratory drilling in an new geologic territory. Suppose a sedimentary basin is thought to contain oil, but has not yet been tested by drilling. Call this Region B. From preliminary geologic and geophysical mapping, it is found that Region B is very similar geologically to Region A (see Figure 7.4). Region A has already been found to contain significant quantities of oil and gas. From this it is *inferred* that Region B will be comparable to Region A in the quantities of oil and gas per unit of area or volume it contains.

Analogy: Comparing things that are similar.

Infer: To conclude or decide based on information that is known or assumed.

The geologic analogy technique is rather crude, but it is the only method available for estimating the size of a potential resource prior to exploratory drilling.

Since this method is basically an educated guess, it may work very well. Often, however, it can lead to predictions that are partially or completely wrong.

b. Estimation Based on the Complete Production Cycle

You have already seen a typical resource depletion curve (Figure 7.2). If you know the actual shape of the beginning of the curve of a resource, and if you have a good estimate of the total quantity of the resource, you can quite accurately extrapolate (predict) the remainder of the depletion based on production rate assumptions.

Figure 7.4 The geologic analogy method.

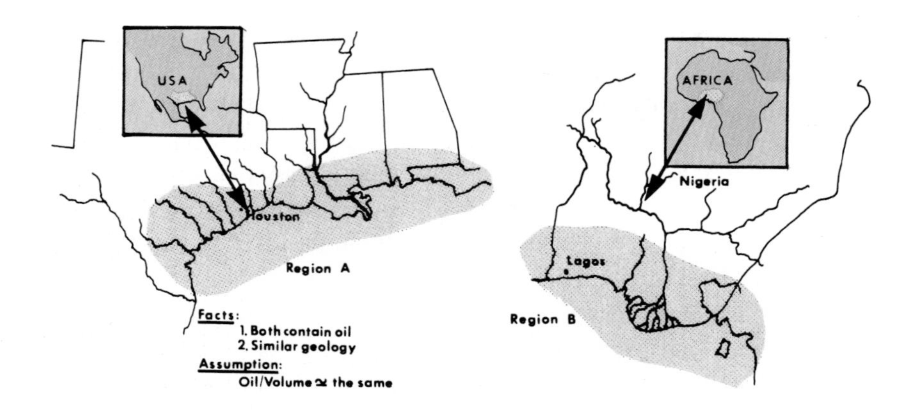

When did Dr. Hubbert predict U.S. crude oil production would peak? When did it peak?

In 1956, Dr. M. King Hubbert, a former oil geologist and research geologist with the U.S. Geologic Survey, predicted the complete production cycle for crude oil in the **continental United States** (Figure 7.5). At that time he predicted that if the accepted figures of 150–200 billion barrels for the ultimate cumulative production were correct, then the production should peak between 1966 and 1971. Production actually peaked in 1970.

In 1971, he made a similar projection for world crude oil production (Figure 7.6). Note that he used two different estimates of the total amount of the resource. Also, note that the larger estimate led to a curve that both rose and fell more steeply. Because of this, the guess as to when 90% of the world's crude oil will be gone is nearly the same in both cases. (Generally, a resource is considered exhausted if 90% of it has been withdrawn. The remaining 10% is too expensive to be worth extracting.) The 2025 A.D. prediction for the exhaustion of the world's crude oil supply is one you will certainly want to watch. It has important implications for your lifestyle, for world politics, and for everyone's future.

?

Why is a resource considered exhausted when 90% of it is used up?

Dr. Hubbert was one of the early prophets of the energy crisis. His 1956 warnings to U.S. oil producers of the oncoming decline in production in the early 1970s were dismissed by many. But the reliability of his projections has earned him great respect and recognition. His projections and conclusions are of great value to all of us.

How should the U.S. prepare for a lack of crude oil?

To summarize, the complete production cycle technique enables one to estimate when production of a resource will peak, and when 90% of the resource is consumed. The technique requires an independent guess of the size of the resource.

c. Estimates Based on Cumulative Industry Data

The complete production cycle method requires an estimate of the total amount of resources available. In many cases, it is hard to get such an estimate.

This obstacle may be avoided if we analyze some of the cumulative statistical data of the petroleum industry. These data can tell us the current position of the industry in its inevitable and irreversible

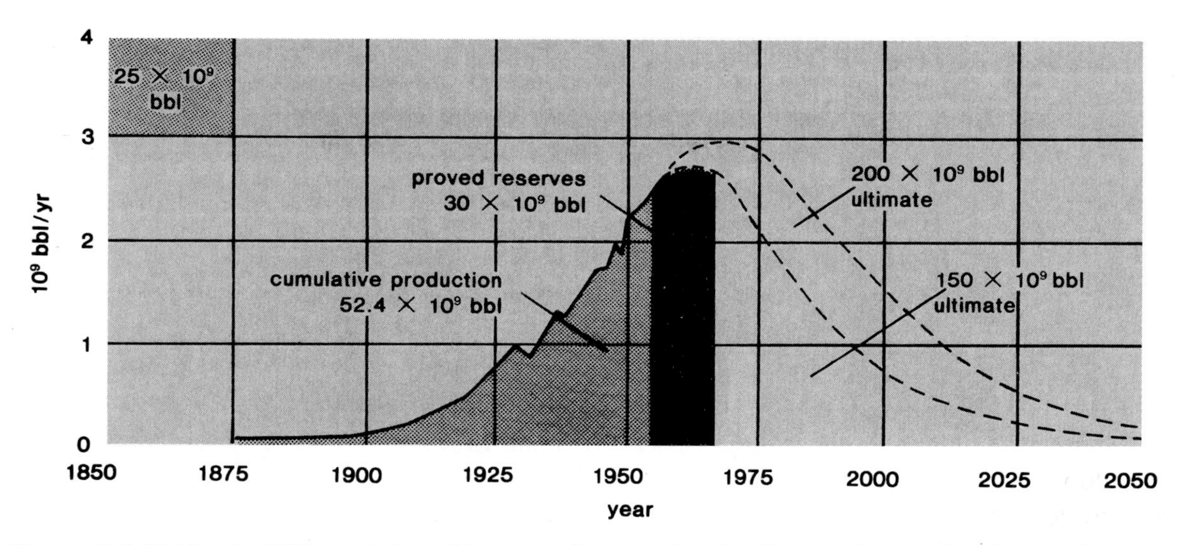

Figure 7.5 Hubbert's 1956 prediction of future production of crude oil in contiguous U.S. (lower 48 states) and adjacent continental shelves. (From M. King Hubbert, 1956. With permission of the author and the American Petroleum Institute.)

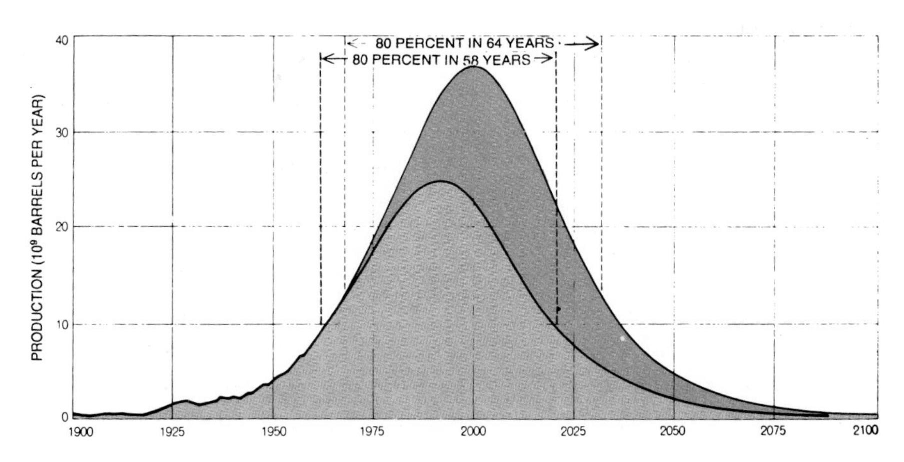

Figure 7.6 The cycle of world oil production is plotted on the basis of two estimates of the amount of oil that will ultimately be produced. The high curve reflects Ryman's estimate of $2{,}100 \times 10^9$ barrels, and the low curve represents an estimate of $1{,}350 \times 10^9$ barrels. (From "The energy resources of the Earth," by M. King Hubbert, Scientific American, © 1971. With permission of the author and Scientific American. All rights reserved.)

evolution. For this purpose, two significant sets of data are: annual production since 1860 (when the petroleum industry began), and annual estimates of proven reserves since 1900.

You can compute the cumulative production from 1860 to any given year, giving you a value, Q_p, for that year (where Q means quantity). You can also obtain the value Q_r for proven reserves, in any year since 1900. The total amount of oil which can be said to have been discovered by any given time is the sum of the cumulative production to that time, plus the proven reserves. This we call cumulative proven discoveries, Q_d. From this definition of Q_d, we have the equation:

Q_p = quantity produced

Q_r = quantity in reserve

Q_d = quantity discovered

$$Q_d = Q_p + Q_r. \qquad \text{(See Figure 7.7)}$$

These three quantities change in predictable ways during a complete normal cycle of exploration and production in a large region

What is the equation that relates Q_p, Q_r, and Q_d?

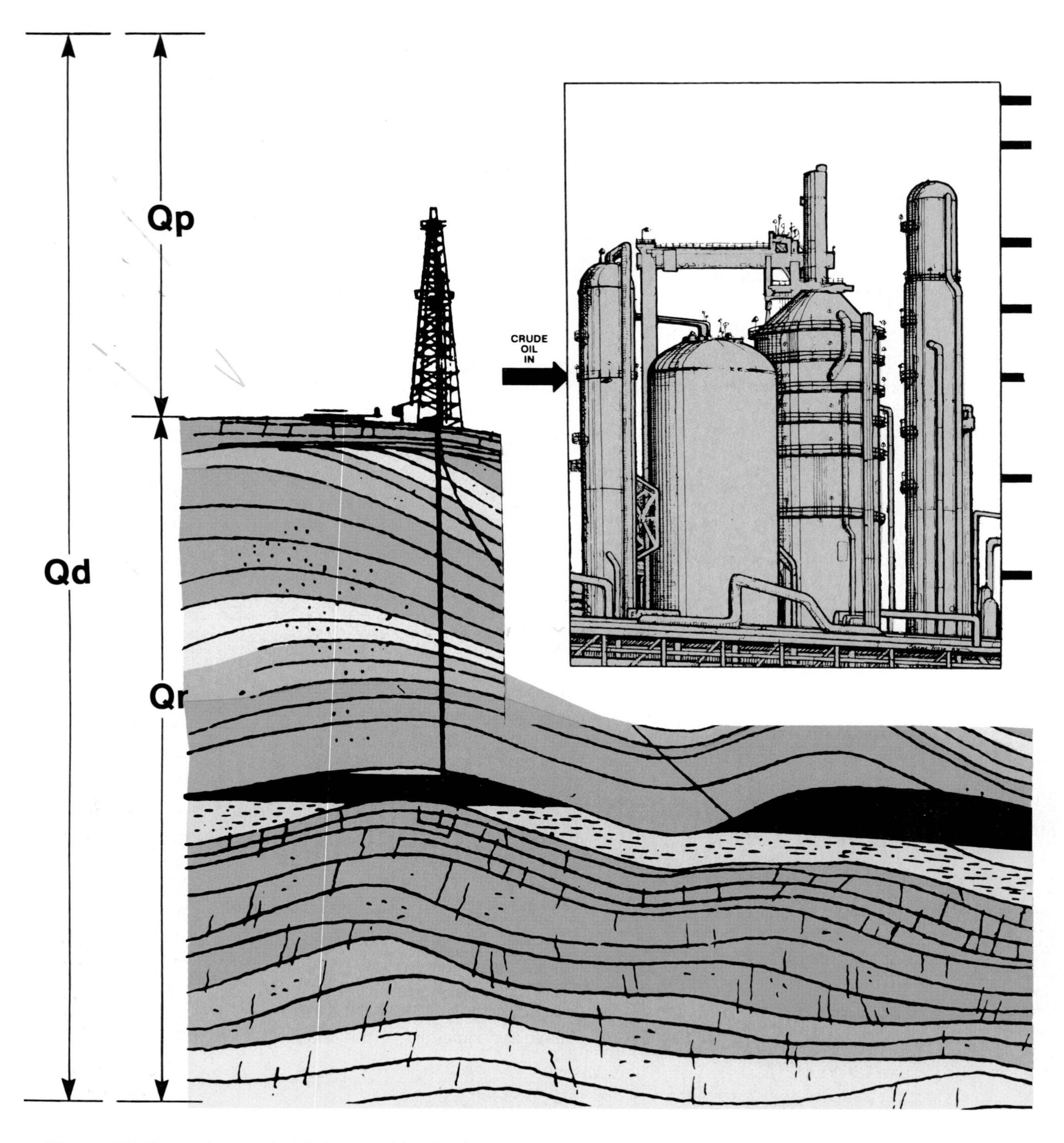

Figure 7.7 Factors involved with the quantities Q_p, Q_r, and Q_d.
(Courtesy Shell Oil Company.)

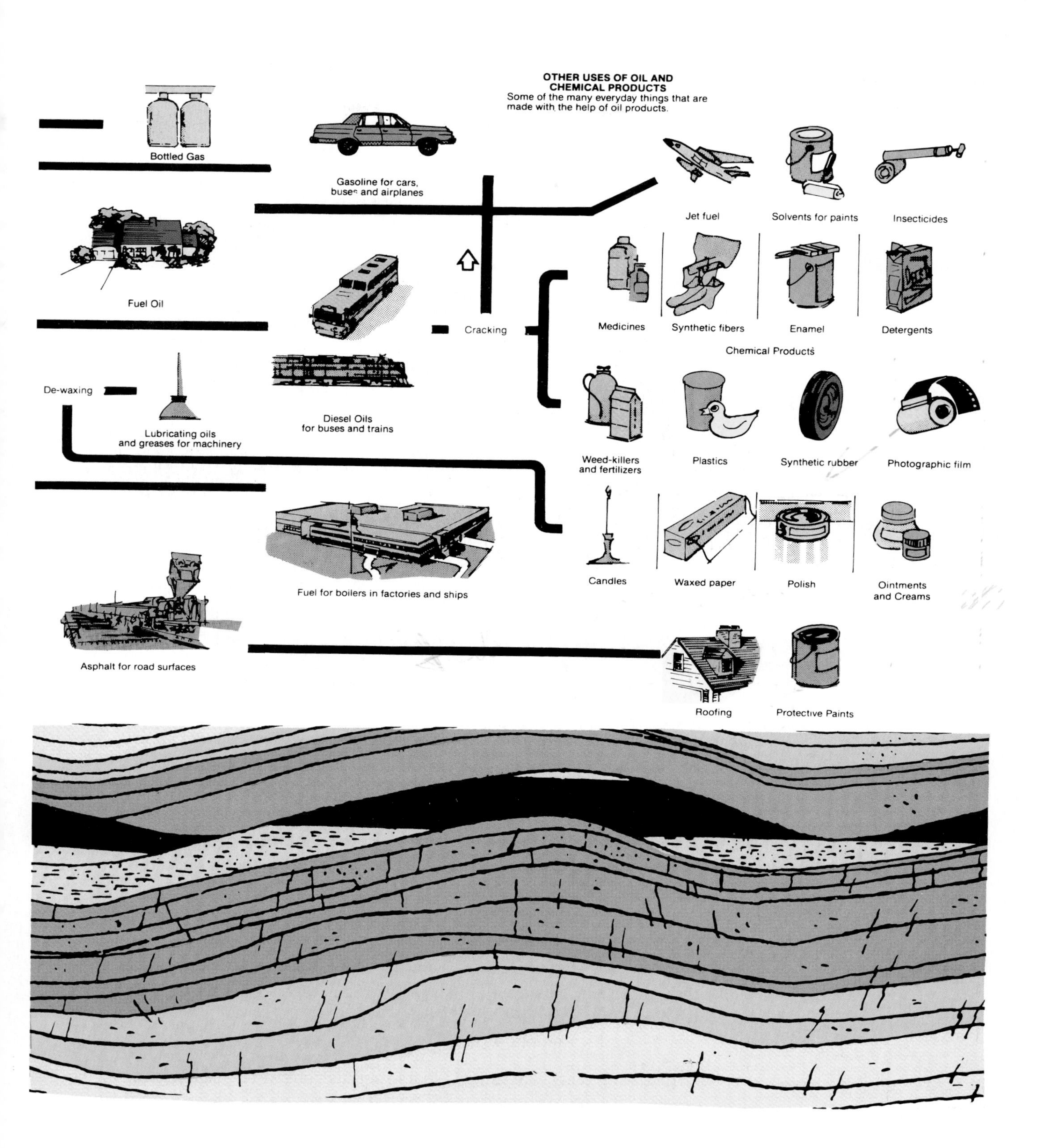

OTHER USES OF OIL AND CHEMICAL PRODUCTS
Some of the many everyday things that are made with the help of oil products.
Bottled Gas
Gasoline for cars, buses and airplanes
Jet fuel
Solvents for paints
Insecticides
Fuel Oil
Cracking
Medicines
Synthetic fibers
Enamel
Detergents
Chemical Products
De-waxing
Lubricating oils and greases for machinery
Diesel Oils for buses and trains
Weed-killers and fertilizers
Plastics
Synthetic rubber
Photographic film
Fuel for boilers in factories and ships
Candles
Waxed paper
Polish
Ointments and Creams
Asphalt for road surfaces
Roofing
Protective Paints

Figure 7.8 The generalized form of curves of cumulative discoveries, cumulative production, and proved reserves for a petroleum component during a full cycle of production. (From *Energy Resources,* by M. K. Hubbert, 1962. With permission of the author and the National Academy of Sciences.)

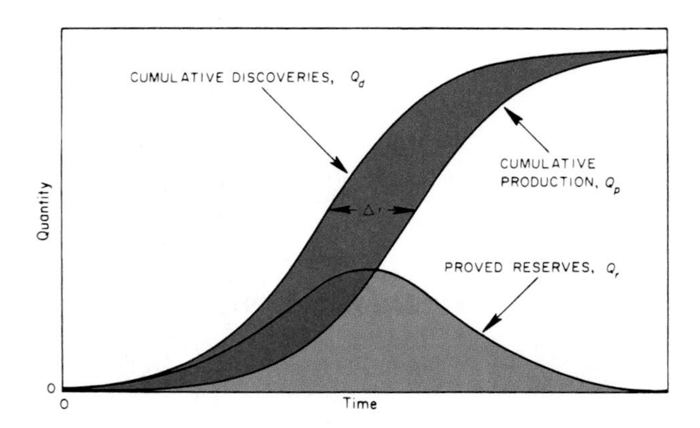

such as the United States. This is shown in Figure 7.8. A large region is specified because for small regions these curves may be very irregular. For large regions, the irregularities tend to cancel one another, and the curves become much smoother.

Curve of cumulative production.

The curve of cumulative production, Q_p, starts slowly as the industry begins. It increases exponentially. However, the growth rate begins to slow as reserves become harder to find. In the middle range, an inflection (turning) point is passed, and production slows. It gradually approaches the ultimate cumulative production.

?

What is the difference between resources and reserves?

Proven reserves in any given region are zero at the beginning (before any discoveries are made), and zero at the end (when the resource is used up). They reach a maximum somewhere in the middle range of the completed cycle. This is shown by the Q_r curve in Figure 7.8.

The curve of cumulative proven discoveries, Q_d, has the same shape as the cumulative production curve, Q_p. It begins at zero and ends at the same ultimate end point as the production curve. Discovery must precede production, however, by some time interval we can call Δt. So, the Q_d curve is to the left of the Q_p curve on the graph. The Q_d curve gives an approximate Δt-preview of the Q_p curve. In other words, if we wish to know what the production will be Δt years later, it will probably be close to where the discovery curve is now.

The main feature of this method of estimating is that it provides a means of predicting, a few years in advance, when production will peak. This prediction can be made without an estimate of the total quantity of oil available.

You can see in Figures 7.9 and 7.10 how well the actual historical data of the U.S. petroleum industry fits such graphs. From Figure 7.10 we clearly see that the Δt is 12 years.

From these graphs we see:

1. $\Delta t \simeq 12$ years. Thus, the Q_d curve acts as about a 12-year preview or warning of the behavior of the Q_p curve.
2. The proven reserves in the United States peaked around 1961.

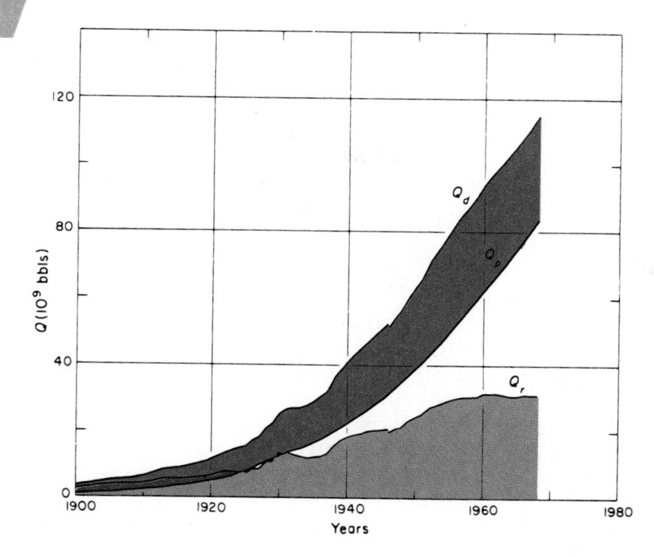

Figure 7.9 Data for the United States, exclusive of Alaska, on cumulative production (Q_p) and proved reserves (Q_r) of crude oil.

(Figures 7.9 and 7.10 from *Energy Resources* by M. K. Hubbert, 1969. With permission of the author and the National Academy of Sciences.)

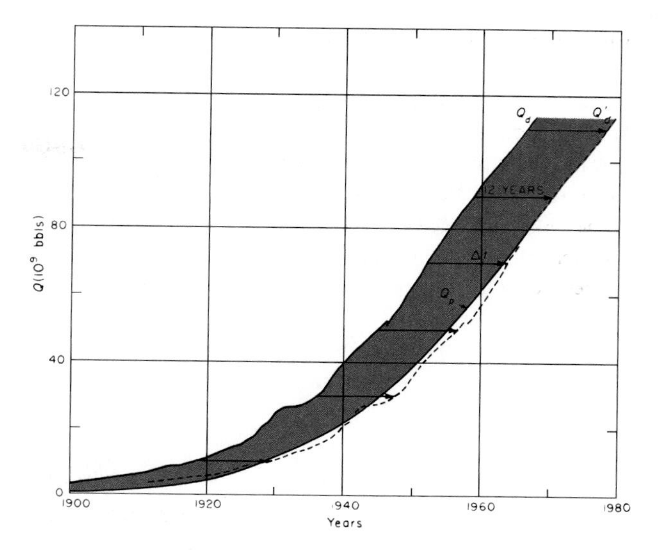

Figure 7.10 Time delay, Δt between United States cumulative proved discoveries (Q_d) and cumulative production (Q_p) of crude oil. The dashed line Q_d reflects the form of the curve Q_d when it is moved to the right, parallel to the time axis, until it most nearly matches the curve Q_p. (Hubbert, 1969, Fig. 8.12, p. 75, with permission of the author and the National Academy of Sciences.)

3. Since the peak rate of discovery occurred around 1957–58, the production rate should have peaked 12 years later, around 1969–70 (since $\Delta t \simeq 12$ years). It did.

4. If we assume that about half the total amount of oil is withdrawn from the ground at the time when the discovery rate peaks (1957–58), the Figure 7.9 tells us that the total amount of oil available in the U.S. is about $85 \times 2 \simeq 172 \times 10^9$ barrels. The estimate of 172×10^9 barrels is in good agreement with the estimates used for the complete cycle projections shown in Figure 7.5.

In summary, cumulative statistical data on annual production and proven reserve estimates enable one to plot graphs of Q_d, Q_p, and Q_r vs. time. Analysis of these curves makes possible the prediction a few years ahead of when production will peak. This prediction can be made without an estimate of the total quantity of resource available. This technique also enables one to estimate the size of the reserve.

How Much Energy?

The amount of energy we have left depends on remaining resources of different fuels. However, oil is sold by the barrel, coal by the ton, and natural gas by the cubic foot. This makes it difficult to compare amounts of energy involved. To make comparisons, we need to know the amount of energy available from a barrel of oil or a ton of coal.

Figure 7.11 A scientist using a bomb calorimeter to determine the energy content of a sample of coal. Electric power utilities do this on a routine basis to make certain the coal they purchase contains the energy they are paying for. (Courtesy of the U.S. Bureau of Mines, Pittsburgh Research Center. Joseph Mills, photographer.)

?

What do we mean by the energy content of a fuel?

The **energy content** of a fuel is the amount of energy released when one unit of mass of that fuel is consumed. A bomb calorimeter is used to determine the energy content of flammable fuels. See Figure 7.11. Note in Table 7.1 how the average energy content varies from fuel to fuel. Oil and natural gas provide more energy per pound than coal. Nuclear fuels have a huge energy content. We can use this table, along with estimates of how much oil, gas, coal and uranium remain in the ground, to gain some idea of the amount of energy available to the United States and the world from these fuels.

To compare easily the energy available from different fuels, we need a common unit of measure. Since we are considering national and world energy reserves and demands, we will use a very large unit, the Quad. A Quad will provide the energy required to run the entire United States for approximately 4.5 days.

7.4 Nonrenewable Resources

The United States relies primarily on these fuels for its energy.

As discussed in Chapter 6, the United States relies primarily on the fossil fuels—coal, oil, and natural gas—for our energy. In 1991, the burning of these fuels accounted for about 88% of our energy consumption. We obtained an additional 8% from uranium fission used in nuclear reactors that year. Another 4% of our total energy came from **renewable** or continuous resources (mostly from water power). The world use pattern is similar.

Because the deposits of fossil fuels and uranium are finite, it is critical that we know how much we have left. Experts strongly disagree on their estimates of these resources. Let us try to get at the reasons for the confusion. In addition, we need to make realistic estimates of how much energy these resources can provide before they are used up.

Figure 7.12 Multiple coal seams outcrop this pristine bluff in the Hoseanna (AKA Lignite) Creek Basin, near Healy, Alaska. The most prominent coal seam is approximately 40 feet thick in this area, known as the "Popovitch Badlands," named after an early prospector. (From Usibelli Coal Mine, Inc.)

Table 7.1 Energy Content of Various Fuels

Fuel	Common Units	Energy per Pound	Energy per Kilogram
Coal	25×10^6 Btu/ton	3,150 Calories (13×10^6 Joules)	6,930 Calories (2.9×10^7 Joules)
Crude Oil	5.8×10^6 Btu/bbl.	4,900 Calories (20.5×10^6 Joules)	10,780 Calories (4.5×10^7 Joules)
Natural gas	1,031 Btu/cf.	5,000 Calories (20.9×10^6 Joules)	11,000 Calories (4.6×10^7 Joules)
Uranium	———	8.86×10^9 Calories (3.71×10^{13} Joules)	1.95×10^{10} Calories (8.17×10^{13} Joules)

Notes: 1,000 calories = 1 kilocalorie = 1 Calorie.
bbl = barrel, cf = cubic foot
Btu = British Thermal Unit

a. Coal

The problem of estimating coal reserves.

To estimate coal reserves you need a great variety of information. You need to know the thickness, extent, and quality of individual **coal seams.** It is also important to know how deeply they are buried and how easily they can be mined. Some coal seams lie close to the surface and can be mined there. Others dip deeply into the earth, even hundreds of feet below the surface. Most of this coal is available only through underground mining methods. Also, if a seam isn't thick

Table 7.2 Nonrenewable Energy Reserves and Resources

Energy Type	Region	Recoverable Proven Reserves	Estimated Total Resource Remaining
Crude oil (billion bbls.)	World	900	1,600
	U.S.	34	70
Natural gas (trillion cf.)	World	4,200	7,000
	U.S.	170	600
Coal (billions of short tons)	World	1,100	6,800
	U.S.	300	1,400
Uranium (u_3O_8) (thousands of short tons)	World*	2,400	4,800
	U.S.	600	1,800
Oil Shale/	World	270	2,300
Tar sands (billions of bbls.)	U.S.	75	1,000

Note: These estimates are an average of the estimates for 1990 reported in various recent studies.
* Uranium resources do not include China, the former USSR, or other former communist areas.
1 short ton = 2,000.00 pounds.
1 metric ton = 2,204.62 pounds.

enough, mining it is just not practical. The structural condition of the rocks enclosing the seam must also be considered. All of this information is necessary for appraising the quality of the recoverable coal.

Total identified coal resources in the United States are about 1.4 trillion tons. An equal amount may be in coal deposits that have not yet been discovered. Reserves of coal are estimated to be 300 trillion tons (see Table 7.2), with reserves of 1.1 trillion tons.

b. Crude Oil

The difficulty in estimating reserves of crude oil.

Estimating resources and reserves of crude oil is a very difficult task. Before the full extent of an oil field can be known, many wells must be drilled, a process that may extend over several years. Furthermore, the oil in a field is never fully recovered. There is always a portion that cannot be economically recovered using current technology. Some reservoirs may yield 90% of their oil. Others may yield as little as 5%. The current average recovery of oil from all the oil fields in the United States is estimated at between 30% and 40%.

World crude oil resources are estimated to be about 1.6 trillion barrels. World reserves are approximately 900 billion barrels, with over half of that located in the Middle East. The United States resources are estimated to be around 70 billion barrels; U.S. reserves are about 34 billion barrels. (See Table 7.2.)

Figure 7.13 The development of crude oil reserves in the Middle East. (Science VU-API/Visuals Unlimited)

Figure 7.14 The flaring and storage of natural gas. (W. Ormerod/Visuals Unlimited)

c. Natural Gas

Natural gas is even more elusive than oil. It may be found with oil, or alone. World resources are estimated to be about 7000 trillion cubic feet. World reserves are placed at 4200 trillion cubic feet. United States resources are estimated to be 600 trillion cubic feet, with reserves of about 170 trillion cubic feet. (See Table 7.2.)

We are much more efficient in extracting natural gas than we are in extracting coal or oil. Because it is free-flowing and often under pressure, natural gas can be extracted at a national average of 80% of identified reserves.

Figure 7.15 Nuclear fuel rods. The rods are under water. The glow is called Cerenkov radiation.
(Science VU-API/Visuals Unlimited)

How to estimate the amount of electrical energy obtainable from a ton of uranium oxide.

U-235 and Pu-239 are radioactive compounds used for energy. You will learn more about neutron bombardment in chapter 8.

d. Uranium

Four hundred fifty tons of uranium oxide (U_30_8) must be used to load a 1000mW nuclear reactor for the first time. About 150 tons per year is needed to keep it going, depending on the reactor's efficiency and on the capacity factor. The capacity factor represents the percentage of time the reactor is producing power at full capacity. One often-used estimate is that a 1000 mW reactor will use 5,500 tons of uranium oxide in its 30-year lifetime. We can use these numbers to estimate how much electrical energy can be obtained from a ton of uranium oxide.

We can expect to get about 78 Quads of energy out of the 600,000 tons of U_30_8 in this country's reserves. Put another way, the 600,000 tons of uranium oxide could fuel 109 1000-mW nuclear reactors through their full 30-year lifetime.

At the present time there are approximately 100 nuclear power plants operating in the United States. The vast majority of these are small than 1000 mW. Even so, these plants will consume most of our uranium reserves by about the year 2040.

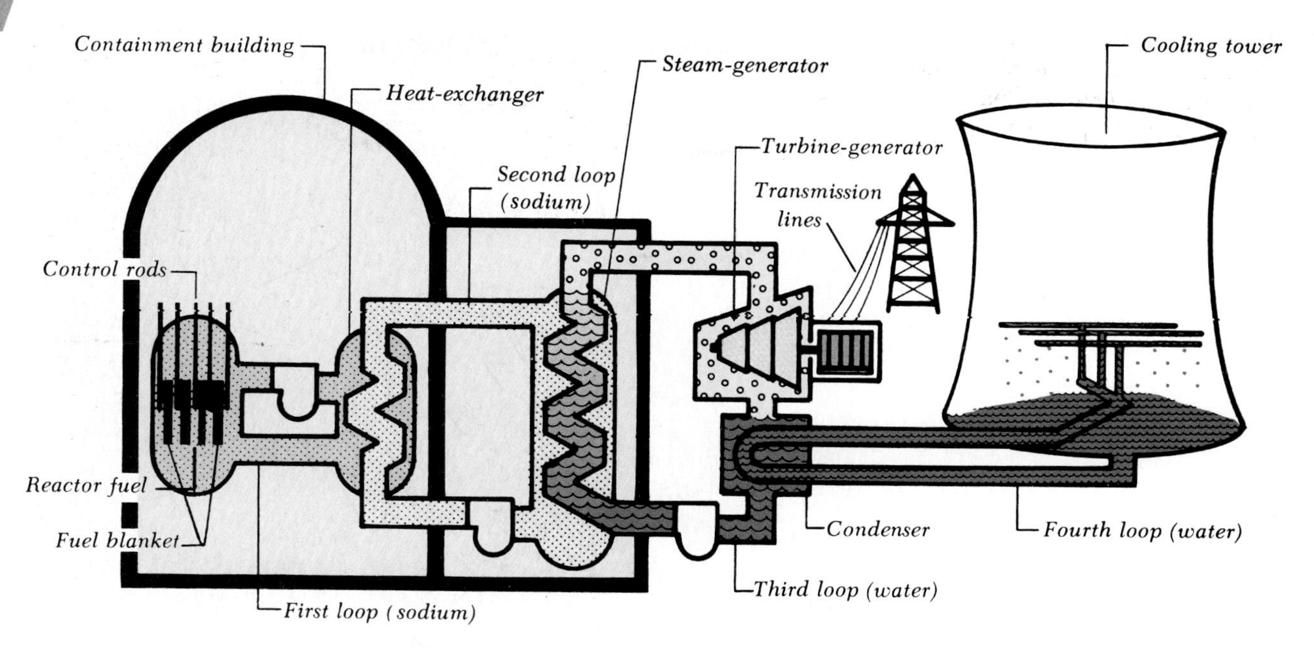

Figure 7.16 Fast breeder reactor diagram. (From USDOE.)

e. Uranium Resources in a Breeder Economy

The energy content of uranium is based on the current inefficient methods of using fuel. The spent fuel contains U-235 and Pu-239, both fissionable. If the fuel cycle is completed and these fuels extracted, the total energy content is increased by about 20%. The fuel cycle will be examined in the next chapter.

The fissionable fuel Pu-239 produced from the inert U-238 by neutron bombardment could be recycled to increase efficiency. Such recycling is the key to the much more efficient "breeder reactor," which is described in the next chapter. If this became the dominant device in the nuclear power system, the efficiency of uranium use could rise to 50% or 60% (instead of the present 1%). The reactor will use one to two tons of fuel per year, instead of 150 to 200 tons. We will also learn that this option makes it possible to obtain energy from thorium ores. The net result is that a nuclear program based on breeder reactors enables you to obtain 60 to 100 times more energy from nuclear reserves. We will discuss this optimistic note further in the next chapter and balance it by considering some of the breeder reactor's disadvantages.

How much more energy may be available from the nuclear option if the breeder reactor is used?

f. Oil Shale and Tar Sands

Oil shale is sedimentary rock containing **kerogen,** a solid organic substance of high molecular weight. When heated, kerogen breaks down. It yields substantial amounts of synthetic crude oil (**syncrude**) and flammable gas.

Why is oil shale important? Synthetic: Not fully of natural origin. Human intervention is required for the production. Syncrude means synthetic crude oil.

Figure 7.17 Oil shale country in Colorado's Grand Valley region. (Courtesy Atlantic Richfield Company [ARCO].)

What is tar sand?

Tar sands are deposits of rock or sediment containing heavy oil or tar-like fossil fuel (bitumen) that is too thick to be pumped to the surface by drilling. Tar sands are very old deposits from which the light hydrocarbons have escaped, leaving the heavy, asphaltic residue behind. The technology for treating tar sands to make synthetic crude oil is relatively simple.

Tar sands and oil shale are of economic interest because the synthetic crude oil they provide can become a substitute for our diminishing supply of crude oil. Oil shale and tar sands will be discussed in the next chapter.

7.5 Comparing Our Nonrenewable Reserves

Comparing the amounts of various U.S. nonrenewable reserves is first a matter of converting the units to Quads. This exercise is summarized in Table 7.3.

To understand the significance of these numbers, we must estimate how much energy the United States will use between 1990 and 2010. Estimating a number such as this is very risky. The crystal ball is foggy at best, and much can change in 20 years. However, projections are necessary for planning ahead.

Estimating the amount of energy the United States will use between 1990 and 2010.

Assume that energy consumption in the United States will remain at approximately 80 Quads/year for the 20-year span. This span will thus require 80 Quads/year × 20 years, or 1600 Quads of energy. (United States energy consumption leveled off in the 1980s, and there are good reasons to assume that consumption will not rise significantly in the years ahead.)

We are now ready to place our various reserve and requirement estimates on a single bar graph. See Figure 7.18.

Table 7.3 Comparison of U.S. Nonrenewable Energy Reserves

Source	Reserve Estimate	Conversion Factor	Quads
Crude Oil	34×10^9 bbls.	181×10^6 bbls./Quad	190
Natural Gas	170×10^{12} cf	0.797×10^{12} cf/Quad	210
Coal	300×10^9 tons	44.3×10^6 tons/Quad	6700
Uranium Oxide (U_3O_8)	600×10^3 tons	7.67×10^3 tons/Quad	80
Syncrude (Oil shale, tar sands)	75×10^9 bbls.	181×10^6 bbls./Quad	410

(Source: obtained by processing the data of Table 7.2)

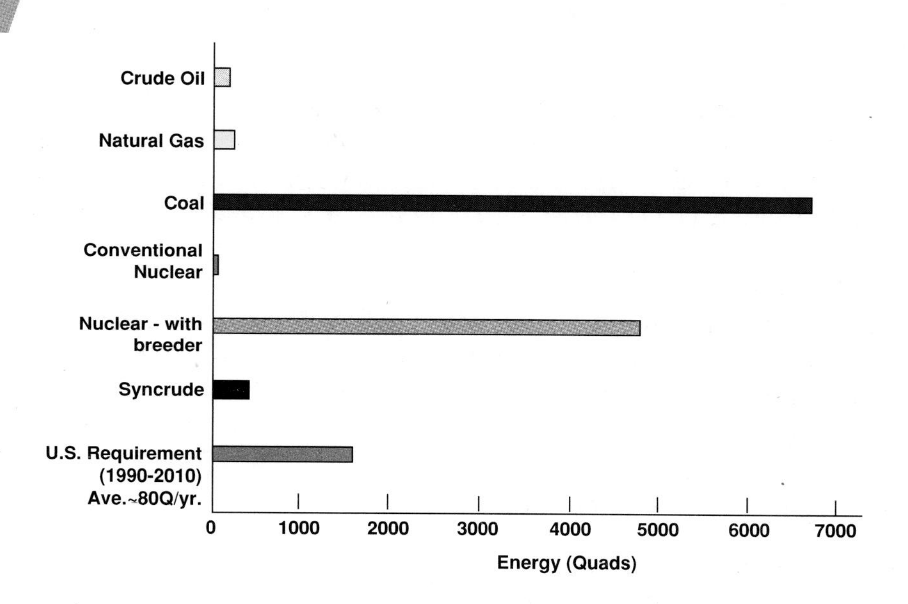

Figure 7.18 Remaining U.S. nonrenewable energy reserves and projected U.S. energy requirements for 1990–2010.

What conclusions might you draw from Figure 7.18?

Figure 7.18 shows that our days of relying on oil and gas are numbered. But what are our alternatives? Without the breeder reactor, nuclear power is not as significant as most people think it is. The breeder reactor option comes with its own peculiar set of problems, which we will consider in Chapter 8. The environmental problems tied to the large-scale use of coal and the fact that coal is a solid may force us to use it only as a transition fuel. The transition could be to a solar-based economy. Coal, however, is an amazing raw material; and there are many ways of converting it to clean fuels or using it as a base for many petrochemical products we require, such as plastics, solvents, epoxies, and so on. However, the greenhouse effect poses an additional concern. The syncrude sources will contribute very little in our twenty-year projection because it will take 10 to 15 years of planning

The greenhouse effect will be discussed in Chapter 12.

Figure 7.19 Hydrocarbons! . . . Hydrocarbons! . . . (Reprinted by permission of Tribune Media Services.)

and construction to put these operations into production. High costs are the major problem. At present, we have not even decided whether to go ahead with using syncrude.

How Long Will Our Reserves Last?

This is one of the most controversial issues of the energy debate. The controversy is fueled by the wide range of answers being given. The primary reason for the wide range of answers is the hidden assumptions behind them. These assumptions are examined in what follows.

?
What variables determine the lifetime of a nonrenewable resource?

7.6 The Static Lifetime

The lifetime of a resource depends on two things: (1) how much we have; and (2) how fast we're using it. This simple approach assumes that the use rate remains constant and that no new discoveries are made throughout the lifetime of the resource. So, "static" (unchanging rate) lifetimes can easily be determined by using the equation:

$$\text{Lifetime } (T_s) = \frac{\text{Reserve}}{\text{Constant Use Rate, } r_0}$$

This give you only a standard for comparison, because no resource is used up at a constant rate. Constant use rate (or consumption rate) is especially unrealistic over long periods of time. The quantity of the resource classified as a reserve also changes because of new discoveries and economic conditions.

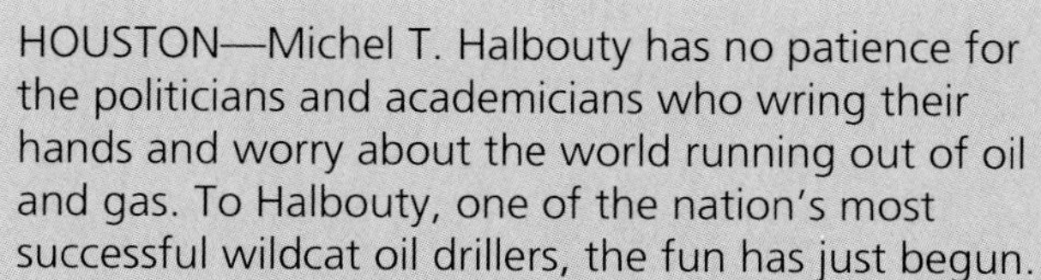

Special Focus

Another View of the Outlook for Oil

HOUSTON—Michel T. Halbouty has no patience for the politicians and academicians who wring their hands and worry about the world running out of oil and gas. To Halbouty, one of the nation's most successful wildcat oil drillers, the fun has just begun.

Hundreds of oil fields are hidden under ice, and thousands of feet of water, and beneath mountains and deserts, he believes. The oil awaits the probes of explorers with nerve, vision, and money enough to go looking for it.

"It's there," said Halbouty, 70, his high, thin voice racing along with excitement. "I tell you, it's there. All we've got to do is go find it."

Halbouty, who pronounces his first name, "Michael," was born and raised in Beaumont, within hiking distance of the Spindletop oil well that started Texas' oil industry. He sharpened his skills as a geologist during the 1930s East Texas boom triggered by Spindletop and has constantly widened his horizons since.

New theories of geology have swept away the old ideas that the formation of oil is a phenomenon isolated to only a few lucky regions of the world, Halbouty says. Oil was deposited in particular types of formations that can be found virtually planetwide, he says.

The Earth is the same as it was, Halbouty says, but scientists are now looking at it differently. And when they look, they are finding more oil.

"There are about 600 oil basins in the world," Halbouty says. "Of course, 160 are producing oil and gas. Two hundred have had very, very little exploration. And 240 have had practically no exploration at all. So you see, you've actually got 440 basins in the world that have not been adequately explored."

Each of the basins could hold scores of oil fields, some with the potentials of an Alaska or a Saudi Arabia or an East Texas, he says. The basins cover vast regions of the earth, millions and millions of square miles awaiting the drilling bit of the wildcatter.

He recalls how the "experts" once predicted, using the best knowledge then known, that East Texas would have no oil, that it would be a waste to even drill there. But hunch-playing wildcatters did drill. And they opened up an oil field that at the time was the richest in North America.

Using data from satellites, Halbouty has prepared maps showing in purple where these potential oil basins lie. There are purple smears across much of Siberia, great blotches in central China and Canada, and in Asia, South America and Africa. Continents on his map are rimmed with purple, making water covered basins along the coasts of the Americas, the Arctic Sea, around Australia and the Pacific coasts of Asia. There are also huge fields of purple marching across the plains, mountains, and deserts of the western United States.

"My God, they are fantastic!" Halbouty says, gesturing at his map, his eyes sparkling. "Think of it!"

Engineering advances also have opened new energy frontiers.

Oil rigs are drilling in deeper and deeper water, penetrating deeper and deeper into the earth, and in conditions of ice and heat and weather that were once thought impossible to challenge.

"Even two years ago, drilling in 200 to 300 feet of water was considered risky," says Halbouty. "Now we're drilling in 6,000 feet of water; and in a few years, we'll be drilling in 10,000 feet of water."

And drillers are challenging rock structures once thought impenetrable. The Western Overthrust Belt along the Rocky Mountains is an example, he says.

Halbouty lives life at a constant run, regularly working 14 to 16 hours a day at the Houston office building that is the headquarters of his multimillion-dollar private company.

He is a striking figure, with flowing silver hair and mustache, and tailored suits. Halbouty, who is known for working long hours, dashes around Houston in a Mercedes-Benz sports car and flies off to distant cities in his private jet.

The author of two books, Halbouty regularly gives lectures and research papers at professional meetings and donates hundreds of hours annually as a government consultant. He was chairman of the Energy Committee in Ronald Reagan's transition team.

But Halbouty is not the stereotypical wildcatter.

The oilman seldom drinks, never smokes and religiously starts each day with a rugged 35-minute workout.

An executive at another oil company says: "He once said he'd like to still be looking for oil at age 110. I think he just might do it."

Halbouty has no doubts.

"I've been in the oil business for 50 years," he says, his eyes twinkling and his voice charged with excitement. "And I still think there are a lot of discoveries to be made."

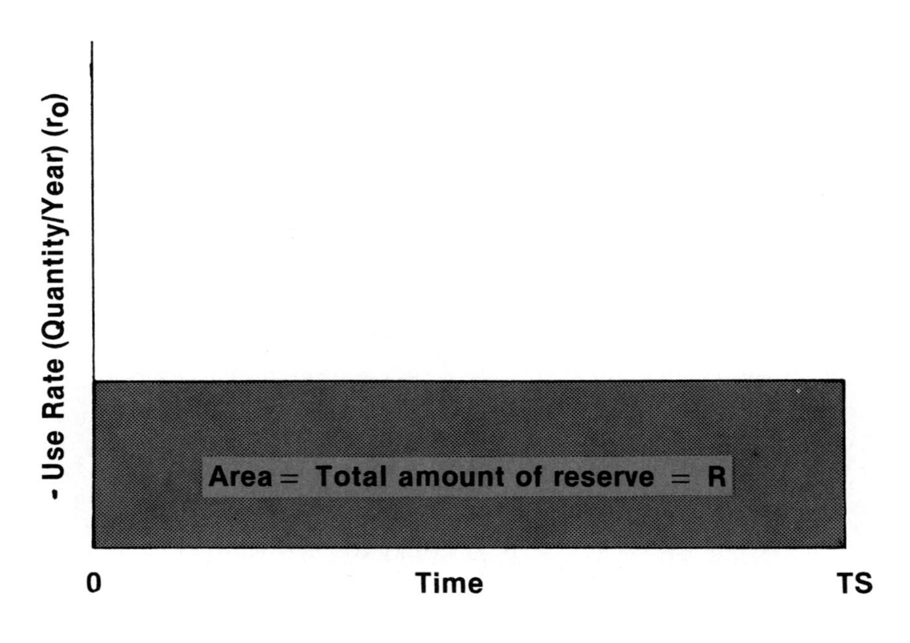

Figure 7.20 Use rate vs. time for a nonrenewable resource that is consumed at a constant rate. Notice that the size of R (a rectangle) equals its length (time) times its width (use rate).

7.7 The Exponential Lifetime

The demand for energy often increases rapidly. The energy problem is partially a problem of growth. Demand grows, but resources are finite. In other words, the numerator in our static lifetime equation is in some ways fixed, but the denominator increases. Thus, to really understand the problem and to make realistic assessments of resource lifetimes, we have to apply our knowledge of the mathematics of growth. We have to be able to deal with the exponential function. The important characteristics of exponential growth were listed in Chapter 4 .

How to determine lifetime if consumption grows exponentially.

To determine the **lifetime** of a resource, we divide the amount of the resource by the consumption rate. However, if the rate of consumption is increasing exponentially, the rate itself is increasing. As a result, our lifetime equation for the *exponential* lifetime becomes:

$$\text{Lifetime } (T_e) = \frac{\text{Reserve}}{\text{Exponentially Increasing Consumption}}$$

Unfortunately, it requires calculus to process this type of equation. To simplify matters, we will use a graph to analyze the situation.

From Figure 7.21 we see that the consumption rate is growing exponentially. We also see that the area under the graph represents the total amount of the resource (R) and that T_e is the exponential lifetime. This graph does not represent reality because no resource is consumed exponentially until the day it runs out.

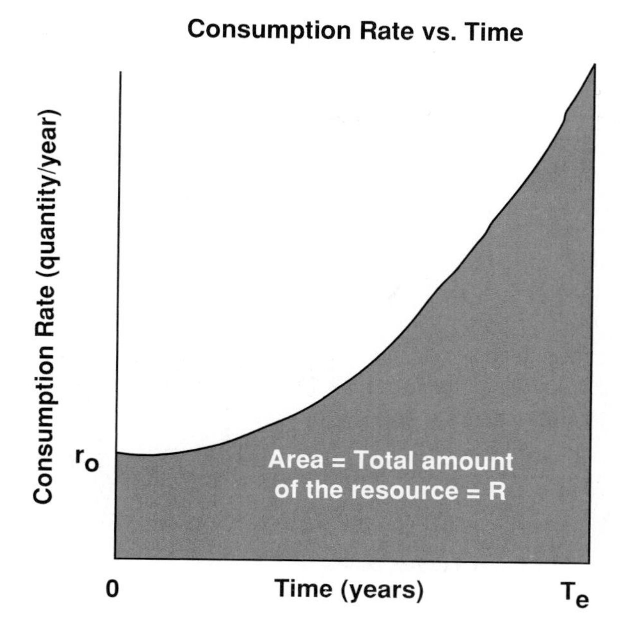

Figure 7.21 The consumption rate versus time graph for a nonrenewable resource that is consumed at a rate that increases exponentially.

7.8 The Way Things Are

As was just stated, no resource is consumed at an ever increasing rate until the day it is exhausted. Increasing rates of demand become harder and harder to fill. This results in higher prices. Demand then slows down.

Lifetimes in terms of the way things really are.

Economics does not allow exponential growth to go on unchecked. As a resource becomes harder to find, costs increase; and the production rate falls. Also, both the static and the exponential calculations assume that no resources will be discovered as new reserves. In the real world, both the known reserves and the use rates change, depending on economics, technology, and world politics. There is, however, some upper limit to the reserves since the Earth (and each country) is finite. Throwing money and machinery at the problem won't produce more reserves indefinitely. See Figure 7.22.

Why lifetime calculations often give different answers.

In addition, lifetime calculations are made more difficult by these uncertainties: Should you assume an increasing or decreasing preference for a certain resource with time? Or, should you assume total dependence? Should you include only reserves? Or, should you try to guess at the extent of the undiscovered resources and assume you will be able to afford to extract them? One key point that must be understood is that the assumptions one starts with determine the lifetime one calculates.

The real world situation regarding reserves is analogous to a bathtub that is being filled while the drain is left open. (See Figure 7.23). The quantity of water in the tub at any given time represents the known reserve. The water coming in represents new economic discoveries. The water that is leaving represents our consumption.

In the early use of a resource, new discoveries are more significant than consumption. The reserve builds up. Eventually, the resource

Hold That Line!

Are we using our energy wisely? This is a key question for people who think soft technology is the answer to conserving Earth's nonrenewable energy resources. Even those who argue against soft technology agree that efficient energy use must be a part of a conservation plan. One way or another, we cannot continue to rely on natural gas and crude oil for most of our energy, because the Earth is running out of both. Both sides of the argument say that we must reevaluate our energy needs, and take a more sensible approach to supplying them.

Karen Ambeau's team at the Pacific Gas and Electric utility in Hayward, California, is helping to make this "sensible approach" into reality for thousands of residential, commercial, and industrial users of natural gas and electricity in the San Francisco Bay Area. Karen's department works with PG&E customers who want to lower their energy requirements by installing energy-efficient appliances, lighting, and heating and air conditioning systems. These systems help reduce operating costs and generate less atmospheric pollution—not to speak of the obvious conservation benefits. The solutions chosen for these PG&E customers are a plus for all concerned: the user of energy, the supplier of energy, and the source of the energy.

The help-wanted ads for Karen's team might look like this: "Marketing Engineer needed to assist large/small commercial/residential customers in analyzing and choosing energysaving, environmentally-friendly appliances/systems. Determine rebate eligibility." And "Construction Consultant wanted; help design energy-efficient homes and offices." On the support side: "Billing Specialist with knowledge of accounting to ensure accurate, timely billings." And "Admin. Asst., good at organizing, skilled in computer data entry and/or word processing."

Some of the industrial and commercial customers served by Karen's department are constructing new buildings and want to start out right, conserving from the beginning in order to avoid costly retrofitting later. Some may be upgrading an existing structure with a new network of appliances, computers, heating/cooling systems, and so on. These customers often do many studies on their own to determine the possible savings. Then the PG&E marketing engineers help to confirm the customer's calculations and make sure they're on the right track. Often the team will have suggestions for altering the customer's plan or choices in some way. Many proposed installations realize enough savings to qualify for a rebate from PG&E.

Karen's team also works with residential customers and small businesses Their needs may be smaller in scale, but their savings are just as important. By installing energy-efficient refrigerators, insulating attics, putting special pads over hot water heaters, and so on, these customers also can achieve savings and receive rebates for their efforts.

Karen enjoys the challenge of her work as an administrator. Much of her time is spent leading meetings, supporting her team members and helping to solve their problems, and participating in situations that need special attention. She sets goals for individuals as well as for the team, and plans the department's budgets. Of course, her knowledge of electrical engineering (she has a B.S. from Tuskegee University) contributes a lot to her career. Every day she uses physics, mathematics, and chemistry in understanding the systems recommended by her staff. Karen says a two-year college degree in a technical skill such as electrical engineering can be an entry point to a career in energy marketing. However, young people interested in advancement to management will need a bachelor's or master's degree.

Karen is much more conscious of energy consumption these days. Because of her work, she looks at everything from refrigerators to amusement park rides in a new light. Instead of seeing just a roller coaster or an electric lawn mower, she thinks about their energy consumption, their stability, or the motors used to run them!

Figure 7.22 "Buffalo shortage? What buffalo shortage? Just give me more money for scouts and guns, and I'll get you all the buffalo you need!" (Stein '77—*Rocky Mountain News.*)

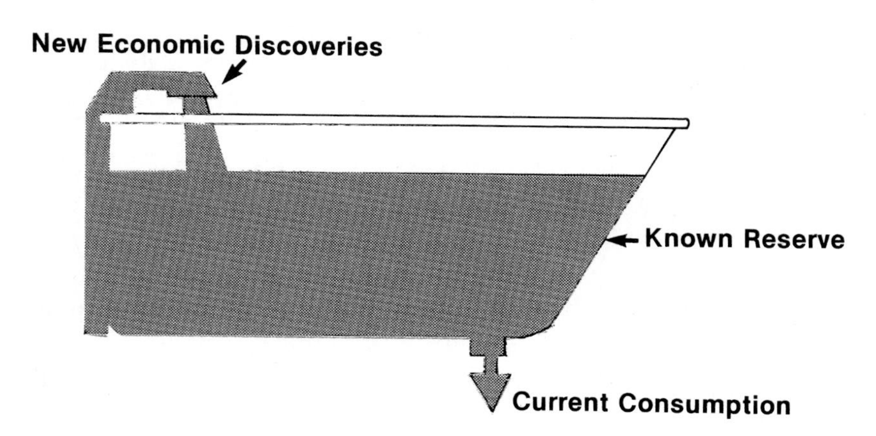

Figure 7.23 The real-world situation regarding reserves. New reserves are being discovered as known reserves are being depleted.

becomes harder to find and reserves are drawn down. The historical depletion pattern outlined at the beginning of this chapter holds true.

Another factor which makes estimating lifetimes very difficult is government-imposed environmental restrictions. We are placing many areas off limits to resource extraction. Some of these constraints are justified, many seem unjustified. Whatever the reason, the resources are not available.

The graphs of Figure 7.24 summarize the relationship between static lifetime (T_s), exponential lifetime (T_e), and real-world lifetime (T_{rw}) for a given reserve (R) of a resource.

What do you conclude from this information?

From the information provided in this section and the data contained in Tables 7.2, 7.3, and Figure 7.18, we conclude that no matter how one determines lifetime, both the U.S. and the world are using up our reserves of oil and gas. We must find adequate replacement energy sources if we are going to continue to maintain the technical level and standard of living the "have nations" enjoy and others hope to attain.

We have also seen that conventional "burner" type nuclear reactors will rapidly consume our uranium reserves. They are not a

Figure 7.24 The depletion of a nonrenewable resource based on three different assumptions. R is the same in each case.

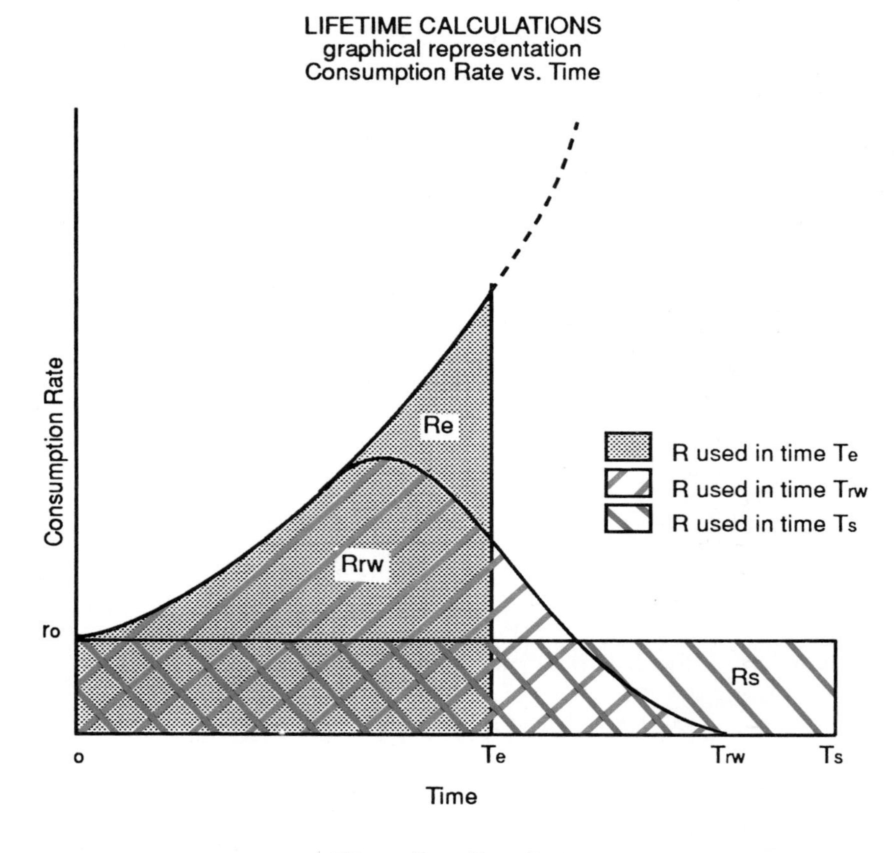

solution. Coal offers some promise if we can solve the technical and environmental problems associated with its use.

As you know, we also have renewable energy resources. These we will label the "continuous" resources. Greatest among them are the solar energy sources. In Chapter 9 we will look at continuous resources and assess the contributions they can make to our energy needs. We will then address providing energy for the future.

> Problems related to the depletion of our nonrenewable resources can be reduced by:
>
> - Improving the efficiencies of machines (automobiles, power plants, furnaces) that consume these resources.
> - Improving the quality of technical devices (catalytic converters, scrubbers, etc.) that reduce the pollution related to combustion of fuels.
> - Expanding the use of renewable energy sources.
> - Examining use patterns to eliminate wasteful consumption.
> - Planting trees and preserving forests to tie up excess CO_2 emissions.
> - Expanding known resource reserves through continued exploration.

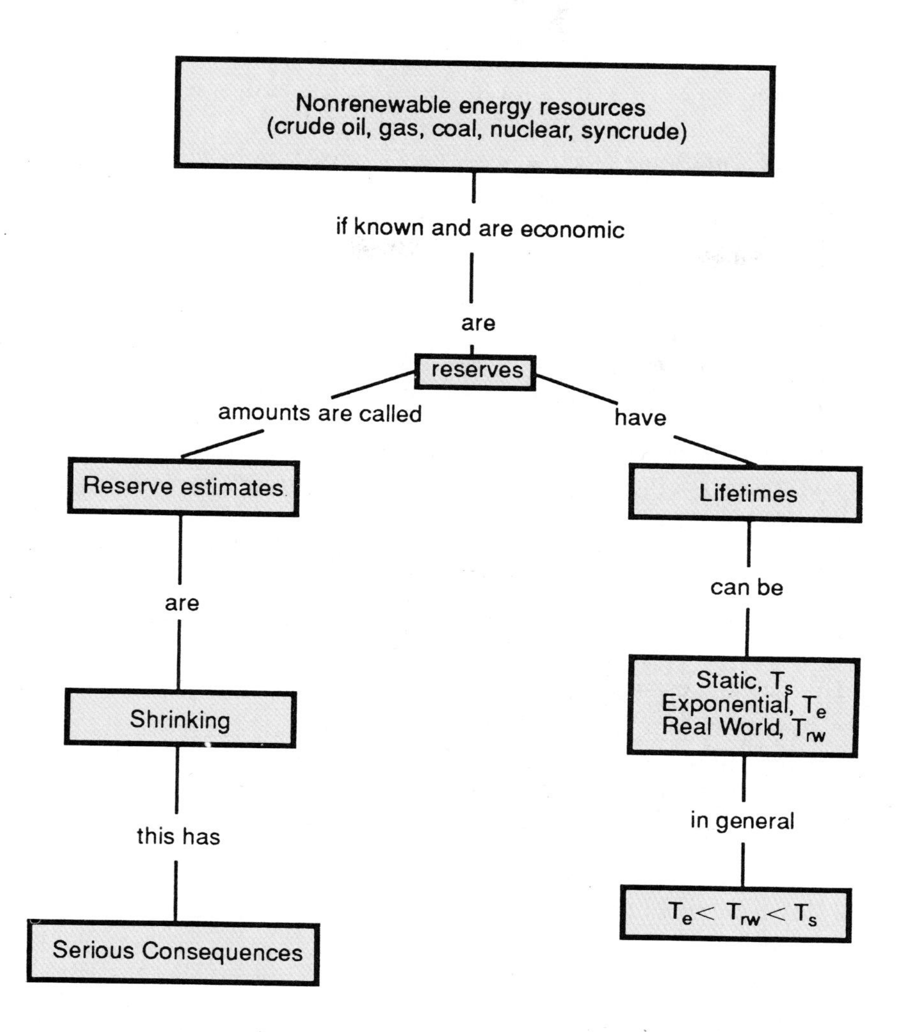

Summary 

The data in this chapter indicate the oil age is drawing to a close. It has been a unique age in the history of humankind—an age of inexpensive, abundant energy and rapid growth in both technology and technology-related problems. As we near the end of this age, we are challenged to use the last of its convenient (though no long inexpensive) energy resources to invent and deploy new technologies and related attitudes that will carry humankind into the next phase of its existence.

References

Averitt, Paul. Coal Resources of the United States, January 1, 1974. *Geologic Survey Bulletin 1412* (Washington, DC: U.S. Geologic Survey), 1975.

- Still the most comprehensive study of U.S. coal resources.

British Petroleum Company *B P Statistical Review of World Energy* (London: The British Petroleum Co.), 1991 volume.

Hubbert, M. King. Nuclear energy and the fossil fuels. *In Drilling and Production Practice* (Dallas: American Petroleum Institute), 1956.

———. Energy resources. *In Resources and Man* (San Francisco: W. H. Freeman & Co.), 1969.

———. *U.S. energy resources, a review as of 1972;* a background paper. (Washington, DC: U.S. Government Printing Office, #527002419), 1974.

Mast, R. F. and others. *Estimates of Undiscovered Conventional Oil and Gas Resources in the United States—A Part of the Nation's Energy Endowment* (Denver: U.S. Geologic survey), 1989.

Master, Charles D. *World Petroleum Resources—A Perspective,* Open-File Report 85–248 (Washington, DC: U.S. Geologic Survey), 1985.

Russell, Paul L. *Oil Shales of the World, Their Origin, Occurrence, and Exploration* (Oxford: Pergamon), 1990.

U.S. Department of Energy. Energy Information Administration. *Uranium Industry Annual* 1991, DOE/EIA—0478(91) (Washington, DC: U.S. Department of Energy), 1992.

World Resources Institute. *World Resources 1992–93* (New York: Oxford University Press), 1992.

End of Chapter Questions ?

Set A

1. What is a resource depletion curve and what does the area under it represent?
2. How can rough estimates of resource quantities be made using geologic analogues?
3. Why is a resource considered exhausted when 90 percent of it is used up?
4. If we are running out of crude oil, why can't we just look for more?
5. List the important differences between the graphs shown in Figures 7.5 and 7.6.
6. If proven U.S. reserves of oil peaked in 1961, then what is the predicted date of oil production decline?
7. Why is it important to use more than one method for predicting oil depletion rates?
8. How are Q_d, Q_p, and Q_r related?
9. How was M. King Hubbert able to predict, almost 12 years ahead of time, when U.S. petroleum production would peak?
10. What do we mean by the energy content of a fuel?
11. What is the difference between resources and reserves?
12. Which nonrenewable resource can provide the greatest amount of energy for powering the United States to and beyond the year 2000?
13. Why are the \$50/pound U_3O_8 reserves larger than the \$15/pound reserves?
14. Does the use of uranium without the breeder reactor make much sense?
15. If a breeder reactor program were to be initiated in the near future, how much fissionable fuel would there be as compared with our coal resources?
16. What is oil shale? Why are we interested in oil shale?

17. What is tar sand? Why is there interest in developing tar sands?
18. What variables determine the lifetime of a nonrenewable resource?
19. What are the implications of the calculated lifetimes for national and world oil and gas reserves?
20. If the fossil fuel age is ending, what's next?

Set B

21. The economics and politics of energy can cause irregularities in the shape of resource depletion curves. Refer to Figure 7.5. Offer an explanation for the large "dip" in the curve between 1920 and 1940.
22. Sketch an "idealized" Q_r curve. Now, suppose that a large discovery is added to the proven reserves in a single year. Modify your sketch to show the effect of this new discovery.
23. Trace Figure 7.8 onto a sheet of unlined paper. Use a ruler to demonstrate that the sum of the heights at given times of the Q_r and Q_p curves equals the height of the Q_d curve. In words, what does this show?
24. Americans use less oil now than in the 1978 peak year (18.85 mb/d). List possible reasons for the decline in consumption.
25. Table 7.1 lists the energy content of natural gas on 1031 Btus per cubic foot. This value is for gas burned at sea level. However, in Denver (elevation 5,280 feet), the heat content is only 840 Btus/cf. Explain why the heat content decreases as elevation increases.

End of Chapter Problems ?

1. Locate (a) the present year, and (b) the start of the oil industry on Figure 7.5. What do you conclude?
2. Suppose the cost of coal is \$25/ton; oil is \$30/barrel; and natural gas is \$0.25/cubic foot. Use Table 7.1 to calculate the cost of each resource per 10^6 Btus. On this basis, which fuel do you prefer and why?
3. Calculate the number of Btus of oil that have been produced in the United States.
4. In the 1970s, the known global reserves of petroleum (crude oil) were estimated to total 455 billion barrels. The world appetite for oil was approximately 85 million barrels a day in 1980.
   a) At the 1980 consumption rate, how long would the known reserve last?
   b) Since the date of exhaustion of the world's crude oil reserve may be close, why is there so little concern?
5. At the present time, the United States has a reserve of about 300 billion tons of coal that can be mined economically using existing technology. Current production of coal is about 990 million tons yearly. Use these two facts to calculate how long U.S. reserves will last under current conditions.

6. If coal production increased to 1.5 billion tons per year, how long would the 300 billion tons of coal last?
7. The total energy consumption of the United States in 1987 was approximately 80×10^{15} Btus (80 Quads). Coal has an energy content of approximately 2.62×10^{7} Btus/ton.
   a) If it were possible to power the entire country on coal, how many tons of coal would this require?
   b) As a yearly consumption rate equal to what you calculated in part a), how long would 300 billion tons of coal last?
8. What do you think is the primary flaw in the type of calculations you did in problems 4 through 7?
9. United States crude oil reserves are estimated to be 34×109 barrels. U.S. crude oil production was 7.4×10^{6} barrels per day in 1991. At that rate, how long will U.S. reserves last? Give your answer in years.
10. The undiscovered recoverable oil resources of the U.S. are estimated to average 72×10^{9} barrels. If these are discovered in the next few years, how many years do they add to the lifetime of our crude oil supply (assuming the 1991 production rate)?
11. The United States assessed resources of natural gas are estimated to average 600×10^{12} cubic feet. Production of natural gas in the U.S. in 1991 was 22×10^{12} cu. ft. At that rate, how long will U.S. natural gas resources last?

Goal

To examine the basic principles of nuclear energy and consider its potential as an energy option.

Nuclear Energy

We nuclear people have made a Faustian bargain with society. On the one hand, we offer an inexhaustible source of energy. But the price that we demand of society for this magical energy source is both a vigilance and a longevity of our social institutions that we are quite unaccustomed to.*

—A. Weinberg, former director of Oak Ridge National Nuclear Laboratory, 1972.

*According to legend, Faust was an old philosopher who sold his soul to the devil in exchange for knowledge and power.

Energy From Atoms

Humans have used most forms of energy since the beginnings of civilization, only nuclear energy is new to us. This is because science and technology had to develop to the point where nuclear events could be detected, understood, and controlled. Our understanding began in the early 1900s. The potential and danger of nuclear energy were brought to the world's attention with the atomic bomb explosion at Hiroshima in World War II. It wasn't until the 1960s that nuclear energy began to make a real contribution to the energy mix.

Several features of nuclear energy make it attractive. It can lessen our dependence on the fossil fuels. It does not cause obvious pollution. It does not add to the "greenhouse" effect. It is potentially an almost unlimited source of energy and can help satisfy our enormous appetite for electricity.

Before we begin to discuss nuclear reactors and how they work (and how breeder reactors make fuel as they run), we must first understand some basic ideas about atoms and how they are put together.

?

What is an atom and how are atoms put together?

41 8.1 The Atomic Nucleus

Today, scientists believe that all matter is built from basic units called atoms. There are over one hundred kinds of atoms. The atoms of any particular kind make up an **element**. For example, one kind of atom makes up the element we call gold; another, silver. All of the elements can be listed on a chart called the Periodic Table (Figure 8.1).

Atoms themselves are believed to be made up of smaller units called protons, neutrons, and electrons. Scientists believe that an atom is mostly empty space, and that almost all of its mass is concentrated at the center in a small, very dense, positively charged **nucleus**. Nuclear particles called **nucleons** are found in the nucleus. Nucleons are of two types, **protons** and **neutrons.** Protons are positively charged, and neutrons are neutral. All nucleons have about the same mass. Moving around the nucleus are the *electrons*. Electrons, on a relative scale, have practically no mass. They have a negative charge. Under ordinary conditions, atoms are neutral because they have equal numbers of electrons and protons. Table 8.1 summarizes the basic properties of protons, neutrons, and electrons.

Table 8.1 Basic Properties of Protons, Neutrons and Electrons.

Fundamental Particle	Symbol	Electric Charge	Relative Mass
proton	p	positive = (+1)	1
neutron	n	neutral = (0)	1
electron	e	negative = (-1)	$1/1837 \simeq 0$

PERIODIC CHART OF THE ELEMENTS

- Gases
- Nonmetal solids and liquids
- Metals
- Transuranium elements

1 H																	2 He
3 Li	4 Be											5 B	6 C	7 N	8 O	9 F	10 Ne
11 Na	12 Mg											13 Al	14 Si	15 P	16 S	17 Cl	18 Ar
19 K	20 Ca	21 Sc	22 Ti	23 V	24 Cr	25 Mn	26 Fe	27 Co	28 Ni	29 Cu	30 Zn	31 Ga	32 Ge	33 As	34 Se	35 Br	36 Kr
37 Rb	38 Sr	39 Y	40 Zr	41 Nb	42 Mo	43 Tc	44 Ru	45 Rh	46 Pd	47 Ag	48 Cd	49 In	50 Sn	51 Sb	52 Te	53 I	54 Xe
55 Cs	56 Ba	57-71 La* Series	72 Hf	73 Ta	74 W	75 Re	76 Os	77 Ir	78 Pt	79 Au	80 Hg	81 Tl	82 Pb	83 Bi	84 Po	85 At	86 Rn
87 Fr	88 Ra	89-109 Act Series	(104) Unq	(105) Unp	(106) Unh	(107)	(108)	(109)									

*Lanthanide Series	57 La	58 Ce	59 Pr	60 Nd	61 Pm	62 Sm	63 Eu	64 Gd	65 Tb	66 Dy	67 Ho	68 Er	69 Tm	70 Yb	71 Lu
†Actinide Series	89 Ac	90 Th	91 Pa	92 U	93 Np	94 Pu	95 Am	96 Cm	97 Bk	98 Cf	99 Es	100 Fm	101 Md	102 No	103 Lr

The transuranium elements (numbers 93-109) art part of the actinide series of elements which as a group occupies a single square in the main figure. The transuranium elements are all produced by nuclear bombardment. They are all radioactive. The rare-earth (lanthanide) series of elements, shown spread out in a horizontal row below the main diagram, also occupies a single square in the larger chart.

Figure 8.1 Periodic table of the elements.

The number of protons in a nucleus determines which element an atom is. The number of protons an atom has in its nucleus is referred to as that atom's **atomic number.** The elements are listed on the Periodic Table by atomic number. The table starts with the simplest and lightest atoms first, and works up to the heavier, more complicated ones.

Much of what has just been said is summarized by scientists with symbols. Study the diagrams in Figure 8.2 and the Periodic Table carefully. It is important that you understand what the number and letter symbols mean. They are the key to understanding much of what we will be covering as we survey the nuclear energy option.

Be sure you know these definitions.

Atomic number: The number of protons in an atom's nucleus.

Mass number: The number of nucleons (protons and neutrons) in an atom's nucleus.

Isotopes: Atoms of the same element that differ in the number of neutrons they contain. Isotopes are named by their mass numbers. For example, U-235 is an isotope of uranium that has a mass number of 235. Another uranium isotope, U-238, has a mass number of 238.

Atoms normally have the same number of protons and electrons, and are electrically neutral.

Relate each symbol in Figure 8.2 to the definitions just given.

Figure 8.2 Element symbols.

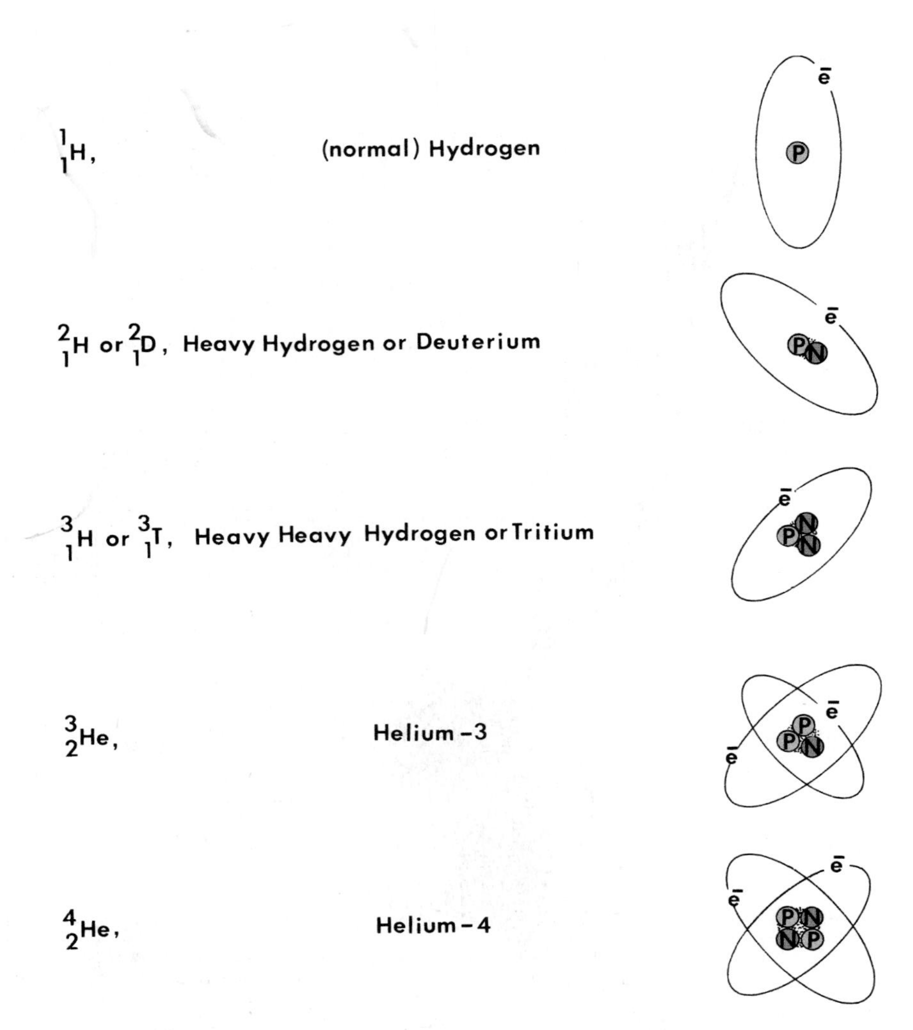

8.2 Radioactivity

Why are some nuclei radioactive?

Radiation is energy in the form of moving particles or waves.

The nuclei of most atoms are very stable. They are put together in such a way that they never change. However, some nuclei are unstable and emit radiation to gain stability. These nuclei are said to be **radioactive.** The reasons for instability vary. Some nuclei have a neutron-to-proton ratio that is too high or too low. Some nuclei are in an excited state, while others are just too heavy for stability. To remedy instability, nuclei decay. Since the conditions of instability differ, the ways nuclei decay also differ. The three most common ways are: 1) α-particle emission, 2) β-particle emission, and 3) γ-ray emission. α, β, and γ stand for *alpha, beta, and gamma,* the first three letters of the Greek alphabet.

Know what α, β, and γ radiations are.

Alpha particles ($^{4}_{2}He$) are the nuclei of fast-moving helium atoms. They are easily absorbed by thin sheets of paper or a few centimeters of air.

Directions: Fill in the spaces in the bottom four rows so that these rows appear similar to the top row. Do not write in your book. Your teacher will provide the details.

Lithium 7 Li 3 3 protons 4 neutrons	Carbon 12 C 6 6 protons 6 neutrons	Neon 20 Ne 10 10 protons 10 neutrons	Zinc 65 Zn 30 30 protons 35 neutrons
Gold ___ ___ ___ ___ protons 118 neutrons	___ 63 Cu ___ ___ protons ___ neutrons	Beryllium 9 ___ ___ ___ protons ___ neutrons	___ 201 ___ ___ 80 protons ___ neutrons
___ ___ Pt ___ ___ protons 117 neutrons	Radon ___ ___ ___ ___ protons 136 neutrons	___ 108 Ag ___ ___ protons ___ neutrons	Lead 212 ___ ___ ___ protons ___ neutrons
Strontium 90 ___ ___ ___ protons ___ neutrons	___ ___ Xe ___ ___ protons 77 neutrons	Thorium ___ ___ ___ ___ protons 142 neutrons	___ 238 U ___ ___ protons ___ neutrons
___ 11 B ___ ___ protons ___ neutrons	Uranium ___ ___ ___ ___ protons 141 neutrons	___ ___ ___ ___ 94 protons 150 neutrons	Neptunium 237 ___ ___ ___ protons ___ neutrons

Exercise 8.1 Nuclear Energy Chart

	Charge (e)	Rest Mass (amu)	Description	Range in Air	Method of Interacting with Matter	Effective Shielding Materials
α	+2	4	Nucleus of helium atom, $^{4}_{2}He$ or $^{4}_{2}\alpha$	few inches	ionizing collisions	paper, dead skin
β	−1	$\frac{1}{1837}$	High speed electron	several ft.	ionizing collisions	lucite, glass, aluminum
γ	0	0	High energy radiation, γ	indefinite	discrete interactions only (direct hits or nearly direct hits)	lead, concrete, water

Figure 8.3 Some properties of α, β, and γ radiation.

Beta particles ($^{0}_{-1}\beta$) are fast-moving electrons, and can penetrate a few millimeters of aluminum or about 100 centimeters of air. As the symbol shows, a β particle has no nucleus, and so its mass number is 0. With no protons to balance the electron, it has an atomic number of –1.

Gamma rays (γ) are electromagnetic radiations of very high frequencies. They have an indeterminate range in matter. On the average, they can penetrate large distances through air, or several centimeters through lead.

You can observe the effects of alpha and beta radiation if you do the cloud chamber experiment described in your lab manual.

Figure 8.3 summarizes some of the properties of radiation. When an alpha or a beta particle is emitted by a nucleus, the atom becomes a new element. What it becomes can be determined by the rules in Exercise 8.2, *Writing Nuclear Equations.* Make sure you understand this information. It is crucial to an understanding of nuclear science.

What do we mean by half-life?

In a sample of radioactive material, all the unstable nuclei do not decay at the same time. Instead, decay is a random event. However, since most radioactive samples contain literally billions of radioactive nuclei, the average rate of decay is "smooth." The amount of time it takes half of the unstable nuclei of a sample to decay into more stable nuclei is called the **half-life.** Each kind of radioactive element has a unique half-life. The half-life can serve as a "fingerprint" for identifying a radioactive material.

A typical radiation intensity-vs-time curve is shown in Figure 8.4. From this you can see that although the half-life for a given radioactive material is a specific amount of time, a radioactive sample theoretically never completely decays. "Half" is always left. Some half-lives are only small fractions of a second, and others are hundreds to billions of years.

8.3 Sources of Nuclear Energy

Nuclear energy is the energy released by a nuclear reaction or by radioactive decay. It depends on changes in the nuclear particles.

Nuclear energy is the energy released by a nuclear reaction (fission or fusion), or by radioactive decay.

Since any nucleus consists of a certain number of protons and neutrons, you would expect that the total weight of the nucleus could be predicted by adding together the individual weights of the particles in it. But in the case of nuclear weights, the whole is not equal to the

Writing Nuclear Equations

Model: atomic mass / atomic no. X ← chemical symbol

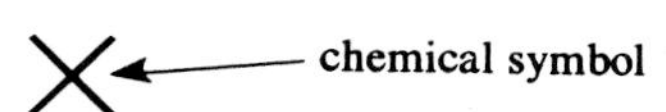

The rules for writing the nuclear equations you will be concerned with are as follows:

1. When a nucleus emits an α-particle, the mass of the atom decreases by 4 atomic mass units and the atomic number of the nucleus decreases by 2 units.

   ex. $^{232}_{90}\mathrm{Th} \longrightarrow {}^{228}_{88}\mathrm{Ra} + {}^{4}_{2}\alpha$

2. When a nucleus emits a β-particle, the mass of the atom is practically unchanged, but the atomic number increases by one unit.

   ex. $^{228}_{88}\mathrm{Ra} \longrightarrow {}^{228}_{89}\mathrm{Ac} + {}^{0}_{-1}\beta$

3. When a nucleus emits a gamma ray, both the atomic number and the atomic mass remain unchanged.

   ex. $^{113m}_{49}\mathrm{In} \longrightarrow {}^{113}_{49}\mathrm{In} + {}^{0}_{0}\gamma$, m = metastable

4. When a nucleus absorbs a neutron, the mass number increases by one and the atomic number remains unchanged.

   ex. $^{238}_{92}\mathrm{U} + {}^{1}_{0}\mathrm{n} \longrightarrow {}^{239}_{92}\mathrm{U}$

5. In all nuclear reactions, the sum of the mass numbers on the left side of the equation equals the sum of the mass numbers on the right side of the equation. The same is true for the atomic numbers.

With these rule in mind, and with the help of your periodic table, complete the following nuclear equations: (Do not write in your book.)

1. $^{222}_{86}\mathrm{Rn} \longrightarrow \underline{\quad\quad} + {}^{4}_{2}\alpha$
2. $^{214}_{82}\mathrm{Pb} \longrightarrow \underline{\quad\quad} + {}^{0}_{-1}\beta$
3. $^{9}_{4}\mathrm{Be} + {}^{4}_{2}\alpha \longrightarrow \underline{\quad\quad} + {}^{1}_{0}\mathrm{n}$
4. $^{235}_{92}\mathrm{U} + {}^{1}_{0}\mathrm{n} \longrightarrow {}^{138}_{56}\mathrm{Ba} + \underline{\quad\quad} + 3\,{}^{1}_{0}\mathrm{n}$
5. $^{14}_{7}\mathrm{N} + {}^{4}_{2}\alpha \longrightarrow {}^{18}_{9}\mathrm{F} \longrightarrow \underline{\quad\quad} + {}^{1}_{1}\mathrm{H}$

"Radioactivity is both a sign and a measure of the instability of certain atoms."—E. Rutherford.

Exercise 8.2 Writing nuclear equations.

sum of the parts! All nuclei (except hydrogen) weigh less than would be expected from the number of particles in them. (See Figure 8.5) In fact, the weight per particle depends on the number of particles, as shown in Figure 8.6.

The weight of the protons and neutrons in a nucleus depends on which nucleus they are in. The curve in Figure 8.6 shows that if light nuclei (atoms near the beginning of the periodic table) could be combined to make a somewhat heavier nucleus (that is, nearer the middle of the periodic table), the nucleus would weigh less than the sum of

From Figure 8.6, which elements have the lightest nucleons?

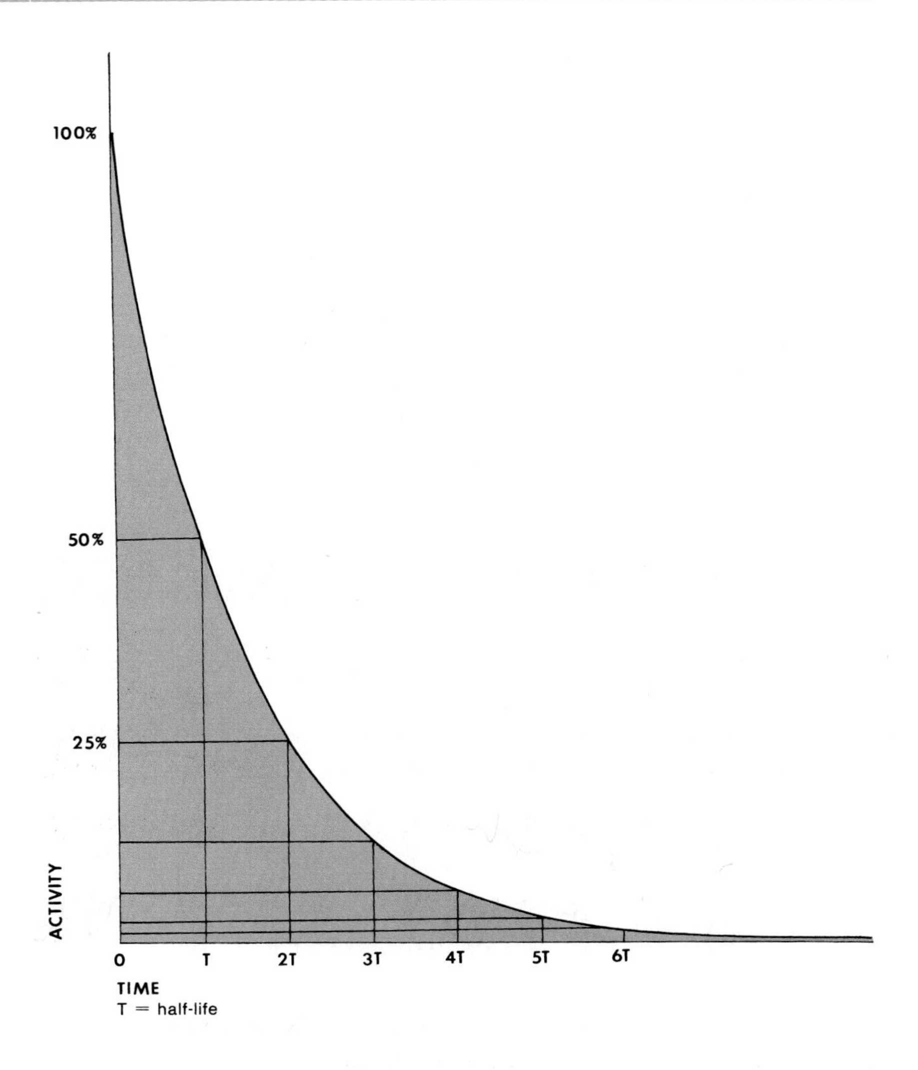

Figure 8.4 The decay of a radioactive sample.

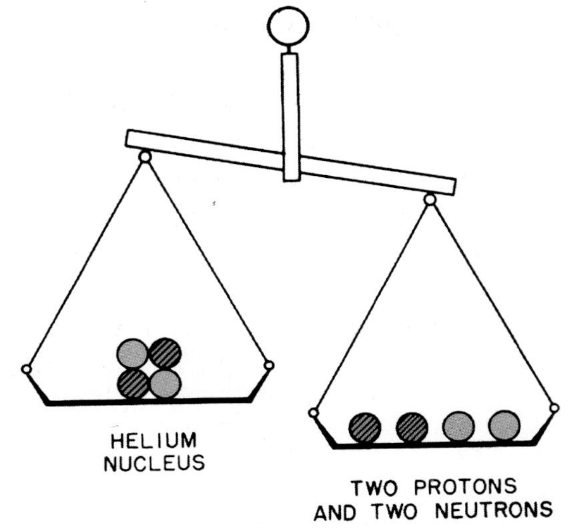

Figure 8.5 A helium nucleus weighs less than the sum of the individual weights of the particles making it up. (USAEC [Atomic Energy Commission])

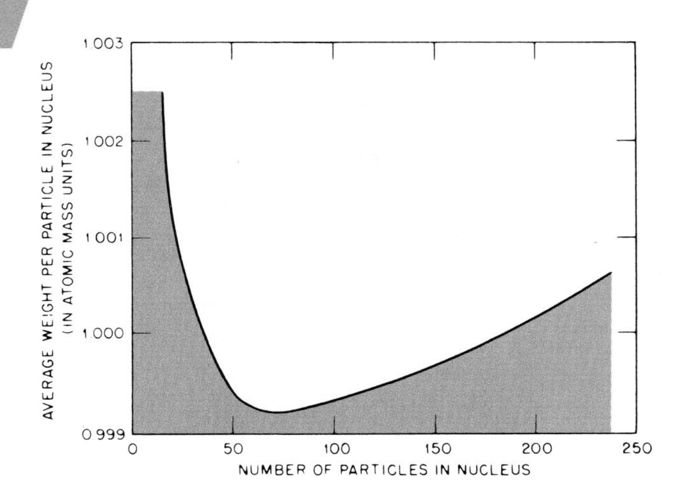

Figure 8.6 Number of particles in a nucleus. The weight per nucleon varies with the number of particles in the nucleus in a significant way. (USAEC [Atomic Energy Commission])

Figure 8.7 Energy comparisons for plutonium. (USAEC)

the original nuclei. It is also clear that if a very heavy nucleus could be separated into parts that fell near the middle of the table, the sum of the product weights would be less than the original (Figure 8.5).

The possibility of combining and splitting different nuclei. Isotopes may also be given their full names, such as uranium 235 or uranium 238.

In both types of nuclear reactions described in the above paragraph, a small amount of matter would actually vanish. Einstein's Special Theory of Relativity accounts for the vanished matter by saying that it would reappear as an incredibly large amount of energy.

$E = mc^2$

The energy released is shown by the equation $E = mc^2$, where E represents energy, m represents the "vanished" mass and c is the speed of light. The amount of energy released in the splitting (fissioning) of one uranium nucleus is not large. However, there are billions and billions of nuclei in a pound of uranium. So, one pound of uranium 235 has the energy equivalence of 1500 tons of coal. See Figure 8.7 for the equivalence for plutonium.

?

What is the difference between fission and fusion?

The two types of nuclear reactions are called fission and fusion. **Fission** is the splitting of a heavy nucleus into two approximately equal **fission fragments** (which are nuclei or lighter elements), accompanied always by the release of a relatively large amount of energy and generally by the loss of one or more neutrons. Fission can

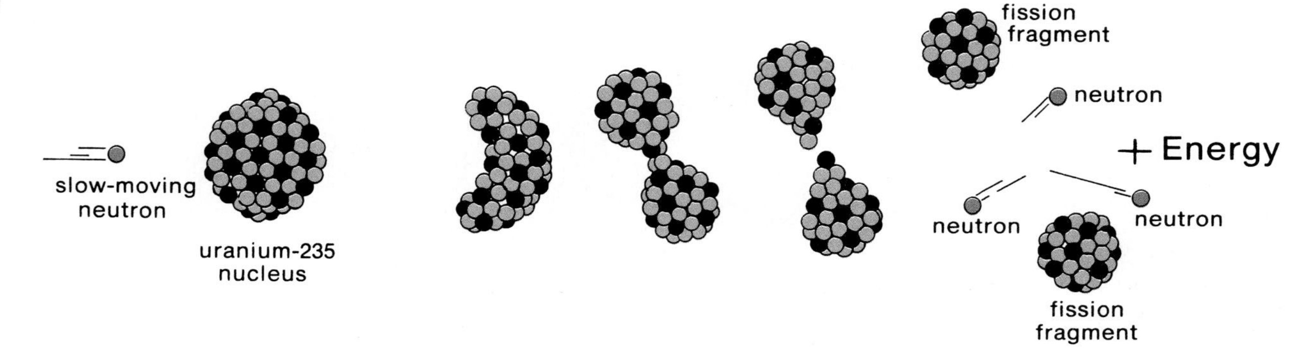

Figure 8.8 A typical fission reaction.

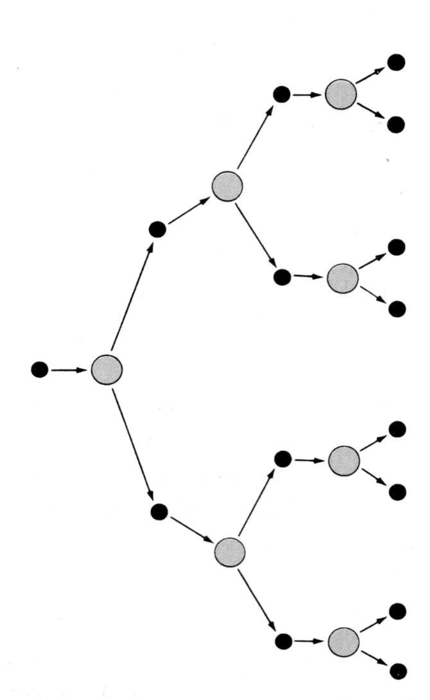

Figure 8.9 Nuclear fission of uranium. A neutron hits the nucleus of an atom of uranium. The neutron splits the nucleus in two parts and creates energy. At the same time, other neutrons are released from the splitting nucleus, and these continue the fission process in a chain reaction. (USGS)

occur spontaneously, but usually is caused by nuclear absorption of gamma rays, neutrons, or other particles (see Figure 8.8). **Fusion** is the formation of a heavier nucleus from two lighter ones (such as hydrogen isotopes), with a release of energy (as in a hydrogen bomb).

45 8.4 Fissionable Isotopes

Pu is the symbol for **plutonium**.

The only naturally occurring **fissionable isotope** is U-235. There are two human-made fissionable isotopes of interest: Pu-239 and U-233.

Pu-239 can be made from U-238, and U-233 can be made from Th-232. These two reactions are diagrammed here:

m = minutes.

d = days.

$$^{238}_{92}U + ^{1}_{0}n \longrightarrow ^{239}_{92}U \xrightarrow[2.35m]{\beta^-} ^{239}_{93}N_p \xrightarrow[2.35d]{\beta^-} ^{239}_{94}Pu \text{ (h.1. = 24,360 yrs)}$$

$$^{232}_{90}Th + ^{1}_{0}n \longrightarrow ^{233}_{90}Th \xrightarrow[23m]{\beta^-} ^{233}_{91}Pa \xrightarrow[27d]{\beta^-} ^{233}_{92}U \text{ (h.1. = 163,000 yrs)}$$

Some typical fission reactions are:

$$^{235}_{92}U + ^{1}_{0}n \longrightarrow ^{138}_{56}Ba + ^{95}_{36}Kr + 3\,^{1}_{0}n + \underline{\text{energy}}!$$

$$^{239}_{94}Pu + ^{1}_{0}n \longrightarrow ^{90}_{38}Sr + ^{147}_{56}Ba + 3\,^{1}_{0}n + \underline{\text{energy}}!$$

Thus **uranium** and **thorium** are the sources of our fission energy fuels. The uranium atoms in natural uranium (as it is taken from the ground) are approximately 99.3% U-238 and 0.7% U-235. The thorium atoms in natural thorium are all Th-232. It must be emphasized that in its initial stages, the fission process is solely dependent upon the isotope U-235.

What are the three fissionable fuels and how are they obtained?

There are two reasons that U-233, U-235, and Pu-239 are fissionable fuels: First, when bombarded with neutrons, they split into lighter elements, releasing huge amounts of energy. Second, when they split, they release more than one neutron, making possible a **chain reaction.** (See Figures 8.8 and 8.9.)

Why are U-233, U-235, and Pu-239 fissionable fuels?

8.5 Fusion Fuels

Fusion involves the combination of light nuclei to produce heavier nuclei and large amounts of energy. The light nuclei used for fusion are two isotopes of hydrogen (**deuterium** and **tritium**), and lithium 6. Fusion is shown in Figure 8.10.

Because deuterium is found in all water, the enormous amount of water available on Earth represents a huge potential source of energy. Tritium, however, represents a different problem. Tritium is made from lithium, and lithium ore is scarce. Further, lithium 6, required for fusion, is only 7.4% of natural lithium. The scarcity of lithium could mean that the total amount of energy which might be realized from fusion on Earth might be no more than what could be obtained from the combustion of the world's fossil fuels.

Using Nuclear Fuels

Wood and coal require little preparation for use as fuels. Even petroleum products are much like the crude oil from which they were refined. Uranium ore, however, must pass through several steps before becoming nuclear fuel. Disposal of nuclear waste is also much more difficult than the disposal of waste from fossil fuels.

8.6 The Nuclear Fuel Cycle

Our current use of nuclear fuels is a one-way process, beginning with mining and ending with storage of waste. Figure 8.11 illustrates the steps in preparing, using, and disposing of nuclear fuels. It also shows how a **nuclear fuel cycle** could be created by the reprocessing of used fuels. Refer to Figure 8.11 as each step is described below.

?

What is the nuclear fuel cycle?

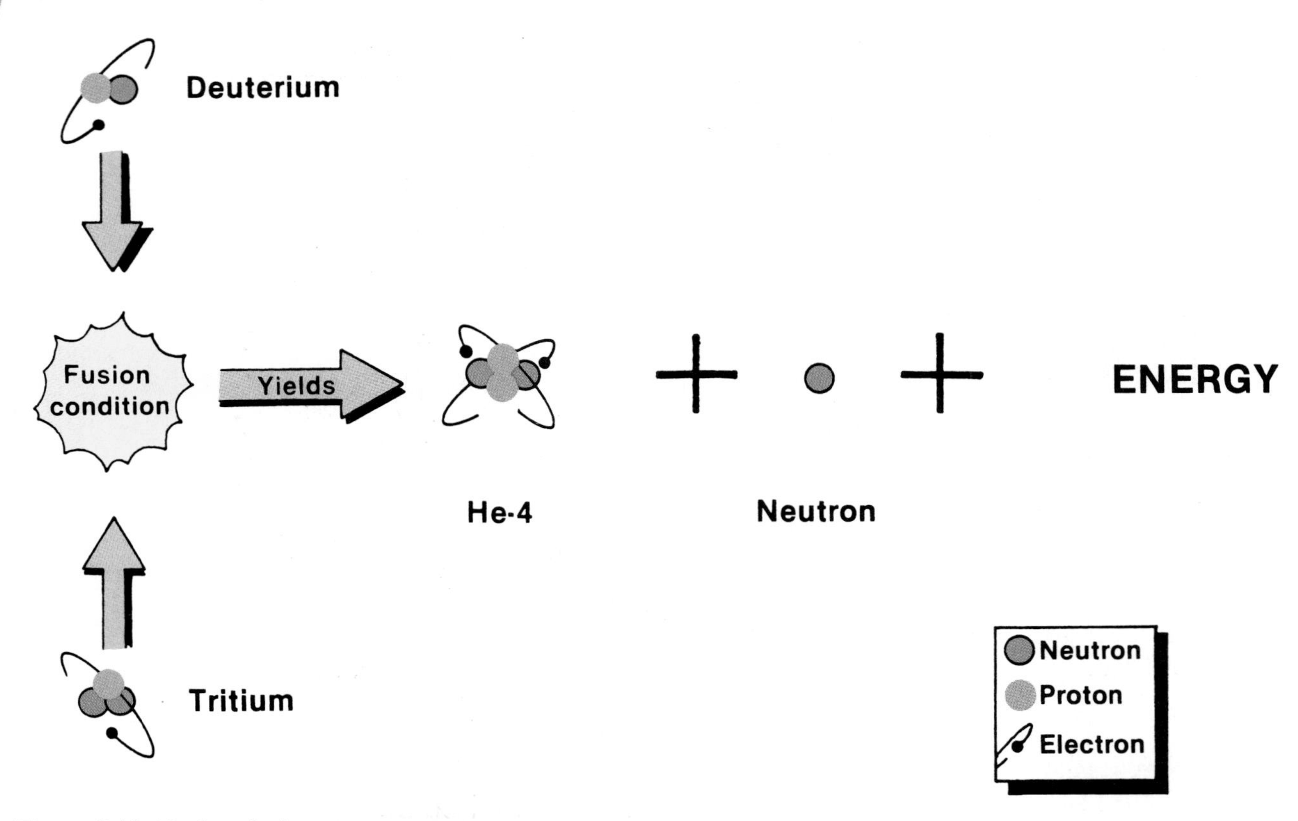

Figure 8.10 Nuclear fusion.

a. Exploration and Mining

Exploration and mining.

Uranium occurs in small amounts in most rock. To be profitably mined, the uranium must be sufficiently concentrated. Uranium fuel production begins with a search for a deposit that is rich enough to mine. Even then, a lot of rock and dirt must be moved in the process. See Figure 8.12. Commercial uranium ore contains only 0.1% to 0.2% U_3O_8 (uranium oxide, the most commonly occurring uranium compound). Uranium is mined both by open pit and underground methods. The extensive mining and processing of uranium must be taken into account when comparing fuels and energy.

b. Milling

Why is uranium ore milled?

The crude uranium ore (U_3O_8) is crushed, sampled, and concentrated as a product called "yellowcake." What is left over when the uranium is removed is called the "mill tailing."

In the past, these leftovers, which contain some radioactive material, have been piled up at the mine/mill site (some 140 million tons in the western states). The wastes are recognized as a potential hazard, and a government-sponsored program is underway to transport them to designated sites for burial.

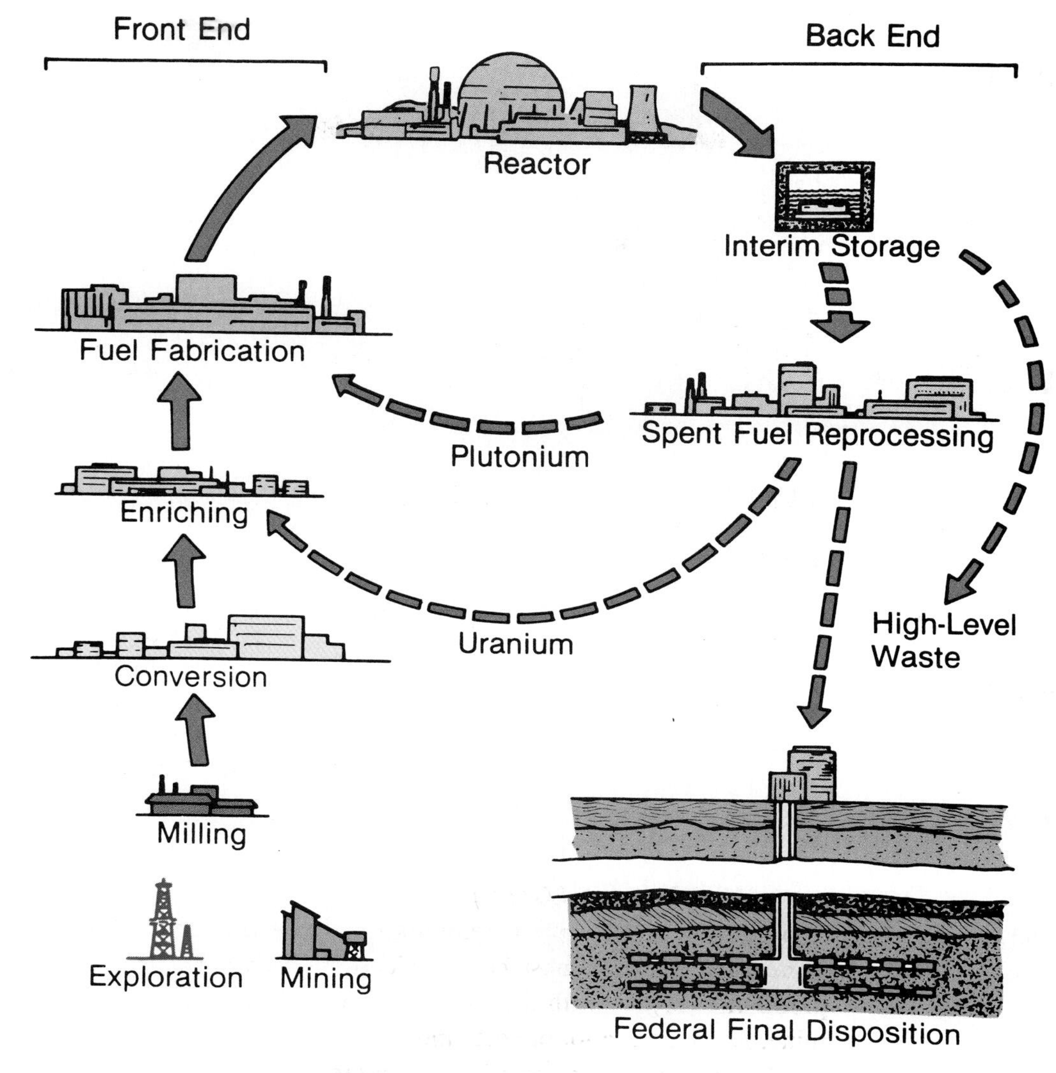

Fuel cycle as it operates currently.

Fuel cycle as it would operate with spent fuel reprocessing and Federal waste storage.

Figure 8.11 The nuclear fuel cycle. (USDOE, Energy Information Administration)

c. Conversion and Enrichment

Why must U-235 be enriched?

Most American nuclear reactors use **enriched** U-235 for fuel. In its natural state, only 0.7% of uranium is U-235. For nuclear fuel rods, this must be increased to 3 or 4%. (The concentration of bomb-grade material is at least 85%.)

Enrichment is a most difficult, energy-consuming step. Since U-235 and U-238 are chemically identical, they must be separated by physical means. Since they differ in mass by only 3 parts in 235 (1.3%), there is little margin to work on.

Figure 8.12 An open-pit uranium mine in New Mexico. (U.S. Bureau of Mines)

Figure 8.13 Yellowcake. (USDOE)

The most common enrichment technique is **gaseous diffusion.** The yellowcake is converted to a gaseous uranium compound, uranium hexafluoride (UF_6), in a conversion plant. This gas is then passed through a porous barrier. The UF_6 molecule containing U-235 is slightly lighter than the one with U-238. It therefore moves a little faster and passes more easily through the barrier. Many such passages (there are hundreds of barriers) build up the concentration of U-235. Gaseous diffusion is a complicated, expensive process. It is the step in using nuclear fuel that is most difficult for a less developed country to do.

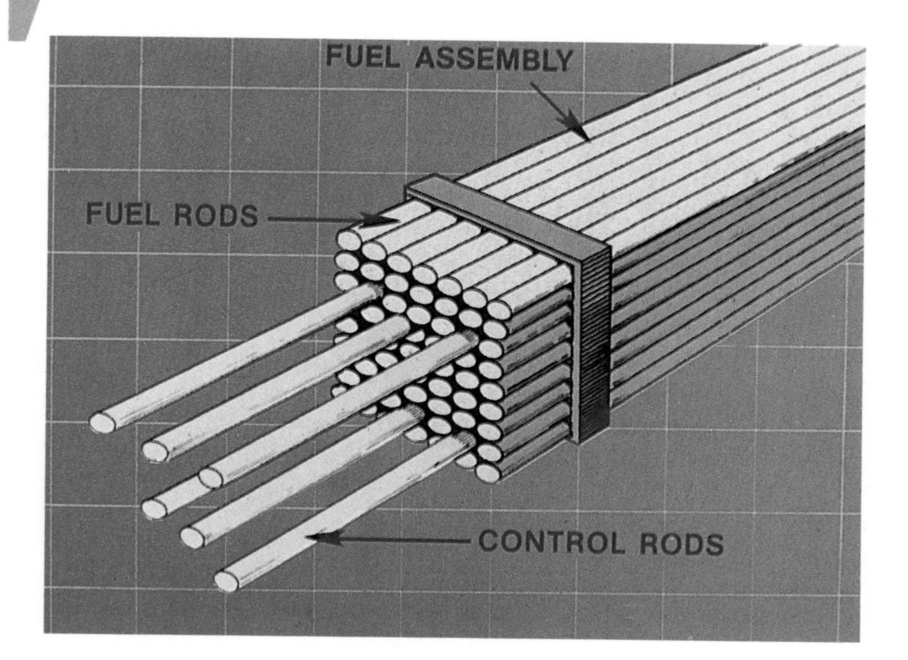

Figure 8.14 Fuel rods in the reactor core. (USDOE)

Enrichment is also possible by newer techniques: the ultracentrifuge, in which the differing masses are separated by centripetal force; or laser enrichment, in which U-235 is selectively activated (excited) by laser light so that chemical separation can then be performed. The perfection of one of these techniques could radically change today's "balance" of nuclear power among various nations.

d. Fuel Fabrication

The enriched gas is converted to the ceramic powder UO_2 (uranium oxide) or UC (uranium carbide). The powder is formed into pellets that are installed in fuel rods.

What is meant by fuel fabrication?

e. Fuel Burning

Fuel rods are transported to the reactor and inserted into the reactor core. The present practice is to replace one-third of a reactor's fuel each year. Unlike fossil fuels, uranium fuel is not totally consumed in ordinary reactors. Only about one percent of the total energy content of all the uranium in the original fuel is converted. The fuel rods need to be removed before all the U-235 is fissioned. This is because of the build-up of fission products that begin to interfere with the overall operation.

f. Spent Fuel Reprocessing

At this stage in the process, highly radioactive "fission products" have built up in the fuel rods. (These are **radioactive wastes.**) The fuel rods also contain some unused U-235 and some Pu-239. The Pu-239 was produced as a result of neutron absorption by some of the U-238 in the fuel rods.

At the present time (in the U.S.), where are used fuel rods stored?

Figure 8.15 Spent fuel rod storage at a reactor pool. (U.S. Council for Energy Awareness)

If the fuel were to be reprocessed, the first step would be to store the fuel rods under water for several months to let the short-lived fission products decay. Currently, this is the only step taken in reprocessing.

At present, the interim storage facilities at U.S. reactor sites are filling up. We are rapidly approaching the point where it will be necessary to either provide some away-from-reactor storage or begin reprocessing. If neither of these options is exercised, some reactors will have to shut down.

What happens when fuel rods are reprocessed?

In reprocessing, fuel rods are dissolved in acid. Radioactive wastes are separated out and prepared for long-term storage. Plutonium is removed and sent to fuel fabrication. Unused uranium is removed and prepared for enrichment. The political problems involved in waste disposal and reprocessing are growing. State after state is now saying "You can't put it here." No one wants to live near a nuclear processing plant or a radioactive waste dump. However, as the debate goes on, the spent fuel rods continue to fill up reactor site interim storage facilities. Tests are progressing at potential sites for the final disposal of **nuclear wastes.**

g. Waste Storage

Why must radioactive wastes be totally isolated?

Fission products (nuclear wastes) are radioactive and can remain so for thousands of years. In assessing the danger to people, you have to consider, in addition to the type of radiation and the half-life, the biological effects of the radioactive material. This will be dealt with in

Figure 8.16 Aerial view of Yucca Mountain. (USDOE)

a later section of this chapter. Because radioactive wastes are highly dangerous to life, they must be kept isolated for thousands of years.

This need for isolation is the real challenge of radioactive waste disposal. The debate is intense and often bitter. Questions raised are both moral and technological. We are, in effect, leaving these materials to our children. After disposal, the wastes will have to be monitored for generations.

What are high-level and low-level nuclear wastes?

Nuclear waste can be divided into two categories—high-level and low-level. High-level nuclear waste is composed of spent fuel from nuclear power plants and material from nuclear weapons production. These wastes are highly radioactive and may not decay to background (safe) levels for thousands of years. Low-level nuclear waste is composed of items that have been contaminated or became radioactive during their use. Tools and protective clothing are examples of low-level waste. These wastes are less radioactive than high-level waste and decay to background levels in less time. In addition to nuclear power plants, low-level waste comes from hospitals, research facilities, industries, and universities.

Why is Yucca Mountain an important area?

Yucca Mountain in southern Nevada is the only site in the United States being studied as a possible permanent storage facility for high-level nuclear waste. In the repository area of the facility located 1,000 feet (305 meters) below the mountain ridge, 77,000 tons of nuclear waste will remain undisturbed from the end of this decade until 12,000 A.D. If you are a rock, 10,000 years is not long; but for humans, that span of time is hard to grasp. The United States has existed as a nation for less than 220 years! The whole history of nuclear power spans less than 100 years.

Figure 8.16 shows an aerial view of Yucca Mountain. Figure 8.17 shows the proposed repository area. Testing is being done to determine whether or not the storage vault will be sufficiently stable to withstand any calamity—natural or otherwise—and protect the environment for the next 100 centuries.

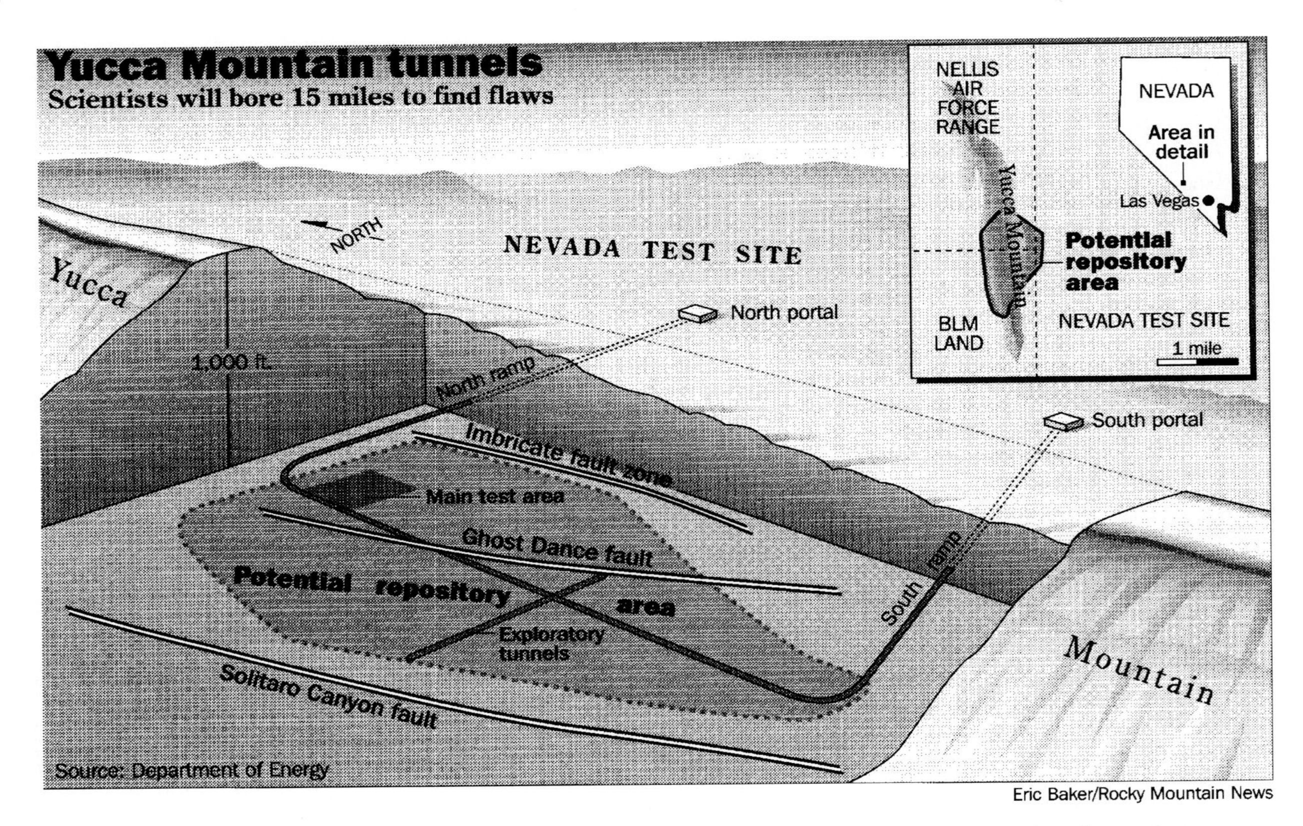

Figure 8.17 The proposed Yucca Mountain nuclear waste repository in Nevada. The cross section shows the potential repository area. (U.S. Department of Energy/Rocky Mountain News)

Where is low-level nuclear waste stored?

Low-level waste is placed in wooden boxes, 55-gallon drums or large metal containers. The material in the containers is packed very tightly together or made into a solid and shipped for disposal. Containers normally are shipped by truck to a low-level waste disposal site. Each state is responsible for the disposal of its own low-level nuclear wastes. Some states have their own disposal sites. Some states form a compact with other states and combine their wastes for disposal at a single site. Making compact agreements has been difficult because most people do not want even low-level nuclear waste near them. Thus, some states are still working to reach an agreement. Federal law requires that this be done.

How does a nuclear power plant work?

8.7 Nuclear Power Plants

Aside from its environmental impact, a nuclear power plant differs from ordinary power plants only in how energy is made available for turning the turbine which connects to the generator. This is illustrated in Figure 8.18.

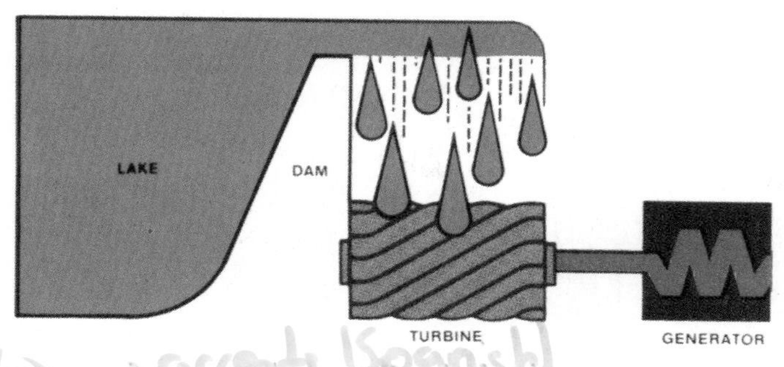

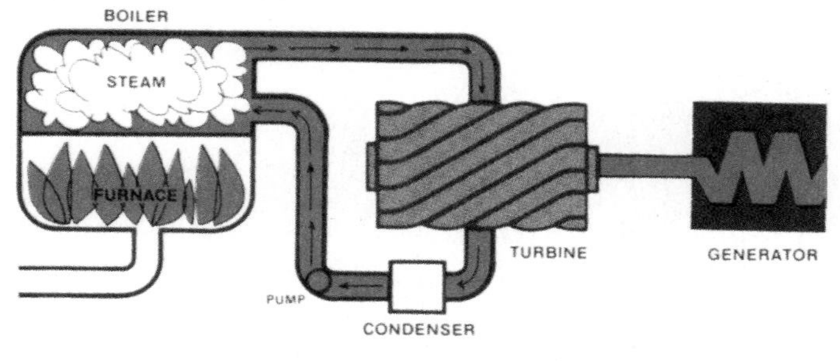

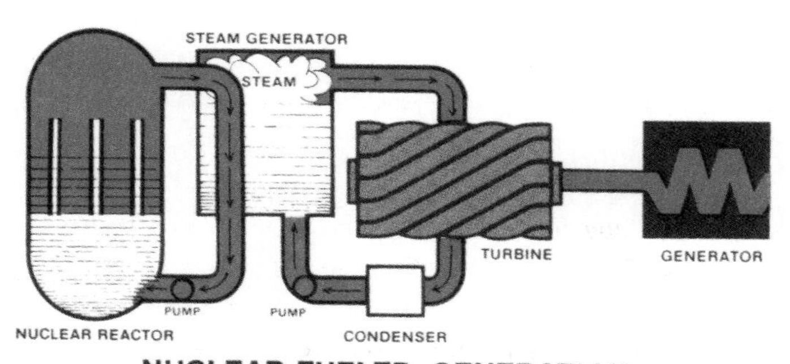

Figure 8.18 Electric generating plants. (Public Service Company of Colorado)

In a nuclear power plant, a **nuclear reaction** produces heat, which is used to produce steam to drive the turbine. The main parts of a nuclear reactor are:

What are the five main parts of a nuclear reactor?

- fuel,
- control system,
- moderator,
- heat removal system, and
- radiation shield.

Each of these parts is briefly described in the following paragraphs; they are also shown in Figures 8.19 and 8.20. Refer to these figures as you read about each part.

Figure 8.19 Nuclear reactor core. (From "Nuclear Reactors," USAEC, Division of Technical Information.)

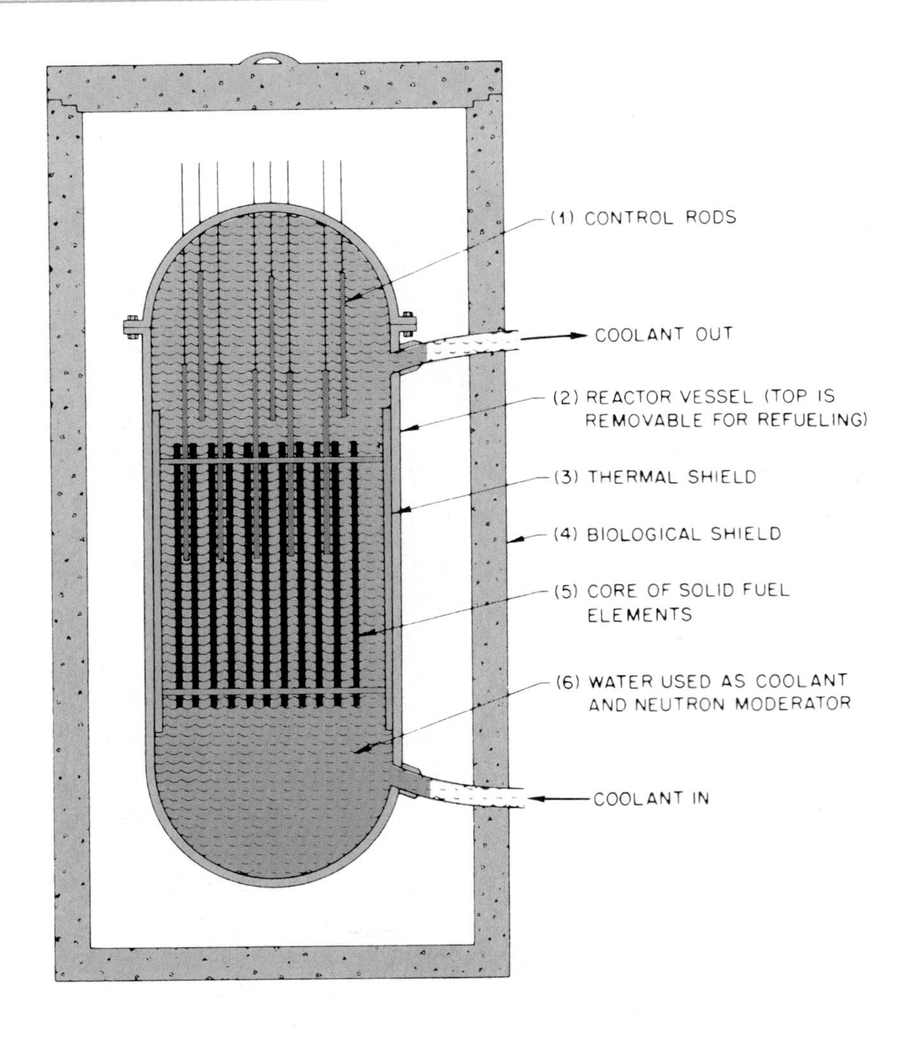

a. The Fuel

Neutrons make excellent bullets for probing the nuclei of atoms. They have meaningful speed and mass when they are produced. They also have no positive or negative charge. This lack of charge enables them to move toward a nucleus uninfluenced by any electrical effects. What usually happens when a material is bombarded with neutrons is that the bombarded nuclei absorb the neutrons. The nuclei then emit alpha or beta particles or gamma rays, and are changed themselves.

Why do neutrons make good bullets to shoot at nuclei?

However, when uranium 235 is bombarded with neutrons, its nucleus fissions into two parts whose weights place them somewhere near the middle of the Periodic Table. (See Figure 8.8.) As mentioned earlier, this process releases a huge amount of energy. This fission process is also accompanied by the release of several fast neutrons. Each new neutron can cause another nucleus to split, if properly slowed down by a "moderator." This releases still more energy and still more neutrons. A moderator is necessary because fast neutrons are not easily absorbed by U-235 nuclei.

What does the moderator do?

How is energy released from nuclear fuel?

All that is needed to achieve a chain reaction is to pile enough enriched uranium metal (suitably interspersed with a moderator, such as

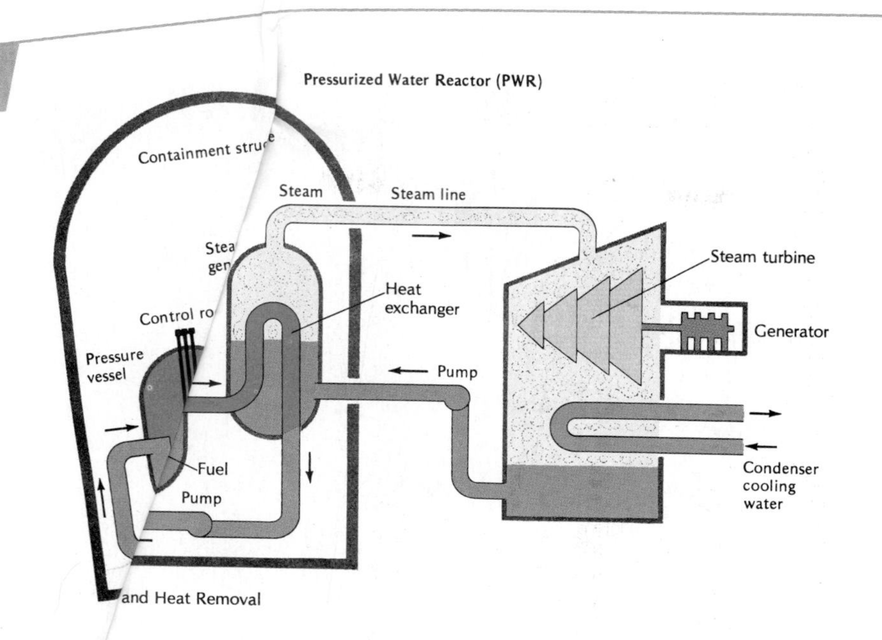

Figure 8.20 A complete nuclear power plant. In the pressurized water reactor, the primary cooling system is closed and under pressure. It exchanges heat energy with a secondary system that provides the steam. (U.S. Council for Energy Awareness)

in one place. The released neutrons have a good chance of absorbed by another U-235 nucleus before escaping. If enough 5 is present (a critical mass), and if the neutrons are allowed to ease rapidly, you have a bomb. If, on the other hand, you control growth in the number of neutrons, you have an energy source that an be used to produce electricity.

The most common fuel for nuclear power plants is uranium 235. Naturally occurring uranium consists of one part U-235 to about 140 parts of U-238. This is not sufficient concentration of U-235 to make a reactor go. Using the gaseous diffusion process, the centrifuge, or laser excitement, it is possible to produce uranium in which the U-235 content has been increased.

A good deal of debate is going on today concerning the size of our nuclear reserves. A fair summary seems to be that uranium reserves are sufficient to fuel the planned reactor program into the next century; but that without new supplies or a new technology, nuclear reactors will make only a small contribution to our energy needs.

b. The Control System

A certain minimum or critical amount of fuel is necessary for a reactor to work. This is called the **critical mass.** In a bomb, an uncontrolled fission chain reaction takes place. In a reactor, the fission chain reaction is controlled. On the average, 2.5 neutrons are emitted per fission. Some leak out of the reactor and are lost. Some are absorbed in the moderator, coolant, and structural material.

What is critical mass?

How do control rods work?

If the reactor is just critical, then there must be one neutron which, after slowing down, is left over to produce further fission. The ratio of the number of fission neutrons available for further fission to the one originally producing the fission is called the reproduction

Figure 8.21 Aerial view of nuclear power plant. (USDOE)

factor, k. For a reactor to be just critical, k = 1. If k is greater than 1 the number of neutrons increases rapidly. If k is less than one, the reactor will shut down.

All reactors have some adjustable neutron-absorbing rods, containing boron or cadmium, called **control rods.** The control rods may be thought of as neutron sponges. When they are pushed into the reactor, the value of k is reduced. When they are pulled out, k is increased. See Figure 8.19.

c. The Moderator

In addition to controlling the number of fission reactions, the speed of the neutrons must be controlled or moderated. Slower neutrons have a greater probability of reacting with the fissionable fuel. The moderating substance, called the **moderator,** must be a material consisting of light atoms. Fast neutrons will lose more energy upon colliding with light atoms than with heavy atoms. Good moderators include graphite, H_2O, or D_2O (heavy water). Most U.S. reactors use water.

d. The Heat Removal System

What is a reactor's heat used for?

As the fission products (and neutrons) collide with surrounding matter, their kinetic energy is quickly converted to heat.

Power plant reactors operate at extremely high power levels (measured in kilowatts or megawatts of heat output), and therefore must be cooled to prevent overheating and melting the core. In these reactors, the heat that is carried away is the primary product of the reactor. The heat is used for steam production.

A forced circulation system carries the heat from the reactor to the steam generator. Various coolants are used, including gases, water, and liquid metals.

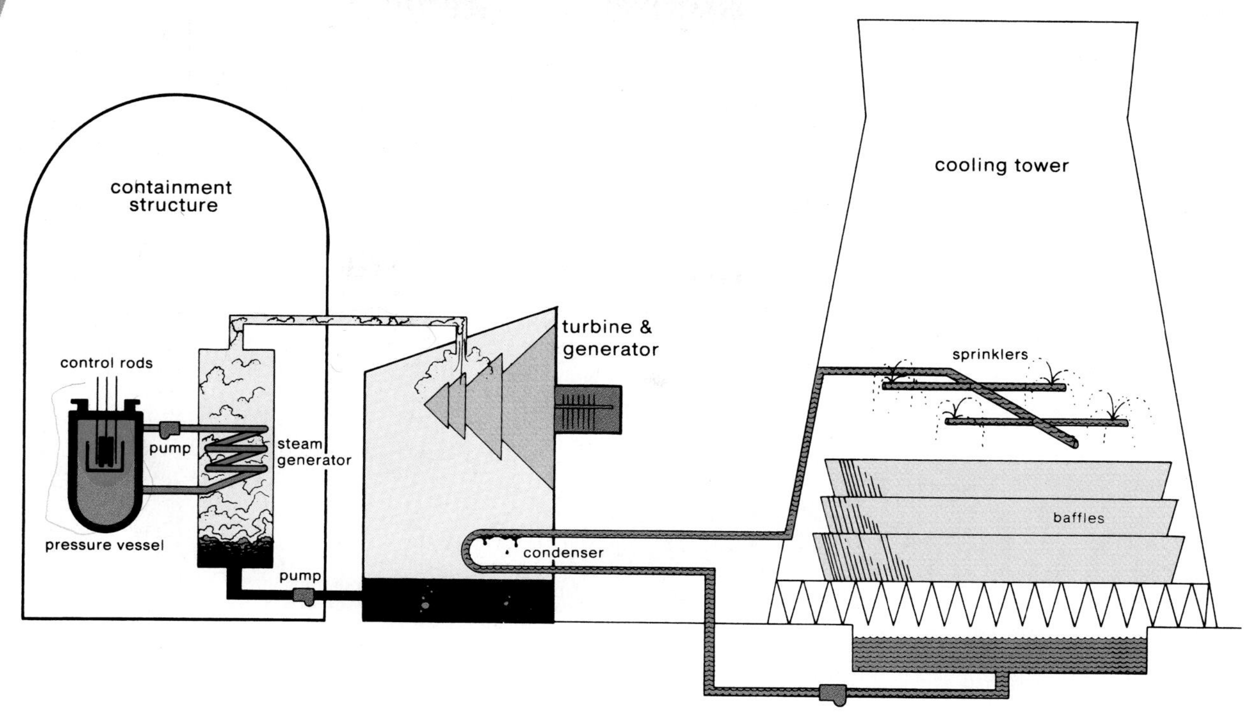

Figure 8.22 The design features of a typical nuclear power plant.

e. The Radiation Shield

Why are reactors shielded?

The part of the released fission energy that does not instantly appear as heat appears as penetrating radiation. Nuclear reactors must therefore be heavily shielded.

Reactors have an internal or "thermal" shield to protect the walls of the reactor vessel from radiation damage. They also have an external or "biological" shield to protect workers from radiation exposure. See Figure 8.19. The internal shield usually consists of a steel lining. The external shield is typically made of several feet of high-density concrete surrounding the reactor installation.

Fission reactions occur continually as the reactor runs. Fission equations have this general form:

$$\text{fissionable nuclei} + {}^{1}_{0}\text{n} \longrightarrow \text{fission products (nuclear wastes)} + \text{neutrons} + \text{energy}$$

The fission products are by far the largest source of radioactive waste in terms of radioactivity. They go through one or more steps of radioactive decay before reaching a stable, harmless end product.

Why are some radioactive wastes dangerous?

Most of the fissionable products decay rapidly and represent no real hazard to humans. A few of them, however, are a problem for one or more of the following reasons: amount produced, long half-life, efficiency of transfer to humans, and metabolism in the human body.

Figure 8.23 The power-generating portion of a nuclear power plant. (USAEC)

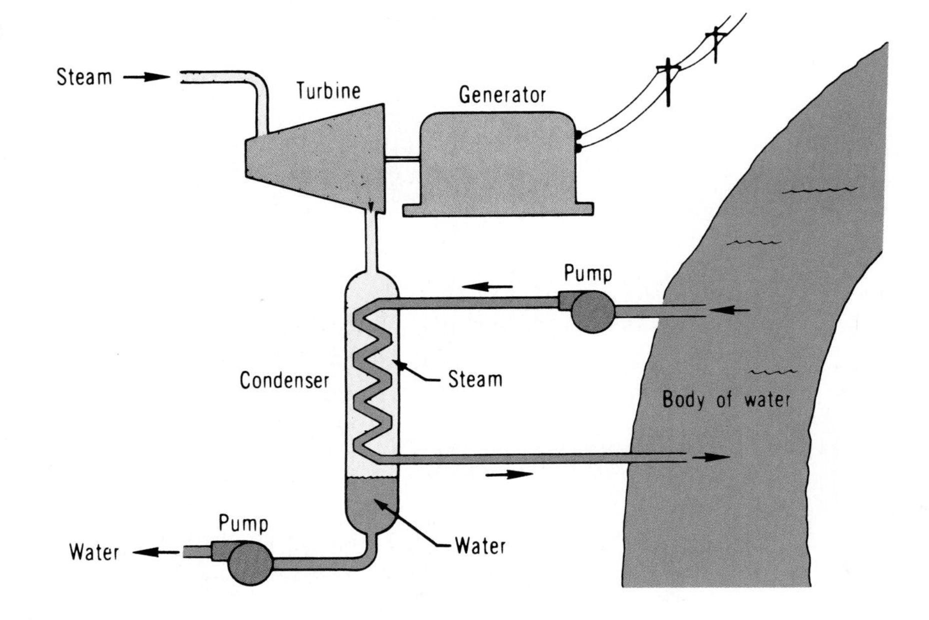

Figure 8.24 Tanks for the storage of high-level radioactive wastes. (From E. I. DuPont de Nemours and Co.)

Our biggest problem with these wastes today is storing them effectively. Much research is being directed toward solving the waste storage problem.

The Pros and Cons of Nuclear Power

?

What are some of the advantages and disadvantages of using nuclear power?

Nuclear energy is the most controversial of all our energy sources. Table 8.2 summarizes the major advantages and disadvantages of nuclear energy. The sections that follow explain other parts of the nuclear debate.

8.8 Biological Effects of Radiation

In the broadest sense, radiation is any event that spreads out in all directions from some source. Hence, the emissions from radioactive nuclei (mostly α, β, and γ) are radiations. Radiation also includes X rays and the cosmic rays that enter our atmosphere from outer space.

Table 8.2 Summary of the Advantages and Disadvantages of Nuclear Power

	Advantages	Disadvantages
Energy Source:	A significant amount of energy is available to us in the form of nuclear energy.	The fission process consumes uranium- and thorium-based nuclear fuels. A significant shift to nuclear power could result in our using up our nuclear reserves in a relatively short period of time (20–50 years).
Operation:	We know how to build and operate fission reactors. We have been doing so for many years.	The fission process produces long-lived hazardous radioactive wastes. Methods of storing them safely are being investigated, but as yet there is no general agreement on how to do this.
Dependency:	A significant shift to nuclear energy will reduce our country's dependence on foreign sources of - petroleum based products.	A shift to nuclear energy could result in a partial dependence on foreign sources of uranium and thorium.
Pollution:	No obvious pollutants such as smoke or ashes are formed by consuming nuclear fuels. Nuclear power does not contribute to the "greenhouse" effect.	The disposal of heat produced by nuclear reactors is a potential thermal pollution problem. Expensive cooling towers and cooling ponds that dissipate heat out into the atmosphere must be constructed to minimize the environmental impact of such large-scale heat disposal. In addition, we must safely dispose of radioactive waste.

For radiations to act in helpful or harmful ways they must interact with the medium they pass through. For example, interaction of α and β, particles with alcohol molecules produces the tracks in a cloud chamber (see Figure 8.26.).

An atom consists of a tiny, centrally located nucleus having a positive charge. Electrons having a negative charge circle the nucleus. Ordinarily the negative charges of the electrons just balance the positive charge on the nucleus. Atoms and molecules tend to be electrically neutral.

What is an ion?

An alpha or beta particle or cosmic ray crashing into an atom will knock electrons loose. What is left of the atom will carry a positive electric charge. An atom fragment carrying an electric charge is called an **ion.** Radiation that produces ions is called **ionizing radiation.** Ions have chemical properties that are different than the properties of the atoms from which they came. (See Figure 8.27.).

Unlike alphas and betas which interact continuously as they enter matter, X rays and γ-rays have discrete interactions with the atoms of the materials they enter. (They must directly hit the particles they

Special Focus

CHERNOBYL

Chernobyl is a nuclear power station located in Ukraine about 60 miles (100 km) north of Kiev. At this nuclear power station there are four 1000 megawatt RBMK-1000 reactors. This type of reactor uses graphite (a carbon substance) as the moderator instead of water to slow down neutrons so that fission can occur. In the RBMK-1000, water rising through pressure tubes inserted in the graphite picks up heat from the fission process and boils to become steam. This steam then drives a turbine-generator to produce electricity. (See Figure 8.25). In the United States water is used to moderate (slow down) the neutrons and remove heat to produce steam.

On April 26, 1986, during an inadequately planned experiment, Chernobyl's power rapidly spiraled out of control. Power levels reached 100 times full power in 4 seconds. Because of this rapid increase, there was a steam explosion and graphite fire which destroyed the reactor. A large amount of radioactivity was released to the environment because there was no containment building around the reactor.

A number of major design flaws of the Soviet RBMK reactor have been identified since the accident. In addition to these problems that were built into the reactor, operators who were conducting the experiment had turned off all automatic safety systems and had failed to follow operating procedures. Both design flaws and human error appear to be the main causes of the accident.

(In the U. S., operators are not allowed to shut off emergency systems without shutting down the plant. The moderator (water) cannot burn. Large reinforced containment buildings are in place to prevent release of radioactivity to the environment even during an accident.)

Source: Edison Electric Institute

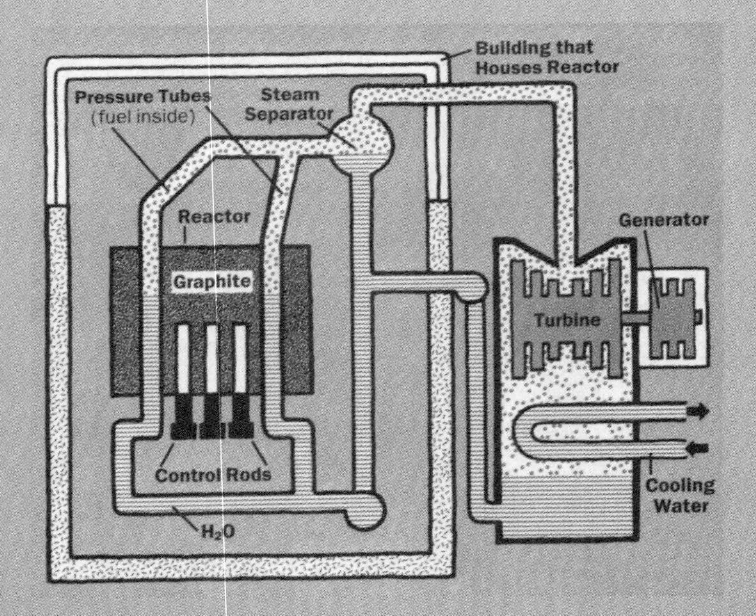

Figure 8.25 RBMK-1000 Graphite Moderated Reactor. (Edison Electric Institute)

Improving the Odds at Hanford

science at work

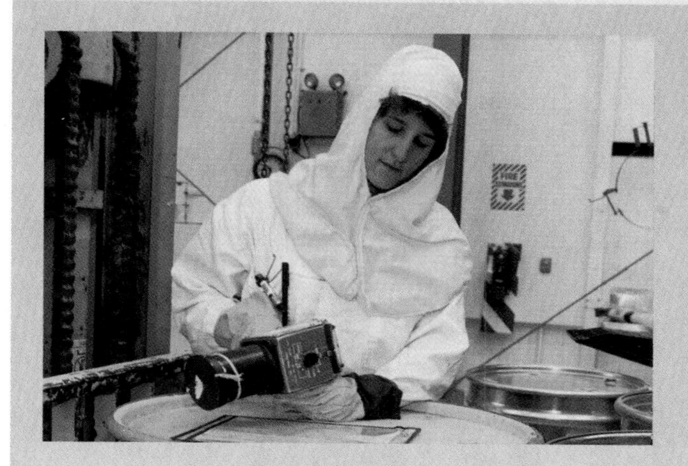

The Hanford Nuclear complex in the state of Washington, was once part of the former U.S. nuclear weapons-production system. Activity there still focuses on nuclear energy, but from a different viewpoint—Hanford is in cleanup mode, and there is much work to be done. Now closed are its nuclear reactor, nuclear waste storage site, and various other facilities for managing nuclear products. These days, contractors reporting to the U.S. Department of Energy are tackling the serious business of cleaning up the contamination at Hanford and similar facilities. Nuclear wastes generated by and transported to Hanford have been stored in shallow burials, open pits and basins, and large metal tanks that are leaking and contaminating the area's groundwater and soil.

Beth Mallory is a senior health physics technician at Westinghouse Hanford Company, one of the firms helping to make Hanford safe again. Beth's job is to monitor the workers there, measuring their exposure to radioactivity and protecting them from both external and internal hazards.

A typical day for Beth starts with a discussion with the workers in the area she is assigned to for that day. Then she begins the more specific work of making sure everyone is protected from exposure to radioactivity, harmful chemicals, and other hazards. Part of this protection is a Radioactivity Work Permit (RWP), which Beth helps to set up for a particular cleanup activity. Each RWP specifies what kind of contamination may be present, what level of radiation to expect, and what protection is required.

Beth uses various instruments and carefully defined procedures in her work. Before anyone starts work on a radioactive pipe, for instance, Beth "swipes" the area. Then she uses a Geiger-Mueller counter to check the level of beta radiation, and other instruments to monitor the alpha and gamma radiation. After determining the levels of radiation present, she uses the information to decide what protection the workers will need. For example, everyone must wear heavy cotton coveralls and canvas boots, with rubber boots over those. Different types of masks are worn based on the immediate environment; they filter out chemicals and/or particulates, and sometimes supply air for breathing when oxygen depletion has been detected.

For the specifics of her job, such as reading the various instruments, Beth was trained by her employer. But she also has a solid understanding of atomic energy, the different types of radioactivity, and the biological consequences of exposure. This helps her communicate with cleanup workers, emphasizing how important it is to be careful and follow all the rules. Her education—she has an Associate in Science degree in Nuclear Technology—included classes in radioactive chemistry, reactor physics, and heat transfer, as well as calculus, human biology, chemistry, and physics.

Beth is doing important work, and she knows it. Federal nuclear facilities still store 100 million gallons of waste in cooling tanks, many of which are cracked and leaking. In tests of the Hanford site, the radiation level of the groundwater was over 400 times greater than the proposed drinking water standard for the area. Until both the commercial and federal sectors of the nuclear industry can develop a long-term solution for nuclear waste disposal, the efforts of people like Beth are of great importance in preventing further damage to our ecosystem.

Figure 8.26 Cloud chamber tracks produced by alpha emissions from a plutonium source. (Argonne National Laboratory)

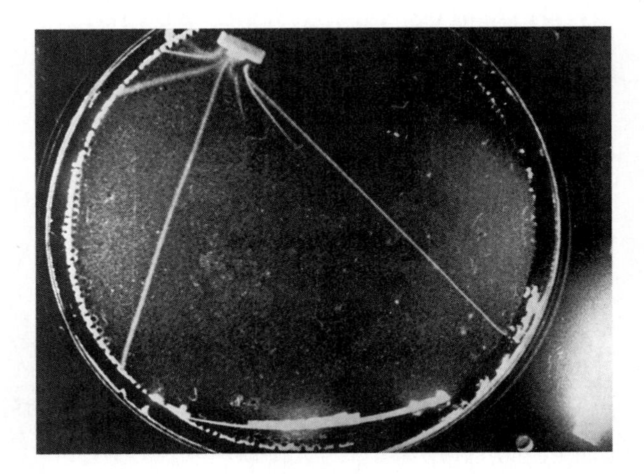

Figure 8.27 Alpha and beta interactions with matter. (USAEC)

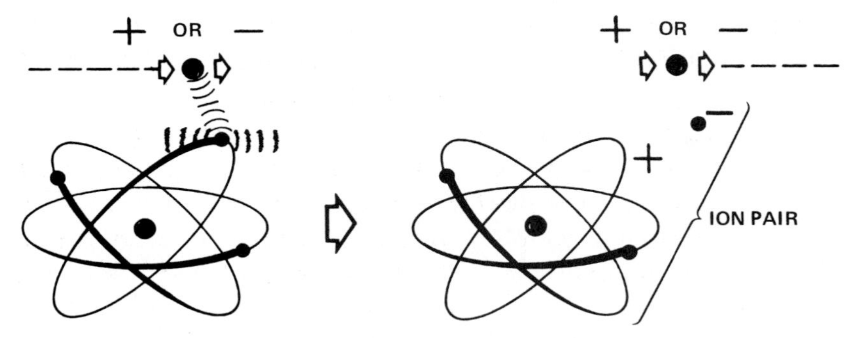

interact with.) These interactions may occur in more than one form, but they all result in the creation of ions. Hence, α, β, and γ emissions, X rays, and cosmic rays are all ionizing radiations.

Like all matter, plants and animals are made of atoms and can be affected by radiation. The basic unit of any living thing is the cell. Each cell is a tiny chemical factory made up of millions of atoms. In it several thousand different kinds of chemical changes are constantly taking place. The average human adult consists of about 50 trillion cells.

How does growth occur in cells?

A species is one kind of animal or plant, such as humans, flies, or oak trees.

Growth occurs when cells divide. The instructions for division and growth are contained in the cell's **chromosomes**. On the chromosomes are the instructions which determine growth, eye color, number of fingers, sex, and so on. Each species has a characteristic number of chromosomes in each cell. As a cell divides, its chromosomes also

Figure 8.28 "Strontium 90." (Reprinted from *The Saturday Evening Post*. Copyright © 1966 by the Curtis Publishing Company.)

Strontium 90 is a radioactive isotope of strontium that easily deposits in bone.

divide, and they line up in pairs. Because one chromosome of each pair goes to each new cell, the new cells are replicas of the old cell. (However, in the formation of sex cells, a sperm or egg cell gets only half as many chromosomes as a body cell would.)

What can ionizing radiation do to cells?

Ionizing radiation can alter chromosomes and hence cause **mutations** or changes in cells. Mutations may be invisible, like a change in one enzyme. Or they may lead to missing fingers, toes, or other visible changes. Mutations caused by ionizing radiation are random. Since living organisms are such complex, nearly perfect functioning chemical factories, very few mutations are believed to be beneficial. See Figure 8.28.

Natural radiations.

What are some sources of the natural radiation we receive?

Humans have always lived in an environment that includes a great deal of natural radiation. It comes both from within the Earth and from outer space. Such radioactive materials as uranium and thorium, and decay products associated with them, exist everywhere in the Earth. The places where they are mined are simply the locations of large concentrations of these minerals. Small amounts of the radioactive gas radon are present in the air we breathe and in the soil.

Cosmic radiation, particles of very high energy which strike the Earth's atmosphere from outer space, contribute both directly and indirectly to the amount of radiation to which we are exposed. Cosmic rays contribute directly by striking our bodies. They contribute indirectly by creating radioactive carbon 14 when cosmic neutrons strike atmospheric nitrogen. Carbon 14 is then quickly converted into $^{14}CO_2$. The $^{14}CO_2$ is utilized by plants in photosynthesis, and the plants are eaten by animals. The radioactive carbon eventually finds its way into our bodies through our food. In fact, the disintegration of ^{14}C results in the liberation of about 200,000 beta particles per minute in the average adult. Potassium 40, which is also in our bodies, liberates approximately 240,000 beta particles per minute in the average adult. Other radioactive materials in our bodies include radium 226, strontium 90, cesium 137, and iodine 131.

Human-produced radiations.

In addition to this natural radiation, humans have created new sources of radiation as we have explored nature and hunted for ways to improve our control and use of nature. Sources of human-produced radiation which contribute to our total exposure to radiation include medical X-rays, radioactive fallout, television tubes, radioactive wastes from nuclear reactors, and so on.

Large doses of radiation can cause severe injury and even death, but what about smaller doses? Though all exposure to ionizing radiation presents some risk, human beings are continuously exposed to radiation at low intensity without any apparent or readily identifiable harmful effects. Just as the body is able to adjust to cuts and bruises and mend the damage, so to a certain extent it is able to adjust to and counteract the harmful effects of small doses of radiation.

In a couple of ways, however, we cannot adjust even to low levels of ionizing radiation. Rates of genetic mutations and all forms of cancer increase with increased exposure.

Genetic damage and cancer production have been the subjects of much public concern. Some scientists believe that low levels of radiation have been producing genetic effects since the beginning of life. Cumulative changes in heredity have apparently helped to accomplish the evolution of plant and animal species . Although this may be the case, most scientists agree that we should not speed up the process of evolution by increasing our radiation exposure.

What is cancer?

Cancer is believed to result from a mutation in which certain cells lose the capacity to regulate their growth properly. In every cell in the body, there is a regulatory gene which controls the rate at which that cell divides. Instead of dividing about 50 times, as a cell normally does, a cancerous cell produces millions and millions of cells. Since these mutations do not involve the sex cells, they are confined to the individual and are not passed on to the offspring.

Penetrating radiation and external hazards.

X rays and gamma rays must undergo discrete interactions (direct hits) with matter before they create ions. Hence they can penetrate deep into wood, water, and the human body. They are thus considered external hazards. People who were a mile or so away from the bomb dropped on Hiroshima suffered radiation effects, even though they were not injured by flying debris, intense heat, or the shock wave created by the explosion.

α and β are internal hazards.

Alpha and beta radiations are not very penetrating, so they are not classified as external hazards. Their range in air, paper, and skin is very short. However, they intensely ionize the material through which they do pass (as is seen in the cloud chamber). This makes them a serious internal hazard. That is why plutonium is so dangerous. Plutonium is a strong alpha emitter. Cancer may result if even a minute amount of it is breathed in and deposited in the lungs.

These facts pose a real dilemma. Surely it makes sense to have one's leg X-rayed if one suspects it has been broken. If the information gained from the X-ray results in the proper treatment of the break, the benefit incurred most likely is greater than the increased risk of cancer or genetic damage.

However, the dangers of increased exposure to ionizing radiation must not be taken lightly. For example, the handling and disposal of our radioactive wastes are serious problems, and how we decide to handle them will indicate the maturity of our generation.

8.9 The Breeder Option

Most of the uranium found in nature (99.3%) is made up of atoms containing 238 protons and neutrons, U-238. This uranium is quite stable and has no practical energy use itself.

The uranium used to fuel today's nuclear reactors is uranium 235 (the remaining 0.7% of natural uranium). When hit with a high speed (thermal) neutron, it will break up or split and produce heat energy, fission products (nuclear wastes), and more neutrons. These neutrons can be used to split more U-235 atoms and produce more energy. Uncontrolled, we have a bomb. Controlled, we have a source of energy. This sequence is summarized as follows:

$$\text{U-235} \longrightarrow \text{FISSION PRODUCTS} + \underline{\textit{NEUTRONS}} + \text{HEAT}$$

(the neutrons loop back to U-235)

As was pointed out earlier, this reaction uses up U-235. That is why our present nuclear reactors are called burner reactors. They use up U-235. Our reserves of uranium 235 are such that if this were the complete story on nuclear energy, there would be little interest in it. The energy content of these reserves is comparable to that in our reserves of oil and natural gas.

How does a breeder reactor make fuel as it runs?

In a breeder reactor, as the U-235 breaks down, some of the spare neutrons produced are captured by the rather useless U-238. When this happens, the U-238 changes (in a series of steps) to plutonium 239. This isotope can be split by neutrons as in the fission of uranium 235 and used to produce heat in a reactor. The same thing can be done to thorium 232, the natural form of thorium. The equations are:

$$^{238}_{92}\text{U} + {}^{1}_{0}\text{n} \longrightarrow {}^{239}_{92}\text{U} \xrightarrow{^{0}_{-1}\beta} {}^{239}_{93}\text{Np} \xrightarrow{^{0}_{-1}\beta} {}^{239}_{94}\text{Pu}$$

$$^{232}_{90}\text{Th} + {}^{1}_{0}\text{n} \longrightarrow {}^{233}_{90}\text{Th} \xrightarrow{^{0}_{-1}\beta} {}^{233}_{91}\text{Pa} \xrightarrow{^{0}_{-1}\beta} {}^{233}_{92}\text{U}$$

Using a breeder reactor to make fuel.

Thus, if U-238 and Th-232, which are natural and mined from the ground, are placed in a breeder reactor and bombarded with neutrons, they can be changed into Pu-239 and U-233 respectively. Both P-239 and U-233 are fissionable. This means they can be used to fuel other reactors. Therefore, a breeder reactor makes fuel as it runs.

Theoretically, our uranium fuel supply could be increased by a factor of 99.3/0.7 = 142. In reality, we cannot build reactors that bombard every uranium-238 atom placed in them.

Engineers have determined that a breeder program is capable of increasing the energy available to us from uranium by a factor of about 60. We also gain access to the nuclear energy available to us in our thorium reserves. We are just beginning to determine the extent of those reserves. The diagram below is a way of illustrating the breeder reaction.

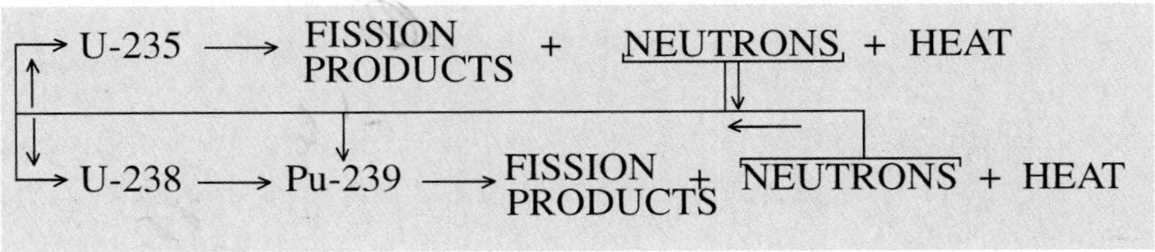

U-235 → FISSION PRODUCTS + NEUTRONS + HEAT

U-238 → Pu-239 → FISSION PRODUCTS + NEUTRONS + HEAT

Once a supply of Pu-239 (or U-233) is built up, U-235 is no longer necessary for the breeder program. However, it is absolutely necessary to have uranium 235 in the beginning.

By careful selection and arrangement of materials in a reactor, the neutrons not needed in the fission chain reaction can be used to convert U-238 and Th-232 into Pu-239 and U-233. Thus, scientists and engineers may be able to make use of most of the uranium and thorium in nature for the release of nuclear energy and the production of electric power. See Figure 8.29.

The advantages of a breeder-based nuclear program are:

- A significant amount of energy is available to us in the form of nuclear energy, especially if the breeder program becomes a reality.
- A significant shift to nuclear energy will reduce a country's dependence on foreign sources of petroleum-based products.
- Because breeders make nuclear fuel as they run, they will greatly extend the lifetime of nuclear fuel reserves. To some extent, the perfection of the breeder implies the end of the energy crisis, at least for a time.

What are some of the advantages of the breeder program?

This is only half of the story. Possible disadvantages of a breeder-based technology include:

- Like ordinary fission reactors, breeder reactors produce longlived radioactive wastes that threaten human health and the environment. If we increase the energy available to us from nuclear fission by a factor of 60 or more, we also increase the quantity of radioactive wastes by the same factor. Presently, there is no agreement on a safe method for storing and disposing of our current wastes. Should we venture into a new program that produces additional wastes without proven storage and disposal techniques?

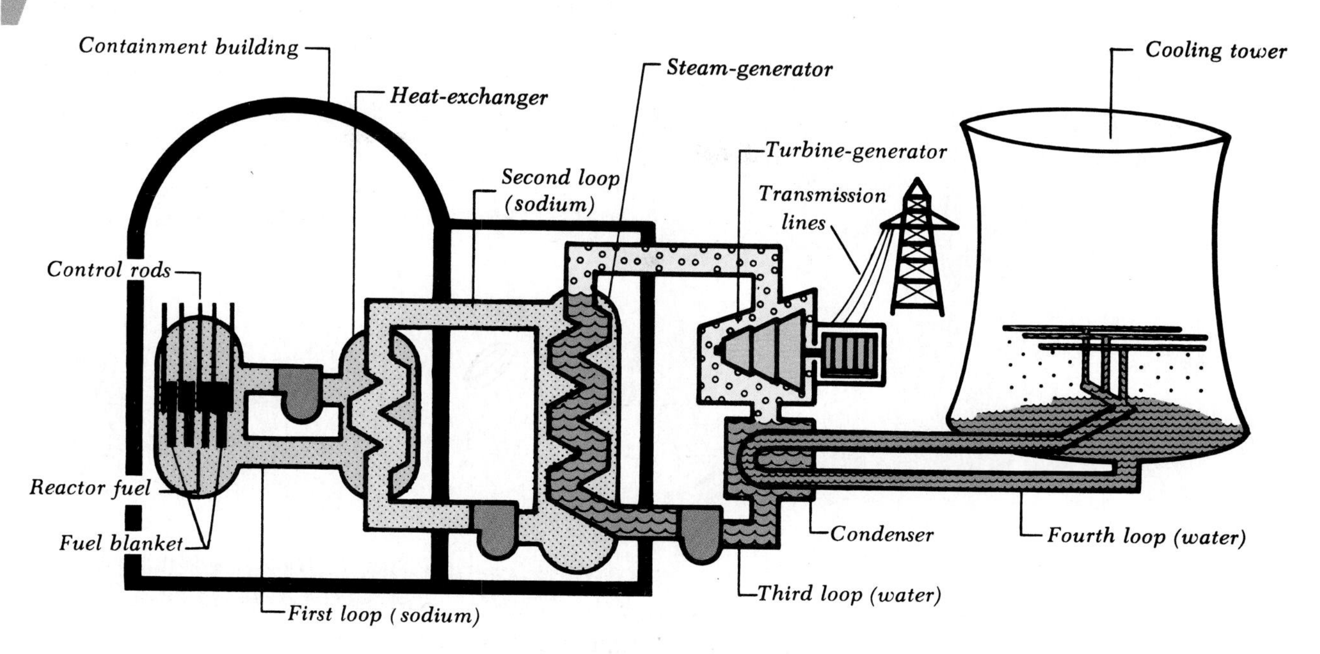

Figure 8.29 A breeder reactor. (USDOE)

- Like ordinary fission reactors, breeders produce large quantities of "waste" heat, which we simply dump into the air and bodies of water. How should this potential thermal pollution problem be handled?
- The fissionable materials produced in a breeder should be used to power new breeder reactors, but they could also be used by terrorists to make nuclear weapons. Some physicists claim the machining of the uranium or plutonium portion of the bomb (the trigger) and the fabrication of all the components must be so precise that most terrorists would have trouble doing it correctly. However, any country that has the capability of producing plutonium 239 and uranium 233 also has the capability of becoming a nuclear power.
- A reactor producing 300 kg of plutonium per year is theoretically producing the equivalent of some thirty or more nuclear bombs. What are the implications of this kind of information?
- Plutonium has been termed the most carcinogenic material known to man. Dr. John Goffman, who has spent the major portion of his career studying the biological effects of nuclear materials, states: "One pound of plutonium represents the potential of producing nine billion human lung cancers. As a toxic substance, it will be in our environment, if released, for the next half million years." Should we go ahead and produce this kind of material by the ton?

What are some concerns related to breeder-based technology?

If you've seen one nuclear war, you've seen 'em all.

Figure 8.30 All God's Chillun got N-Power. (Copyright © 1975 by the Washington Star. Reprinted with permission of Universal Press Syndicate. All rights reserved.)

Gas core reactor power plant.

Because of the magnitude of these problems, and because of the promise of breeder-based energy, scientists and engineers are looking at alternative breeder reactor designs. One such alternative is the gas core reactor power plant. This reactor has a low inventory of fissionable material. If as little as four kilograms of fissionable material are removed from the reactor (less than a critical mass), the reactor will shut down. Fuel is processed on site. A high fuel burnup is featured. Waste production is drastically reduced.

Other scientists are working on transmuting longlived nuclear wastes to isotopes that are shortlived. These possibilities, if successful, could make the breeder option an acceptable one to the American public. Unfortunately, the investigation of these possibilities and the tooling up will require money and time. We can't look forward to their reality until well after the year 2000.

8.10 The Fusion Future

The sun and other stars generate energy by nuclear fusion. Fusion involves joining together the nuclei of two atoms, resulting in the release of energy. Normally nuclei repel each other. This is because all nuclei are positively charged, and like charges repel each other. However, if the nuclei can be brought very close to each other, the force of nuclear attraction becomes stronger than the repelling electrical force,

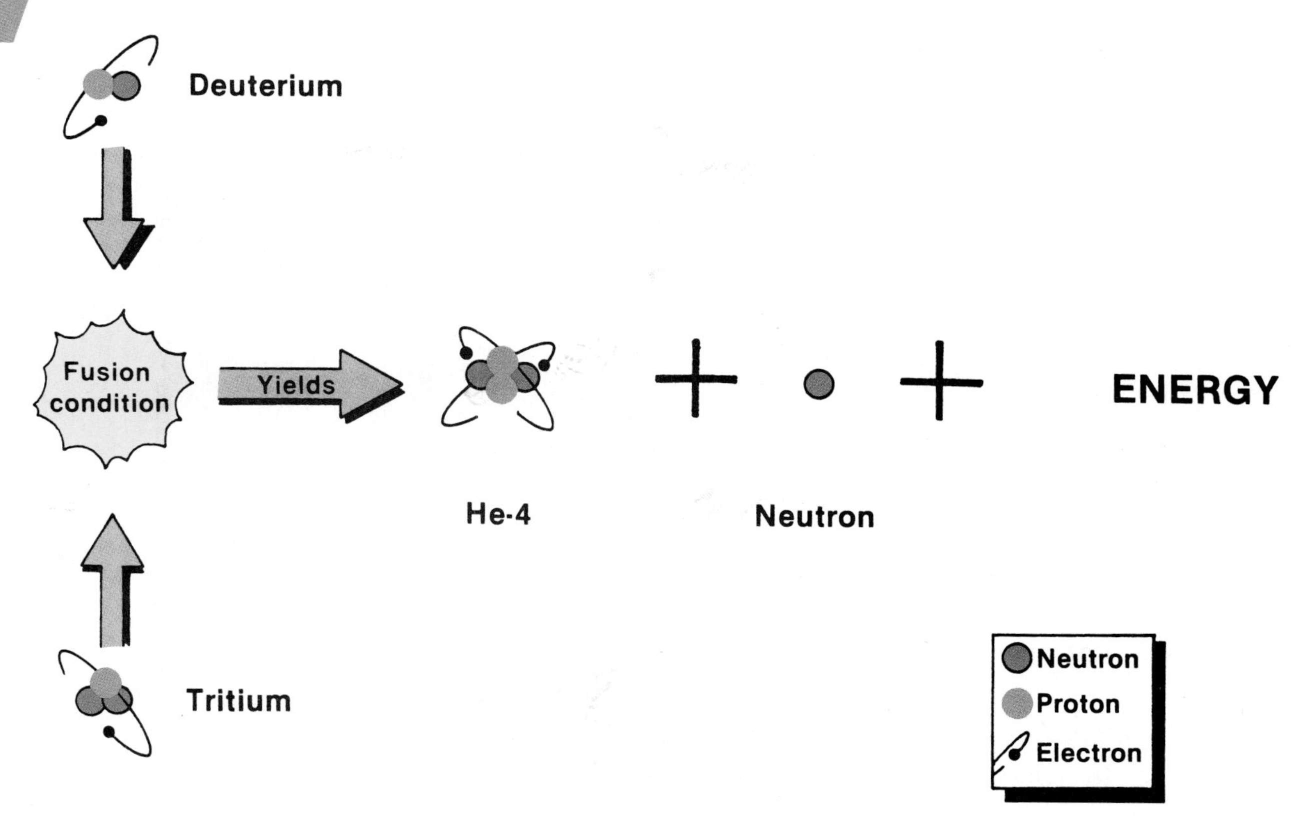

Figure 8.31 Nuclear fusion.

and fusion takes place. To get the nuclei close enough, the fuel for the fusion process (isotopes of hydrogen) must be heated to about 100 million degrees (Celsius, Fahrenheit, or Kelvin). At this temperature, the nuclei are moving fast enough so that fusing conditions are met when they move together. A heavier element is formed, neutrons are produced, and a huge amount of energy released. See Figure 8.31.

The major reason it has been so difficult to accomplish controlled fusion on Earth is the problem of heating something up to 100 million degrees and containing it. Normally we contain gases in bottles and cans. However, any bottle or can would vaporize long before the 100 million degree temperature was reached. No known material substance exists as a solid or liquid at such high temperatures. Two attempts to side-step this problem are being tried. One is **magnetic confinement fusion,** the other is **laser fusion.**

Magnetic confinement fusion.

The idea in magnetic confinement fusion is to contain the hot nuclei, called a **plasma,** in a strong magnetic field often referred to as a magnetic bottle. One of these bottles is shaped like a doughnut. It is produced by bending a circular coil of wire into the shape of a doughnut. This is called a torus. When electric current is passed through the coil, a magnetic field is produced both in and around the torus. If charged particles are placed inside the torus where the dough of a doughnut would be, they cannot get out. They are trapped in a magnetic bottle. An electric current is then driven through the plasma and

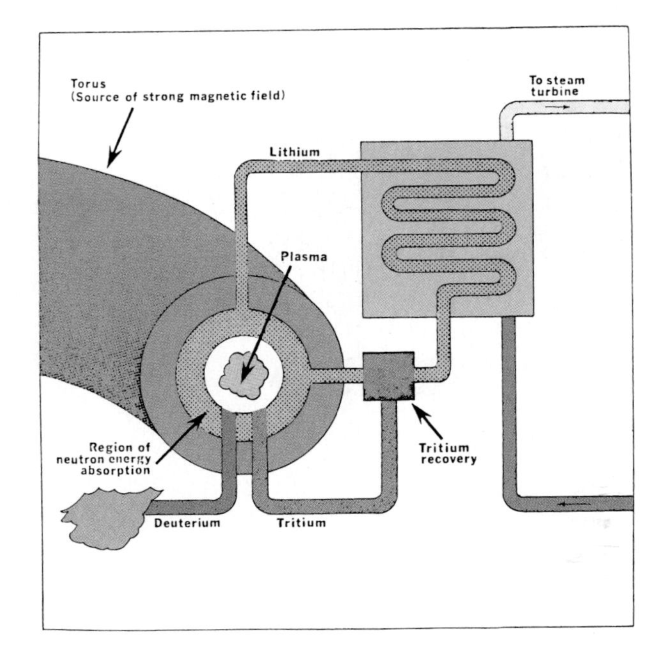

Figure 8.32 Magnetic confinement fusion. (From PEEC Packet: Energy for the Future, National Science Teachers Association.)

heats it (as in a microwave oven) to fusing temperatures. The heat produced is drawn off and exchanged to water for steam production. See Figure 8.32. That is how it should work. Technical difficulties with this process have kept teams of scientists and engineers busy since the late 1940s. The goal is to have the plasma produce more energy than the apparatus consumes.

Laser fusion.

Another method of accomplishing fusion is to embed some heavy hydrogen (deuterium) inside a small glass pellet. If the pellet is zapped with a series of powerful laser beams, the outside layer evaporates almost instantly. The counterforce generated by the rapid expansion of the outer material drives the remaining portion inward. As the material is driven inward, it is forced into a smaller volume and is heated by compression. At the high densities and temperatures generated, the fuel will fuse. (See Figures 8.33 and 8.34). The fusion chamber in this case is spherical, like a basketball. Lasers are mounted like spokes on a wheel to give perfect geometry. So far, no laser fusion device has transferred energy to a pellet rapidly enough to ignite plasma. Teams of scientists continue working on that goal.

The advantages of fusion.

Fusion power has a number of advantages over most future energy sources. These include: (1) Abundant fuel in the form of deuterium is available to all countries, because deuterium is found in all water. (2) Fusion involves no chemical combustion that contributes to air pollution. (3) There is no threat of diversion for making weapons. Perhaps most important, (4) there is no possibility of nuclear explosion, nuclear runaway (meltdown), or reactor-core cooling problems.

There is a major problem in assessing the contribution of fusion. No one knows for sure whether it can be accomplished regularly under controlled conditions in laboratories and power plants.

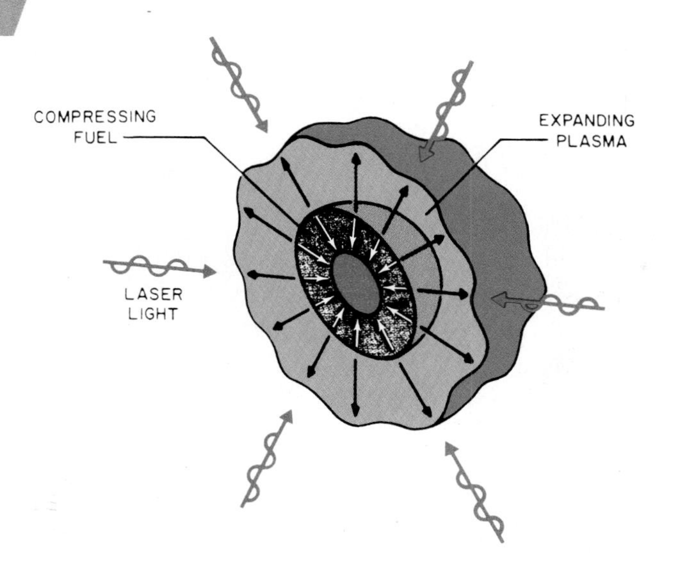

Figure 8.33 The technique of laser fusion. (From Los Alamos Scientific Laboratory.)

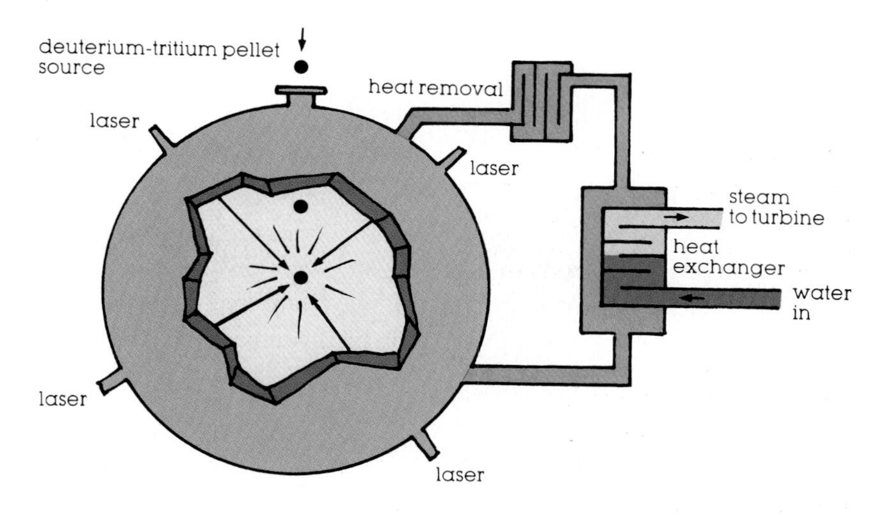

Figure 8.34 The laser fusion chamber.

The Equations of Fusions

The reactions of interest are:

$$ {}^{2}_{1}D + {}^{2}_{1}D \longrightarrow {}^{3}_{2}He + {}^{1}_{0}n + \text{energy} $$

$$ {}^{2}_{1}D + {}^{2}_{1}D \longrightarrow {}^{3}_{1}T + {}^{1}_{1}H + \text{energy} $$

$$ \text{and } {}^{2}_{1}D + {}^{3}_{1}T \longrightarrow {}^{4}_{2}He + {}^{1}_{0}n + \text{energy} $$

It is difficult to make tritium (T) from deuterium (D). However, there is another way to produce tritium atoms:

$$ {}^{6}_{3}Li + {}^{1}_{0}n \longrightarrow {}^{4}_{2}He + {}^{3}_{1}T + \text{energy} $$

The deuterium-deuterium reactions are much more difficult to accomplish than the deuterium-tritium reactions. Unfortunately, the world's supply of lithium (Li), from which we can make tritium, is small. Hence, until we increase our ability to run the deuterium-deuterium reactions, the fusion option is limited.

No energy will be commercially available from fusion before the twenty-first century. Even if a breakthrough occurs, it will take years to move from the demonstration of feasibility to the reality of large-scale power production.

?

What is the future outlook for nuclear power?

8.11 The Future of Nuclear Power

At the present time, nuclear power is not expanding as an energy option in most of the world. U. S. electric utilities currently have no plans to build new nuclear power plants. This is because of a number of social, political, and economic concerns that must be addressed. These concerns center around these questions:

What are some of the social and political issues that relate to the use of nuclear energy?

a. What are the long-term effects of exposure to low levels of radiation?
b. Where will a repository for high-level waste be built?
c. Where will low-level waste be disposed?
d. Can nuclear waste be disposed of and kept out of the environment for thousands of years?
e. Can nuclear waste be transported safely?
f. Are further security measures needed to protect against terrorism?

Nuclear power will not move forward until the public has satisfactory answers to these questions. It is important to know all sides of the nuclear power issue before intelligent decisions are made. Ask questions and get information from all sides, and then make up your mind. The references for this chapter can help you begin that search.

Summary

- Nuclear energy is the only new source of energy available to us. It is used as a source of heat to make steam for electric power generation.
- In nuclear fission, heavy nuclei are bombarded with neutrons, made unstable, and caused to split. This splitting results in the production of lighter, but unstable, nuclei. Heat is produced in the process. Unfortunately, the lighter nuclei are radioactive waste. Since portions of this waste have undesirable biological effects on all living things, they cannot be allowed to enter our ecosystem.
- Extra neutrons from the fission process can be used to produce more nuclear fuel. This is done in a breeder reactor. Unfortunately, this new nuclear fuel can also be used to make nuclear bombs.
- Nuclear fusion has the potential for providing huge amount of energy for the future. However, technical problems must be overcome. So far, humans have been unable to release this energy in a controlled, safe manner.
- Before nuclear power expands as an energy option, serious social, political, technical, and economic issues must be addressed.

To solve the nuclear dilemma, we must either:

- Give up on the nuclear option and safely store the nuclear waste that currently exists.

-or-

- Carefully research nuclear waste disposal options, alternative breeder reactor designs, fusion and reactor technologies. At the same time, a meaningful public debate must bring public acceptance of a safe, reliable way to use nuclear power and handle all related nuclear waste.

References

Edelson, Edward. *The Journalist's Guide to Nuclear Energy* (Washington, DC: U.S. Council for Energy Awareness), 1987.

Lillie, David W. *Our Radiant World* (Ames, IA: Iowa State University Press), 1986.

League of Women Voters. *A Nuclear Power Primer: Issues for Citizens* (Washington, DC: League of Women Voters), 1982.

Lenssen, Nicholas. Confronting Nuclear Waste In State *of the World* (New York: W. W. Norton & Company), 1992.

Martocci, Barbara and Greg Wilson. *A Basic Guide to Nuclear Power* (Washington, DC: Edison Electric Institute), 1987.

Russ, George. *Low-Level Radioactive Waste: Building a Perspective* (Washington, DC: U.S. Council for Energy Awareness), 1986.

U.S. Department of Energy. *Managing the Nation's Nuclear Waste* (DOE/RW-0263P), 1990.

U.S. Department of Energy. *Site Characterization Plan Overview, Yucca Mountain Site* (DOE/RW-0198), 1991.

End of Chapter Questions and Problems

1. What is an atom, and how are atoms put together?
2. List the symbol and atomic number of each of the following:
   a. Oxygen
   b. Nitrogen
   c. Copper
   d. Helium
3. How many protons does each atom of the following elements have in its nucleus?
   a. Aluminum
   b. Lithium
   c. Phosphorus
   d. Carbon
4. What information does the mass number of an element give?
5. How many electrons does each atom of the element potassium have?

6. What kind of electric charge does each of the following atomic particles show?
   a. Proton
   b. Electron
   c. Neutron
7. How do unstable nuclei gain stability?
8. Complete the following nuclear equations:

   a. ${}^{234}_{92}\text{U} \longrightarrow \underline{\qquad} + {}^{4}_{2}\text{He}$

   b. ${}^{214}_{83}\text{Bi} \longrightarrow \underline{\qquad} + {}^{0}_{-1}\beta$

9. Complete the following nuclear equations.

   a. ${}^{114}_{60}\text{Nd} \longrightarrow \underline{\qquad} + {}^{4}_{2}\text{He}$

   b. ${}^{116}_{49}\text{In} \longrightarrow \underline{\qquad} + {}^{0}_{-1}\beta$

   c. ${}^{235}_{92}\text{U} + {}^{1}_{0}\text{n} \longrightarrow {}^{147}_{57}\text{La} + \underline{\qquad} + 3{}^{1}_{0}\text{n} + \text{energy}$

   d. ${}^{27}_{13}\text{Al} + \underline{\qquad} \longrightarrow {}^{30}_{15}\text{P} + {}^{1}_{0}\text{n}$

10. Use the rules for writing nuclear equations given in the text to do the following:

    a. ${}^{241}_{95}\text{Am} \longrightarrow \underline{\qquad} + {}^{4}_{2}\alpha$

    b. ${}^{27}\text{Al} \longrightarrow \underline{\qquad} + {}^{4}_{2}\alpha$

    c. ${}^{144}_{58}\text{Ce} \longrightarrow \underline{\qquad} + {}^{0}_{-1}\beta$

    d. ${}^{209}\text{Pb} \longrightarrow \underline{\qquad} + {}^{0}_{-1}\beta$

    e. ${}^{27}\text{Al} + {}^{1}_{1}\text{H} \longrightarrow {}^{28}_{14}\text{Si} + \underline{\qquad}$

    f. ${}^{239}_{94}\text{Pu} + {}^{1}_{0}\text{n} \longrightarrow \underline{\qquad} + {}^{144}_{58}\text{Ce} + 2{}^{1}_{0}\text{n}$

    g. ${}^{235}_{92}\text{U} + {}^{1}_{0}\text{n} \longrightarrow {}^{99}_{42}\text{Mo} + \underline{\qquad} + 2{}^{1}_{0}\text{n}$

    h. ${}^{23}\text{Na} + {}^{1}_{1}\text{H} \longrightarrow {}^{23}_{12}\text{Mg} + \underline{\qquad}$

    i. ${}^{55}_{26}\text{Fr} + {}^{0}_{-1}\beta \longrightarrow \underline{\qquad}$

    j. ${}^{68}_{30}\text{Zn} + {}^{1}_{0}\text{n} \longrightarrow \underline{\qquad} + {}^{4}_{2}\alpha$

11. Strontium 90 (Sr-90) has a half-life of 30 years. If a 100-gram sample of Sr-90 decays for 60 years, how many grams of Sr-90 remain in the sample?
12. Complete the following fission reaction:

    ${}^{235}_{92}\text{U} + {}^{1}_{0}\text{n} \longrightarrow {}^{136}_{55}\text{Cs} + 2{}^{1}_{0}\text{n} + \underline{\qquad} + \text{energy}$

13. Plutonium 239 has a half-life of 24,360 years. Experts tell us that society must wait for ten half-lives until long-lived wastes will cease to be health and environmental threats. If a high-level waste storage program for plutonium were begun in 1990, in what year would these plutonium wastes be "safe"?
14. Two protons and two neutrons are distinctly heavier than a helium nucleus, which consists of two protons and two neutrons. What happened to the matter that was lost when the helium nucleus was formed?

15. How can scientists obtain energy from atoms by "splitting" and "fusing" them?
16. List the three fissionable isotopes.
17. Describe what happens in a chain reaction.
18. If our only source of tritium is Li-6, and if the only fusion reaction we can get to work requires tritium, how much potential fusion energy can there be?
19. Scientists take advantage of which differences in physical properties when separating U-235 from U-238?
20. What are the five major components of a nuclear reactor?
21. What must happen to fertile material before it can be used in a nuclear reactor?
22. Nuclear reactor cores do not have "accelerators," but they do have "brakes." How do these "brakes" work, and what is their composition?
23. Explain the function of moderator materials in a nuclear reactor.
24. What are some of the advantages and disadvantages of using nuclear power?
25. How do alpha and beta particles usually change the atoms they smash into?
26. How often do mutations *improve* a species? Why?
27. List the sources of radiation we all receive, even if we are not near a nuclear reactor.
28. Why are alpha and beta radiation sources much more dangerous inside of you than outside of you?
29. What is a breeder reactor?
30. How does a breeder reactor make fuel as it runs?
31. List two kinds of pollution that would increase with the widespread use of breeder reactors and one kind of pollution that would decrease.
32. A breeder reactor produces Pu-239. For what purposes other than fueling nuclear reactors can the Pu-239 be used?
33. By how much might the lifetimes of our nuclear energy sources be extended if the U.S. committed itself to the use of breeder reactors?
34. Which of the fusion reactions is the easier to make work?
35. What do you think is the future of nuclear energy? Defend your opinion.

Goal

To examine the energy sources that can be alternatives to the use of oil, natural gas, coal, and nuclear power.

Energy Alternatives

Energy itself is not the problem, but rather appears as an instrument for social purpose misunderstood and misused.

—David Rose

All our energy sources are dwindling or problematic: Crude oil reserves are shrinking. Natural gas seems to be following a similar pattern but at a slower rate. Coal presents special challenges because it is a solid and because of environmental concerns. And the nuclear option has not been accepted by the public.

Can any alternative sources of energy do for us what oil, gas, coal, and nuclear power have done? The answer is yes. In what follows, we will examine various energy sources that are available.

?

What are synfuels? Why is there interest in them?

Synthetic Fuels

By manipulating naturally occurring materials, humans can produce new substances called **synthetic fuels** (synfuels). Synthetic fuels originate in the processes of coal gasification and liquefaction, heating of oil shale, and refining of fuels from tar sands.

9.1 New Fuels from Coal

Coal is easily converted to electricity at electric power generating plants, but cars and trucks are built to run on liquid fuels. (An exception is electric vehicles.) Most of the homes in the United States are heated with natural gas, and many people cook with gas. Thus, changing coal to gas and a liquid makes sense if it can be done economically.

Why gasify or liquefy coal?

About 90% of our nation's fossil fuel are coal. However, most of the nation's energy consumption (about 65%) is of oil and gas. Coal represents only 23% of the total consumption. To reverse this trend, while maintaining high environmental standards, the United States could convert some of its vast reserves into clean gaseous and liquid fuels suitable for power generation, transportation, and residential and industrial uses.

Both coal **gasification** (conversion to gas) and **liquefaction** (conversion to liquid and solid fuels) require high temperature and pressure. Since coal is mostly carbon, with only a small amount of hydrogen, hydrogen must be added to make synthetic hydrocarbons. Water is the cheapest source of hydrogen.

Coal can be converted to three types of gases:

1. High-Btu (or high energy) gas which can be directly substituted for natural gas.
2. Medium-Btu gas which can be used for:
   - **a.** utility boilers
   - **b.** industrial fuel
   - **c.** electric power
   - **d.** chemical feedstocks.
3. Low-Btu gas for electrical power generation.

The major steps in coal gasification are shown in Figure 9.1. Hard coal is ground into a fine powder, then sprayed into a gasifier where it reacts with hot steam under high pressure. The resulting gases

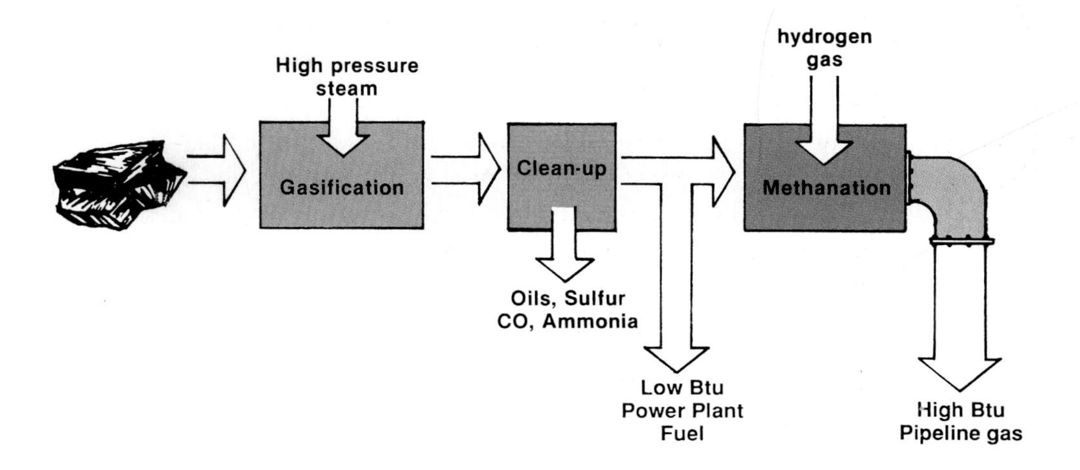

Figure 9.1 The coal gasification process.

are cleaned up. Some gas is drawn off and used as a power plant fuel. The rest is made into a more valuable gas in the methanation process. This gas can be used for home heating purposes.

Advantages of coal liquefaction.

Coal liquefaction in the United States is not as well developed as coal gasification. However, it has two advantages over gasification:

1. Petroleum substitutes produced from liquefaction can be used easily for the wide spectrum of petroleum needs.
2. Gas is produced as a byproduct when producing liquids and solids from coal.

The process can produce as much as three barrels of synthetic liquids from each ton of coal.

What are some of the problems associated with coal gasification and liquefaction?

For both gasification and liquefaction, some environmental problems must be overcome. Large quantities of water are consumed in both these processes. As a rule of thumb, processing a pound of coal uses about 1.5 to 3 pounds, or about 2 quarts, of water. This is about twice the water requirement of an electric power plant of the same energy output. Since much of the coal to be gasified is located in the semi-arid West, this is a major concern. Also some water must be treated before it is discharged.

Recovery and treatment systems will also be needed, to minimize air pollution. Solid wastes, such as ash, require disposal.

Then, there is the whole net energy question. It takes energy to process coal and change it to oil or gas. Does the final product provide enough energy to justify the whole process?

Finally, at the high temperatures used in these coal conversion processes, molecules known as "polycyclin aromatic hydrocarbons"

Figure 9.2 Oil shale location map. The five basins shown make up the Green River Formation.

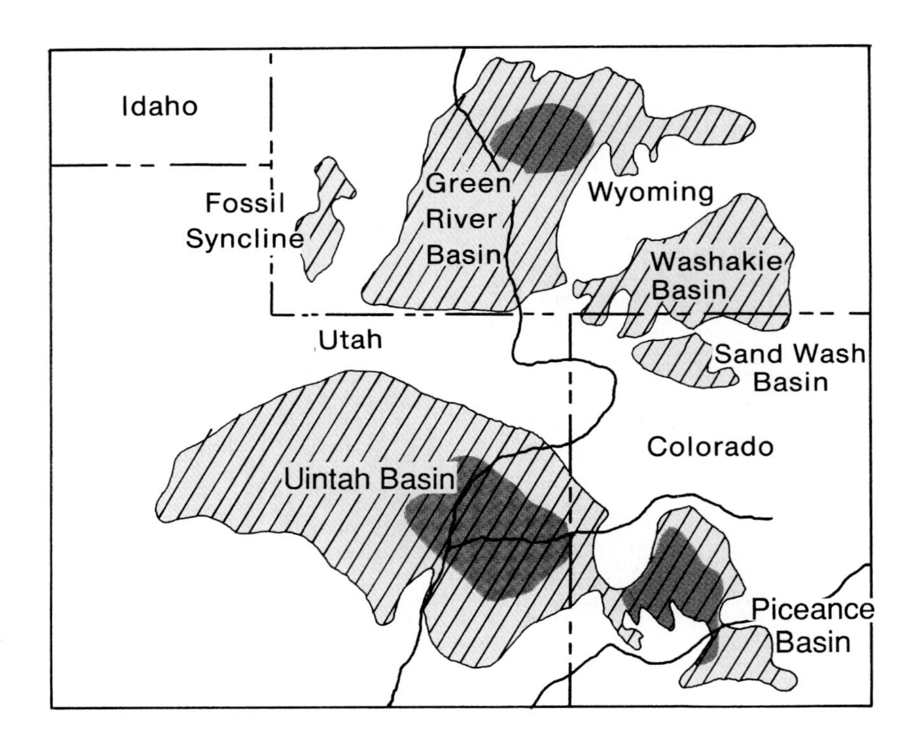

(PAH) are formed. There is evidence that many of the PAH's are carcinogenic, that is, cancer-causing. This problem must be solved before the synthetic fuels can be safely made or used.

Because of all these problems, obtaining significant amounts of energy from most synthetic fuels is progressing slowly. However, methanol (readily obtainable from coal and an excellent oxygenated fuel) can be used as a motor fuel (combined with gasoline or by itself).

 9.2 Oil Shale

Why is oil shale important?

Oil shale is a sedimentary rock (marlstone) containing a high-molecular-weight organic solid called **kerogen.** When heated (**retorted**), the kerogen breaks down. It yields substantial amounts of synthetic crude oil and hydrocarbon gas. The worlds's largest reserves are found in the Green River formation located in the Rocky Mountain region of the western United States. See Figures 9.2 and 9.3. One ton of oil shale may yield as much as 140 gallons of oil. To be of potential commercial interest, the yield must average at least 25 gallons per ton, and the oil must sell for at least forty dollars per barrel.

Special Focus

General Operations in Coal Gasification

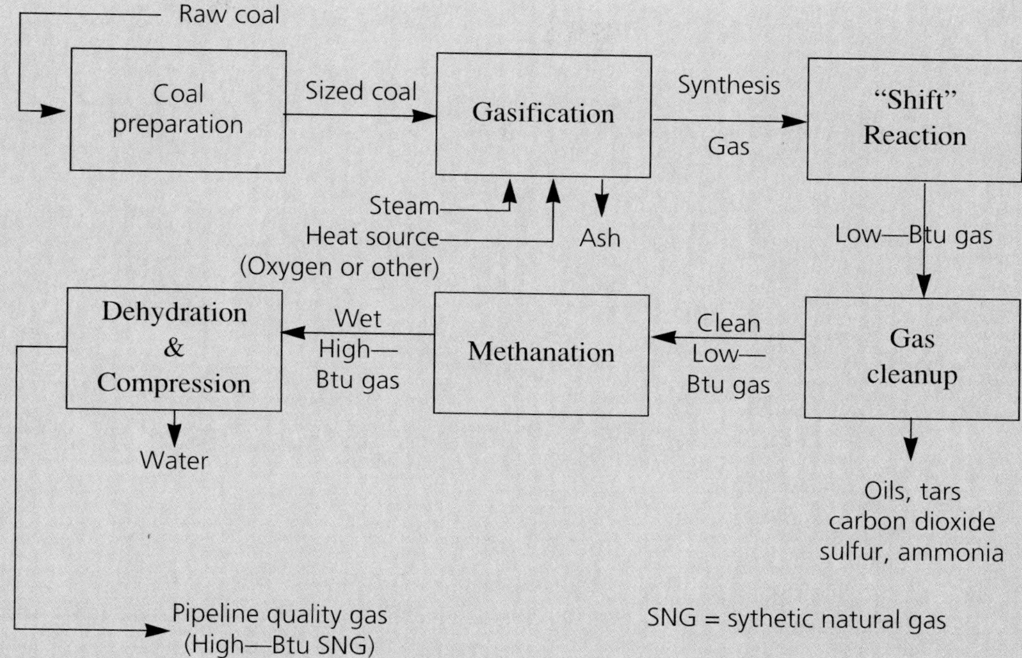

Summary of the Chemistry of Coal Gasification

- *Gasification*

Crushed and pulverized coal is fed into the gasification vessel. In the vessel, the coal interacts with air (or oxygen) and hot steam in an environment of high heat and pressure to produce a synthetic gas. The reactions are:

$C + H_2O \xrightarrow{heat} CO + H_2$ (gasification)

$C + O_2 \longrightarrow CO_2 + heat$ (burning)

$C + 2H_2 \longrightarrow CH_4$ (direct hydrogenation)

- *Synthetic Gas*

The synthetic gas produced in the gasifier is a mixture of gases:

CARBON MONOXIDE, CO	20%
HYDROGEN, H_2	40%
METHANE, CH_4	11%
CARBON DIOXIDE, CO_2	28%
MISC. IMPURITIES	1%

- *Water-Gas Shift*

The shift reaction increases the energy content of the gas mixture so that it is sufficient for electric power generation.

$CO + H_2O \longrightarrow CO_2 + H_2$

- *Methanation*

Methanation increases the energy content of the synthetic gas to the point where it can be directly substituted for natural gas.

$CO + 3H_2 \longrightarrow CH_4 + H_2O$

$CO_2 + 4H_2 \longrightarrow CH_4 + 2H_2O.$

Figure 9.3 Oil shale country in Colorado's Grand Valley region. (Atlantic Richfield Company [ARCO])

What are the advantages of using oil shale?

The primary advantage of oil shale is that it is a fossil fuel. The synthetic crude that results from the heating of the shale can be refined. This changes it into all the products we now obtain from the refining of ordinary crude oil. We don't need to make major adjustments to use the products of oil shale development. Our present automobiles, trucks, furnaces, and motors don't have to be modified. Also, some of the by-products are raw materials for the petrochemical industry.

The most common method for developing oil shale consists of mining the shale, then crushing the rocks into fist-sized chunks. These chunks are further crushed to grain-sized particles of rock which are then fed into the top of a tall (20 stories) retort tower. See Figure 9.4. Here the shale is heated in the absence of air (retorted). The high temperature breaks the solid kerogen molecule into liquid and gaseous vapors. The vapors are fed into a condenser where synthetic crude oil collects. Some of the flammable gas is fed back into the retort to provide the heat necessary for the breakup of more kerogen. Retorted (spent) shale exits from the bottom of the tower. The large quantity of spent shale must be disposed of. See Figure 9.5.

List some of the problems associated with the development of oil shale.

The development of oil shale causes environmental damage. The land is disrupted, air may be polluted at the retort and refinery, new towns are built in remote areas, and large amount of water are consumed in the waste disposal process.

Net energy is another concern related to oil shale development. Do you receive enough energy from the synfuel to justify the large energy expenditure that went into producing it?

Some of the problems related to oil shale development are reduced by heating (retorting) the shale underground. This is accomplished by drilling and fracturing the shale, reducing it to rubble, and then retorting the shale in place. See Figure 9.6.

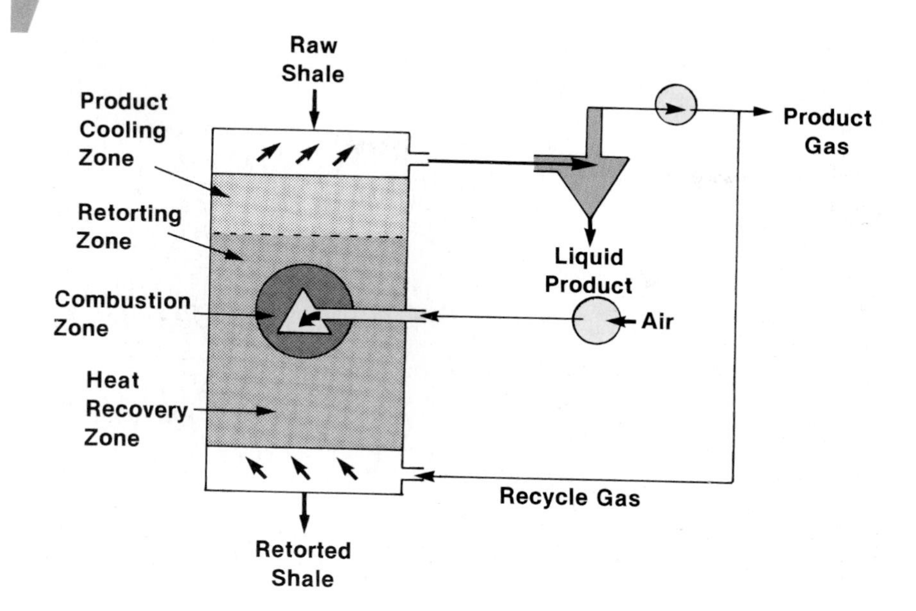

Figure 9.4 A surface retort used to extract the synthetic crude from oil shale. Raw shale is introduced at the top of the retort vessel. Retorted shale is removed at the bottom. Oil and gas are taken off as a vapor at the top of the retort. (ARCO)

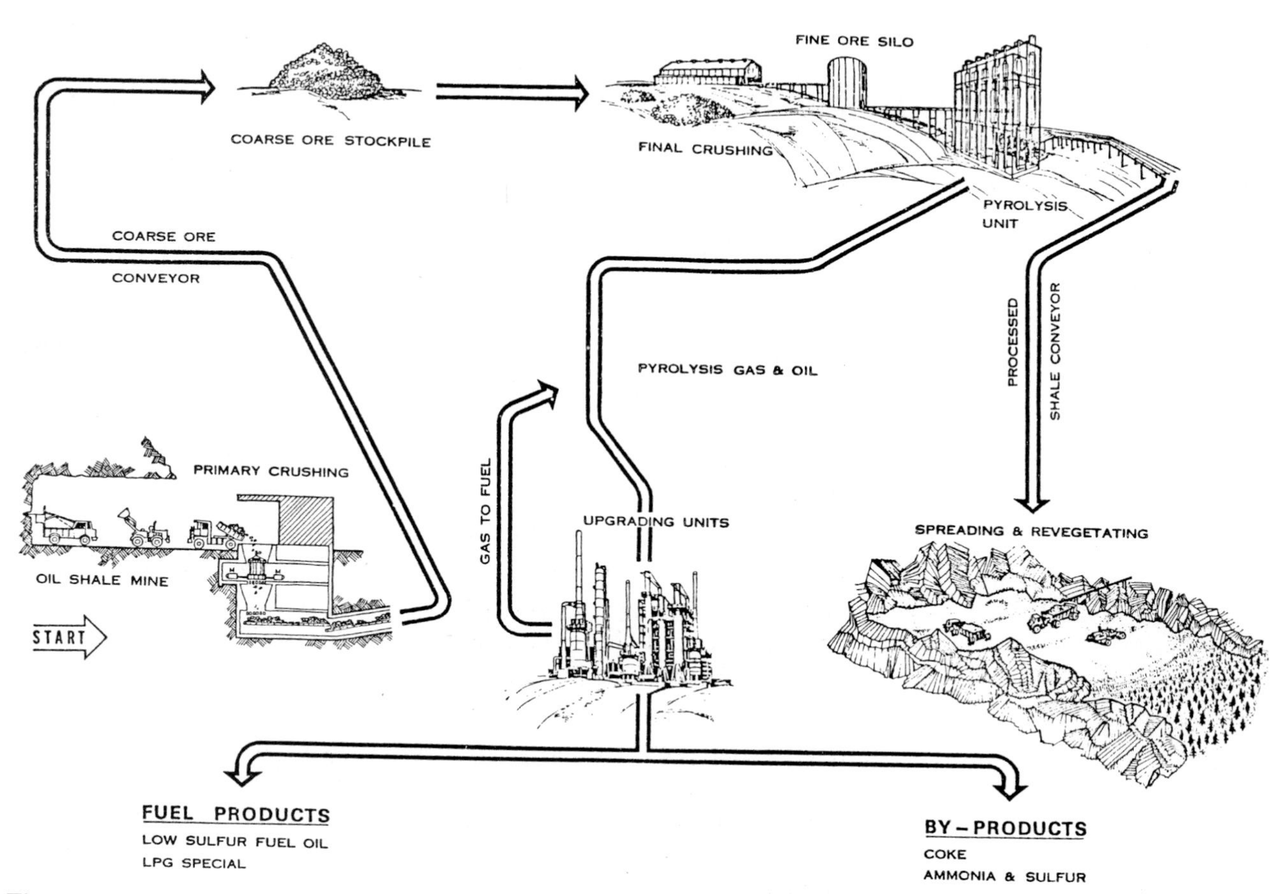

Figure 9.5 Oil shale processing. (ARCO)

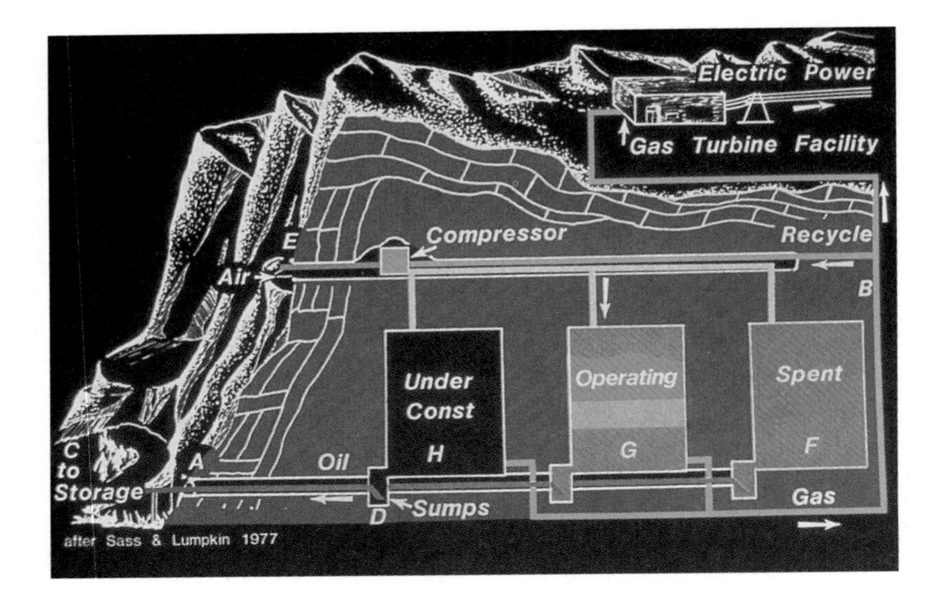

Figure 9.6 Underground (in situ) oil shale development as it might be constructed. Synthetic gas is drawn off and used to generate electricity. Synthetic crude oil is placed in storage. (U.S. Bureau of Mines)

The synfuel collects in a depression (called the sump) and is then pumped out. This method substantially reduces the problems of waste disposal and of water consumption. Research continues in an effort to perfect this **in situ** technique.

At present, very little is being done with oil shale development. The world price of oil is too low for any profit to be realized. Oil shale resources in the United States total more than 4 trillion barrels of potential oil. However, to be of commercial interest, shales must yield from 25 to 65 gallons or more per ton. Less than 15 percent of our oil shale resources would provide that high a yield.

9.3 Tar Sands

What are tar sands?

Tar sands are deposits of rock or sediment containing a heavy oil- or tar-like fossil fuel substance (**bitumen**) that is too thick to be pumped to the surface by drilling. Tar sands are very old deposits from which the light hydrocarbons have escaped, leaving the heavy, asphaltic residue behind. The Canadian tar sands are a mixture of 84 to 88% sand and clay, 8 to 12% bitumen, and 4% water. Bitumen does not flow at room temperature, but it flows freely when heated to about 80° C (180° F).

Tar sands are hydrocarbon deposits. The raw material can be changed to a whole range of fuels, from gases to heavy furnace oils and solids. These are the fuels on which our present economy depends.

In Canada, the overburden is removed from a drained muskeg (swamplike) area by hugh draglines. Rotating bucket-wheel excavators then scoop up the tar sand and dump it on a conveyor belt that carries it to the extraction plant. In the summer, tar sands look like a fine-grained asphalt road mix.

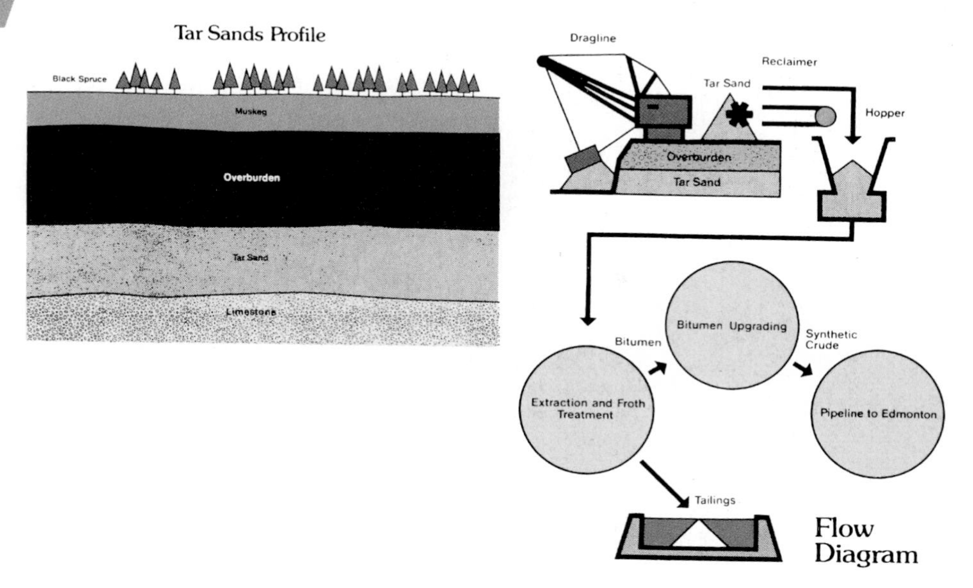

Figure 9.7 Tar sands development. (Courtesy Syncrude Canada Ltd.)

In the extraction plant, the tar sands are mixed with chemically treated water at 80° C (180° F) in huge horizontal rotating drums. This mixture is then pumped into separation cylinders where the sand and clay settle to the bottom and the bitumen floats to the surface. The sand and clay (the tailings) are disposed of near the plant. The bitumen is then upgraded and piped to a refinery. This whole operation is summarized in Figure 9.7.

Why such interest in a material that is so difficult to extract? The tar sands in Alberta alone may contain the equivalent of 1 trillion barrels of petroleum. See Figure 9.8. This is more than the petroleum resources of Saudi Arabia's oil fields. In addition, a similar deposit in Venezuela holds as much as 2 trillion barrels. A deposit in Russia is estimated to be somewhat less than 1 trillion barrels.

Many of the tar sands can be surface-mined. However, techniques for extracting deep-lying deposits will have to be perfected.

Tar sand deposits in the United States are small compared with those in Venezuela, Canada, and Russia. The current low price of crude oil has greatly curtailed development of tar sands. In the meantime, developers need to address environmental issues and study the net energy question.

Local Options

?

Name some nonsolar energy options that are of local interest.

As our fossil fuels run low, the heat energy stored in the Earth's interior **(geothermal)** and the mechanical energy of waves and the tides begin to look more attractive. None of these can contribute more than a fraction of the total energy that will be needed in the future. Nonetheless, in certain locations they may be important.

9.4 Tidal Energy

What causes the tides?

Tidal energy has its source in the gravitational interaction between the earth and the moon. Its relative contribution will be small. It may be

Figure 9.8 Tar sands location map of Alberta, Canada. (Courtesy Syncrude Canada Ltd.)

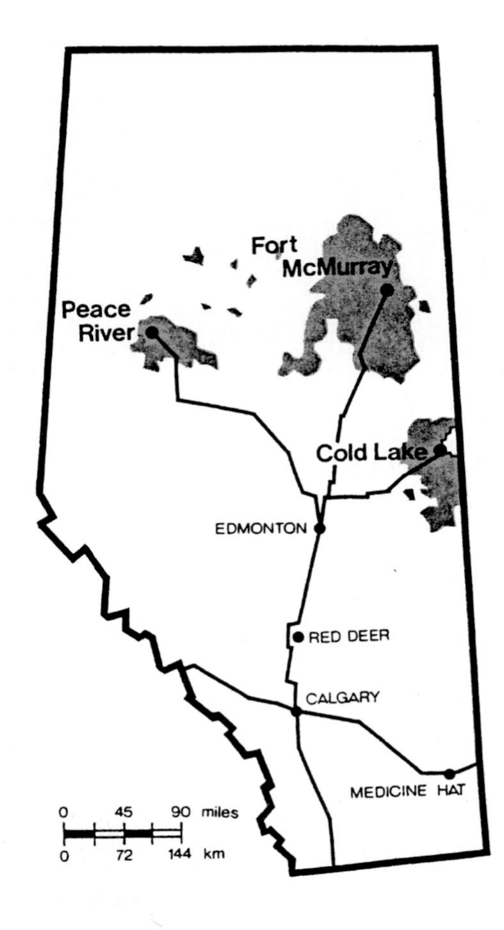

important, however, at some sites where energy is expensive and the rise and fall of the tides is large. A distance of about 16 feet (five meters) between low and high tide is needed for a site to be considered. With the method usually used, the water is dammed in a reservoir at high tide, then allowed to run out through a turbine. The turbine has reversible blades, so it can spin both when the tide comes in and when it goes out. See Figure 9.9.

What is the global potential for tidal energy?

There are few suitable sites for tidal energy generation around the world. Sites in the Bay of Fundy are the only ones available to the lower U.S., although there is impressive tidal power potential at the Cook Inlet site in Alaska.

9.5 Ocean Waves

Energy is also available from ocean waves. The kinetic energy carried by these ocean oscillations comes from wind and ocean current interactions.

Energy in waves.

Waves have considerable energy. Ask any surfer! An active region may have as much as 10,000 watts/m^2 of wave front. Several clever devices designed to extract this kinetic energy are undergoing small-scale testing.

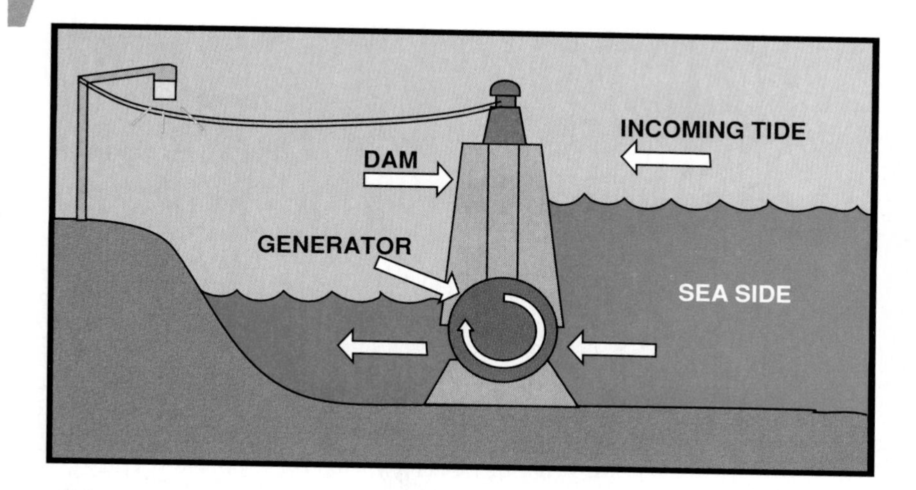

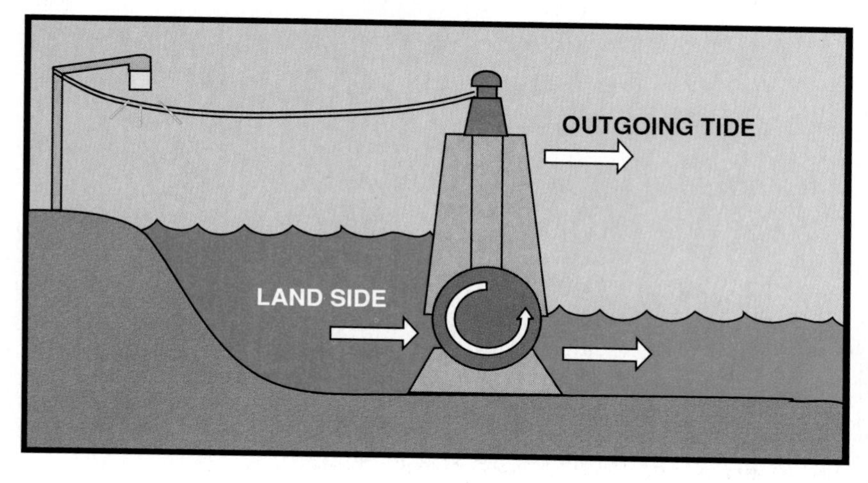

Figure 9.9 At a tidal power station, both the incoming tide and the outgoing tide are held back by a dam. The reversible blades on the turbogenerator allow electricity to be produced both as water flows into the reservoir and as it leaves. Tidal power sites usually are large bays with small openings which can be dammed.

There is energy in both the horizontal thrust that drives the surf board and in the vertical lifting motion. The wave power which lifts an ocean ship is often many times the power available from the ship's engines.

How can wave energy be tapped?

Most experimental devices are designed to use the vertical energy component. In one such device, air is compressed by being forced into a chamber (by the wave rise) through a one-way valve. The compressed air then turns a small turbine. In another, the waves force water up a standing pipe (to several times the wave height), and the water can then turn a turbine.

The use of wave energy may be limited to seacoast towns. The conversion device must be inexpensively manufactured and the problems of durability and energy transmission to shore must be economically solved.

9.6 Geothermal Energy

The origin of geothermal power.

Geothermal energy, the natural heat of Earth, promises to be an important supplemental power source in certain areas around the world.

Figure 9.10 The Geysers.
(From Pacific Gas & Electric Company.)

The 500 mW of electrical generating capacity at the Geysers geothermal installation near San Francisco is the largest in the world. See Figure 9.10.

Geothermal energy uses the heat produced by natural processes under the Earth's surface to provide energy. These processes occur at great depths everywhere on Earth, but the heat must be concentrated close enough to the surface to be useful. Geothermal reservoirs provide hot water or steam that can be used for heating and cooling buildings, processing foods, producing other consumer goods, and generating electricity. See Figure 9.11. Geothermal energy is the major energy source in Iceland.

Using The Sun's Energy

The solar option is useful for three major end-use categories: space heating; electricity; and, liquid and gaseous fuels.

9.7 Solar Heating and Cooling

On the average, enough **solar energy** strikes the roof of most American homes to provide for most or all of their total heating needs. This is true throughout the entire year.

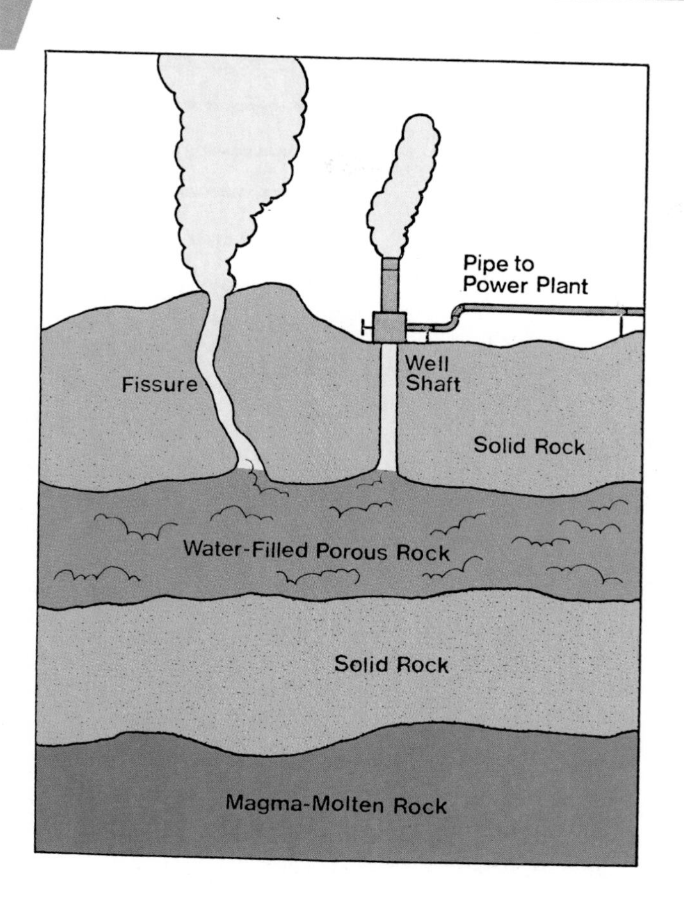

Figure 9.11 A vapor-dominated geothermal system. (From PEEC Packet: *Energy for the Future*, National Science Teachers Association.)

a. Active Solar

What is meant by active solar?

Active solar heating systems work like this:

Flat plate collectors usually are installed (on the roof or ground near the building) on the sunny side and covered with transparent glass or plastic. Between the cover and a black plate is an air space. Black is used because it is an efficient absorber of sunlight. The transparent cover traps heat in the collector much like glass does in a greenhouse. See Figure 9.12.

Water or air is circulated (in pipes) through the collectors to absorb captured heat and carry it to a storage tank (usually in the basement).

If air is circulated, the heat is absorbed in hot rocks. If water is circulated, the storage tank is usually a large tank of water. Fans or pumps, powered by electricity, deliver the heat to the various rooms of the house. See Figure 9.13.

If solar cooling is also desired, the flat-plate collectors must be replaced by parabolic reflectors. This kind of system is much more expensive.

b. Passive Solar

What is meant by passive solar?

The simplest way to make use of the sun's energy to heat a home is called "passive" solar. The strategy is called passive because no outside energy is required to operate fans or pumps. The key elements of the system just sit there and perform their tasks.

Figure 9.12 Flat plate collector.

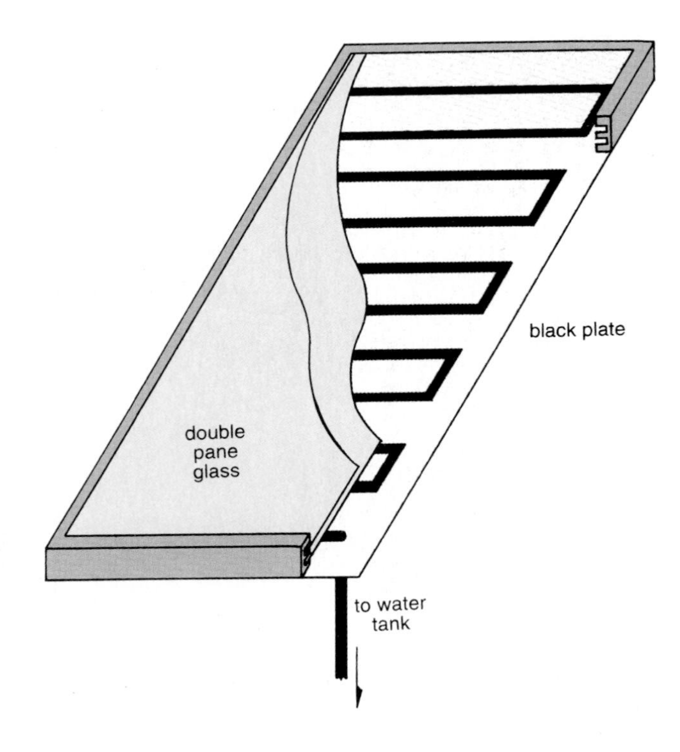

Figure 9.13 An active solar home.

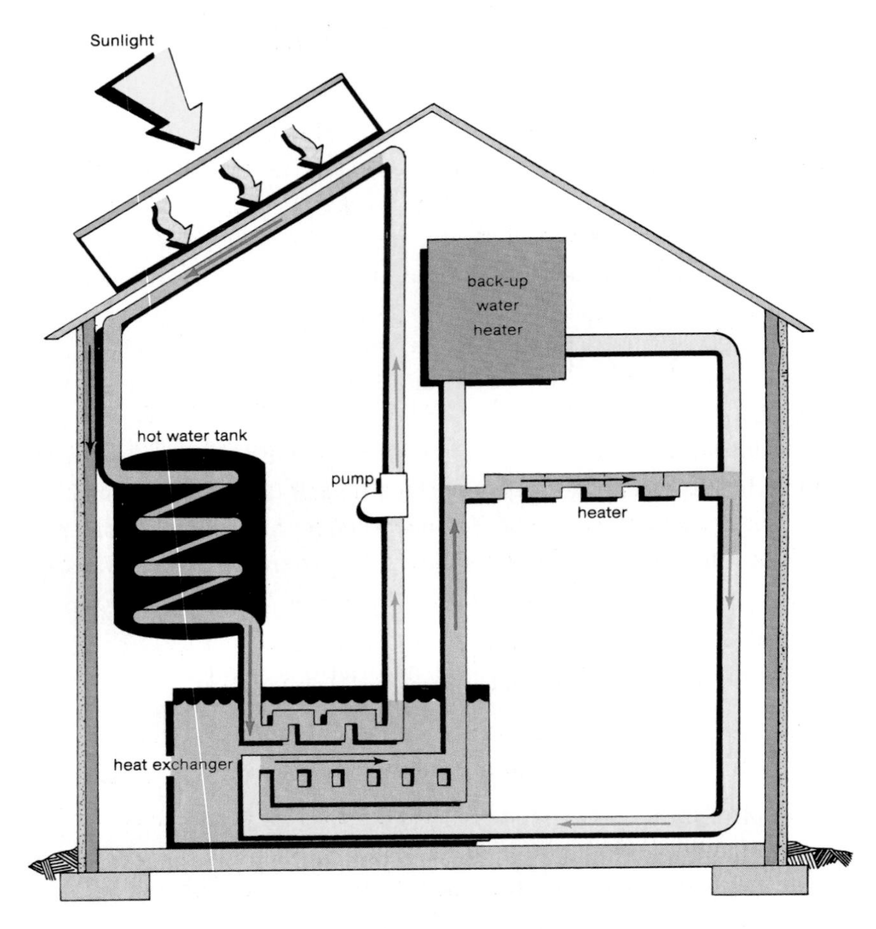

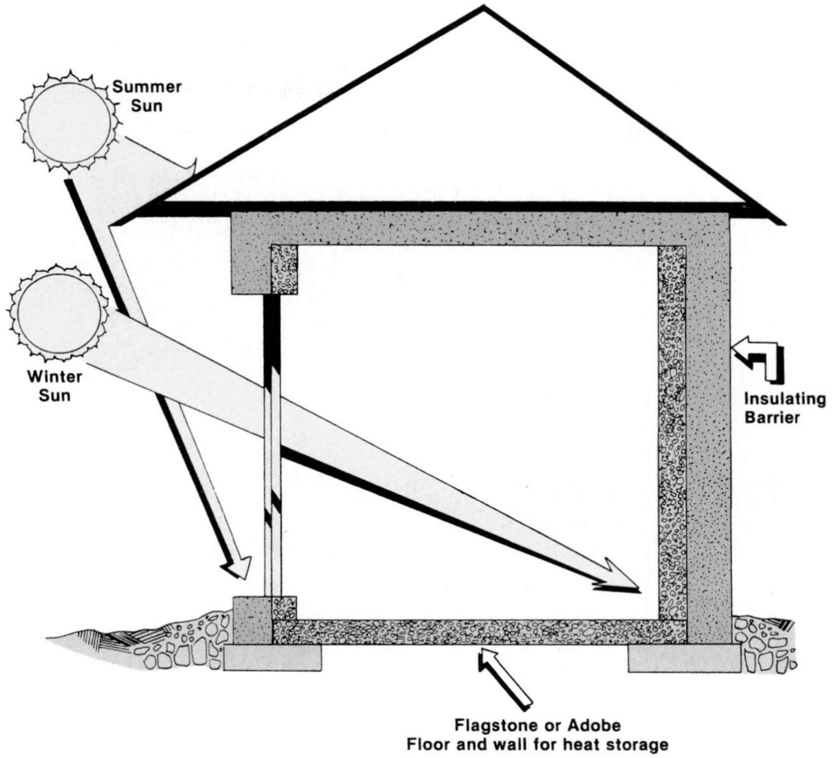

Figure 9.14 A passive solar home.

In passive solar homes, the familiar elements of the building itself—walls, floors, windows, and other features, along with the landscaping—help collect, store, and distribute the sun's energy. Figure 9.14 illustrates these ideas.

The basic ideas behind passive solar are:

- The home faces south, to capture the greatest amount of solar radiation.
- The south-facing window area is maximized, and all others are minimized. Windows have double or triple panels or high tech (low-E) design.
- Roof overhangs or shades block out the high summer sun to cut cooling costs. Recessing the windows accomplishes the same thing. In the winter, the low-angle sun rays are allowed to enter.
- **Thermal mass** in the interior absorbs and stores energy in the daytime and radiates it at night. The thermal mass can be a dark brick or stone wall, or dark tiles on a concrete floor.
- Insulated drapes or shutters can be opened in the daytime and drawn to provide insulation at night.
- Deciduous trees on the south side shade and cool the house in the summer. The sun is allowed to enter in the winter when the leaves have fallen. Coniferous trees make a good windbreak when planted on the north side of the home.
- Well-placed vents help with summer cooling.

Figure 9.15 An earth-sheltered home that is both functional and attractive. (Designers: Tom Ellison and John Carmody. Underground Space Center, University of Minnesota.)

Passive solar systems are simple to construct and require the same building materials that are used in normal home construction. A well-thought-out combination of superinsulation, passive solar, and active solar strategies can take care of all of a home's heating, cooling, hot water, and humidity requirements. All the local utility company must provide is enough electricity for running appliances.

Combining passive strategies with the underground placement of a home seems to be gaining some popularity. Moderate soil temperatures dramatically reduce the total heating and cooling energy requirements of a residence. Proper placement of a dwelling in the ground and the correct location of insulation are necessary for good performance. Usually three walls are in the ground. The south wall is exposed and designed to let the sun's rays penetrate the interior only during the winter months. Some earth-sheltered homes have earth roofs, other do not.

What is an earth-sheltered home?

In addition to their significant energy savings, earth-sheltered homes have the potential to withstand tornadoes, and they have long-term design life and negligible exterior maintenance. However, acceptance has been low. This is probably because they do not look like most other homes, and people may have visions of feeling trapped in a cave. This is primarily an architectural problem. When the principles of handling the **earth-sheltered** environment are understood, a subterranean architecture will most certainly evolve. The homes will be limited in their beauty, quality, and individuality only by the abilities of their architects and engineers. See Figure 9.15.

The economics of solar heating.

The initial costs for installing solar heating systems are still quite high, unfortunately. It is hoped that by the year 2000, the cost (when spread out over 20 years) will be competitive with other types of heating. Because sunshine is unpredictable, storage must be provided. To

Nature's Light and Power Company

science at work

The sun—the source of all life on Earth—is a central focus in D. Wayne Robertson's life. He works with many different systems that harness the sun's energy. Wayne's interest in solar energy isn't new, but it took a while for him to put it to use. In college he majored in art, and also studied political science. Later he worked at a variety of jobs, and his career path took a good number of twists and turns before he reached his current vocation. When Wayne began to build his own house, he wanted to incorporate environmentally friendly technology, including solar heating and electricity. Today his stereo, computer, kitchen appliances, and heating system all get their power from solar panels in his yard. Like many solar homes, Wayne's has a backup wood-burning heater, but he burns less than a cord of wood a year.

Wayne is the sales manager for Solar Electric Specialties in Willitts, California. He sells solar systems and equipment to people and businesses all over the world. Sometimes solar power is needed because a home or other structure is in a remote region, far from traditional power grids. Sometimes the solar source is "remote" by just a few feet—for instance, to provide light in a bus-stop shelter, solar power may be more economical than digging up a sidewalk to reach an underground power source.

Besides photovoltaic panels and solar generators, Wayne also supplies solar chargers for batteries used in boats, RVs, farm equipment, and other machinery that may sit idle for long periods. He helps to design solar power systems around MAPPS (modular autonomous photovoltaic power supply), for specific—and sometimes unusual—situations all over the world. For instance, he has set up solar power for water pumping systems in Africa and Jamaica, and communications systems in several national forests. Solar-powered communications repeaters on mountaintops help radio waves travel around physical obstacles and over long distances. Travelers to remote areas of Nepal and Tibet have carried solar power packs made by Solar Electric. Irrigation control systems and gate openers can be powered by solar cells, as are many of those emergency call boxes you see along the freeways.

On his own, Wayne studies many of the engineering and physics principles involved in his work, and he's learned specific facts about solar energy systems on the job. His understanding of basic scientific thinking helps him to analyze his customers' needs and to design systems for solving their problems. Colleges do offer two-year degrees in electrical engineering, but Wayne would like to see more programs designed for young people who want to specialize in alternative energy sources. He is a member of the Renewable Energy Development Institute, which plans to create a college specifically for training people in this field.

What about the future? Solar energy is both ancient and newborn. Wayne says there is much room for exciting research, creative solutions, and business opportunities in the field. Interest in solar energy flagged during the 1970s and 1980s but is now on the rise again. Even utility companies supplying traditional forms of electricity are looking into solar, which helps to make solar more acceptable to the general public. The cost of solar systems is coming down, too. According to Wayne, "People who need solar the most," those in developing countries, for instance, "can afford it the least, and financial institutions need to be less hesitant to fund solar installations."

keep costs down, the storage is usually enough for only two sunless days. After that an auxiliary heating system must be used. This additional heating system adds to the expense.

The passive system concept makes a lot of sense. However, scarcely any existing homes are faced correctly for fully utilizing passive solar strategies. A custom-built home on a carefully chosen lot is best, but this is too expensive for most of us. We can, nonetheless, improve insulation, caulk the cracks, and make the best use of what we have.

Wood as a fuel.

c. Wood

Our most familiar biological fuel is wood. After accounting for as much as 90% of our total energy consumption in the mid-nineteenth century, wood has dropped to under 0.5%. There are signs of a limited revival. For instance, the wood stove is making a comeback in areas with low population density and lots of trees.

Unfortunately, many fireplaces were installed for appearance and enjoyment—not for fuel efficiency. Many of them actually lose energy, because warm home air used for combustion is drawn up the chimney. Areas where many wood stoves and fireplaces are in constant use are experiencing a good deal of pollution related to wood burning. Some areas have banned, others are considering banning, their use—at least on high-pollution days.

Wood will make only a small contribution to our nation's energy future. This contribution will be in areas of low population density and where wood is abundant and inexpensive.

How can the sun be used to produce electricity?

9.8 Solar Electricity

Solar energy can be harnessed in several ways for producing electricity.

What is the purpose of STEC?

a. Solar Thermal Energy Conversion (STEC)

Solar thermal energy conversion is a collection system that concentrates enough sunlight onto a boiler or a fluid (water or heat-conducting oil) to make large quantities of steam. The steam in turn is used to spin a turbine which rotates the coil of a generator which produces electricity.

Two methods are being extensively researched. The first method is called the *distributed collector concept.* In its most common form, a long reflecting trough having a parabolic cross-section concentrates solar energy onto a collector tube. A heat-conducting oil flows through the tube and into a heat exchanger, where the oil transfers its heat to water and produces steam. Excess heat is stored for use at night and on cloudy days. See Figure 9.16.

Using acres of mirrors to track the sun.

The second method seems even more promising, because higher temperatures are produced. A field of computer-guided mirrors (heliostats) tracks the sun and focuses the sun's rays onto a boiler which is mounted on top of a central receiving tower. Here the radiant solar energy is absorbed and used for producing steam. See Figure 9.17.

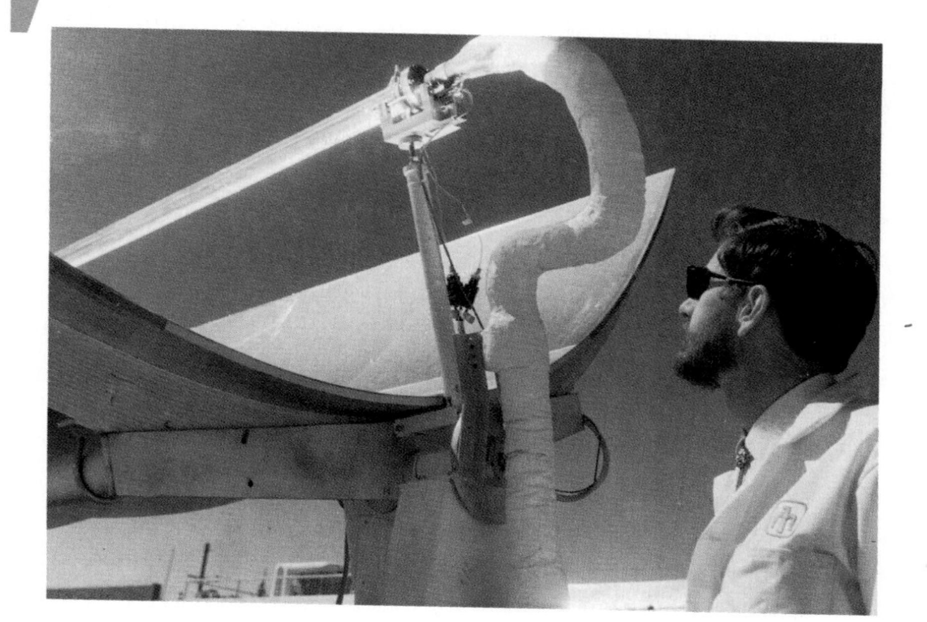

Figure 9.16 The distributed collector concept. (From USDOE, Sandia Laboratories.)

Figure 9.17 Diagram of a solar thermal power plant. (Courtesy Southern California Edison Company.)

The main advantage of both methods is that sunshine is free. In addition, the environmental impact of these systems is relatively minor.

For this approach, only direct sunlight is usable. This restricts solar thermal power plants primarily to the sunny areas of the country. There are no basic technical limitations in this method. The main questions are overall efficiency and economics. One key consideration is space, as sunlight is diffuse and must be collected over a wide area. It is estimated that in the southwestern United States, approximately 26 square kilometers (10 square miles) would be needed to operate a 1,000-megawatt plant working at an average capacity of 60%. This is enough power to supply a city of a million people. At present, there is no economically feasible method for storing heat for use at night and on overcast days.

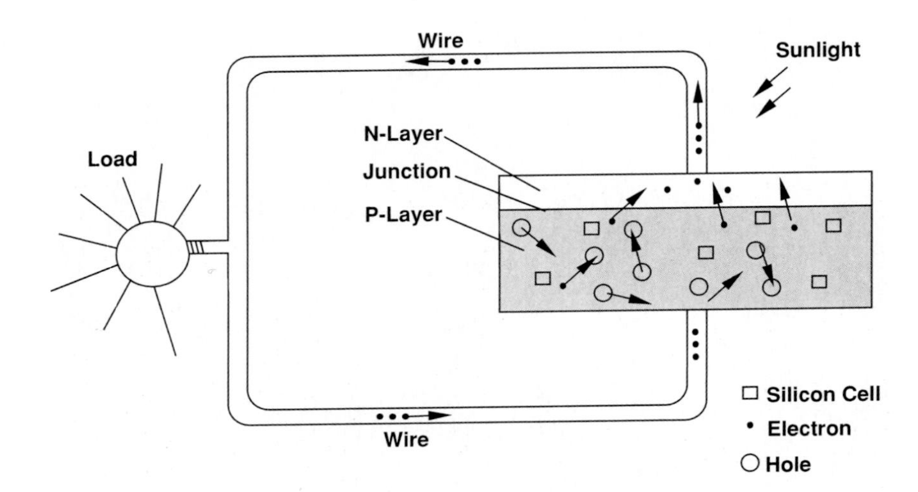

Figure 9.18 Diagram of a solar cell. (From Solar Energy Research Institute.)

Southern California Edison Company is building a commercial solar thermal power plant in Barstow, California. It should be operating in 1995.

b. Solar Photovoltaic Energy

How do solar cells work?

Solar radiation can be converted directly to electricity in a **solar cell.** A beam of sunlight is made up of little particles called **photons.** If they carry enough energy, the photons can knock electrons loose from the atoms they strike. Solar cells combine this property of light with the unusual properties of a **semiconductor.** A semiconductor consists of a junction between two dissimilar materials. A typical arrangement is shown in Figure 9.18.

The N-layer is transparent to light and very thin. Photons of light entering this region knock electrons out of silicon atoms. The electrons flow in one direction across the junction and the "holes" they leave move in the other direction. This sets up a potential difference, a voltage. If circuitry is provided as shown, current will flow with electrons moving toward the negative terminal and "holes" in the opposite direction. Thus, electric power is produced. This is called the **photovoltaic effect.**

Solar cells have been used for years to power highway call boxes, offshore buoys, and other remote devices. Once installed, they essentially require no maintenance. They are now economical for use in homes in remote areas.

The chief barrier to widespread use of solar cells is cost. However, much current research is being done particularly in "thin-film" technology, and so research breakthroughs and mass production should lower the cost significantly. This should make photovoltaics commercially competitive.

Solar cell arrangements having enough capacity for electric power production can be constructed. See Figure 9.19. One thousand watts, or one kW, of power is about enough for many household uses.

Figure 9.19 Solar photovoltaic power farm. (USDOE)

Such an arrangement costs approximately $2,500.00 (1990 dollars). These arrangements can boost the efficiency of power companies, making it possible for them to use less fuel, cause less pollution, and avoid constructing additional modern, pollution-controlling power plants.

c. Wind Power

What causes wind?

The wind's energy originates in the uneven heating of the earth. The sun's rays strike the equatorial regions almost directly, but they approach the poles at an angle (see Figure 9.20). This causes largescale currents in the atmosphere. Hot air rises from the tropical regions, flows toward the poles, and sinks to Earth there. A flow of cooler air goes back across the surface toward the equator. Wind patterns would be simple if Earth were a smooth, solid sphere, and if it were not rotating. The planet's axial spin breaks this simple flow into the major wind belts, the prevailing westerlies and trade winds. Differences in local surface conditions (mountains, oceans, forests, etc.) provide the almost infinite variety that makes wind and weather so hard to predict.

The advantages of wind power.

Using the wind's energy is not a new idea. It has been used for centuries for grinding grain, moving sailing ships, and pumping water. In the early twentieth century, six million small windmills of about one horsepower each dotted the Midwest. They were mainly used for pumping water. In the 1930s the inexpensive electricity provided through the REA (Rural Electrification Administration) put most of the windmills out of business. However, a rise in fuel prices, coupled with environmental concerns, has revived interest in wind machines as a source of electricity.

Wind power is relatively cheap and non-polluting. It has features which are well adapted to farm and remote site use. This eliminates

Figure 9.20 *a*. Radiant energy hitting the Earth's surface at an angle, as at point D, is less intense because it must pass through a greater thickness of the atmosphere than that coming straight down, as at C. *b*. The energy carried by rays A-B is spread over a greater area on the inclined surface (2) than on the perpendicular surface (1) and so produces less heating per unit area. (From *Physics of the Earth*, by Robert B. Gordon. New York: Holt Rinehart and Winston, Inc., 1972.)

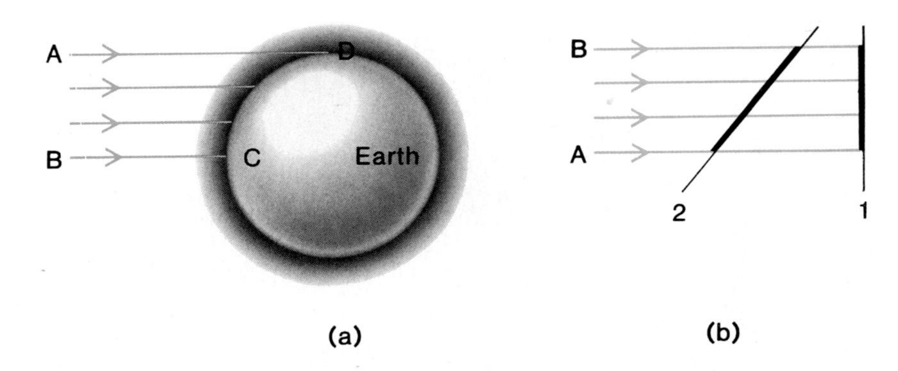

the need for long and expensive transmission lines. But before the wind can provide meaningful amounts of power for us, several major problems must be solved.

Some problems related to wind power.

There are different wind-driven generator designs. The most important distinction is between the horizontal-axis machines (Figure 9.21) and vertical-axis machines such as the Darrieus rotor (Figure 9.22).

The horizontal-axis machines generally have the higher power factors (as shown on Figure 9.23). The vertical-axis machines have the advantage of not requiring steering into the wind and allowing placement of the generator at the base of the machine. Such placement has the disadvantage of putting all the wind machine's weight on the pivot. At present, the vertical-axis machines are considered mostly suitable for smaller machines while the very large machines are all horizontal-axis devices.

Other considerations enter into wind machine designs. The intended use is crucial. If water is to be pumped, then a high torque (or turning force) is required to enable the wind machine to start with a heavy load on it. The multibladed Jacobson windmill of the old Midwest and the Dutch windmill thus gave away efficiency for torque. If the machine is designed to generate electricity, a high starting torque is not required and a higher power coefficient can be obtained.

Erratic source of energy.

The wind as a source of energy is erratic, like solar energy. On the average, wind machines have capacity factors of 25 to 30%. (A capacity factor is the rate of energy delivered to the total energy which could be delivered if the machine ran at its rated capacity all the time.) This means that wind machines either need significant storage capacity or need backup. Both of these are expensive.

What are other possibilities involving wind?

Wind-generated electricity can be stored in batteries. This is done in many small scale operations. However, battery storage at present is extremely expensive. Other storage options are available. Some of them, like hydrogen production, still require much research. The most practical systems at present are those which would take advantage of a large grid of interconnected wind machines. Interconnection averages power over a large area, increasing the odds that some machines are

Figure 9.21 Horizontal-axis wind turbine. (From Energy Alternatives: A comparative analysis. Science and Public Policy Program, University of Oklahoma. Photo by Sandia Laboratories)

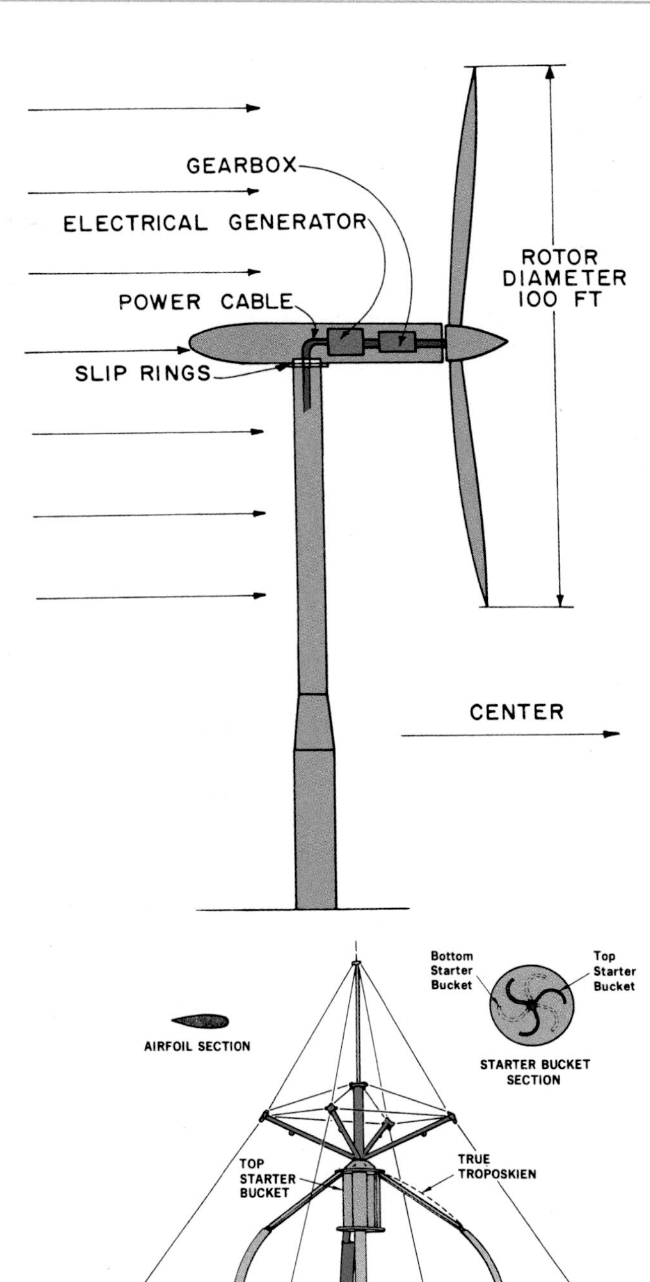

Figure 9.22 Vertical-axis wind turbine. (USDOE, Sandia Laboratories)

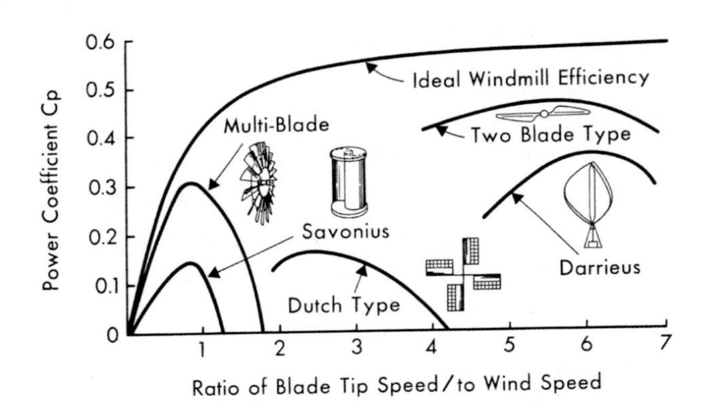

Figure 9.23 Typical performances of wind machines. (USDOE)

Figure 9.24 California windmill complex—part of a growing independent power industry. (Pacific Gas and Electric Company)

generating power. It is also likely that an interconnected grid system like this would include some nuclear or fossil fuel backup generating capacity. (See Figure 9.24.)

How can solar energy complement wind energy?

Solar energy and wind energy can be used to complement each other. The wind is likely to be blowing when the sun doesn't shine, and vice versa. So, connecting a solar generator to a wind generator would be more reliable than using either alone.

Another sort of grid is being discussed in the Southwest. There, high winds blow above rivers where several hydroelectric projects are located. If the wind machines were used exclusively to generate electricity when wind energy was available, and the water was allowed to accumulate behind the dams until needed, hydropower would be available when wind power wasn't.

Wind power is not a single answer to the energy problem, even though it has massive potential. Used imaginatively, in connection with other sources, it can be an important component of the energy mix of the future. How important will depend on money, on the dollars invested in it by the government, and private utilities. Wind might satisfy up to 5% of our energy needs in a couple of decades.

d. Ocean Thermal Energy Conversion (OTEC)

How does OTEC work?

The biggest collectors of energy on Earth are the oceans. This fact makes possible the whole concept of ocean thermal energy conversion (OTEC). Ocean thermal energy conversion uses temperature differences between surface waters and ocean depths to generate electricity. Basically, this is how it works:

1. In the tropics the ocean's top layer, heated by sunlight and mixed by wind and waves, is relatively warm (80° F/27° C). The lower, dark layers (1,500–4,000 feet down) are cold (40° F/4.5° C). A power plant in the ocean would draw warm water from the surface to heat a working fluid such as ammonia, propane, or Freon in a closed container until it evaporates.
2. Confining the fluid to a small container would produce pressure that rotates a turbine, powering a generator. Cold water drawn from the depths would cool the working fluid until it condenses back into a liquid. The entire cycle would then be repeated.

All this takes place at a power plant on a large floating platform. Electricity can either travel to land through cables for conventional uses or be used to extract hydrogen from sea water. Hydrogen can replace fossil fuels in many ways. Electricity could also be used to combine nitrogen from the air and hydrogen from the water to make ammonia. This is the primary ingredient for fertilizer. (See Figure 9.25.)

Problems related to OTEC development.

The temperature difference between deep and shallow ocean waters represents a continual and considerable source of energy. However, this process is still highly speculative. The potential for capturing this power is largely unproved because little experimentation has been done. Many questions remain: Can a design and materials be found that will resist the corrosive power of sea water? What impact will mixing warm and cold water have on aquatic life or ocean cycles? Is a net energy yield possible? What are the legal and political considerations? Finally, the cold water contains large amounts of dissolved carbon dioxide which would be released upon warming. What long-term environmental effects would this have?

e. Orbiting Solar Satellite Energy

How can solar satellites provide energy to people on Earth?

Putting solar collectors in outer space and relaying energy back to Earth is an appealing idea. The solar radiation reaching the Earth could supply more than the world needs. The idea is to put solar collectors in orbit and to beam the captured energy back to Earth in the form of microwaves. Advantages of such an undertaking are that solar radiation is more intense in outer space and the sun shines continuously. The clouds that interfere with collecting solar energy near the Earth's surface would have no effect on orbiting collectors.

Figure 9.25 An ocean thermal power plant. For size comparison note the helicopter. (Lockheed Missiles & Space Co., Inc.)

The orbiting satellites would have solar panels more than forty square miles in area. A single power station might provide as much as 5,000 megawatts of power. This is about half the present capacity of New York City's generating plants. The microwaves, transmitted by the satellite, would be received by a ground-based antenna some five miles in diameter. Here the microwave energy would be converted into alternating current electricity and distributed for use. (See Figure 9.26.) Princeton physics professor Gerard K. O'Neill calculates that a 5,000 megawatt satellite station and its ground receiver could possibly produce electricity for less than the 8 to 12 cents a kilowatt-hour consumers now pay for electricity from coal-fired power plants.

What are some of the problems associated with the solar satellite idea?

The economics of collecting and utilizing this energy presents a major obstacle to scientists and engineers. It has been suggested, for example, that we mine the moon for raw materials for building the space stations and collectors. However, a closer examination of this idea puts it in the realm of pure fantasy. Not all the needed raw materials are found on the moon. Also, the production of steel and special alloys is a complex operation even on Earth. It is difficult to explore for and develop mineral deposits in isolated regions on Earth. The advisability of attempting similar operations on the moon seems questionable at best. Another problem is that little is known about the short- or long-term effects of exposing living organisms (including humans) to

Figure 9.26 An artist's conception of solar satellites beaming microwave energy back to Earth. (NASA)

microwaves. Scientists generally believe that exposure is probably not healthy. A more specific answer to the problem will require more study.

How would a nation defend its solar satellites? Clearly, if a significant portion of a nation's energy supply were orbiting the globe, it would have to be defended. Would this prompt the development of a space-oriented military? Would "Star Wars" become a reality? What would be the price tag for that?

In a project of this nature, energy is being captured, relayed to Earth, and retained for a time. This is energy that otherwise would not have reached the Earth. If this is done on a large enough scale, the Earth will become warmer. What are the long term implications of this? Will we change our climate and start melting polar ice?

Figure 9.27 Cross-section of a hydroelectric dam. (Adapted from Hydroelectric Handbook, 2nd ed., by Creager and Justin. New York: John Wiley & Sons, Inc.)

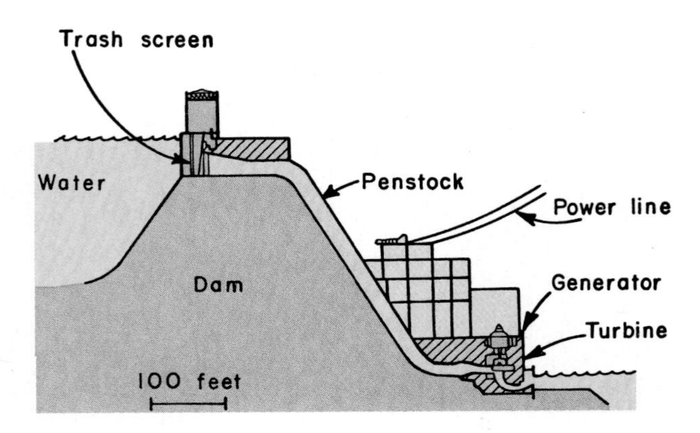

Finally, can we justify spending billions on solar space stations when human suffering on Earth is so widespread? Calculations may indicate that space-produced energy is economical, but do these calculations include all the hidden costs?

One thing is sure: a society powered by an energy system located in space would be much more dependent on technology than our society is.

f. Water Power

How is water power used?

Water power is another use of solar energy having a long history. Water is evaporated by solar heat, lifted and carried by the winds. It has energy stored in many forms. It has gravitational energy that is converted by hydroelectric power plants. Water flowing from a height has kinetic energy. This energy can be used to turn a water wheel or a modern turbine (Figure 9.27.).

What is the future of water power in the U.S.?

We are using a fairly large percentage of our available **hydropower** already. Many of the undeveloped sites are in areas of great scenic beauty, however, and are protected by legislation such as the Scenic Rivers Act. (See Figure 9.28.)

Future development of hydropower in this country may proceed in two directions. There is growing interest in using the energy available from small dams and from undammed flowing water ("non-dam" hydropower). These installations would use totally immersible turbogenerators placed in rivers or in artificially constructed diversions. They could also be used in aqueducts, irrigation ditches, and so on. Such systems would be small and of local interest only. They could be important components of the "appropriate technology" approach to energy which we will consider in the next chapter.

g. Energy from Trash

Municipal trash has an average energy content of about 4,500 Btu/lb.

Various cities throughout the world burn trash to produce electric power. This is because municipal trash is mostly paper, cardboard, plastic, and food scraps. However, mixed in with that flammable trash are bottles, cans, and a variety of other materials. If they are not

Figure 9.28 Aerial view of Hoover Dam on the Colorado River. (U.S. Bureau of Reclamation)

removed ahead of time, they melt in the boiler and then condense as a hard scale on the inside walls of the boiler. This scale must be removed periodically at great expense.

Various ways are being sought to separate municipal trash into its various components before it is burned. Figure 9.29 diagrams one such proposal. It would be so much easier if trash were separated before being picked up. In many cities, such as San Francisco, such "curbside recycling" of separated trash is already a reality.

Even if trash is separated, burning paper and other biological materials adds to air pollution. Scrubbers must be added to the incinerators.

9.9 Fuels from the Sun

?

How can the sun be used to provide liquid and gaseous fuels?

Wood (a form of **biomass**) was the first solar energy option to be an important source of non-food energy. Food biomass was the first energy source. The conversion process is photosynthesis in which radiant solar energy causes CO_2 and H_2O to combine to form carbohydrates. The energy stored in the carbohydrates is released when they are digested, burned, or decomposed.

The efficiency of this process is not impressive. Much of the radiant energy that strikes a planet's surface is reflected and lost. Even more of it is not of the proper wavelength for photosynthesis. The plant may not, for reasons of its biological cycle, be able to make use of the energy. All in all, less than one-tenth of one percent of the incident energy is used in photosynthesis. Plants, therefore, do not impress us as technological wonders when compared to 15% efficient solar cells or 50% efficient solar thermal collectors. But when we remember that the "construction" of these solar converters (plants) is accomplished by throwing seeds on the ground, our attention is recaptured.

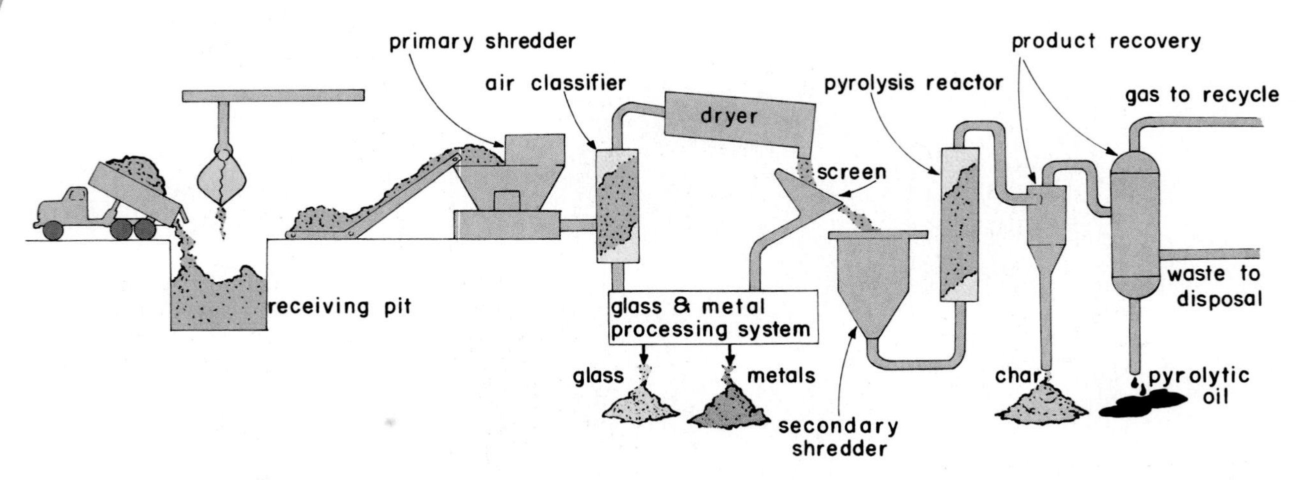

Figure 9.29 A proposed resource recovery plant. (From Energy Alternatives: A Comparative Analysis, Science and Public Policy Program, University of Oklahoma.)

Biomass is stored solar energy.
What are biofuels?
What can biofuels be used for?

Living materials that can be used as fuels are called **biofuels.** (Biofuels may also be referred to as biomass.) Biofuels are living organic material such as trees, grass, crops, and seaweed or other algae. Municipal solid waste (trash) can also be included as it consists mainly of biofuel products (paper, cardboard, food residues). The energy stored in the biofuels is derived from photosynthesis. The energy may be released by direct combustion (burning), or by converting biofuels into charcoal and liquid or gaseous fuels. The byproducts (leftovers) of biofuel can be used for food, fertilizer, and chemicals. Biofuels can be used to produce electricity, heat, steam, and transportation fuels to reduce the use of nonrenewable sources.

a. Sources of Biofuels

Many of the biofuels now available for energy are waste materials left over from other processes. Some typical sources and examples are:

- forest products—sawdust, bark, paper pulp, wood shavings, scrap lumber, wood dust, and paper,
- agricultural and food-processing waste—fruit pits, walnut shells, rice hulls, corn cobs, manures, and sugar cane residue,
- municipal sewage and solid waste.

Converting residues and other wastes to energy also solves waste-disposal problems.

Residues are another source of biofuels for conversion to energy. Examples of forest residues are wood material or "slash" left in the forest after cutting and harvesting timber, noncommercial timber, and diseased trees. Agricultural residues include corn stalks as well as straw from rice, wheat, barley, and oats.

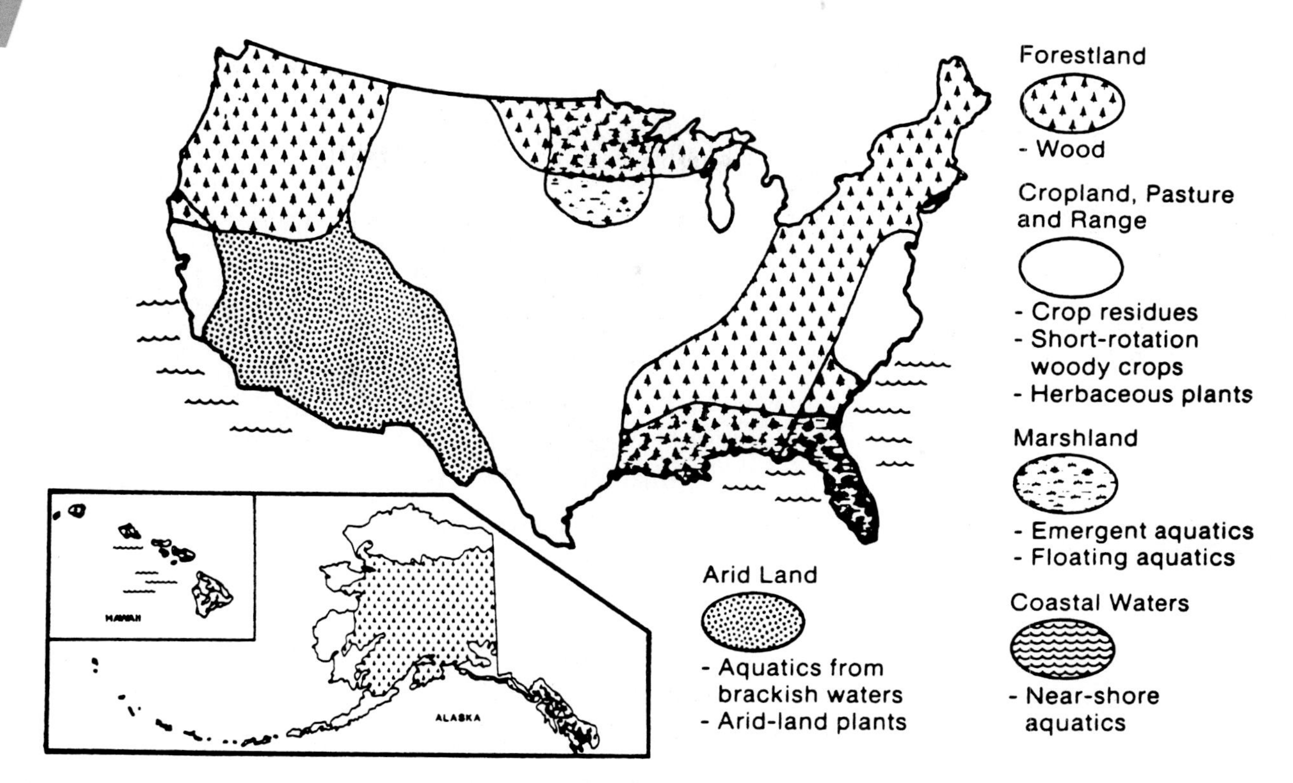

Figure 9.30 Biomass resources areas in the United States. (From Solar Energy Research Institute.)

High-yield, high-energy crops such as sugar cane, sugar beets, and sweet sorghum, or rapidly growing trees such as eucalyptus, willow, and sweet gum can be grown specifically for use as biofuels. Existing technology for short-rotation forestry can be adapted to biofuel tree plantations. The annual yield of usable material from managed short-rotation tree farms could be as much as 10 short tons per acre (22,000 kg/hectare). Organic materials for biofuels could be grown in nearly every region of the country. (See Figure 9.30.)

b. Conversion Processes

Biofuels may be converted into gaseous, liquid, or solid fuels. This is illustrated in Figure 9.31. The type of fuel you end up with depends on the conversion process.

Basically there are two types of biofuel energy (bioenergy) conversion processes: thermochemical conversion and biochemical conversion. See Figure 9.32.

1. **Thermochemical conversion.** The thermochemical conversion process uses heat to produce chemical reactions in biofuels. Examples of such conversion techniques include direct combustion (burning), and **pyrolysis** (heating in the absence of air). In direct combustion, the product is heat which may be used to produce steam for electric power generation or to power

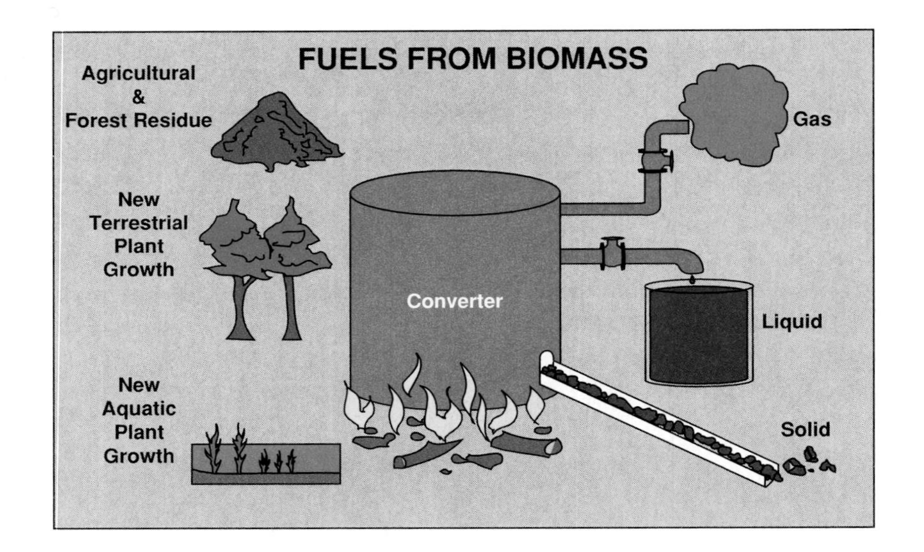

Figure 9.31 Fuels from biomass. (USDOE)

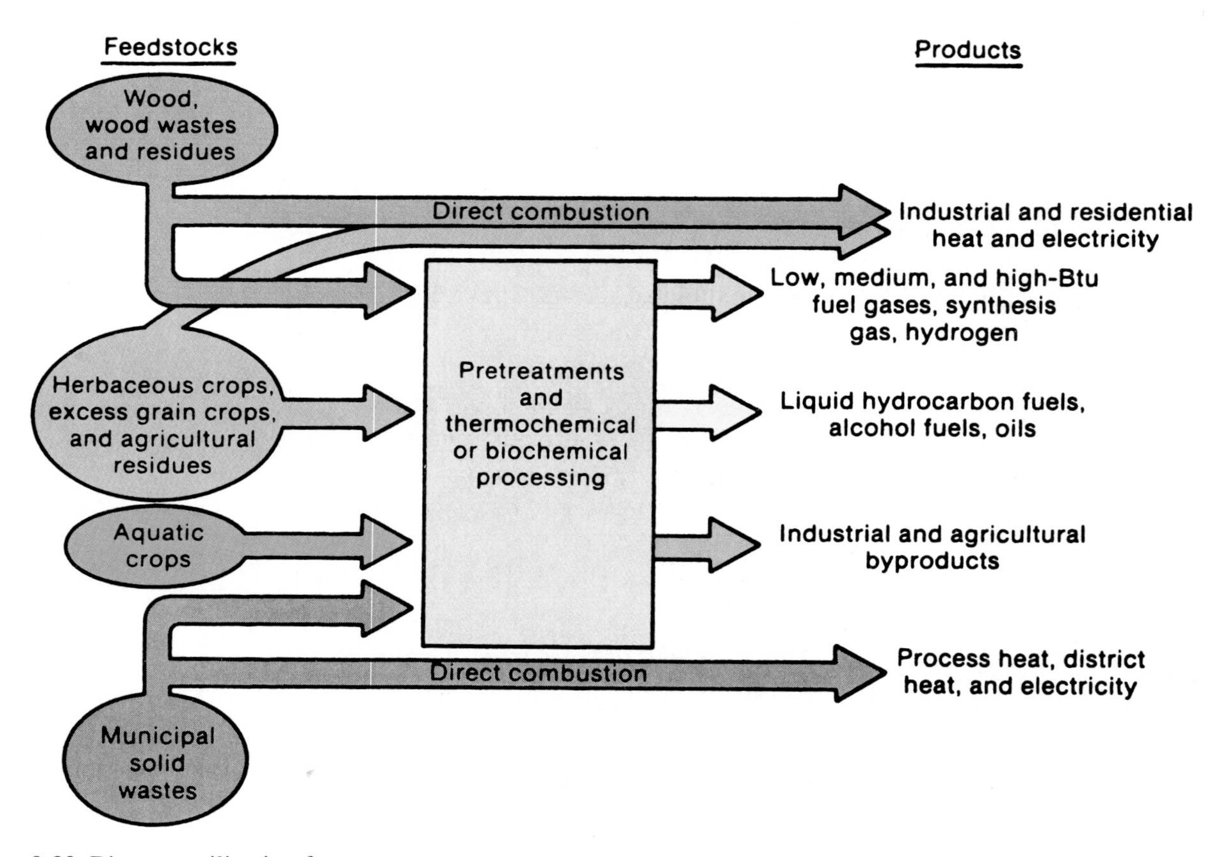

Figure 9.32 Biomass utilization for energy. (From Solar Energy Research Institute.)

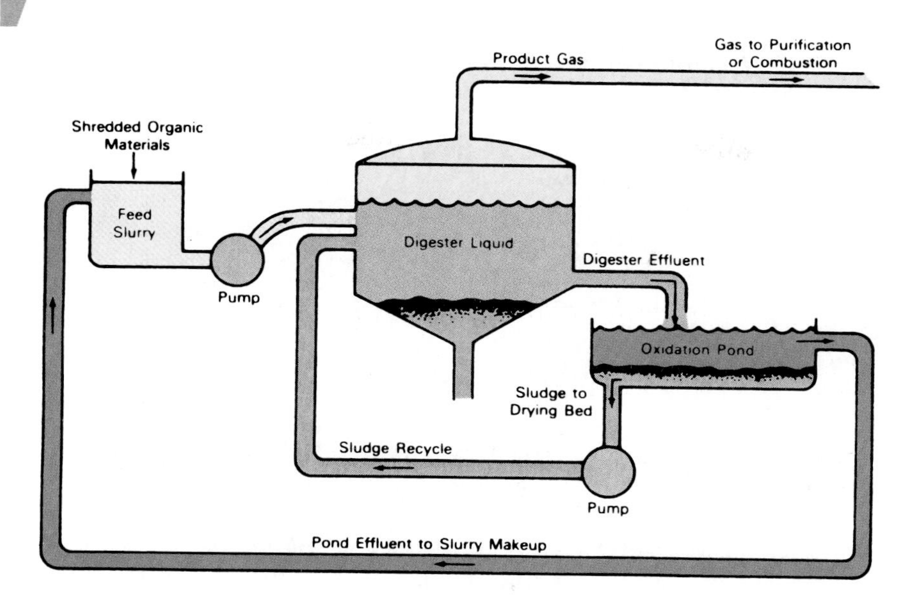

Figure 9.33 Plan for a unit for continuous conversion of organic material to methane by anaerobic (without oxygen) fermentation. (USDOE)

industrial processes or heat homes. Pyrolysis breaks down biofuels into liquids such as crude oil, flammable gas mixture, and solids (carbon and ash).

2. **Biochemical conversion.** Biochemical conversion (bioconversion) is a chemical reaction caused by treating high-moisture biofuels with enzymes, or with fungi or other microorganisms. These conversion techniques produce either liquid or gaseous fuels. Two processes are used today: anaerobic digestion and fermentation. **Anaerobic digestion** is the controlled decay of organic material in the absence of oxygen. Manure, agricultural wastes, municipal solid waste, paper, seaweed, and algae all can be converted by anaerobic digestion to produce methane gas.

Figure 9.33 shows a possible unit for the continuous conversion of organic material to methane by anaerobic fermentation.

Sewage treatment plants have used anaerobic digestion for many years to treat waste and generate methane gas. It is also possible to capture and burn the methane gas formed by natural anaerobic degradation of municipal solid waste in old landfills. The methane gas produced in these processes can be used as a direct substitute for the natural gas used to heat most American homes.

Fermentation is a natural process in which a living organism (yeast) decomposes carbohydrates (such as starch, sugar, or molasses) into ethyl alcohol (ethanol) and carbon dioxide. (See Figure 9.34.). Research is being done on using acids and natural enzymes to convert cellulose into glucose for fermentation. This step is necessary because cellulose, the most important carbohydrate component of wood and plant residues, does not easily ferment. A mixture of 10% ethanol or methanol (from coal or natural gas) and 90% gasoline is usable in any

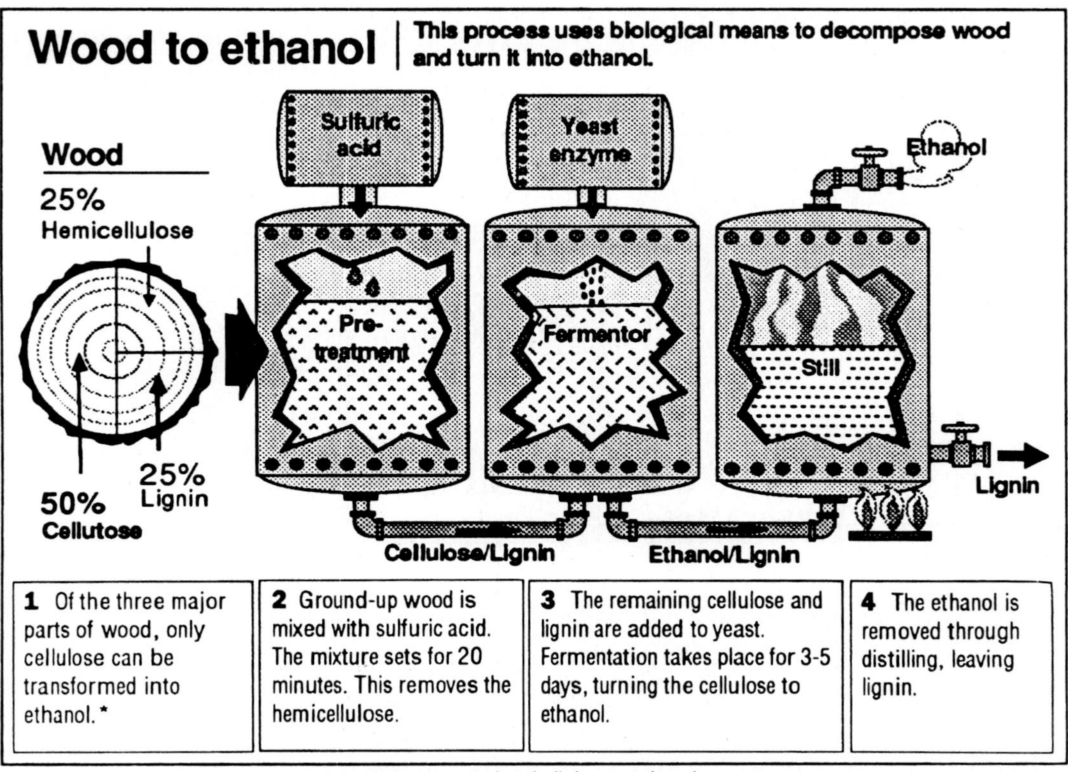

Figure 9.34 A wood-to-ethanol process. (Reprinted with permission from the Rocky Mountain News.)

internal combustion engine without any modification of the carburetor. The ethanol fuel now being widely used is made primarily from grain in conventional distilleries, by methods originally developed for beverage alcohols. The demand for alcohol/gasoline blends is increasing because alcohol can substitute for lead as an octane enhancer.

Because alcohol molecules contain oxygen, the exhausts of cars that burn alcohol/gasoline blends contain less carbon monoxide than the exhausts of gasoline-burners. Since carbon monoxide is a major air pollutant in many American cities, some areas are beginning to require the use of alcohol/gasoline blends.

Methanol-blend fuels also have been field tested successfully. Methanol (methyl alcohol) can be produced from biofuels by several processes. Using methanol in place of diesel fuel almost eliminates sulfur emissions, and greatly reduces other pollutants usually emitted by diesel-powered vehicles. Producing methanol from biofuels is expensive, though.

c. The Future of Biofuels

The municipal solid waste problem in the United States is growing rapidly. The traditional use of landfills is proving unacceptable because, land for future landfills is not available.

Present efforts are concentrating on incineration, which is meeting with public opposition because it may cause air pollution. An alternative to incineration would be to gasify the refuse and then use the gas for methanol production.

An even more exciting option for the future is fuel efficiency: If the average car in the United States ran 40 miles on a gallon of fuel (which is possible), and if the number of cars on the road remained at roughly what it is today, then the biomass generated from forestry, agricultural wastes, and municipal trash could provide energy for all of those automobiles.

Note: If the byproducts (leftovers) from biofuel production (called mash) are continually plowed back into the fields where the biofuels are produced, the biofuels can be regrown continually. The byproducts contain the seeds and nutrients (fertilizer) necessary for healthy plants. Nature provides the rest—sunlight, water, and carbon dioxide.

Energy farms specializing in fast-growing crops can produce high energy yields. These include silviculture (tree plantations); grain farms for fuel alcohols; freshwater farms growing algae, duckweed, and water hyacinth; marine (ocean) farms; and marginal lands growing grasses, oil-bearing plants, and plants with high hydrocarbon contents. Oils from some plants have compositions similar to that of diesel fuel, while others produce materials that can be refined like petroleum.

Biofuels will become more widely used only if they are no more expensive than conventional energy sources. The cost-effectiveness of biofuels as an energy resource depends largely on site-specific circumstances. Compared to fossil fuels, biofuels have a lower energy content per ton, and they must be used near their source of production to minimize transportation and handling costs. A guaranteed long-term source of fuel is also essential for any project, especially industrial-scale applications. Finally, the process of converting the biofuels into energy must be reliable, efficient, and cost-competitive with conventional energy-producing systems. The equipment costs for gasification, pyrolysis, and liquefaction must be reduced before these processes will be widely used.

As with any energy option, environmental effects must be carefully investigated to ensure that the biofuels are intelligently used and managed. The benefits of using biofuels for fuel also must be weighed against the benefits of using them to create other economically valuable products, or from allowing them to return nutrients to the soil through natural decay. Land use, combustion and processing byproducts, and wildlife effects must all be considered.

Summarize the future of biofuels.

Because global reserves of oil and natural gas are shrinking, because coal is a solid fuel and its direct use presents special environmental challenges, and because the public has not accepted the nuclear option, we can:

- gasify and liquefy coal
- develop local energy options such as geothermal power and tidal energy
- use the sun's energy to:

1) heat and cool buildings
2) provide electricity
3) produce solid, liquid, and gaseous fuels

Summary

In this chapter, we have examined our energy alternatives. Synthetic fuels enable us to obtain fuels like the oil and gas we so heavily rely on at the present time. We have examined the renewable (sustainable) energy options. These options are always with us. They include the secondary solar sources (wind, waves, hydroelectric power, and biomass), and direct solar options (active and passive solar, STEC, photovoltaic cells, OTEC, and solar satellites). Some of these options produce minimal amounts of energy. However, they are still of interest because they can be significant in terms of local needs. Others offer significant amounts of energy on a national scale. They all have a relatively small negative environmental impact.

Solar applications are many and varied. Some are simple, such as passive solar and flat-plate collectors. Some, such as photovoltaic cells, STEC, and OTEC, require major engineering efforts. Solar satellites require a space program and military capability.

References

American Solar Energy Society. *Assessment of Solar Energy Technologies* (Boulder, CO: American Solar Energy Society), 1989.

Anderson, Bruce (ed.) *Solar Building Architecture* (Cambridge, MA: MIT Press), 1990.

Goldemberg, Jose, et. al. *Energy for a Sustainable World* (New York: John Wiley), 1988.

Lumpkin, Robert E. Recent progress in the direct liquefaction of coal. *Science.* February 19, 1988.

Moretti, P. and L. Divone. Modern windmills. *Scientific American.* June 1986.

National Research Council. *Geothermal Energy Technology* (Washington, DC: National Academy Press), 1987.

Pimentel, David, et. al. Environmental and social costs of biomass energy. *BioScience.* pp. 89–94. February 1984.

Shea, Cynthia Pollock. *Renewable Energy: Today's Contribution, Tomorrow's Promise* (Washington, DC: Worldwatch Institute), 1988.

Wells, Malcolm *Underground Buildings* (Brewster, MA: Malcolm Wells), 1990.

Zweibel, Kenneth. *Harnessing Solar Power: The Photovoltaics Challenge* (New York: Plenum), 1990.

End of Chapter Questions

1. Distinguish between nonrenewable and continuous energy sources.
2. Why would anyone want to change coal into a gas or a liquid when it works perfectly well as a solid fuel?
3. What environmental concerns are associated with coal gasification?
4. If it is possible to make coal into a more useful gaseous fuel, why isn't the U.S. doing it on a large scale?
5. Why is there interest in oil shale and tar sands?
6. What are some of the problems related to the development of oil shale and tar sands.
7. Why are geothermal energy and the tides called local options?
8. From a theoretical point of view, is there enough power available in the solar radiation that falls on the U.S. to fulfill national demands for power?
9. Name the two categories of solar heating.
10. Describe the advantages and disadvantages of the two types of solar heating systems.
11. If you were considering living in an earth-sheltered solar-heated home, what might be (a) your concerns and (b) what things would you like?
12. Because sunlight is so spread out (diffused), what must be done to it to allow its heat to generate electricity?
13. How do photovoltaic cells work?
14. Why would anyone want to use photovoltaic cells to produce electricity when the power from them costs several times as much as the power from an electric power company?
15. What causes the wind?
16. List the necessary conditions of a region where it might be advantageous to use wind energy today.
17. Explain why the reliability of a wind system coupled with a solar system would be much higher than the reliability of either alone.
18. Justify the inclusion of Ocean Thermal Energy Conversion (OTEC) in the category of "solar energy."
19. How would the utilization of ocean thermal gradients satisfy one of the biggest disadvantages of solar energy?
20. What does a hydroelectric plant do.
21. Describe two ways of using hydroelectric energy in addition to the building of large hydroelectric dams.
22. Give examples of materials that are classified as "biomass" energy sources.

23. What are the two most feasible processes for converting biomass into energy?
24. Why doesn't the U.S. supply all of its domestic energy from our forests, since they represent 300 Quads of energy just standing there?
25. Why are liquid fuels important?
26. Explain how the same food grain can be used to operate farm machinery and to provide protein for cattle.
27. Discuss the statement: "Sunshine is free; solar energy is not."
28. List five competitive uses of biomass.

Goal

To examine our energy options. To begin to sort out our options as a basis for future planning.

Strategies for Using Energy

The energy problem should be not how to expand supplies to meet the postulated extrapolative needs of a dynamic economy, but rather how to accomplish social goals elegantly with a minimum of energy and effort.

—Amory B. Lovins

Figure 10.1 Freeway traffic.
(National Renewable Energy Laboratory)

Abundant energy is woven into the fabric of our daily activities and is a major factor underlying the strength of our economy. Modern technological societies are built on the assumption that clean energy supplies will be readily available.

The United States' pattern of energy use has emerged from its large land area, low population density, and many natural resources. Except for countries like Canada and Australia, most nations do not have comparable features. The energy consumption patterns in Canada and Australia are similar to those in the U.S. The entire infrastructure of cities, highways, and industries was developed with abundant and relatively cheap energy sources.

Abundant and cheap energy can no longer be guaranteed for years to come. Domestic oil and gas reserves are depleting, coal and nuclear sources have unique problems, and solar energy requires special adaptations to meet our needs. We will have to examine our energy situation carefully if we wish to ensure adequate supplies at reasonable costs. In this chapter we will examine some strategies that can enable us to reach that goal.

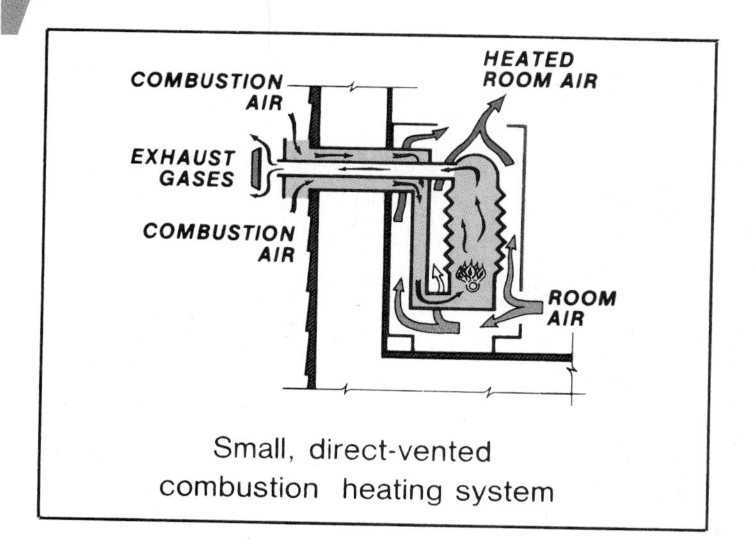

Figure 10.7 Small, direct-vented combustion heating system. (Courtesy Denver Energy Resource Center.)

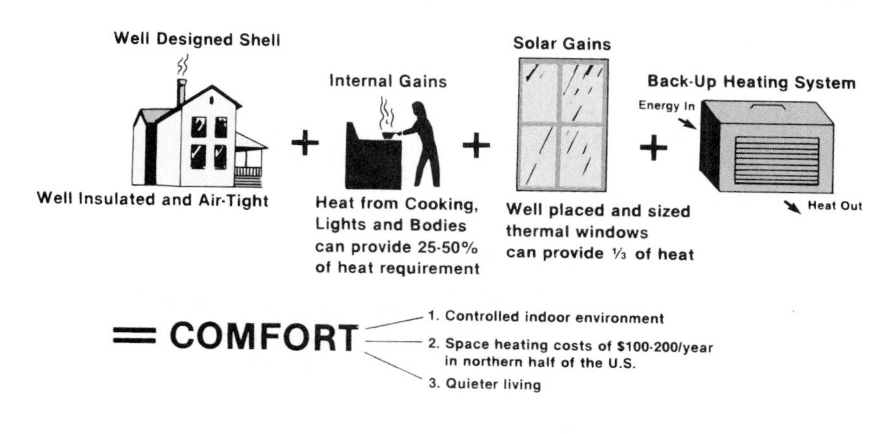

Figure 10.8 The superinsulation strategy.

house. Wood stoves and fireplaces are not recommended for superinsulated homes. Stoves tend to overheat easily. Also, because it is difficult to make them airtight and limit their combustion air to an outside source, they lower indoor air quality. Figure 10.8 shows the strategy of superinsulation.

With superinsulation, the initial building costs increase by about 5 percent. The payback time is typically five years.

10.2 High-Mileage Cars

In the 1960s and 1970s, the average fuel rate (miles per gallon) for passenger automobiles in the United States was less than 14. In contrast, the 1992 rate had risen to about 23. Not only that, but the average rate for the *new* cars sold that year was 28. Table 10.1 indicates that this is just the beginning. Right now, a buyer can choose among several cars that are rated at over 50 miles per gallon. Several prototype cars (designed and being tested) are giving around 70 miles per gallon, and cars on the drawing board should do even better than that.

Table 10.1 Fuel Economy for Passenger Automobiles

Car	Fuel	Fuel Economy		Curb Weight		Power	Passenger Capacity
		(liters/ 100 km.)	(miles/ gal.)	(kilograms)	(pounds)	(horsepower)	(persons)
Commercial (1993)							
Geo Metro XFi	gasoline	4.2	56	737	1,621	49	4
Geo Metro	gasoline	4.9	48	750	1,650	55	4
Geo Metro LSi	gasoline	4.9	48	797	1,753	55	2
Honda Civic HBVX	gasoline	4.5	52	952	2,094	94	5
Suzuki Swift HB	gasoline	5.7	41	809	1,779	72	4
Prototype							
VW Auto 2000	diesel	3.6	66	780	1,715	52	4–5
Volvo LCP 2000	multi-fuel	3.4	69	707	1,555	52	2–4
Renault EVE +	diesel	3.4	70	855	1,880	50	4–5
Toyota lightweight compact	diesel	2.4	98	650	1,430	56	4–5
Design							
Cummins/NASA Lewis Car	multi-fuel	2.9	81	1,364	3,000	70	5-6

Adapted from Energy for a Sustainable World, *World Resources Institute,* Washington, D.C.

Figure 10.9 Geo Metro's standard 1.0 liter, 3 cylinder engine features electronic fuel injection for lively response and excellent drivability. With an average (city/highway) mileage of 55 mpg, it is one of the most fuel efficient cars in the world today. (From Chevrolet Motor Division, General Motors Corporation.)

What is the major reason for improved fuel efficiency in American cars?

How have these dramatic gains been achieved? The major reason is a reduction in weight. In the 1960s and early 1970s, the typical American car weighed about 3000 pounds (1384 kilograms). As a general rule, as the weight goes down, the mileage goes up. See Figure 10.9.

These weight reductions were made possible mainly through the use of lighter gauge steel and aluminum. Another factor is the use of composite parts. Advances in the chemistry of plastics led to a whole new family of structural materials called composites. **Composites** are a combination of high-strength non-metallic fibers embedded in a matrix (usually epoxy). These are commonly called plastic parts but are more correctly described as fiber-reinforced composites. Not only can the chassis (body) of the car be made of composite material, but so

What are composites?

can the wheels, drive shafts, connecting rods, and suspension systems. At present, most passenger cars contain about 250 pounds of composite parts. If more composites are used, the present weight of a typical car can be reduced up to 50% in the future. Combining that with the development of the ceramic engine and other strategies, who knows what kind of fuel economy we will get in the year 2020. For example, the Cummins/NASA Lewis Car is an exception to the rule of weight reduction. It has a ceramic (adiabatic) engine and gets 81 miles/gallon.

What major factor will lead to a large increase in higher mileage cars?

One of the major hurdles that must be crossed before all this occurs is that of public acceptance. Many believe that good fuel economy means a sluggish, slow vehicle. However, the Volvo Light Component Project 2000 vehicle gets 65 miles per gallon but accelerates from 0 to 60 miles per hour in only 11 seconds. Many people also believe that high fuel economy means a tiny, cramped vehicle. However, most of the new high efficiency cars and prototypes listed carry four or five passengers comfortably. What about safety? Aren't fuel-efficient cars unsafe? Again, good engineering design can improve the structural strength and safety of even very small cars. (Ceramic engines and other car parts made of nonbiodegradable materials may also bring about disposal problems that should be anticipated.)

What about expense? Studies show that using more plastics will reduce the cost of owning and operating a car in the United States by $150 to $250 per year because of longer product life, cheaper repairs, more corrosion resistance, and lower insurance rates.

10.3 More Efficient Appliances

United States refrigerators consume about 7 percent of the nation's electricity—the energy output of about 25 large electric power plants. A 1972 refrigerator with a top mounted freezer and automatic defrost typically uses about 2,000 kWh of electricity per year. A similar model sold in 1992 runs on about 1,000 kWh a year. If every household in the United States had the most efficient refrigerator currently available, the electricity savings would eliminate the need for about 12 large nuclear or coal fired power plants. See Figure 10.10.

How significant might a switch to more efficient refrigerators be?

This is only the beginning! Similar savings are possible with other appliances—light bulbs, stoves, freezers, washers, dryers, furnaces, and so on.

Although energy conservation may be less exciting than controlled nuclear fusion experiments or space-based solar collection systems, the benefits of conservation are enormous. These include: A cleaner environment, reduced world tensions, and an increased opportunity for larger numbers of people to enjoy some of those benefits we refer to as the "good life."

What are some of the major benefits of an effective energy conservation program?

Energy Conversion and Storage

Although they are not energy sources, several methods for converting and storing energy deserve some mention as they can help us use energy more efficiently. Some of these strategies are described in the next two sections.

Figure 10.10 Energy-efficient refrigerators.

10.4 Energy Conversion Technologies

What are some energy conversion techniques?

a. Magnetohydrodynamics (MHD)

Magnetohydrodynamics (MHD) is the science that deals with the interaction between a magnetic field and a flowing ionized (charged) gas. A gas mixture is ionized if its atoms have lost one or more electrons. Heating to 3,000-5,000° F ionizes it, causing it to become an electrical conductor.

An MHD electric generator is much simpler than a conventional electric generator. It requires no turbine or other rotating machinery. In an MHD power plant, powdered coal burns fiercely in a chamber and produces temperatures high enough to ionize the combustion gas molecules in the chamber. This gas is squirted, through a nozzle, into a powerful magnetic field. In the magnetic field, the positive ions move in one direction and the negative ions in another. The resulting current is drawn off by electrodes. It is believed that MHD electric power generation (Figure 10.11) could raise the 40% efficiency of most existing electric power plants to at least 60%.

How does fluidized-bed combustion increase efficiency and improve air quality?

b. Fluidized-Bed Combustion

Fluidized beds are simple devices that add the fuel (usually pulverized coal) to a much larger mass of small, red-hot particles. The particles the coal reacts with are called the sorbent. The efficiency of combustion and of heat transfer is high because of the turbulent mixing and

Self-Contained and Self-Sustained

science at work

On 4,500 acres in southwest Kansas, Reeve Agri Energy is nothing like the old-fashioned family farm it once was. Employing 30 to 35 people as well as several members of the Reeve family, the company is a complex, profitable ecosystem that conserves more than one of Earth's nonrenewable resources.

Oxygenated fuels are important to United States energy needs now that oil is less plentiful, more expensive, and contributing too much to pollution. Ethanol—the same form of alcohol found in beer and whiskey—is mixed with gasoline to provide the cleaner-burning, higher-octane automobile fuel you know as "unleaded plus" or "super-unleaded." Every year, the Reeve facility produces 9.2 million gallons of ethanol. The process starts with corn, molasses, and other material high in sugars and starches, and water from the Ogallala aquifer that underlies much of the Midwest. The plant uses many energy-efficient tools, such as heat exchange systems and electricity from natural-gas generators.

But ethanol is only part of the story. A byproduct of the ethanol production is used to feed the Reeve cattle. After cooling, sifting, and removal of water, the stillage that remains is heavy in protein. The starch used for the ethanol production is replaced in the form of corn, alfalfa, and milo, and some vitamins and minerals are added. This enhanced mash is then given to the 21,000 head of cattle raised on the ranch. It's important to keep it wet, because drying the product would take as much energy as producing the ethanol in the first place.

Further down the ecosystem line, cattle manure is used to fertilize the surrounding cropland. The leftover hot water from the ethanol plant is cooled and used to raise white tilapia, a mild-flavored warmwater fish. This same water, nutrient-rich after housing the fish, is then returned to the land in irrigation.

Many branches of science contribute to the Reeve effort. A remarkable assortment of people contribute their talent and knowledge—farmers, veterinarians, microbiologists, nutritionists, attorneys, accountants, and those who run the ethanol facility—and Lee Reeve has to communicate with all of them. He sees every day the value of understanding scientific ideas. When the family added the fish breeding operation to their business, he learned a lot about biology and ecology, and was glad for the good scientific beginnings his high-school textbooks gave him. Lee has a B.S. in Agricultural Economics from Kansas State. He also knows the value of community college instruction, and emphasizes the importance of on-the-job training such as apprenticeship programs.

Critics of ethanol say it's too expensive to produce and that our tax dollars should not be spent to make it. But there's no doubt ethanol is a cleaner fuel than oil, and supplies of oil are decreasing. According to Lee, the critics should remember the First and Second Laws of Thermodynamics. We can't make new energy, but we can take advantage of its transformation from one form to another.

Reeve Agri Energy is an excellent example of economic development that contributes both jobs and products in a setting that does not harm the environment or waste energy. Lee wants to see other industries evolve from and support one another, just as his family's business has. "The first requirement of success is to find out what happens in nature, and then try to duplicate that, not fight it."

Figure 10.11 MHD generator electrical system. (USAEC)

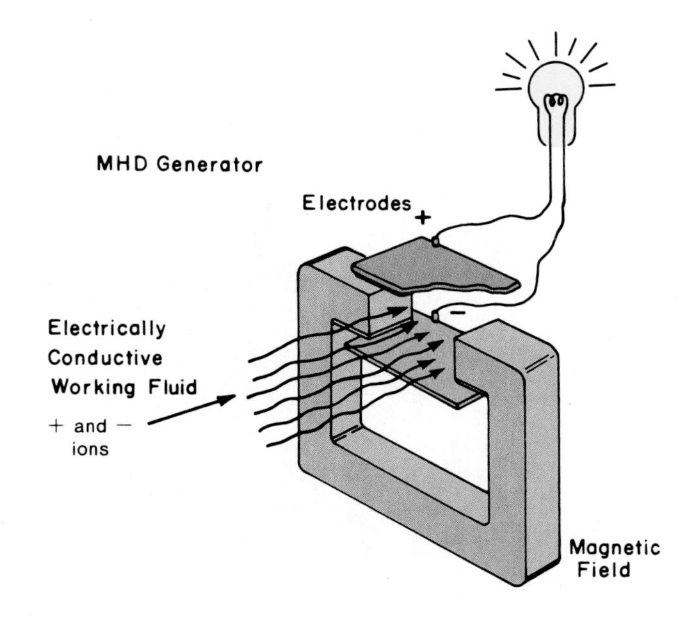

Figure 10.12 The fluidized-bed combustion process. (E. Stratos Tavoulareas. Reproduced with permission from the Annual Review of Energy and the Environment.)

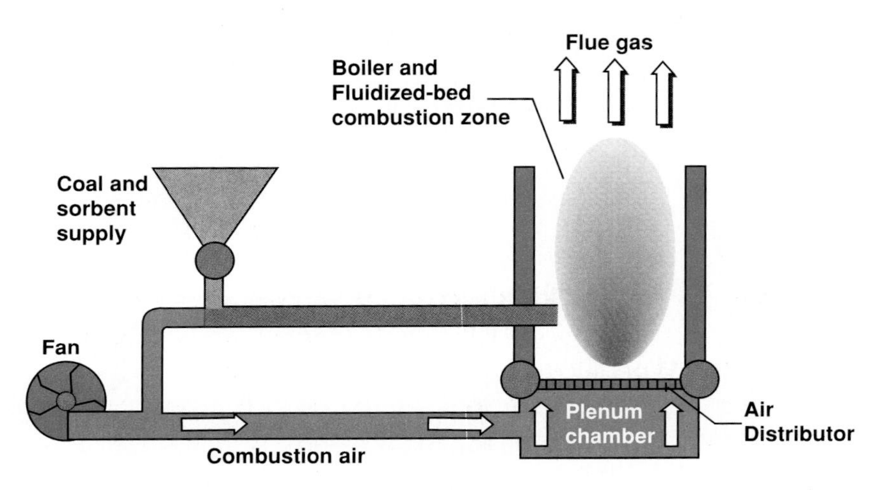

The plenum chamber contains air under high pressure.

large surface area of the particles. Current research is attempting to perfect the process and adapt it to large electric power generation plants.

Figure 10.12 illustrates the fluidized-bed combustion process. Coal and particles (sorbent) are injected into the boiler, while air is blown upward through the air distributor in the bottom of the boiler. In the boiler, coal is burned efficiently, and sulfur dioxide (produced from sulfur impurities in the coal) reacts with a sorbent-related chemical to form calcium sulfate. The calcium sulfate can be removed as a dry harmless solid.

Fluidized-bed combustion is of interest both because it improves efficiency and because it reduces sulfur oxide and nitrogen oxide emissions at electric power plants. This means that less fuel is burned and air quality is improved.

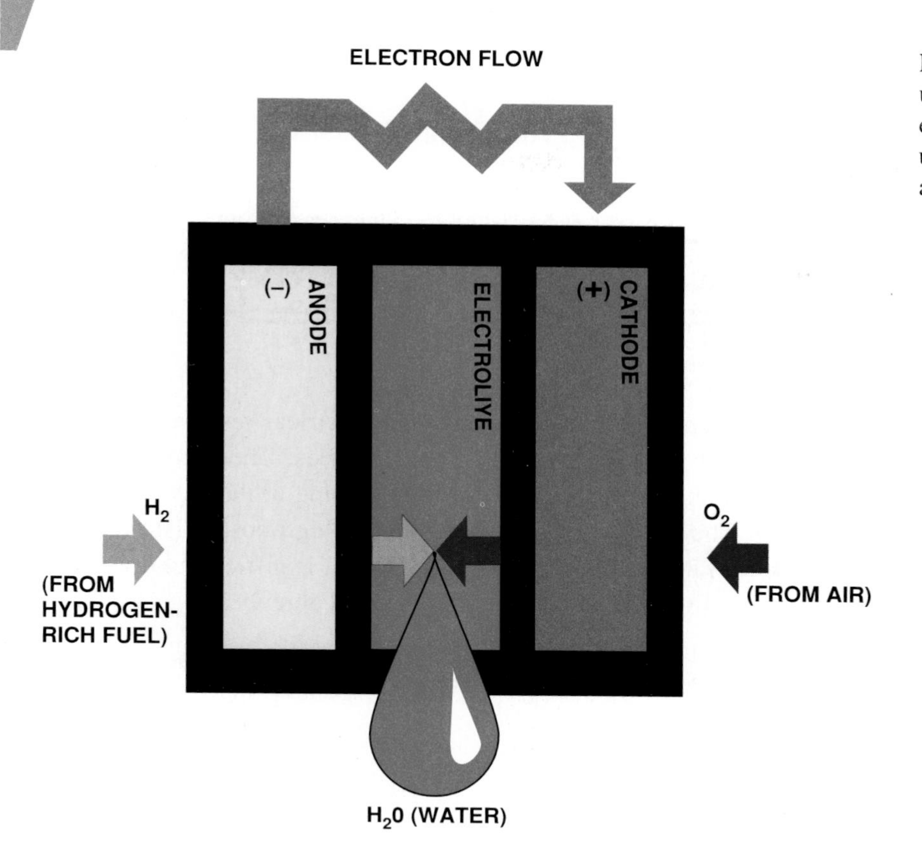

Figure 10.13 A simplified fuel cell using hydrogen and oxygen. The electron flow that results can be used to power any of the electric appliances we all use. (USDOE)

c. Fuel Cells

What is a fuel cell?

A fuel cell generates electrical energy directly from chemical energy. It is somewhat like a battery. However, it differs from a battery in that the chemical energy, rather than being stored, is fed into it continuously. In most fuel cells, hydrogen is combined with oxygen to give water plus energy.

Fuel cells have many advantages over other forms of generation. They have good efficiency. The only moving parts are fans and pumps. They are quiet and pose little pollution threat (if they use gas as a fuel) since the waste products are carbon dioxide and water (although carbon dioxide adds to the greenhouse effect). If hydrogen gas becomes an energy storage technique, fuel cells could be used to put back together the hydrogen and oxygen originally separated by electrolysis at some huge, distant power plant.

d. Heat Pumps

What is a heat pump?

Heat pumps are devices (such as air conditioners or refrigerators) which move heat around, rather than producing it. They are similar to air conditioners, with a reverse cycle for heating. In the winter, the refrigerant (colder than the outside air) picks up heat from the outdoors and releases it inside the house. See Figure 10.14.

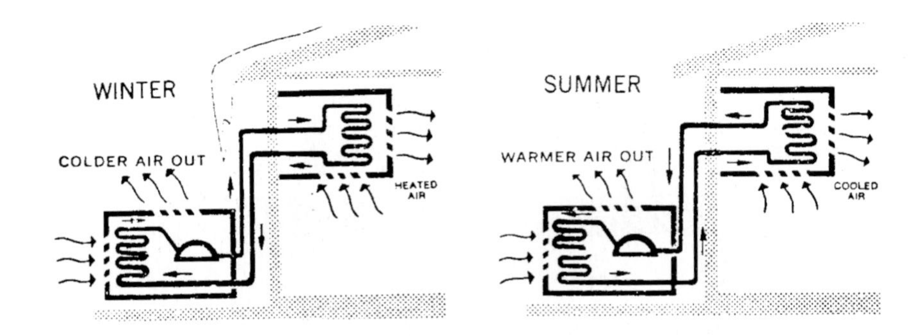

Figure 10.14 The operation of a heat pump. (Reprinted from *Popular Science* with permission. Times Mirror Magazines, Inc., Frank R. Buonocare (artist), copyright © 1979.)

Heat pumps are more efficient than electrical resistance heating and somewhat more efficient than gas furnaces. They are clean and don't need a chimney (their only chimney being at the electric power company). The main drawback is the initial high cost. Also, they do not work well in very cold climates, because it is difficult to draw heat from outside air which is below zero degrees Fahrenheit (–17.8 ° C).

10.5 Energy Storage Techniques

?

What are some energy storage techniques?

a. Hydrogen Storage

We have already mentioned that electricity can't be stored (except in small quantities). One solution to this problem is to use surplus electricity to electrolyze water into hydrogen and oxygen.

$$2H_2O_{(l)} + \text{electricity} \longrightarrow 2H_2(g) + O_2(g)$$
$$(l = \text{liquid}, g = \text{gas})$$

Then when energy is needed, the hydrogen can be burned and the energy recovered. Hydrogen can be stored and transported much as we store and transport natural gas today (but usually in steel cylinders). It can be burned rapidly in furnaces and cars to produce heat and motion or burned slowly in fuel cells to produce electricity.

Hydrogen storage could become very important if photovoltaic cells become inexpensive. We could run our cars on hydrogen, and water would come out the tailpipe.

How does pumped storage work?

b. Pumped Storage

Because electricity cannot be stored in large quantities, and the demand for electricity fluctuates a great deal, electric power companies must maintain a large reserve generating capacity, which sits idle much of the time. One way of leveling the demand is to pump water uphill and store it behind a dam during off-peak hours. Then during high demand periods, the water can be allowed to turn the turbines in a hydroelectric plant.

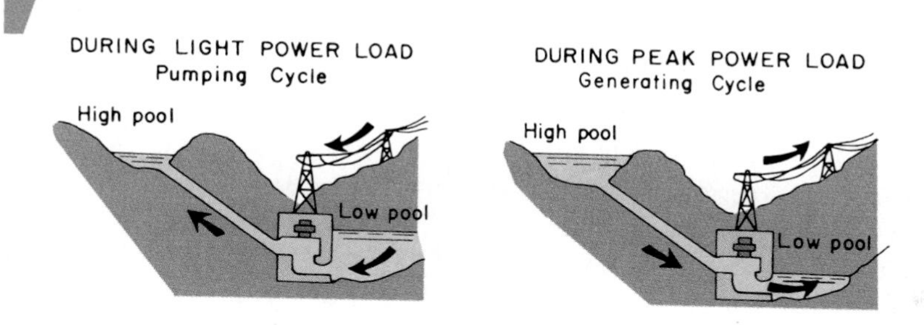

Figure 10.15 Operation of a pumped storage plant. (From Department of Water Resources, California Resources Agency.)

Of course, electricity must be used to run the pumps. However, even though the reversible turbine (pumps) are only 66 percent efficient (34 percent of energy is lost in the storage step) the difference between the cost of peak and off-peak power often makes them practical.

c. Heat Storage

How can solar energy be stored for use at night?

One problem with the use of solar energy is that every night the sun goes down. This is when the heat is needed most. To solve this problem, heat must be stored for night-time use. Storage is often in dark-colored bricks and tiles, along with large tanks of water. These are called thermal mass.

What are eutectic salts and how might they be used?

The tanks of water are used for heat storage only, not as a source of drinking water. So, a useful substance called a eutectic salt can be added to the tanks. A eutectic salt is a solid at room temperature and a liquid at 50°–65° C (120°–150° F), the temperature of solar-heated water. The solar-heated water melts the eutectic salt in the daytime. At night, the salt solidifies as it cools, releasing the stored heat. The amount of stored heat given off when the salt solution cools and solidifies is many times what would be emitted if the solution remained a liquid as it cooled. This makes it possible to store much more heat in a smaller amount of water, saving space. The heat released at night could be used for heating water tanks and for space heating.

Comparing Sources—How Much is Available?

When planning for the energy needs of a large region or nation, it is useful to know the quantity and sources of energy available. These facts, combined with environmental goals, conservation strategies, and the use of efficient technologies, are key elements in wise energy planning. The next two sections summarize data on energy availability in the United States.

10.6 Energy Available from Nonrenewable Reserves

Figure 7.18 illustrated how nonrenewable resources may be compared in terms of the amount of energy still potentially available from each of them. It must be remembered that as reserves are used, some resources become new reserves. Thus, the situation for oil and natural gas may not be quite as bad as Figure 7.18 implied.

What is the status of nonrenewable energy reserves in the U. S.?

One may conclude that our crude oil and natural gas reserves are small compared to our demands. We should, therefore, reduce our reliance on them and emphasize sources that can more easily meet our demands in environmentally acceptable ways.

10.7 The Continual Resources—A Comparison

What are the continual resources?

Spaceship Earth does not have to depend entirely on stored energy, as some forms are renewed continually. The largest continual energy source is the sun. Direct uses of sunlight include solar heating, cooling, and solar electric power production. Sunlight not only is an energy source itself, but also can be converted into stored sources. The storage results from photosynthesis or other natural processes. Wind, warm water, and biomass (wood, crops, etc.) are all stored solar energy.

In addition to solar energy, other continual sources of energy deserve consideration. Earth's interior is hot, but conduction is very slow. The major heat flow to the surface is from granitic rocks in upper layers. At some places in the Earth's crust, molten material is close to the surface. Volcanoes, hot springs, and geysers are visual evidence of this. If conditions are right, this heat energy can be useful to us.

The other continual source is tidal energy. The gravitational attraction of the moon periodically pulls the oceans away from the Earth's center and then lets them fall back. This mechanical energy can be extracted from the energy stored in the Earth-moon system and can be used for human purposes.

?

If the continual options were ranked in terms of how much power they can deliver on a national basis, what would that ranking be?

Table 10.2 shows a comparison of the power supplied by the continual resources with human demand for power. The numerical comparison is restricted to the United States because we have reasonably good data here. However, the relative comparison is true for the world as a whole. In discussing continual resources, we use units of power per area. The table shows the unit kilowatts per acre or kilowatts per hectare on the 2,310 million acres of the lower 48 states. This supply is compared with the power requirements in the U.S., 1.2 kW/acre for 1991. (That figure was obtained by converting 81.5 Quads of energy used in that year to kWhs, and dividing it by the 8766 hours in a year and by the area of the United States.)

Table 10.2 Continual Energy Sources in the United States

	kW/acre	kW/hectare
Solar Energy (at ground level)	720	1800
Winds (at surface)	43	110
Tides	0.02	0.05
Geothermal	0.02	0.05
Photosynthesis	0.4	1.0
Hydroelectric Power	0.2	0.4
U.S. Consumption, 1991	1.2	2.8

The United States requires a little more than a kilowatt of power per acre on the average. Table 10.2 shows us what an impressive demand for power that is. Though small when compared with the magnificent charity of the sun, only one of the other continual sources—wind—could provide that much power by itself. Wind is a solar product and is not restricted to certain locations. There is a lot of wind blowing across the great open spaces of this country. Even though Table 10.2 shows the maximum estimates for the other sources (tides, geothermal, photosynthesis, hydropower), none of them individually can power our nation.

At first glance, we note that solar energy could easily supply all our needs.

Appropriate Technology

10.8 Appropriate Technology: A Strategy for Using Energy

Appropriate (soft) technology is neither a source of energy nor a way of converting or storing energy. Instead, it is a strategy for using energy wisely. Soft technology attempts to both lower demand and promote the use of renewable resources in a social and political climate based on the following beliefs: (1) smaller is usually better; (2) people should become less dependent on technology, not more dependent; and (3) whenever possible, people should be able to understand and control the devices and systems on which they depend. This strategy is summarized below.

a. Renewable Resources

The advocates of appropriate technology believe that our major energy sources must be the renewable (continual) sources, such as sun, wind, and vegetation. These sources are always with us, whether we use them or not. We must spend "energy income," not deplete our capital (like fossil fuels).

?

What are some of the major ideas of the appropriate technology strategy? What are some of the concerns regarding the full adoption of this approach?

b. Diverse Sources

Under the soft technology option, our energy supply should come from several sources, with each source making only a modest contribution to the whole. Our future risks would then be distributed among many diverse low technologies. Most of these technologies are already known to work well.

Minimizing our reliance on fossil fuels hedges our bets, making us less vulnerable in times of war or natural disaster. Also, the environmental impact is lessened, manageable, and reversible. Never again should we allow ourselves to become totally dependent on one or two energy sources.

No single source is best for all needs. We can find the most appropriate technology for each purpose by considering the quality, size, and complexity of the energy needed.

Figure 10.16 Many cattle roam on land in remote areas where power lines are nonexistent or very expensive to maintain. It is appropriate, in these cases, to use photovoltaic systems to pump and maintain water supplies for cattle. (Photo by Carrol E. Hamon.)

c. Simplicity

What is the advantage of simple technology?

"Appropriate technology" implies that the energy collection and distribution system should be relatively low-technology (simple), so that large numbers of people can understand and use it without having to acquire sophisticated skills. Hard technologies and power complexes are viewed as alien, remote, and uncontrollable. They are run and maintained by a faraway, technical elite. Decisions about who shall have how much energy at what price are centralized, a politically dangerous trend. The appropriate-technology path has a lower initial cost because of its technical simplicity, small unit size, and low overhead. It is adaptable to mass production. There are negligible distribution losses.

d. Matching Size to End-Use

Why might smaller be better?

Energy systems should be matched in size to end-use needs. The scale and complexity of centralized grids not only make them politically inaccessible to citizens, but also increase the likelihood and size of malfunctions, mistakes, and deliberate disruptions. A small fault (such as malfunctioning circuit breaker) or a few discontented people can "turn off" a country. In times of social stress, when grids become a likely target for dissidents, the energy sector can be protected by decentralization.

e. Matching Quality to End-Use

Why match quality to end-use?

Similarly, energy quality should be matched to end-use needs. So-called "waste" heat from power plants and some industries could be used to perform the low-quality tasks of heating water, buildings, and residences near them. Where we want only to create temperature differences of tens of degrees, we should meet the need with sources whose potential is tens or hundreds of degrees, not with flame and

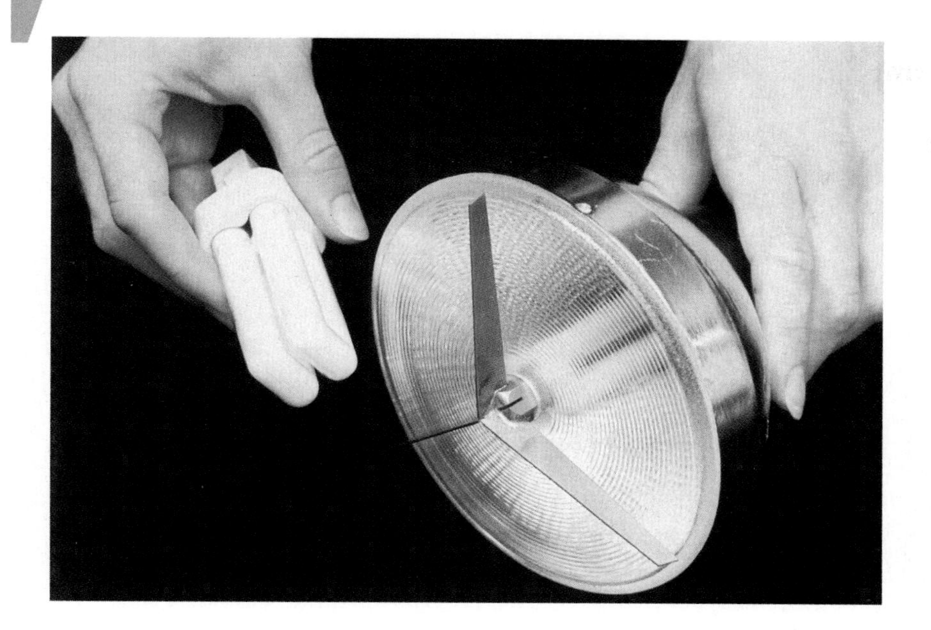

Figure 10.17 A compact fluorescent light bulb at the left and a patented small heat sink at the right. (USDOE)

nuclear temperatures of hundred and thousands of degrees. For some applications, electricity is appropriate and indispensable: electronics, smelting, subways, most lighting, some kinds of mechanical work, and a few more. These applications are already oversupplied.

f. Efficiency

Another soft technology belief is that energy should be used more efficiently. We should strive to do more with less energy through strategies like conservation. If the problem is to move yourself from point A to point B, maybe you could take a train instead of a car. If you must go by car, one weighing 1,800 kg may do just as well as one weighing 3,600 kg. For shorter trips, you might consider walking, bicycling, car-pooling, or mass transit. Instead of using an elaborate "climate control" system, you can dress to suit the weather. An attic fan might make you as comfortable as an air conditioner can. Recycling may accomplish much of what expanded resource extraction provides.

g. Energy Equity

Soft technology strategies recognize the problem of energy inequity. Today a small percentage of the world's people consume the bulk of its energy reserves. While hard technological energy systems continue this inequity, soft technology approaches offer an opportunity to reverse this injustice without major social and political unrest. Soft technologies are socially effective. This is true especially in poor countries that need such scale, versatility, and simplicity even more than we do. These systems can directly benefit the more than two billion people who have no electric outlets.

Equity means fairness.

Figure 10.18 Two projections of future energy needs. *a*. The traditional approach. *b*. The appropriate technology prediction.

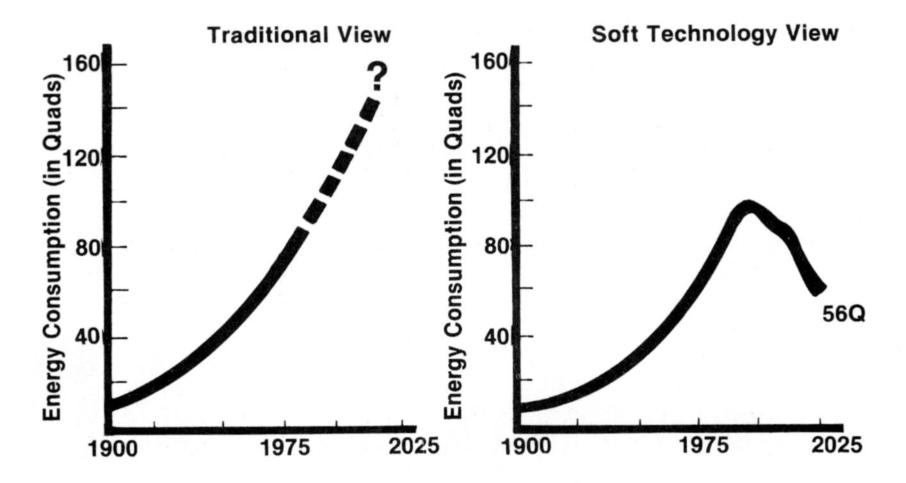

10.9 Can Appropriate Technologies Power a Nation?

The traditional approach to projecting future energy needs involved plotting past consumption and noting that as population increased and standards of living rose, so did energy consumption. It was thus assumed that since population was expected to increase and the standards of living would also grow, more and more energy would be required as the years went by. See Figure 10.18a. There was no end in sight. No one asked, Is there a better way to get from here to there?

a. The "Yes" Answer

The appropriate technology advocates claim we've been asking the wrong questions. Asking how much energy we need fails to deal with questions like: Are we using our energy wisely? Can we heat our homes another way? Can we live comfortably and yet be in harmony with our natural surroundings? The answer to such questions is that there is a better way. We can live as comfortably tomorrow as we live today, and with less energy than we use now. Figure 10.18b shows this energy projection.

How can we live better and use less energy? Figure 10.19 summarizes the appropriate-technology response to that question. It is based on a three-part strategy: 1) identify the task; 2) improve efficiency; and 3) find the cheapest and best source to supply the need.

It is encouraging that United States energy consumption decreased in the early 1980s when we started down the path of appropriate technology and conservation.

b. The "No" Answer

Because the appropriate-technology approach calls for dramatic changes in our present social system, it has come under severe attack. Some objections include:

What are some of the concerns expressed about the adoption of the appropriate technology option?

1. Increasing local control will not guarantee democratic values or the solution of technical problems. Some local, small-scale institutions are as impersonal and rigid as multinational corporations.

Figure 10.19 How to Live Better and Use Less Energy.

Space and Water Heating and Air Conditioning	Liquid Fuels for Transporation	Electricity
Building shells can be designed to keep heat in during the winter and out during the summer. Superinsulation can reduce a home heating bill to $50–$75/month or less, even in harsh climates. Using passive solar is next most efficient. Flat-plate collectors of solar energy provide hot water.	By decreasing car weight and using other techniques, by 2020 we could have a fleet of cars and trucks that use less than ¼ the energy used in the 1980s. The total use of energy for transportation should drop by 50% in the next 40 years. At that level, we could comfortably meet our needs with liquid fuel derived from crop and forest residues which are now waste.	Electricity is needed for home appliances, lighting, computers, and industrial motors and should be reserved for those purposes. If we cease using electricity for space and water heating, electricity is already oversupplied. Bulbs now available provide the light of a 75-watt incandescent bulb, yet only use 18 watts. Refrigerators are being improved each year and computer-controlled motors are more efficient. With wiser usage, hydropower + wind power could provide almost all our needs. Photovoltaics may be the electricity source of the future.

2. There is a place for both large-scale and small-scale technology. One does not exclude the other. Smaller is not always better. With dispersal, pollution control is more difficult, less responsive to regulation, and hardly more environmentally sound. It is easier to remove pollution at one centralized power plant than it is to control the smoke from the chimneys of homes that burn wood or coal. Individual ownership presents the major problem in the regulation of pollution from automobiles. Also, those who find power transmission lines and bill boards unsightly are not going to welcome household windmills in the neighborhood.
3. Under present economic conditions, the costs of the appropriate technology path are prohibitive. Even though the lifetime cost for such strategies as solar panels and passive systems are acceptable to some, first-time costs are still prohibitive for many people.
4. Interconnected power supply grids enable utilities to work around system failures and prevent human suffering. When a local system fails and the outside temperature is

Figure 10.20 Domestic natural gas production. (USDOE)

below zero, a backup system is a must. Technology may be part of the problem, but it is also part of the solution.

5. It is unrealistic to assume that the industrialized world can switch to an appropriate technology base in only 20 to 25 years. Our society is built to run on oil and gas (or comparable substitutes). Free market economic measures require a deliberate and slow transition away from this. Recent history has shown us that nations can only briefly (and then only in times of great perceived danger) gain wide acceptance of policies which reduce expectations, without resorting to severe repression of individual freedom. New energy technologies generally take 30 years or more to see even limited commercial use.
6. All energy production by whatever method results in environmental changes. These changes may be what limits total world energy production and consumption rates. It is not simply a case of which technology is used.

?

What energy strategies do you feel are best for the present and the future—both for yourself and your country?

Energy Policy

An energy policy is a plan that is put together by the government. To be effective, it must have broad support from both the business community and the public.

There is little disagreement on the overall value of having an energy policy. Our economy requires an adequate and affordable supply of energy, but the use of energy affects the environment in many ways. Potential energy supply disruptions from unreliable sources make energy a national security issue. Free market forces don't guarantee clean air or reliable supplies.

The problems of putting together an energy policy are large. Governmental interference with market forces often creates more

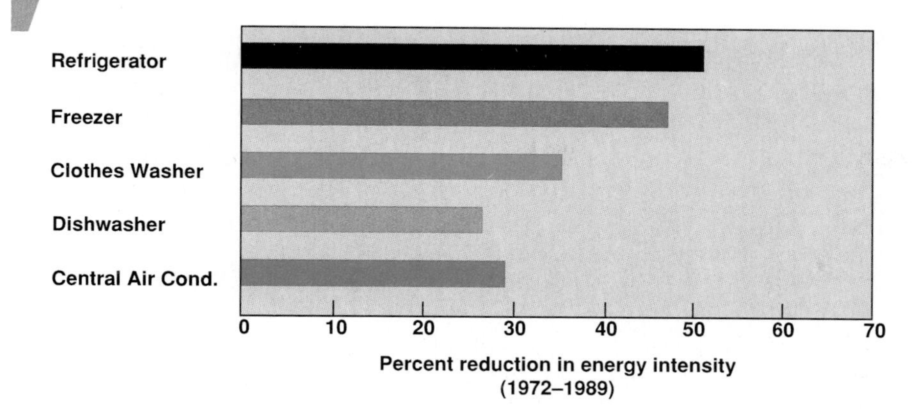

Figure 10.21 Energy intensity is the amount of energy used per unit of activity. In the case of a refrigerator, it can be the amount of energy used to run the refrigerator for one year. The bar graph shows the percent reduction in the energy intensity of new U.S. electrical appliances from 1972 to 1989. The refrigerator figure refers to a refrigerator-freezer. (Source: *Energy Efficiency and Human Activity* by Lee Schipper and Stephen Meyers.)

problems than it solves. Many Americans waited in long lines in their automobiles to buy gasoline after the government used price controls and supply rationing in response to the Arab oil embargo in 1973. Also, our economic system is geared primarily to reward short-term gains. Most people and businesses focus on quick profits. This makes it difficult to target long-term issues and research projects.

If we can overcome these problems, an energy policy should build mechanisms where business and government can work together to:

1. Provide the research and development (R&D) for those technologies that can advance energy efficiency. Federally initiated R&D programs on energy-conserving technologies have already saved taxpayers billions of dollars. These programs targeted fluorescent lighting, low-emissivity (low-E) coatings for windows, and high-efficiency refrigeration. Well-conceived federal R&D can continue to reinforce private industry initiatives. Figure 10.21 illustrates the potential for such R&D efforts. Improving energy efficiency offers the greatest opportunities for reducing our dependence on energy imports, reducing the environmental impacts of energy use, providing time to expand our energy options, and lowering the costs of the consumer products we make.
2. Encourage a balanced and mixed energy supply, including renewables and alternatives to oil and gas. For the short term, improved efficiency has removed the word "crisis" from the energy-supply situation. However, because of shrinking reserves of oil and natural gas in the United States, coupled with environmental concerns and the geographic locations of known global oil and gas reserves, it is wise to develop energy alternatives and address the depletion problem.
3. Lessen the conflict between environmental interests and energy industries so that natural resources can be utilized in an environmentally acceptable manner.

Figure 10.22 Solar energy. (USDOE)

It is true that ecological diversity must be preserved. It is also true, though, that some plots of land are much more diverse and ecologically more valuable than others. The careful selection of sites for energy exploration and extraction, coupled with the application of appropriate technology and environmental knowledge, should enable us to use natural resources without destroying the surrounding environment.

4. Determine the role taxes should play in reducing energy consumption and related environmental problems.

In 1992, federal and state taxes on gasoline amounted to about 25¢ a gallon in the United States. In Japan, the tax was $1.62 a gallon, and in Italy the tax is more than $3.00 per gallon. Experts from think tanks and academic institutions argue that the most effective way to reduce oil consumption is to tax it. Taxes hit everyone, but some are hit harder than others. The challenge is to maximize the benefits and minimize the losses. This won't be easy when some will lose so much.

The goal of any energy policy will be to accomplish the above four tasks and at the same time minimize government interference in people's lives.

What is the National Energy Strategy?

In February 1991, the National Energy Strategy was published by the U.S. Department of Energy. It laid the foundation for a more efficient, less vulnerable, and environmentally sustainable energy future. It presented a strategy for producing and using energy. It contained

Figure 10.23 Alternative fuel vehicle. (USDOE)

Figure 10.24 The decisions. (Wright—The Providence Journal-Bulletin.)

more than one hundred ideas for building our energy future. Starting these plans is a shared responsibility of the American public, the business sector, educators, and all levels of government.

We desire major changes in our energy delivery system, changes that will require unwavering commitment from the people, from our political leaders, and from industry. Building that commitment is one of the great challenges of our time.

Summary

The wise use of energy includes a variety of strategies:

1. Conservation—superinsulated buildings, high-mileage vehicles, more efficient appliances.
2. Energy conversion and storage techniques.
3. Knowledge of a variety of energy sources, including the quantity of energy they can provide and the environmental impacts related to their development and use.
4. A plan or policy for using energy that:
   - **a.** supports increased efficiency R&D.
   - **b.** encourages a balanced and mixed energy supply.
   - **c.** lessens the conflict between environmental issues and nationa resource use.
   - **d.** determines the role taxes should play in reducing energy consumption and related environmental problems.

References

Electric Power Research Institute. In search of a national energy strategy. *Epri Journal,* January/February 1991.

Flavin, Christopher. Building a bridge to sustainable energy. *State of the World* (New York: W. W. Norton), 1992.

Geller, Howard. The role of federal research and development in advancing energy efficiency: A $50 billion contribution to the U.S. economy. *Annual Review of Energy, Volume 12* (Palo Alto, CA: Annual Reviews), 1987.

Goldemberg, Jose, et al. *Energy for a Sustainable World* (New York: John Wiley), 1988.

Lovins, Amory B. *The Negawatt Revolution* (Old Snowmass, CO: Rocky Mountain Institute), 1990.

Mellde, Rolf W. Advanced automobile engines for fuel economy, low emissions, and multi-fuel capability. *Annual Review of Energy, Volume 14* (Palo Alto, CA: Annual Reviews), 1989.

Ogden, Joan M., and Robert H. Williams. *Solar Hydrogen: Moving Beyond Fossil Fuels* (Washington, DC: World Resources Institute), 1989.

Schwartz, Peter. What happened to the energy crisis: The dilemma of an energy decision maker in a dynamic world. *Annual Review of Energy, Volume 12* (Palo Alto, CA: Annual Reviews), 1987.

Shipper, Lee and Stephen Meyers. *World Energy: Building a Sustainable Future* (Stockholm, Sweden: Stockholm Environmental Institute), 1992.

Shurcliff, William A. Superinsulated Houses. *Annual Review of Energy, Volume 11* (Palo Alto, CA: Annual Reviews), 1986.

Smil, Vaclav. *General Energetics: Energy in the Biosphere and Civilization* (New York: John Wiley), 1991.

Solar Energy Research Institute. *The Potential of Renewable Energy: An Interlaboratory White Paper* (Golden, CO: Solar Energy Research Institute), 1990.

Tavoulareas, E. Stratos. Fluidized-bed combustion technology. *Annual Review of Energy and the Environment, Volume 16* (Palo Alto, CA: Annual Reviews), 1991.

U.S. Department of Energy. *National Energy Strategy: Powerful Ideas for America* (Washington, DC: USGPO), 1991.

End of Chapter Questions

1. What are some methods Americans are using to conserve energy?
2. There are many good arguments for conservation. One is that conservation can be put into effect almost immediately. What is another?
3. What major change in individual behavior must occur before the U.S. can have a successful energy conservation program?
4. List the five critical features in the design of a superinsulated home.
5. What has been the most important factor in increasing automobile efficiency?
6. What are some benefits of an effective energy-conservation program?
7. Energy conversion technologies are not sources of energy, but they save energy. Why? Briefly describe how each of the energy conversion technologies work.
8. Describe how any of the seven energy conversion and storage techniques listed could be used in "smoothing out" solar-produced electricity.
9. Explain why the reliability of a wind system coupled with a solar system would be much higher than the reliability of either alone.
10. Briefly describe how each of the three energy storage techniques work.
11. Distinguish between nonrenewable and continual energy sources.
12. Why are crude oil and natural gas not good energy sources for the future?
13. What are the secondary solar options?
14. If energy from tides and from Earth's interior are really as insignificant as Table 10.2 indicates, why look to them as potential energy sources?
15. From a theoretical point of view, is enough power available in the solar radiation that falls on the U.S. to fulfill national demands for power? Justify your answer.
16. Present an argument against the appropriate-technology strategy.
17. In biology you learn that the basis for a species' endurance is genetic variation. In other words, in order to be able to withstand "rough times," a population needs to be diverse. How is this principle applied in the arguments for "appropriate technology"?
18. Discuss the statement: "Heating your home to 70° F using electricity from a nuclear power plant is like eating your breakfast using a front-end loader."
19. How can using taxpayers' money to pay for the R&D of more efficient devices be justified?
20. Why is it better to depend on several energy sources rather than to depend on just one or two?
21. Can conflict between environmental groups and energy developers be lessened? Justify your answer.
22. Give one argument *for* and one *against* raising taxes on energy use.

Goal

To build an understanding of the importance of having adequate quantities of high-quality water for modern societies.

Water: Quantity and Quality

Of all the substances that are necessary to life as we know it on Earth, water is by far the most important, the most familiar, and the most wonderful; yet people know very little about it.

—Thomson King

How does almost every human activity involve the use of water?

In 600 B.C., Thales, one of the earliest Greek philosophers, said, "Water is the original substance of the universe. Out of it everything has been made. To it, everything must ultimately return." He was not too far from the truth. Water is the only substance necessary for all organisms; every life process, down to the function of each cell, demands water. Ancient civilizations fought over water and collapsed for lack of it. Because land without water is land without life, water controls the political geography and the economic life of nations. Too much brings floods, too little brings drought and famine.

Water is also important as a carrier of other substances. In its long journey from the clouds to the faucet, water picks up or dissolves a little bit of almost everything it touches. Rain washes the air, removing dust, fumes and microscopic living organisms. Water flowing over the Earth's surface becomes turbid or cloudy as it gathers impurities such as silt, sand, mud and clay. As it flows through swampy areas, water picks up unpleasant colors, tastes, and odors from decaying plant and animal life. As water seeps into the ground, it dissolves minerals from rocks and soils.

All these impurities can cause water problems in the home and in industry. However, the problems created by natural processes are small compared to those which can result when municipal and industrial wastes are placed into streams and lakes.

No matter how much water is used and reused, it is never really consumed. Instead, water recycles. When this cycle becomes overburdened, water pollution occurs. A major offensive against water pollution started with the Water Quality Act of 1965 and the Clean Water Restoration Act of 1966. All citizens must become more aware of water as an important resource to take care of and use wisely.

Earth's Water

11.1 Water Distribution in the World

What portion of the world's water supply is available for human use?

Water seems abundant on Earth, covering almost three-quarters of its surface. But of all that water, less than one percent is available for human use. The 99% we can't use is mainly found in the oceans, which are too salty for most human uses. The rest of the 99% is fresh water, but is locked in remote icecaps and glaciers.

Most of Earth's fresh water is locked up in icecaps and glaciers.

The oceans contain more than 97% of all water on Earth, about 1320 million cubic kilometers (317 million cubic miles) of water. The Antarctic icecap alone covers 15.5 million square kilometers (6 million square miles) and contains 86% of the world's frozen water.

Figure 11.2 summarizes the global water supply. Table 11.1 provides related data.

a. Surface Waters

Rivers are an important source of fresh water. In addition, since rivers carry surface runoff back to the sea, they help maintain the world's water balance. Figure 11.3 shows the world's major river basins.

Figure 11.1 Aerial view of the Antarctic. (Ann Bancroft)

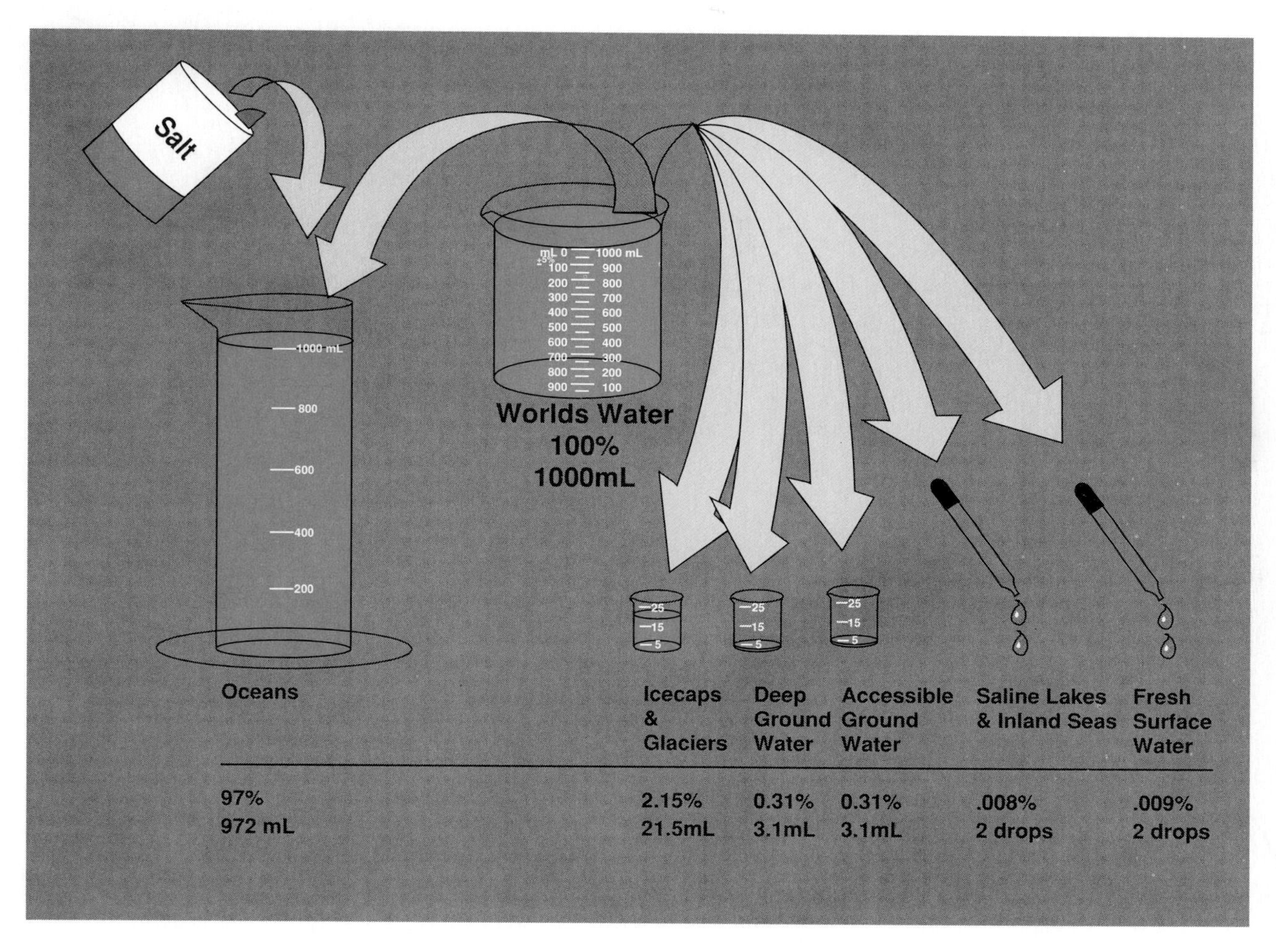

Figure 11.2 The global water supply.

Table 11.1 The World's Estimated Water Supply

Location	Surface Area (square miles)	Water Volume (cubic miles)	Total Water (%)
Surface Water			
Freshwater lakes	330,000	30,000	.009
Saline lakes and inland seas	270,000	25,000	.008
Stream channels average	—	300	.0001
Water Below Surface			
Water in soils	—	16,000	.005
Groundwater within half a mile of surface	50,000,000	1,000,000 .31	
Deep-lying groundwater	—	1,000,000	.31
Other Water			
Icecaps and glaciers	6,900,000	7,000,000	2.15
Atmosphere (at sea level)	197,000,000	3,100	.001
World oceans	139,500,000	317,000,000	97.20
TOTAL (rounded)	394,000,000	326,000,000	100.00%

Why are freshwater lakes so important to humans?

The Earth's land areas are dotted with hundreds of thousands of lakes which are important in supplying domestic water to many communities. The volume of all large freshwater lakes in the world totals nearly 125,000 cubic kilometers (30,000 cubic miles). The Great Lakes and other large North American lakes contain about 26% of all fresh water in the world. Large freshwater lakes in Africa contain 29% of the world's supply and Asia's large lakes (primarily Lake Baykal in the Soviet Union) contain about 21% of the total.

Saline lakes throughout the world contain almost as much water as freshwater lakes, but their distribution and usefulness to people are very different. The Caspian Sea contains about 75% of the total water

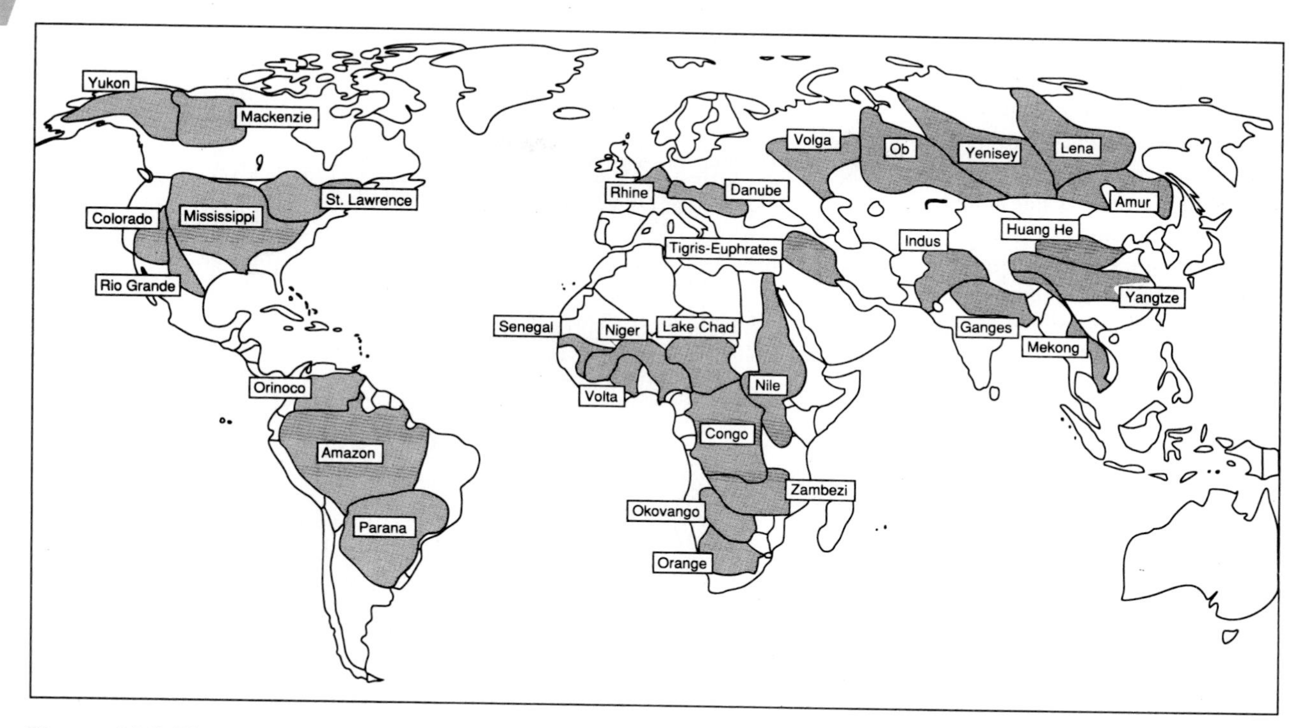

Figure 11.3 The world's major river basins. (World Resource Institute)

content of saline lakes. Most of the remainder is in Asia. North America's shallow Great Salt Lake is comparatively insignificant in terms of its water content.

b. Groundwater

How significant are groundwater supplies?

Groundwater is water found below the Earth's surface in porous rock layers and in soils. While people obtain most of their water from rivers, lakes and reservoirs, water under the ground is also important. In Germany, more than 70% of the water supply comes from groundwater; in Israel, this figure is about 54%; and in Britain and the United States, it is about 20%.

Groundwater may be near the surface, only 2.5 to 3 meters (8–10 feet) underground, or as deep as 800 meters (0.5 mile) below the surface. Tremendous amounts of water—more than 30 times the water in all the world's rivers and lakes—exist as groundwater.

Why is soil moisture vital to life?

Above the saturated zone of groundwater, a small amount of water is held within the soil. See Figure 11.4. This is a very small percentage of the Earth's total water, but it is vital to life. Practically all the Earth's vegetation depends on natural soil moisture, which, in turn, depends on the proper functioning of the water cycle.

?

What are the two most serious threats to ground water supplies?

Two serious threats to groundwater are increasing pollution and overuse. Since the **recharge** (replacement) rate of groundwater is slow, pollution affects these water supplies for centuries. In addition, pumping water out of an aquifer faster than it can be recharged depletes this important source of water.

Figure 11.4 Underground water lies in both an unsaturated zone and a saturated zone. At the top of the saturated zone water is held in a capillary fringe by surface tension. At any one spot, the water table is the point in the saturated zone where the water is under a pressure equal to atmospheric pressure. Its position is indicated by the water level in shallow wells.

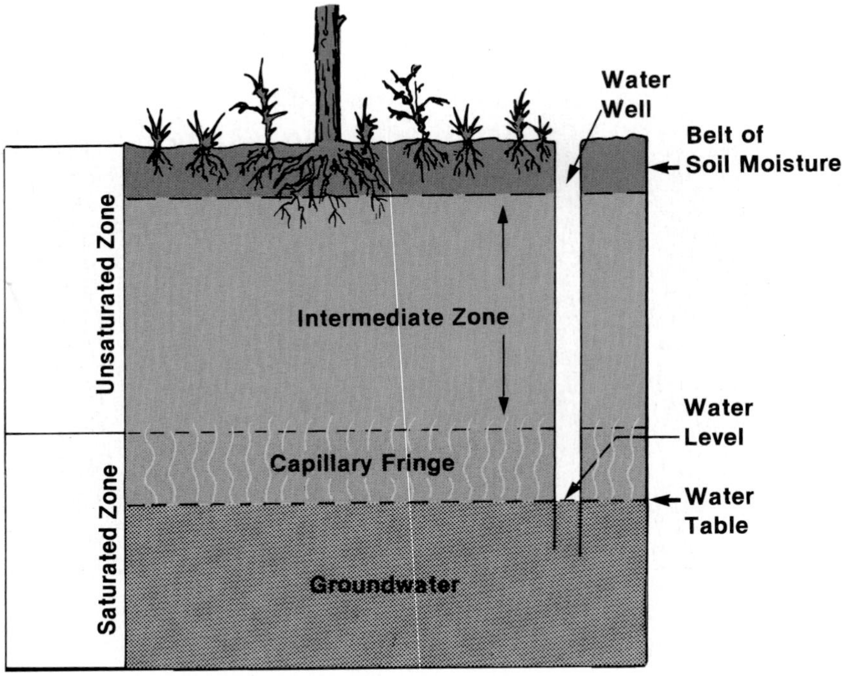

c. The Problem of Fresh Water

The amount of usable fresh water may become critical because people have become so numerous and the activities of a modern economy use and process so much water. Many regions are already experiencing water shortages. If current trends of population growth and increased water use continue, lack of fresh water will threaten the vitality of many regions.

Name the two largest users of fresh water, and indicate their approximate use by percentage.

Human use of water accounts for one tenth of the total renewable supply and about one fourth of the stable supply. Agriculture claims the "lion's share," about 70% of the world's water use. Roughly a third of the present-day harvest comes from irrigated croplands. Industry is second, using one-quarter of all water. Production of energy from nuclear and fossil-fueled power plants is the greatest single industrial water user. Water provides the source of steam that drives the turbine generators, and it cools power plant condensers.

Water's seeming abundance has made society complacent about the need to manage it and adapt to the limits of a fixed supply. Warning signs appear in the form of polluted water supplies, depletion of groundwater, and falling water tables.

Why must we conserve our supplies of limited fresh water?

As water shortages develop and competition for limited supplies increases, people must develop new water strategies to conserve this valuable resource. Without such strategies, industrial activity will stagnate, projects to increase food production to feed a growing population will fail, and rationing of drinking water will become common.

Figure 11.5 Irrigated cropland in an arid region. (U.S. Soil Conservation Service)

11.2 Water in the United States

a. The Water Budget

What is a water budget?

One way to study the water supply in an area is to set up a **water budget**—a type of balance sheet showing the water available in different parts of the water cycle. Figure 11.6 presents a water budget for the United States. Data is given as millions of gallons per day (Mgal/d). From this figure we see that 4,200,000 Mgal/d of moisture enter the United States in the form of precipitation, mainly rain and snow. Water leaves the United States land mass in a variety of ways. It **evaporates** from moist surfaces and **transpires** from plants. (These losses are grouped under the term **evapotranspiration.**) The total evapotranspiration over the United States averages 2,800,000 Mgal/d. Both surface and groundwater leave the United States, flowing into the oceans, Canada, and Mexico. This total outflow amounts to 1,300,000 Mgal/d.

Finally, some water is bound into products (like concrete), crops, and animals, or otherwise removed from the water environment of a region. This is referred to as consumptive use. For the United States it totals 92,000 Mgal/d.

The water budget is based on averages for the 48 adjacent states. Actually, two-thirds of the precipitation falls in the East and one-third in the West. Even the western states show considerable variation: the annual precipitation of the Mojave Desert of California is a low 5 centimeters, while in the Olympic Mountains of Washington, it is 250 centimeters . Each region has its own water budget.

Since water does not disappear, the input should equal the output. Thus: $P \sim ET + TO + CU$. The slight difference of 8,000 Mgal/d is due to estimates and rounding off numbers and is not significant.

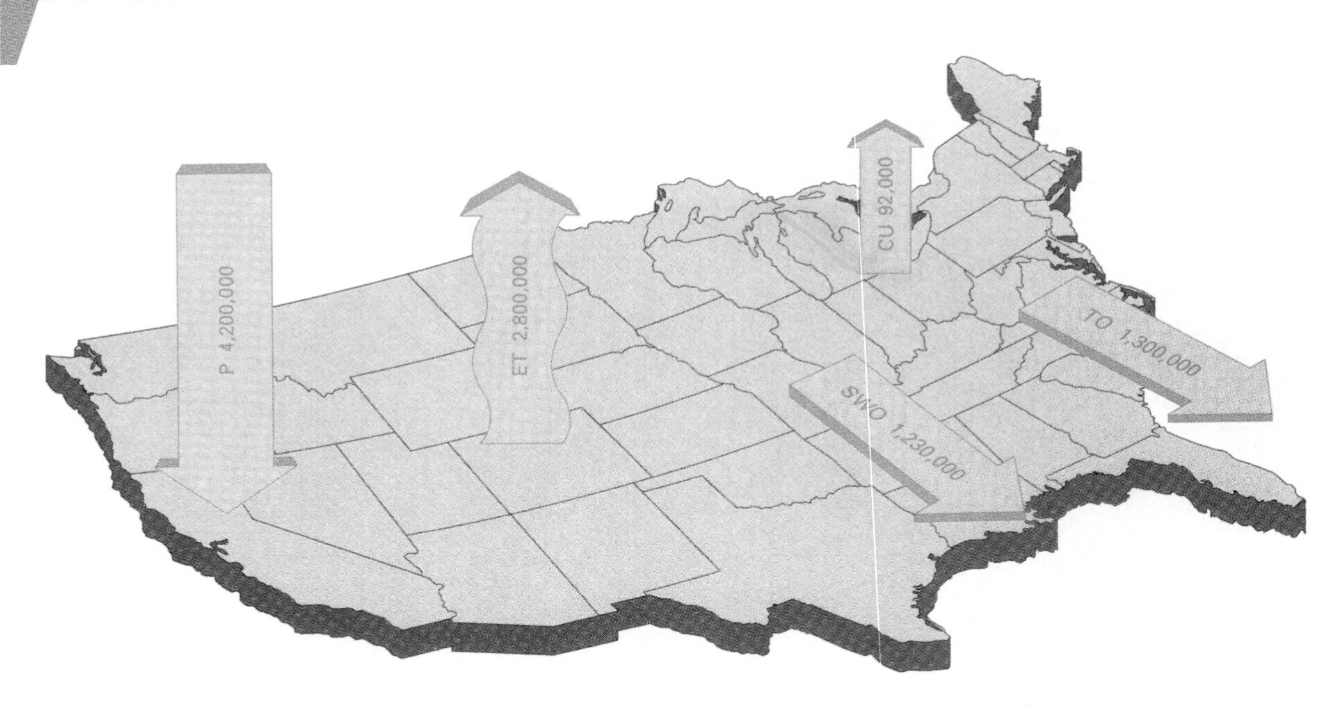

Figure 11.6 Estimated water budget for the conterminous United States. Data given in millions of gallons per day (Mgal/day). Abbreviations: P, precipitation; ET, evapotranspiration; CU, consumptive use; SWO, surface-water outflow to the oceans, Canada, and Mexico; TO, total surface and groundwater outflow to the oceans, Canada, and Mexico. (Source: USGS)

b. Human Water Use

Almost every human activity involves the use of water in some way.

Think about the ways we use water. Water for drinking is a necessity for life. In addition, we use water for cooking, washing dishes, bathing, washing clothes and flushing the toilet. We use water for our gardens and for recreation. Almost every human activity involves water either directly or indirectly.

Conversion factor: 3.785 liters = 1 gallon.

In the average American home, each person uses about 300 liters (80 gallons) of water per day. This use is summarized in Figure 11.7. From this figure we see that almost 75% of the water used in the home is used in the bathroom. Can you think of ways to use water more wisely at home?

Use Table 11.2 to compare home and commercial, agricultural, and industrial water use in the United States.

Table 11.2 summarizes U.S. water use. From this table we see that home and commercial use is only about 11% of the total picture. The remainder is used by industry, for electric power generation, and by agriculture.

Agricultural water use is primarily for irrigation. Much can and is being done to reduce irrigation losses. Irrigation ditches can be lined with clays, concrete or plastics to reduce seepage into the ground. Spray irrigation can be reduced on hot afternoons. **Trickle irrigation** techniques release water closer to the plant roots.

c. Availability

Because of its dry climate, increasing population, and agricultural demands, much of the western half of the United States is faced with

Figure 11.7 Average U.S. indoor home water use. (U.S. Department of Housing and Urban Development)

Table 11.2 Average U.S. Water Use

Sector	Percent	Use/Person/Day
Domestic (home)/ Commercial	11.5	587 liters = 155 gal
Industrial/Mining	8.2	416 liters = 110 gal
Thermoelectric Power	38.6	1960 liters = 518 gal
Agriculture	41.7	2112 liters = 558 gal

water-supply problems. (Figure 11.8) In the midwestern and western regions of the United States, low precipitation has led to greater use of underground water. Huge underground reservoirs which have been filled through the centuries are now being used at a rate greater than their recharge rate. "Mining" of water, accompanied by a drop in the water table, has occurred in the Central and San Joaquin Valleys of California, south-central Arizona, and throughout the Ogallala aquifer underlying the midwestern United States. The Ogallala aquifer may have less than 30 years of useful life left, and in some localities depletion of underground water will occur even sooner. Water tables in portions of the West are falling as much as 15 to 90 centimeters per year!

What is meant by "mining" water?

With adequate precipitation and numerous rivers, the eastern part of the United States seems well endowed with water. The problems there have to do with large population centers and with pollution of lakes, rivers, and groundwater.

Water Management

While we cannot increase the overall supply of fresh water, we can manage it more effectively. One approach involves increasing water supplies through building dams and diverting water to areas of

?

Describe the two major approaches for managing water.

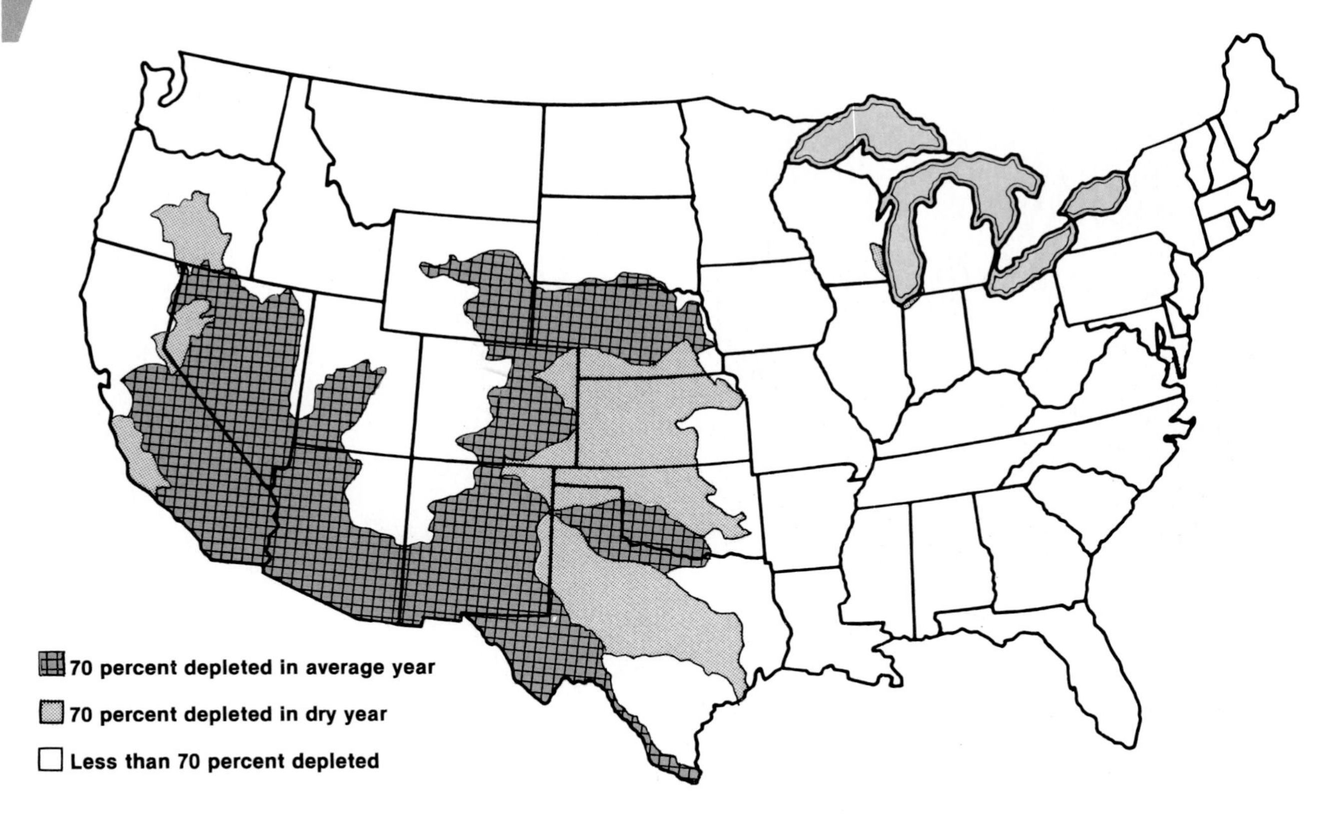

Figure 11.8 Water-deficit regions in the United States. (U.S. Water Resources Council)

greatest needs. A second approach emphasizes using water more efficiently and conserving water supplies. Both approaches are needed to solve our growing water problems.

11.3 Dams and Reservoirs

List some of the benefits and problems associated with the damming of water.

Early in the development of agriculture, people began irrigating crops and building dams to control water. Water stored behind dams could be released as needed, assuring crops could flourish. This was essential for growing crops in arid areas such as Israel and Egypt. The construction of dams, aqueducts, canals, and pipes to store and carry water from areas of abundance to areas of need has grown with the growth of human population and with the growth and need of water by industry.

Dams store or impound water which can be used for irrigation, for drinking and home use, for generating electricity, and for industry. A dam regulates the rate of water flow downstream, thus reducing flooding. Electricity generated by water flowing through turbines can be transmitted long distances to population centers where electricity is needed. All of the water used in generating electricity is returned to the stream after use.

Figure 11.9 Lake Dillon was formed by damming Colorado's Blue River (a tributary of the Colorado River). Some of the impounded water is used by the Denver metropolitan area. It is diverted through a tunnel (23 miles long) under the continental divide. (Denver Water Department)

Figure 11.9 shows the recreational value of impounding water. In this particular case, the lake created improved the scenery, and the people it displaced built new homes on the lake shores. The lake and stream that flow in and out provide excellent fishing, swimming, water skiing, and sailing. Ice fishing is popular in the winter, along with ice skating and other winter activities.

Sometimes, however, problems created in damming rivers outweigh their advantages. Building a dam and impounding water alters scenic areas, displaces people, and alters natural wildlife habitats. A reservoir prevents low-impact recreational activities such as whitewater rafting, stream fishing, and wilderness hiking. A dam interrupts the natural stream flow, disrupts natural fish migrations, and alters the water's temperature and oxygen content.

Water losses from a reservoir are tremendous. Large amounts of water evaporate from the surface of a reservoir, and even more water seeps into the ground. For example, 270,000 cubic meters of water evaporate from Lake Powell per year, enough water to serve the needs of a city of 500,000 people. As evaporation of water leaves dissolved particles of salt behind, the water remaining in the reservoir becomes saltier. When water with too much salt is used for irrigation, soils become increasingly salty, eventually becoming too saline for agriculture.

Water in the reservoir is slower-moving and calmer than the river or stream entering it. In the faster-moving stream, sand and soil particles are carried in the water. In the reservoir these particles, called silt, settle to the bottom. Each year during the spring runoff, as water from the stream slows down upon entering the reservoir, more silt is deposited. Eventually, the reservoir fills up in this process of siltation.

Figure 11.10 The Roberts Tunnel is located in the Rocky Mountains of Colorado. It carries water from the west side of the Continental Divide, through a 23-mile-long tunnel, to the east side. The purpose is to provide more water to the large population in the Denver Metropolitan Area.

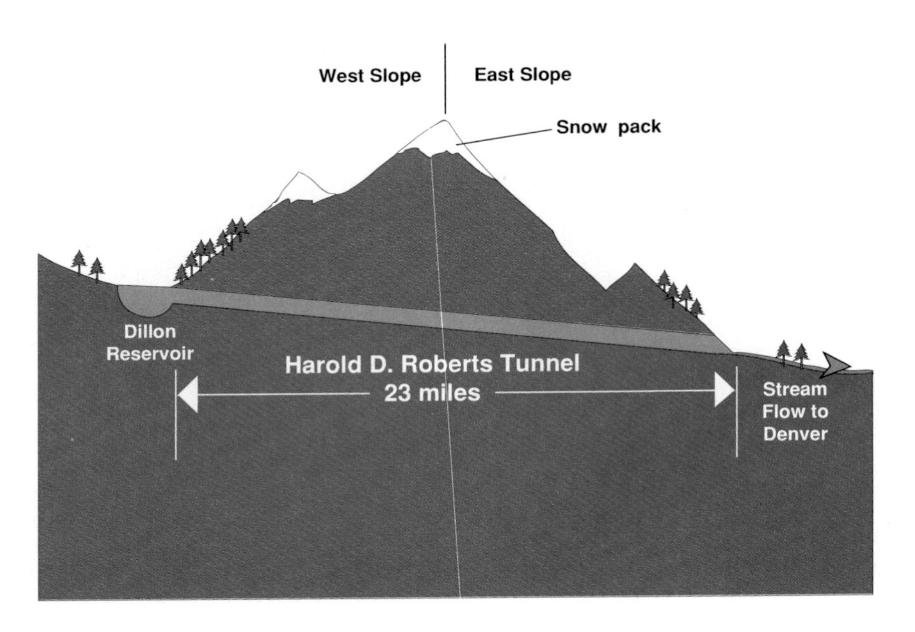

11.4 Water Diversion Projects

What is meant by water diversion?

Channeling or diverting water from a water-rich to a water-poor area also has mixed blessings. Extensive systems of channels and man-made aqueducts carry water to dry, thirsty southern California. In 1913 the Los Angeles aqueduct first brought water from the Owens River in central California to Los Angeles. Later a canal was built to carry water from the Colorado River to the Imperial Valley east of San Diego.

Recently other, very costly, water projects have been proposed to carry water from northern California to the southern part of the state. Proponents of these projects claim the water is essential for the economic growth in southern California. Opponents feel the projects are too costly, encourage waste of a precious resource, cause increased salinity of soils and other ecological disruption.

11.5 The Colorado River Basin and Water Law

The Colorado River, one of the major rivers in the United States, drains much of the American Southwest. It extends more than 1,400 miles from its headwaters in north central Colorado to its mouth in the Gulf of California. With hundreds of tributaries, the Colorado River basin drains a vast area—242,000 square miles in the United States and 2,000 square miles in northern Mexico.

The Colorado River basin includes some of the driest lands in the United States, and so water of the Colorado River is precious. The water resources of the river have been the subject of major legal battles; many landmark cases of water law involve the use of Colorado River water. By controlling its water, people have not only changed water distribution, they have also changed the scenic splendor of the Colorado River.

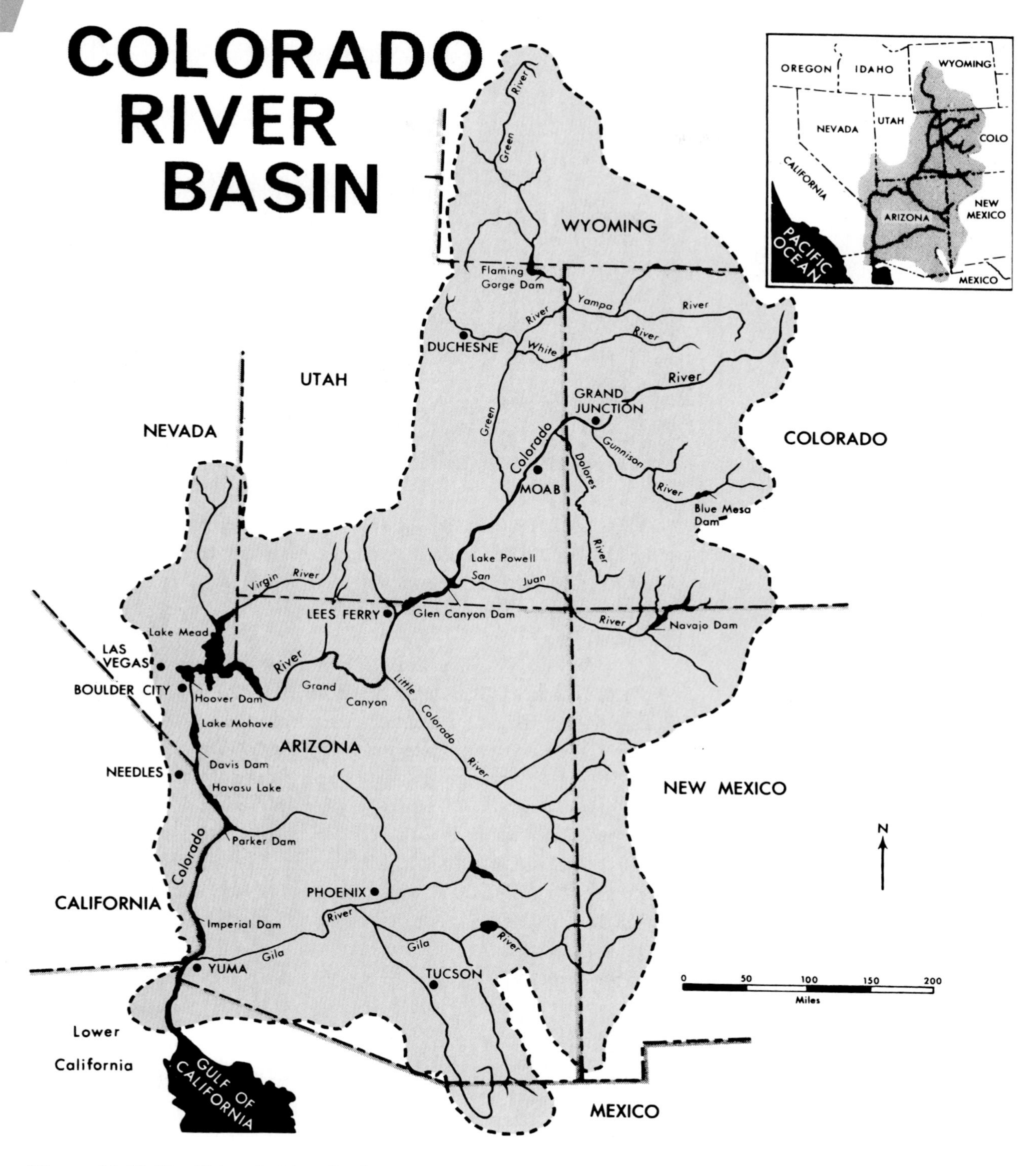

Figure 11.11 The Colorado River Basin. (USGS)

Figure 11.12 The Grand Canyon with the Colorado River below.
(Ivo Lindauer)

The history of the development of the Colorado River is highlighted by brilliant engineering achievements, production of large supplies of electrical power, agricultural successes, and legal power struggles. The original flow of this mighty river is now almost completely tamed and altered.

The first use of water in the Colorado River basin was for irrigation. The Anasazi Indians built small ditches, diverting water to small fields. Modern irrigation practices date from the 1850s. At first only stream bottom lands were reclaimed, and the facilities were simple. By the 1890s, it was recognized that storage reservoirs were needed in order to provide a reliable source of water for crops during the latter part of the growing season. It was also necessary to store water from one year to the next to guard against particularly dry years. One of the first laws regarding Colorado River water was the Reclamation Act passed by Congress in 1902. Various diversion projects and dams were planned and built, each to address a particular local problem of water need.

When Rocky Mountain National Park was created in 1915, the Colorado River flowed southwesterly from its origin in the Park across the high Colorado Plateau into southeastern Utah, and down through northwestern Arizona. It slashed through a wilderness of mountains, plateaus, and deserts. The Colorado River traveled 1,000 miles through deep gorges, including the spectacular and famous Grand Canyon. The river then bent south, forming the boundaries between Nevada and Arizona, Arizona and California, and Sonora and Baja California in Mexico. Finally, the Colorado River flowed into the Gulf of California.

For purposes of water distribution and control, the Colorado River basin was divided. Lees Ferry in northern Arizona was chosen as the division point. (See Figure 11.11) The Colorado and its tributaries above Lees Ferry were "upper basin;" those below, "lower basin." In

1922, use of river water was portioned out by an agreement (the Colorado River Compact) among the upper and lower basin states and the federal government. The compact allocated 7,500,000 acre-feet of water use to each of the two basins. Later, in a 1954 agreement, the United States guaranteed Mexico the delivery of 1,500,000 **acre-feet** of water per year. In years of low water, both upper and lower basins were to share equally in supplying water to Mexico. Thus the 1922 compact was essential in appropriating water equally to both parts of the river basin, as the states (see Figure 11.13) had become bitter rivals for water.

In spite of these agreements, the mighty Colorado River no longer flows to the sea. Its water is being used up. South of Yuma, Arizona the remnant of the once mighty river now sinks out of sight into the sands. Where has the Colorado River gone? Who used it up?

It became apparent that the natural flow of the Colorado River could not supply all the uses contemplated by the seven Colorado River basin states. In addition, it was obvious that the lower basin states, particularly California and Arizona, were growing much more rapidly in population and water use than were the upper basin states. The upper basin states were concerned that the lower states would legally appropriate all water. Many people in Colorado even charged that the U.S. Congress deprived them of water that was their birthright, while giving California and Arizona all the development funds they could spend.

Appropriate: to take to oneself in exclusion of others; to claim or use as by an exclusive right.

Saving the Colorado River required a federal policy directed at helping all seven states develop their compact share. The Bureau of Reclamation's inventory of possibilities for river regulation, irrigation, and power generation stimulated the technical and political leaders in the upper Colorado River basin to accept and aggressively promote the comprehensive development of the upper basin. The Upper Colorado River Basin Compact, signed in 1948, led to the Colorado River Storage Project Act and the authorization for the construction of four large storage reservoirs capable of holding 33,583,000 acre-feet of water for river regulation, power generation, and consumptive use. These storage reservoirs are Glen Canyon Dam and Lake Powell on the Colorado River in Arizona and Utah; Navajo Dam and Reservoir on the San Juan River in New Mexico and Colorado; Flaming Gorge Dam and Reservoir on the Green River in Wyoming; and Blue Mesa Dam and Reservoir on the Gunnison River in Colorado.

The upper division states were opposed and harassed from both Arizona and California during the initial filling of the storage units of the Colorado River Storage Project, especially during the filling of Lake Powell behind Glen Canyon Dam. It was also during this period that the upper states recognized that the average streamflow of the Colorado River was only 14.8 million acre-feet annually, far less than the 26 million acre-feet estimate that had been used as the basis for the Colorado River Compact in 1922. Tree ring studies confirmed this realization. (See Figure 11.15.) Thus upper basin states were fearful that future allocation laws would require upper basin states to give up some of their water rights.

On the average, how much water is available from the Colorado River? How much water was allocated by the Colorado River Compact?

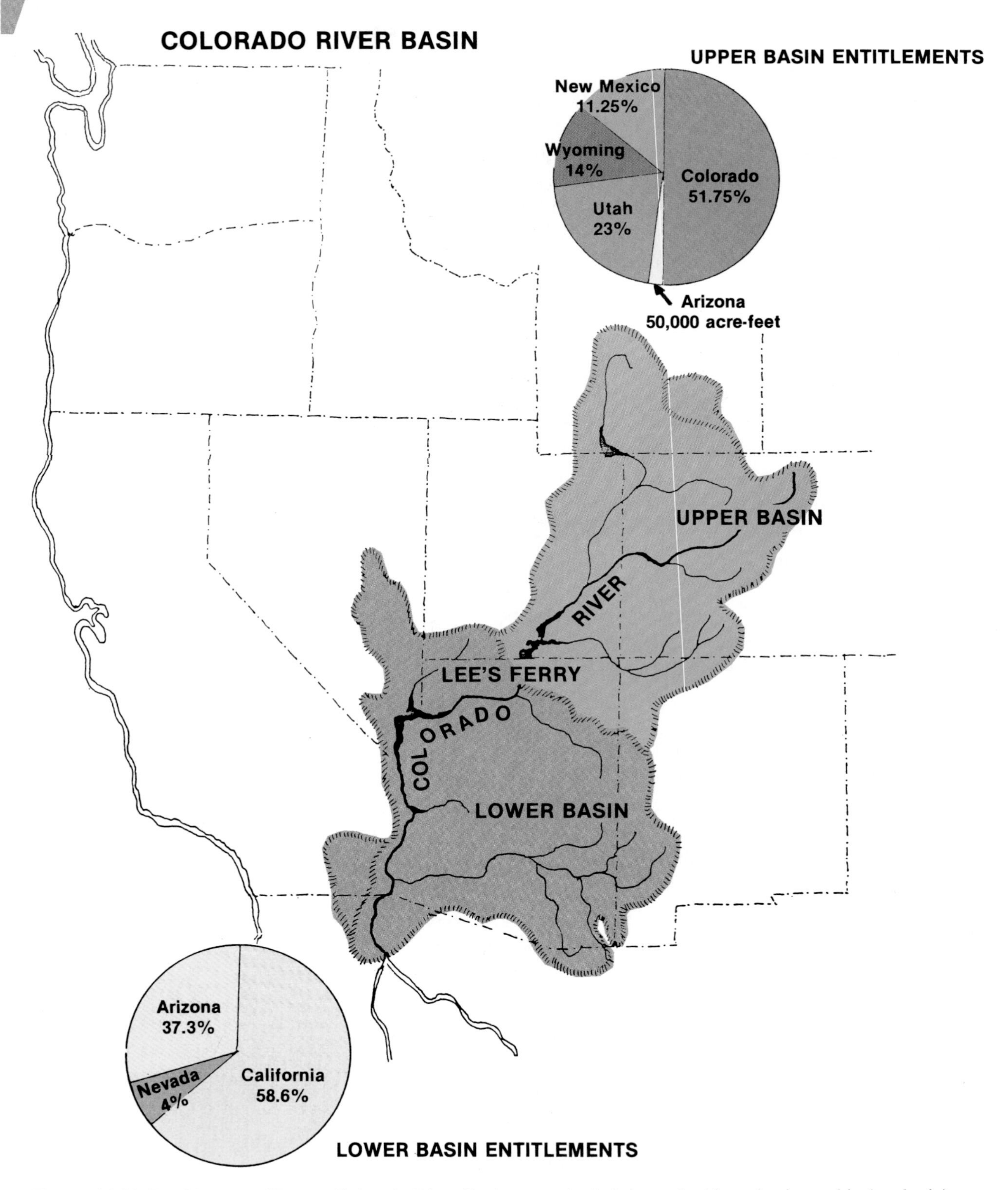

Figure 11.13 The Upper and Lower Colorado River Basin watershed. A watershed is a physiographic (geologic) division. The Colorado River Compact divided states in the Colorado River Basin (watershed) into upper and lower basin states. The upper basin states are Colorado, Wyoming, New Mexico, and Utah. The lower basin states are Arizona, Nevada, and California. This division is a legal/political division. Entitlements to water were granted as shown. (From Water Education Foundation, 717 K Street, Sacramento, California 95814.)

Figure 11.14 Lake Powell was created by Glen Canyon Dam. (John S. Flannery/Visuals Unlimited)

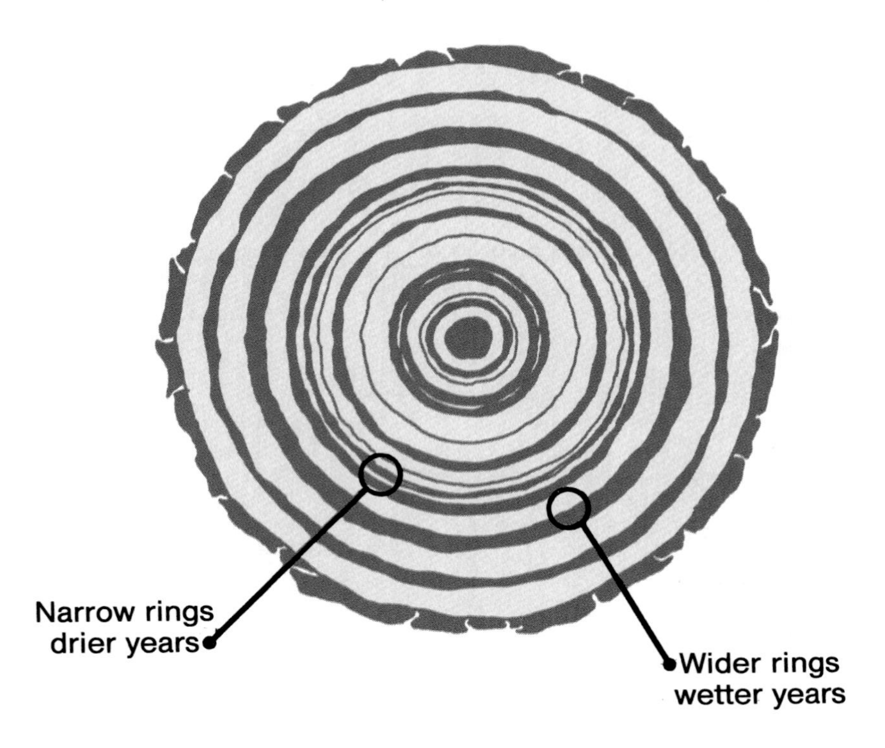

Figure 11.15 The interpretation of tree rings.

After several years of negotiations between upper and lower basin states, the last of the reclamation laws, the Colorado River Basin Project Act, became law in 1968. This law is truly a basin-wide comprehensive law aiming to balance resources and need throughout the entire basin.

Through all these projects, the Colorado River has become totally utilized, or in the words of critics of these projects, "the river was plumbed to put water on arid lands and to generate electricity." The Colorado River is no longer natural, but neither is it dead and gone.

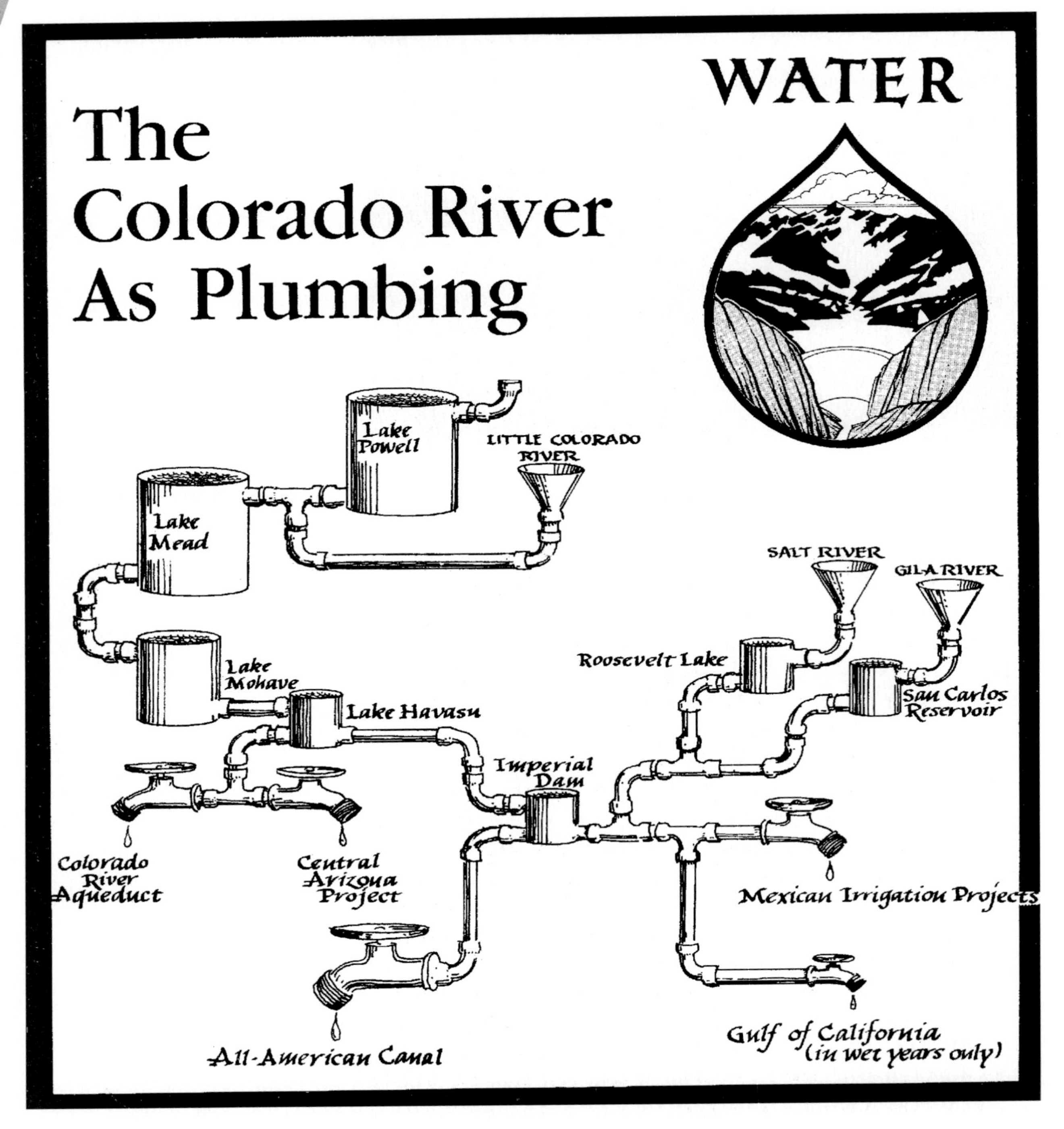

Figure 11.16 The Colorado River as plumbing. (Reprinted with permission from *Western Water Made Simple,* Island Press, 1987, copyright © 1987 High Country News.)

Figure 11.17 Trickle irrigation is a strategy for delivering water to the root zone of plants.

With the Federal Water Pollution Control Act of 1972, people have become increasingly concerned with the increased salinity (salt) in the Colorado River. About half the salt may be from natural sources, half from human influence. At its headwaters, the average salinity is less than 100 milligrams per liter (mg/L), but it progressively increases downstream until at Imperial Dam below Lake Mead salinity averages approximately 800 mg/L. Projections indicate that the salinity may rise to nearly 1100 mg/L by the year 2010. Should this occur, agricultural, municipal, and industrial use of water in Southern California would be severely impacted.

Engineers are trying various procedures to reduce or eliminate the problems of scale build-up in boilers and pipes, damage to agricultural land, and the high cost of desalination. These mainly involve modifying irrigation practices above Lake Powell—lining irrigation ditches to prevent water loss and salt build-up in soil, and using techniques to increase irrigation efficiency once water reaches the crop. Diversion of water away from natural sources of salt is also being tested.

List some of the measures being tried to reduce water-related problems in the Colorado River basin.

Recreational activities in the Colorado River basin are now beginning to influence the direction of development and legal actions concerning water policy. People are beginning to appreciate as never before that the natural landscapes of the Colorado River are unique in the country and probably in the world.

11.6 Managing Groundwater

Air travelers often notice great circles of green on the brown landscapes as they fly over the Great Plains. These circular fields of corn, alfalfa, and other crops are irrigated by automatic center-pivot irrigation systems. Each circle has a shallow well in its center and a rotating sprinkler system that delivers water to the field.

Figure 11.18 Center-pivot irrigation. Each circle in the photo has a diameter of one-half mile and an area of about 51 hectares (126 acres). (U.S. Soil Conservation Service)

Figure 11.19 The great Winter Park Sinkhole of 1981. Some 11 meters across and over 38 meters deep, this sinkhole caused over 4 million dollars in damages. It consumed parts of two streets, a house, 2 Porsches, and one end of an olympic-sized swimming pool, as well as disrupting utilities and tying up traffic for weeks. (Florida Sinkhole Research Institute)

Water for this irrigation comes from the Ogallala Formation, a vast aquifer extending from Texas north to the Dakotas. This use of water seems beneficial. However, when an aquifer is pumped faster than the water can be replaced, the area is left without sufficient groundwater. Overpumping of the Ogallala aquifer has lowered the water table and is increasing pumping costs to a prohibitive level. Some farmers in the area are returning to dry-land farming.

Another problem related to groundwater depletion is **subsidence.** As water is removed from water-holding rock layers, empty spaces are created. Pressure from overlying material can compress some earth materials, resulting in a lowering of the land surface, or subsidence. Subsidence rates of 5 to 10 centimeters per year have been observed in the San Joaquin Valley of California, in Texas, and in Florida. Subsidence cannot be reversed and once an area has collapsed, the water-holding capacity of the underground aquifer is diminished.

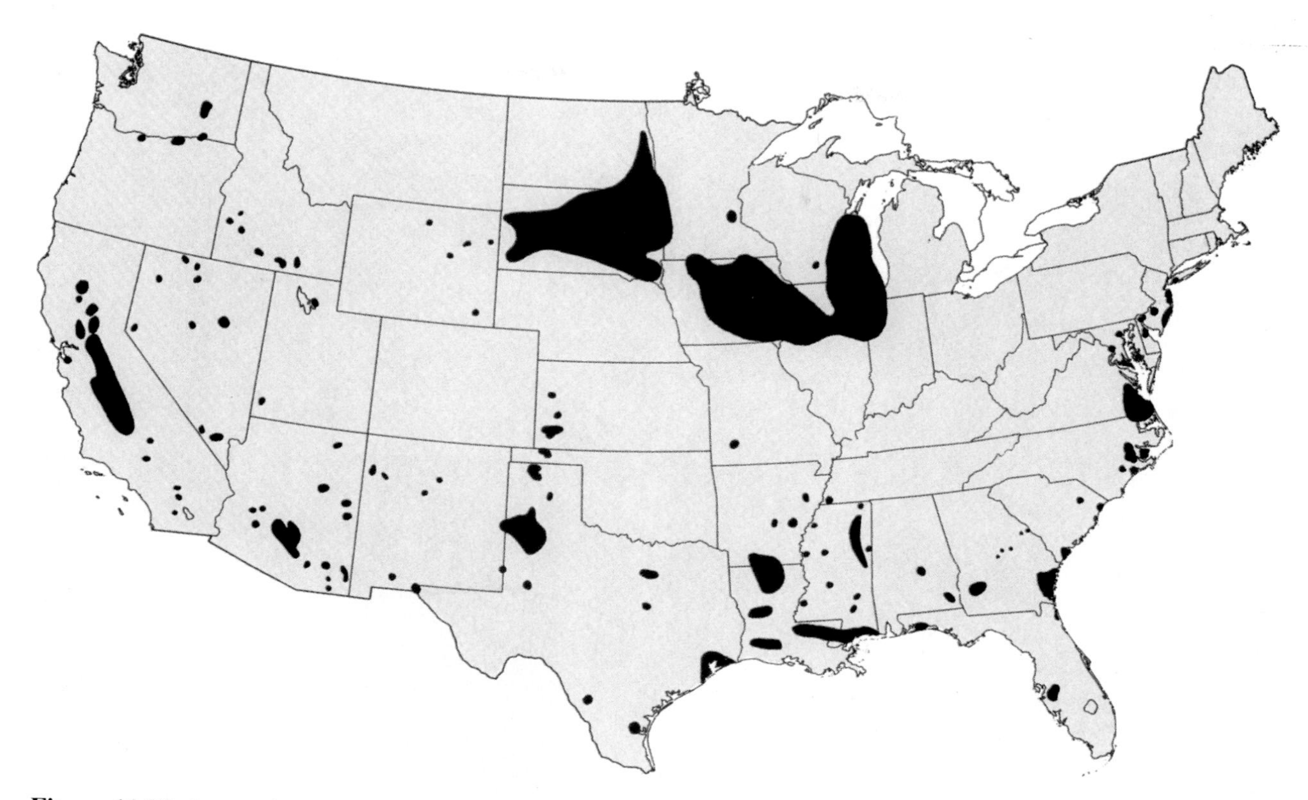

Figure 11.20 Areas of water-table decline or artesian water-level decline in excess of 40 feet (12 meters) in at least one aquifer since predevelopment. (USGS)

How are U.S. groundwater supplies being damaged?

Along a seacoast, subsidence can lower the land below sea level so the land either becomes flooded or dikes must be built to keep out the sea water. In addition, sea water may move in, making the aquifer salty and useless for drinking and irrigation.

Hydrologists currently are working on methods to increase groundwater through artificial **recharge,** that is, pumping water back into the ground. With one method natural stream water is channeled into wells, increasing natural infiltration of water through the soil. Water soaks down to the aquifer and fills it. Another recharge method is to feed in water from industrial cooling and wastewater. Water is pumped into recharge wells rather than being withdrawn. Care must be taken not to pollute groundwater during recharging.

11.7 Desalination

What is desalination, and why is it of interest?

People die of dehydration if they drink sea water. This is because the high concentration of salt in sea water draws water out of body cells. In trying to find ways of making sea water usable by humans, scientists have studied sea gulls. Sea gulls are able to obtain usable water from sea water because they have a membrane system that allows them to separate the salt from sea water and cough out the excess salt.

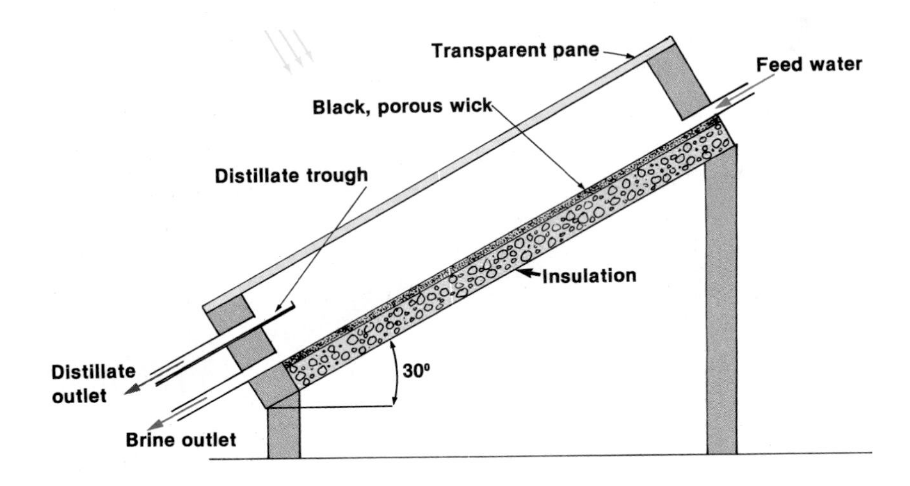

Figure 11.21 The principle of evaporative desalination.

Figure 11.22 This Landsat satellite image shows a large iceberg that broke away from the Ross Ice Shelf of Antarctica in October, 1987. The iceberg measured over 153 kilometers long and 36 kilometers wide (approximately 96 × 23 miles). This is twice the size of Rhode Island. (Earth Observation Satellite Company, Lanham, Maryland)

In copying the sea birds' technique, engineers have designed a membrane for desalinating sea water. Salt water under pressure is forced through a selective membrane that permits only the passage of water molecules. The salt is left behind. This process is costly and uses a great deal of energy, but new technologies may make it more cost effective in the future.

Another method for removing salt from sea water is evaporative desalination, which shows promise. This may be used in seaside communities where solar energy can be used efficiently in evaporating the water. See Figure 11.21.

11.8 Water from Icebergs

In November, 1987, a huge iceberg broke away from Antarctica (Figure 11.22). The iceberg, twice the size of Rhode Island and hundreds of meters thick, is made up of great quantities of fresh water. This is because the salt remains in the liquid, as sea water is frozen.

What if this iceberg could be towed and its water used? It would contain enough water to supply Los Angeles for 600 years! The idea of towing icebergs sounds wild, and no one knows whether it is even feasible. Saudi Arabia's former King Khalid was so intrigued with the idea of towing icebergs to the Middle East that he funded research into the possibility. A French engineering firm concluded that it could be done, but towing a typical iceberg would cost $80 million and take 6 to 12 months. What the ecological consequences would be, and whether enough water would be available by the time the iceberg reached its destination, are some questions that still need to be answered.

Why is there interest in towing icebergs?

11.9 Cloud Seeding

What is cloud seeding?

Some scientists and engineers have tried to modify the weather by cloud seeding. Flying over certain types of clouds and sprinkling them with silver iodide crystals causes the formation of ice crystals and water droplets, which precipitate as snow or rain.

Weather can be modified in certain areas in this way, but how cloud seeding affects overall weather patterns is unclear. It may increase rainfall in one locality at the expense of another. In addition, because cloud seeding requires rain clouds, it is not effective in very dry areas, which rarely have rain clouds. There is also some concern about using silver iodide to induce a cloud to give up its moisture. Silver iodide is a poison that may, in sufficient quantities, harm plants, animals, or people. Finally, legal questions remain unanswered. Do the people in one state have the right to remove water that might otherwise have fallen in another state?

11.10 Water Conservation

A variety of factors place limits on our ability to expand water supplies to a region. Some factors are higher energy prices, water laws, increased competition for water, and higher water prices. Thus, if the supply cannot be increased, the resource must be used wisely.

Wise water usage includes both using new technologies that require less water and having a water conservation ethic. According to this ethic, resources such as water are valuable, and it is wrong to waste them.

?

List some ways you can save water at your home.

A variety of technical solutions are available for the home. These include ultra-low-flush toilets, low-flow sink and showerheads, space-filling bottles added to toilet tanks, and short cycles on dishwashers and washing machines. The volume of water used for lawn watering during summer months can be huge. Carefully planned landscaping, featuring less grass and more native plants that require little water, can bring large savings. Automatic car washes can wash a car with a small amount of water or with recycled water. Plumbing-supply stores, lawn and garden shops, and your local water supplier can provide other ideas for saving water.

Table 11.2 shows that on a national basis the greatest water savings can be made in electric power generation and in agriculture. In

Figure 11.23 Low-water landscaping uses native grasses, trees, plants, and other strategies.

agriculture, open, unlined irrigation ditches should all be lined with cement or plastic or replaced with closed pipes. Unlined ditches can lose 40–50% of the water flowing through them before it reaches the crops. Crop sprinklers, which often waste up to half the water used, can be replaced by drip irrigation systems, which deliver water directly to the root area and thus lose only 5–10% of the water to the atmosphere.

The use of water at electric power plants can be cut by one-fourth with dry cooling towers. These towers circulate water in pipes instead of evaporating it in open air. Unfortunately, dry cooling towers require more energy to operate and cost more to build.

11.11 The Florida Everglades: A Case Study

A look at the Everglades region and its history shows how people almost ruined a fragile ecosystem. Until recently, the importance of swampy wetlands has not been appreciated. Most people in Florida viewed swamps, bogs and mud as problems to be dredged, ditched and drained. Now, almost too late, people realize that the nation's most exotic swamp needs to be preserved.

The Everglades is a broad, swampy region of southern Florida that extends 160 kilometers (100 miles) from the shores of Lake Okeechobee to the ocean (Figure 11.24). The water from Lake Okeechobee does not flow to the ocean in a well-defined river; instead a wide sheet of water flows slowly through the swamp on its way to the ocean or Gulf. The water in the Everglades never runs deep, ranging from only a few centimeters to no more than two meters.

Water depth determines the plant communities. Sprouting from the shallow water are vast areas of sawgrass, a tall grasslike plant with slender saw-toothed leaves. The sawgrass grows out of a bed of **muck,** a rich soil produced by the slow, centuries-long buildup of decaying plants. On

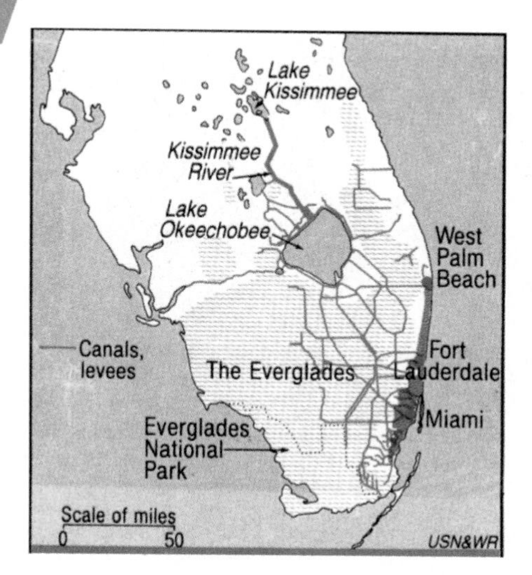

Figure 11.24 Southward flow of water essential to the Everglades is siphoned away by drainage canals. (Copyright, Feb. 24, 1986, *U.S. News & World Report*)

Figure 11.25 Tree islands in the Everglades. (Harold Hungerford)

scattered outcrops of bedrock, tree islands dot the "river of grass" all along its length (Figure 11.25). Here hardwood trees, including live oaks and mahogany, teem with wildlife. These islands provide nesting grounds and shelter for many species of birds, mammals, and reptiles. **Sloughs,** areas with slightly deeper water, are largely free of sawgrass and are dominated by free-floating plants such as the white water lily.

The Everglades are always changing. In a typical year, rains drench lower Florida from May through October and the wetlands flow with an abundance of water. The rainy season is followed by a six-month dry season. Before the rains return, much of the Everglades turns to mud and then to dry, cracked earth. The balance of wet and dry seasons is important to plants and animals adapted to these conditions. During the wet season the sawgrass swamp is covered with a meter of water, and the plants grow rapidly. If this wet growing season continued all year long, plants would choke out the swamp, and forests would invade the area. However, during the dry season the water table drops. The sawgrass dries up and turns yellow. Lightning-caused fires are part of the natural system during the fall and winter,

Figure 11.26 Alligator in 'gator hole. (Bruce S. Cushing/Visuals Unlimited)

but only the tops of the sawgrass are burned. The roots, still covered by a few centimeters of water, are undisturbed. Tree islands, too, are generally safe from the fast-moving fires.

As the drought continues and the mud dries, most of the aquatic life would be threatened if it weren't for the most famous Everglades reptile, the American alligator. The alligator is often referred to as the "keeper of the 'Glades" because biologists have found that the alligators' life style helps maintain the marsh ecosystem. Alligators scoop out large depressions with their tails, creating 'gator holes that collect water. During the dry winter season 'gator holes provide refuge for fish, turtles, snails and other water-dwelling animals (Figure 11.26).

The plants and animals of the Everglades have adapted to this complex cycle of seasonal growth, fire, and drought. The wide spectrum of habitats support a very diverse set of plants and animals that are all interconnected.

Now Everglades National Park, established in 1947 to preserve this unique ecosystem and the migratory birds that go there to breed and nest, is in danger of environmental collapse. The number of wading birds has declined 90% since 1936. Between 1962 and 1981, park biologist Bill Robertson found that the breeding populations of all bird species declined at least 50%. Alligator populations have declined because water control projects flooded the mounds on which they lay their eggs. Deer populations also suffered by flooding. Deer feed on vegetation in the marshes, and tree islands provide dry land where deer can rest and breed. When flooding occurs, some deer become stranded on islands and starve.

How did these problems occur for the Everglades? What is being done to turn around this tide of destruction?

In an effort to build Florida as an agricultural state, water from the wetlands and excess water from Lake Okeechobee was channeled,

Figure 11.27 Canal southwest of Miami is part of flood control network that starves the Everglades of water. (Gerald Davis)

and wetlands were drained. Farms replaced many former swamplands. Water development projects grew until there was a maze of 2240 kilometers (1400 miles) of canals, dikes, levees, and pumping stations throughout the lower third of Florida (Figures 11.27 and 11.28).

To accommodate both agriculture and the concerns of citizens wanting to preserve the Everglades, the U.S. Army Corps of Engineers designed several water conservation districts, guaranteeing that the park would receive at least a minimum annual water delivery. In 1967, an extension to a canal was dug into Conservation Area 3 to serve as a new water route to the park. Designed to get water to the park quickly and in large quantities, the new canal eliminated any remaining trace of the wetlands' historic sheet-flow pattern. Flooding then became a problem. The park was getting too much water, too often, and in too concentrated a stream. Water released during the dry season flooded the areas around 'gator holes, so that fish were farther apart. To nesting birds this meant loss of easily accessible prey during critical periods. Release of water during wet periods increased the water level, flooding alligator nests.

One more problem plagued the Everglades: runoff of water from the new agricultural lands led to **eutrophication** of water in Lake Okeechobee, the main water source for the Everglades. That is, the runoff from fertilized fields added nutrients to the water and increased algae growth, which choked out fish populations.

It was once thought that areas of land could be preserved forever by making them into national parks. But national parks are not

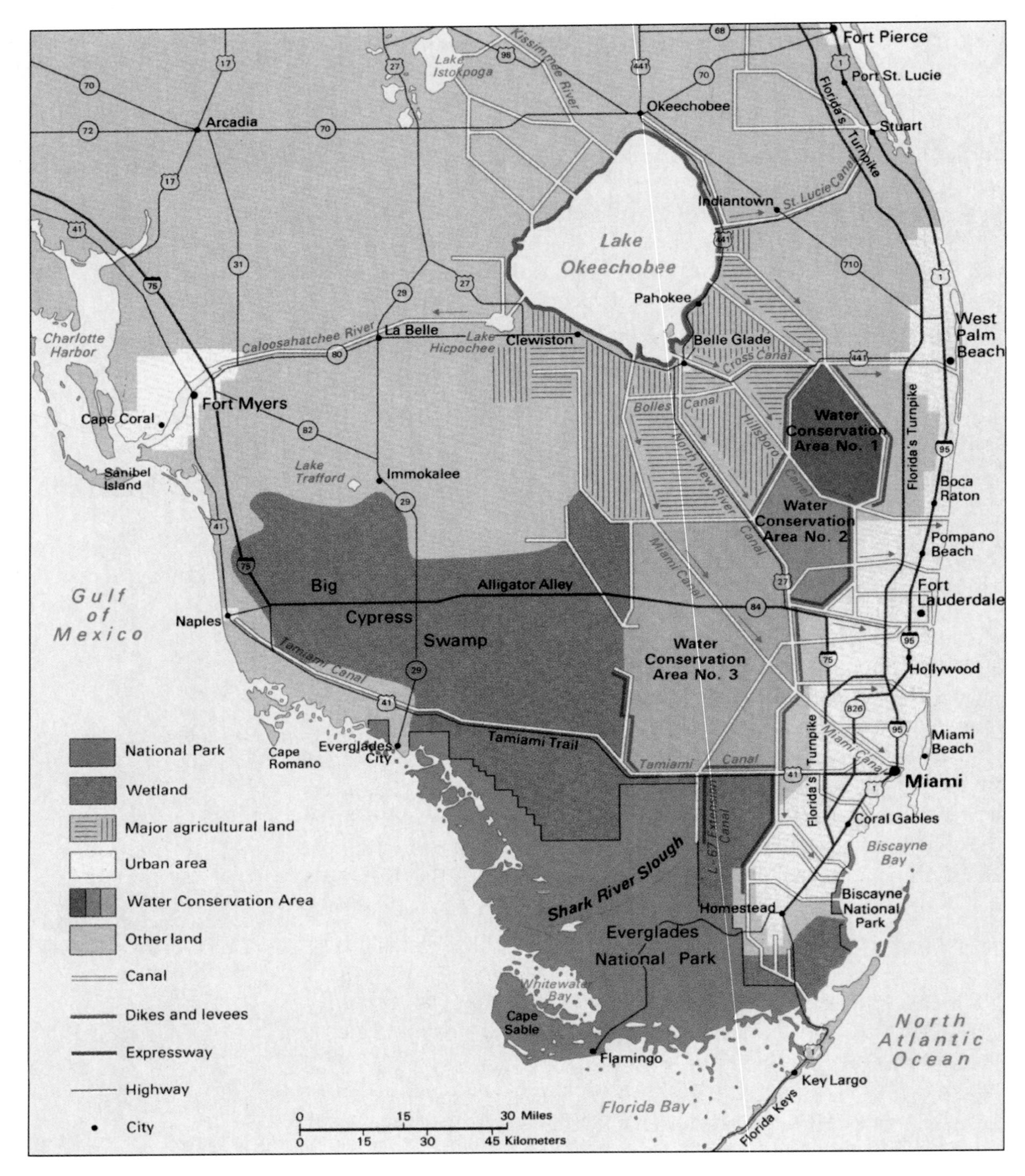

Figure 11.28 The problem and the solution. The natural sheet flow of water in the Everglades was cut off by an extensive system of canals, locks, dikes and levees that severed Lake Okeechobee and the Kissimmee River from the Everglades ecosystem and split the Everglades into three main parts: the Everglades Agricultural Area; Everglades National Park; and a large expanse of wetlands subdivided into three Water Conservation areas. Flooding in the Park and other problems resulted from the changes. Plugging some canals and cutting gaps in levees is restoring a more normal water flow. (From The 1988 Science Year, *The World Book Annual Science Supplement*. Copyright © 1988 World Book, Inc. Reproduced with permission.)

Figure 11.29 Florida panther kitten. (Joe McDonald/Visuals Unlimited)

isolated islands. They are greatly impacted by what happens outside their boundaries. Since water quantity, quality, and timing are at the root of the Everglades' problems, they must be the focus of the solution.

The South Florida Water Management District, the Corps of Engineers, the National Park Service, and the private agricultural interests are the principal players when it comes to saving the Everglades. These groups must move quickly to accomplish three tasks: (1) They must clearly define what "restore" means. It is hard to accomplish any task if there is not a clear goal. (2) They must develop a plan to reach their goal. Must some lands be removed from agricultural production? Should price supports for the sugar growers be removed? How are nutrients best removed from agricultural runoff, and how can this be paid for? (3) They must develop the leadership to ensure that the principal players work together to accomplish the task. The U.S. Secretary of the Interior, the governor of Florida, and the directors of the principal agencies and associations are all charged with the mandate to save the Everglades. The public must be responsible for holding them to that task. A recent agreement between the sugar growers and various governmental agencies may prove to be a significant step forward.

What three tasks are required to save the Everglades?

Pollution of Water

The causes of **water pollution** fall into two broad categories: (1) untreated or inadequately treated wastes from easily identified points, such as sewage treatment plants; and (2) waste from non-point or diffuse sources, such as silt or fertilizers washed into a stream from many farms during heavy rainstorms.

11.12 Point and Non-Point Sources

Distinguish between point and non-point sources of water pollution.

Point sources include pipes from cities and industries dumping untreated sewage into waterways and oceans; sewage-treatment plants that remove some, but not all, pollutants; feedlots in which animals are confined in a small space; and oil spills. The materials that flow out of a pipe or tank are called the **effluent.**

Non-point sources spread pollution over a wide area. These sources include runoff which carries sediments from erosion due to activities such as logging, fire, construction, or farming; runoff of chemical fertilizers or pesticides from agricultural lands; drainage of acids, minerals, sediments, and toxic metals from abandoned mines; precipitation of acid rain; and untraceable oil spills or dumping of hazardous wastes. Non-point pollution is of growing concern in the United States because it is more difficult to control than pollution from point sources.

57 11.13 Major Water Pollutants

What is a water pollutant?

A water **pollutant** is any substance picked up by water which makes it impure. Chemically pure water is not found in nature because water dissolves so many substances. Some substances, not actually dissolved by water, are suspended in or dispersed by water.

What is meant by "pure" water?

Drinking water is not pure water. To make water suitable for drinking, many suspended solids are removed and harmful bacteria destroyed, but many substances still remain in solution. The taste of drinking water varies because different dissolved minerals give water distinctly different tastes. Thus the term "pure" when used in a water pollution sense, means water in which no substance is present in sufficient concentration to prevent the water from being used for normal purposes. Different standards are set for water depending upon its use, because water clean enough for agricultural use or clean enough to support a healthy aquatic ecosystem may not be clean enough for drinking. Over 2000 substances can be found in drinking water. For each substance there is an acceptable level, above which harmful effects can result.

Water quality standards change from time to time as new information becomes available. The acceptable levels of a particular substance may be changed as we learn more about the effects of a particular pollutant. For example, until the 1960s, the acceptable level of selenium in drinking water was 0.05 mg/L. It was then dropped to 0.01 mg/L. It has now returned to 0.05 mg/L. Selenium is found as a trace element in soils and is a metabolic requirement in trace amounts. However, selenium is toxic when ingested at high levels. Selenium itself does not dissolve in water, but compounds containing selenium are soluble. Levels of 2.0 mg/L (40 times today's acceptable levels) have killed goldfish.

Typical flow diagram of water from lake to you.

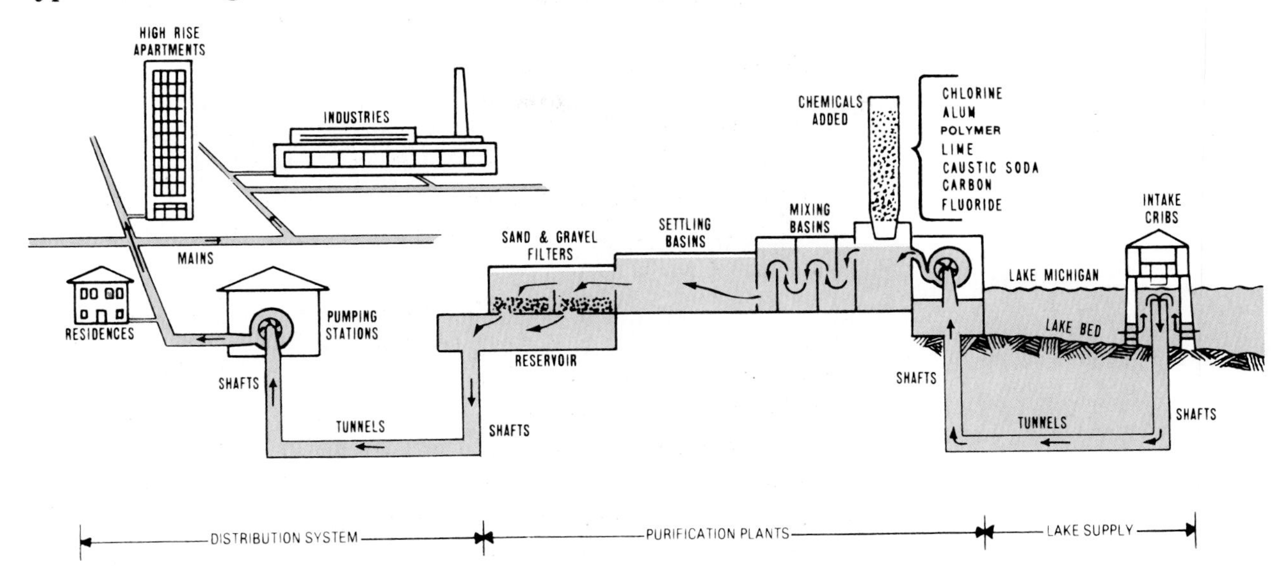

Figure 11.30 Flow diagram of a large municipal water treatment system. (Department of Water, City of Chicago)

Water pollutant categories.

Water pollutants can be divided into the following categories:

- **disease-causing agents:** bacteria, parasites, and viruses
- **inorganic chemicals:** salts, acids, and toxic metals
- **synthetic organic compounds:** detergents, oil, industrial wastes, pesticides and solvents
- **fertilizers:** plant nutrients from agricultural runoff (mostly nitrates and phosphates)
- **sediments:** soil, silt, and clay from land erosion
- **oxygen-demanding wastes:** sewage, animal manure, and some industrial wastes
- **radioactive materials**
- **thermal pollution:** heat from industrial and electric power plants

a. Disease-Causing Agents

Parasites and microbes are particularly common in water in the "Third World" countries in which drinking water standards are not as strict as those in the United States, Canada, and Europe. In 75% of the world, water purification standards are low or entirely absent. Where sanitation is lacking, an estimated 10 million people will die each year of waterborne diseases. Bacteria, viruses, protozoans, and roundworms are found in water contaminated by human and/or animal feces. The obvious solution is to prevent untreated sewage from entering drinking water supplies and to treat all drinking water to kill harmful organisms.

Summarize the steps in typical United States water treatment.

Methods of treating water in the United States have not changed in decades. In a complete treatment plant, water is disinfected with chlorine. Chlorine kills bacteria and microorganisms. Various chemicals are then added to coagulate minerals, to remove suspended particles, and to neutralize unpleasant tastes and smells. Then more chemicals are added to remove the corrective ones. The water is filtered through sand or charcoal, and chlorinated again to prevent contamination as the water is distributed through the community's system.

Although chlorine kills bacteria it is not capable of destroying all of the hundreds of viruses that can be waterborne. Other processes remove some, but not all viruses. So far, the only known way to eliminate them all is to boil the water.

b. Inorganic Chemicals

Why are we concerned about inorganic chemicals that dissolve in water?

Many chemicals that dissolve in water are very toxic. Heavy metals such as lead, mercury, copper, arsenic, and chromium inhibit or destroy enzymes essential to life. Metals affect decomposers as well as higher forms of life. Adding them to an aquatic system can be quite destructive. These pollutants may be absorbed by the bottom mud and released whenever bottom deposits are disturbed.

Contamination of water by mercury is common, because mercury is used for so many purposes. Mercury compounds are found in dental fillings, furniture polishes, floor waxes, antibacterial and anti-mildew powders, medicines, fungicides for seeds, fluorescent lights, air conditioners, and paints. They are used in making plastics, paper, clothing, and film. Mercury dumped into rivers as an industrial waste was once thought to be safe because liquid mercury is relatively inert, and it was believed that the mercury would settle into the river sediment. However, two Swedish scientists discovered that anaerobic bacteria (bacteria not requiring oxygen for their life cycles) found in murky stream sediments could change relatively inert mercury into highly toxic methyl mercury. This transformation occurs more readily in slightly acidic waters.

Methyl mercury poisoning has been reported in Japan, Mexico, Sweden, Iraq, and the United States. In Japan, 52 people died and 150 suffered serious brain and nerve damage from methyl mercury discharged into Minamata Bay by a chemical plant. The methyl mercury in the water was absorbed by fish, and people became contaminated by eating the fish.

c. Synthetic Organic Compounds

Compounds such as detergents, oil, industrial wastes, pesticides and solvents can cause a multitude of problems. Oil and grease get into water from industries, from automobiles, from offshore oil drilling operations, pipeline leaks, and tanker spills. Damage to aquatic ecosystems can be drastic and long-lasting. Following an oil spill in Massachusetts, the populations of polychaete worms, which are resistant to oil, increased in numbers while almost all other intertidal animals declined. Species diversity was severely reduced and did not begin to recover until three or four years after the spill.

Figure 11.31 An oil-covered seal in Prince William Sound attempts to shake off the result of its encounter with the 1,000 square-mile oil slick that occurred when the Exxon Valdez ran aground. (Bill Nation/Sygma)

Sample	Concentration (ppm)
Water	0.00005
Plankton, mostly zooplankton	0.04
Blanket weed algae	0.08
Shrimp	0.16
Atlantic silverside minnow	0.23
Chain pickerel (predator fish)	1.33
Green heron (predator bird)	3.54
Herring gull (scavenger)	6.50
Merganser duck (predator)	22.8
Cormorant (preys on large fish)	26.4
Ring-billed gull (preys on large fish)	75.5

Figure 11.32 Concentrations of toxic DDT, DDE and DDE residues in samples from an estuary on Long Island, New York. The values are in parts per million wet weight of the whole organism. Because of results like this, DDT is no longer used in the United States. (Part of a table by G. M. Woodwell, et al., *Science* 156:821–824, 1967. Copyright © 1967 by the American Association for the Advancement of Science.)

Cleaning up oil spills in rivers is even more difficult than in the ocean. Rivers carry toxic material for miles, damaging wildlife and contaminating drinking water along the way. Cleanup crews use plastic "booms" to contain the oil, which is then vacuumed off the surface of the water by special tankers. Picking up oil is a slow process. A moving river tends to break up the oil, making it even more difficult to scoop up.

Second only to oil spills, sudsy synthetic detergents cause considerable concern. In addition, many detergents contain plant nutrients, enhancing the growth of algae and aquatic weeds. This can kill fish and cause foul odors as the amount of dissolved oxygen in the water becomes depleted.

Pesticides may kill many organisms in addition to mosquitoes or flies. Also, they can build up in aquatic food chains, contaminating foods used by humans. See Figure 11.32.

d. Fertilizers

Plant nutrients from agricultural runoff can also cause algal blooms (population explosions), depleting fish populations as water becomes

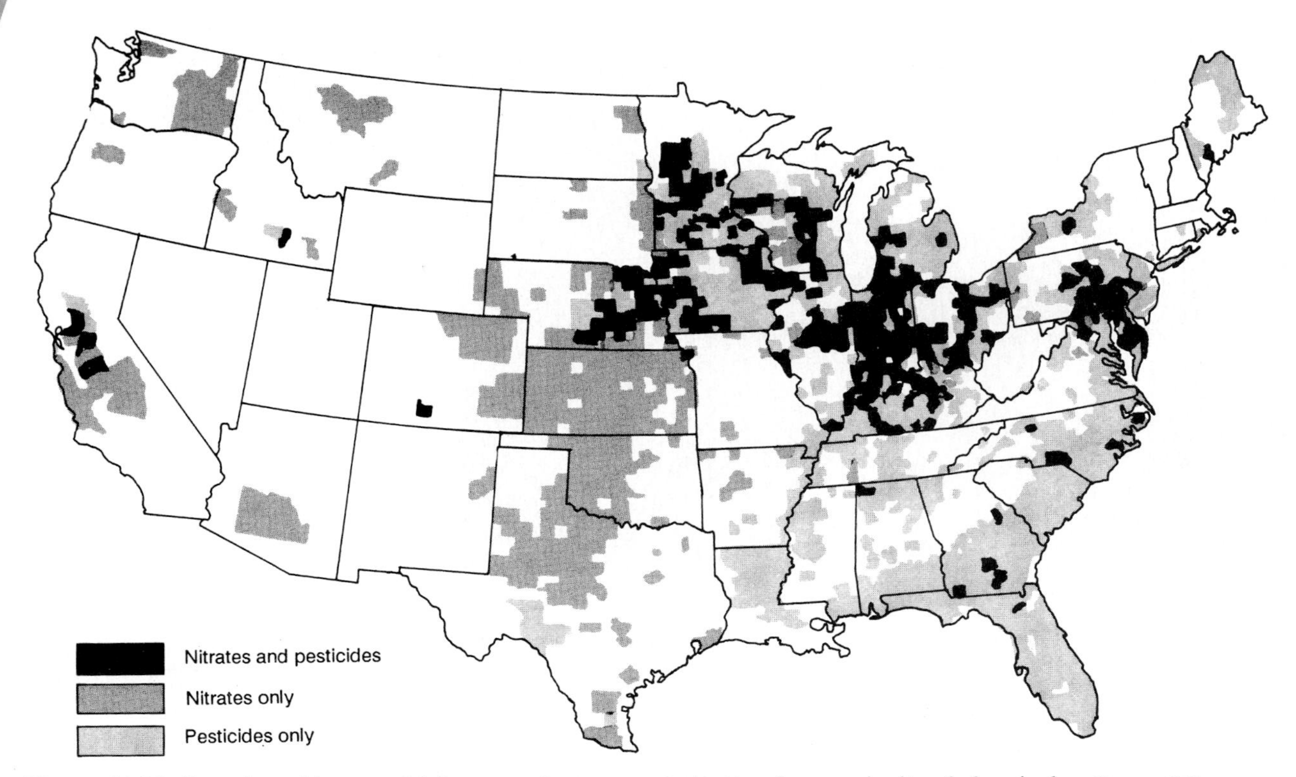

Figure 11.33 Counties with potential for groundwater contamination from agricultural chemicals. (Source: U.S. Department of Agriculture, 1987. The Magnitude and Costs of Groundwater Contamination from Agricultural Chemicals: A National Perspective. Staff Report AGES870318. Economic Research Service. Washington, D.C.)

clogged with vegetation. The balance of the ecosystem is upset, water becomes stagnant and foul, and dissolved oxygen declines.

Excessive use of nitrogen-rich fertilizers results in nitrate residues which dissolve and seep into groundwater. See Figure 11.33. Soil organisms convert the nitrates to nitrites, and water-containing nitrites can be especially dangerous to the health of infants. The nitrites enter their red blood cells, interfering with the cells' ability to carry oxygen.

e. Sediments

Soil, silt, and clay eroded from land are deposited in water bodies. As reservoirs become filled, aquatic life is affected, fish populations decline, and dissolved oxygen is reduced.

f. Oxygen-Demanding Wastes

Sewage, manure, and industrial wastes enter water ecosystems as natural runoff from land; or untreated human or animal wastes may be dumped into rivers. Some of these wastes also come from decaying vegetation and from industries such as food processing plants, paper mills, and oil refineries. Decomposition of these products by aerobic bacteria depletes the amount of dissolved oxygen, causing fish populations to decline. The aquatic ecosystem becomes unbalanced and the water may give off foul odors.

Figure 11.34 Canada geese overwintering on a cooling pond next to an electric power plant in Baldwin, Illinois. (Photo courtesy of Illinois Power Company.)

g. Radioactive Wastes

Erosion of naturally occurring radioactive rock, mining and processing of radioactive materials, nuclear power plants, and nuclear weapons testing may result in pollution by radioactive wastes. When radioactive wastes become part of drinking water, they are extremely toxic. Radiation damages cells within a person's body. Radiation can lead to genetic defects passed on to an offspring, or can cause damage to the individual, such as radioactive burns, miscarriages, cataracts, leukemia, and various cancers.

h. Thermal Pollution

The steam used to drive turbines is condensed and the excess heat may be released into waterways. Increasing the temperature of a body of water affects the entire ecosystem. The composition of the ecosystem changes as a result—cold-water fish cannot survive and are thus replaced by warm-water species. The amount of dissolved oxygen in water also decreases. Since increased temperatures affect plants as well as animals, species of both plants and animals in the thermally altered ecosystem change. Lakes that normally freeze in winter may not freeze because of the heat discharged into them. Figure 11.34 shows Canada geese overwintering far north of their normal winter range at a pond thermally heated by a power plant.

 11.14 Pollution of Aquatic Ecosystems

List and describe three indicators of water quality.

Flowing aquatic ecosystems such as streams and rivers have different water pollution problems than standing ecosystems such as lakes and ponds. However, three indicators of water quality are important in both lakes and rivers: (1) the concentrations of dissolved oxygen (DO), (2) the biological oxygen demand (BOD), and (3) the coliform bacteria count.

Table 11.3 Biological Oxygen Demand

Type of Water	BOD (mg/L)
Pure water	0
Typical fresh natural water	2 to 5
Domestic sewage	hundreds
Sewage after treatment	10 to 20

a. Dissolved Oxygen (DO)

The **dissolved oxygen** or DO content is the amount of oxygen gas dissolved in water. At a temperature of 20° C (68° F) and normal atmospheric pressure, the maximum DO is 9 parts of oxygen per million parts of water (9 ppm). DO level is an important indication of the ecological health of a waterway. If the DO level drops below 4 ppm, fish populations decline.

b. Biological Oxygen Demand (BOD)

In breaking down organic wastes dumped into aquatic ecosystems, decomposing bacteria use dissolved oxygen. The amount of this depletion is called the **biological oxygen demand** (BOD). Bacterial decomposition may reduce the DO content so much that some aquatic organisms die. Water is considered seriously polluted when the BOD of the decomposers cause the DO to fall below 5 ppm. Compare the typical BOD values shown in Table 11.3.

c. Coliform Bacteria

Another measure of water quality is based on the number of **coliform bacteria** in the water. Coliform bacteria are intestinal microorganisms that are found in soils and in human and animal feces. Although most of these bacteria are harmless, their presence indicates that harmful microorganisms, which can cause such diseases as viral hepatitis, cholera, dysentery, or encephalitis, may be there also. Bacteria can be grown in the laboratory, producing visible colonies that can be counted. Samples of water considered safe to drink by the Environmental Protection Agency (EPA) if they produce no more than one coliform bacterial colony per 100 milliliters of water. The EPA recommended level of water safe for swimming produces no more than 200 colonies per 100 milliliters.

d. Natural Purification

At a site where untreated sewage is added to a stream, bacteria start feasting on the sewage. The BOD increases enormously. In areas immediately downstream, the DO levels drop drastically and fish die. Fish do not die from the sewage directly, but from a lack of oxygen.

Describe the changes in a flowing river as it moves downstream from a source of organic pollution.

Flowing rivers have a remarkable ability to dilute many wastes and renew their DO content if not overloaded with pollutants. Further downstream, the amount of sewage decreases because bacteria have decomposed most of the organic material. BOD levels decrease and

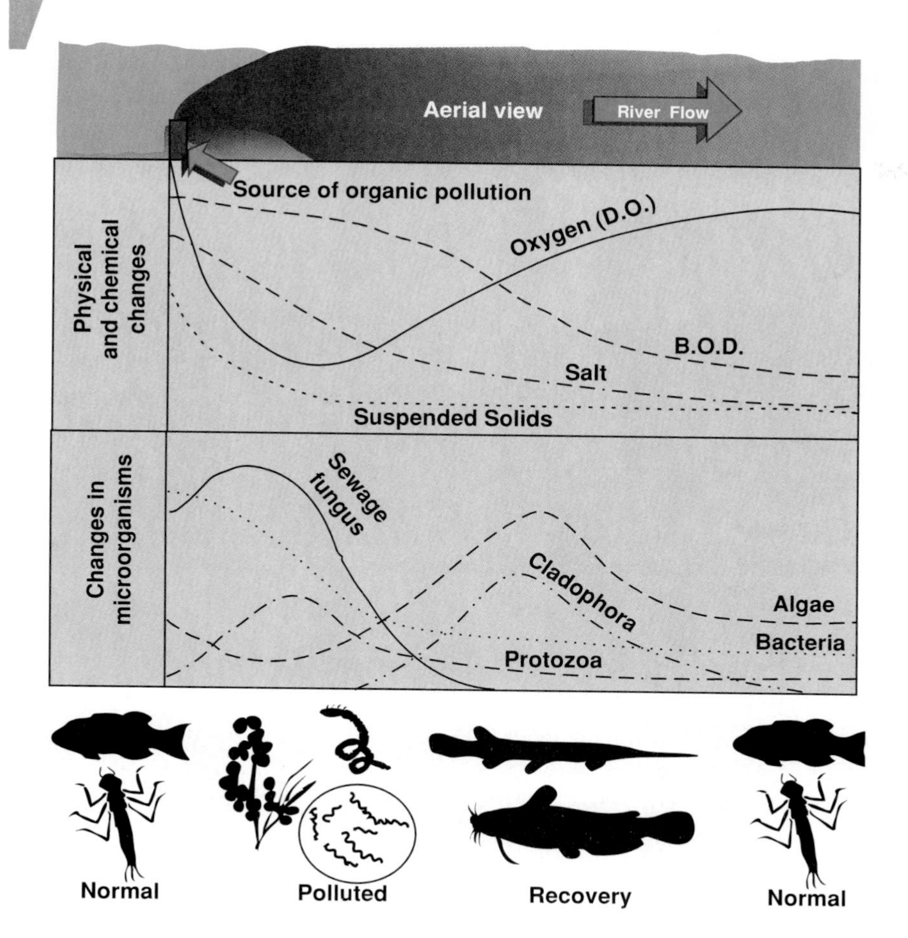

Figure 11.35 Typical changes in water chemistry and biology in a river below a source of organic pollution. (Adapted from The Biology of Polluted Waters, H. B. N. Hynes, Liverpool University Press, 1978.)

DO increases. Some oxygen comes from air mixing with water in the stream and some is replenished by photosynthesis of aquatic plants. The stream begins to repurify itself (Figure 11.35). Because of their ability to purify themselves, most rivers can recover fairly rapidly from a discharge of biodegradable pollutants.

If additional untreated sewage is added before recovery is complete, the river becomes polluted again. Such polluted rivers (which unfortunately are found in many densely populated areas all over the world) have no fish, have a high bacterial count, appear muddy to blue-green in color, and smell from the odors of decay.

Additional problems occur when nonbiodegradable wastes and toxic substances are dumped into streams and rivers. Bacteria have no effect on those pollutants. Through the tightening and enforcing of treatment standards, many rivers in the eastern United States are cleaner now than they were 30 to 40 years ago. Rivers such as the Hudson and the Potomac, once "flowing sewers," have regained fish and other wildlife species.

In lakes and ponds water flows more slowly, so they have less ability to purify themselves than streams and rivers do. Thus, pollution problems become magnified in slower moving waters.

a

Figure 11.36a A typical oligotrophic lake. This kind of lake is characterized by a lack of algae and clear blue water. In Oregon's Crater Lake, a small white disc can often be seen as deep as 100 feet, compared to only about 5 feet in eutrophic lakes. (Alex J. Horne)

b

Figure 11.36b A typical eutrophic lake. A major characteristic of such lakes is the abundance of blue-green algae, also called cyanobacteria, which give the lake a yellow-green color. Algae are a nuisance, particularly when they die and decay. In this photo a thick scum of dead algae is shown as a light-colored band just offshore. (Alex J. Horne)

11.15 Eutrophication of Lakes

Describe an oligotrophic lake.

All freshwater lakes have various stages of development. When an area drained by a lake (called a drainage basin) has few nutrients, the lake is nutrient-poor or **oligotrophic.** These lakes support little plant life; they are crystal-clear with low algae populations, have high DO levels, and support populations of fish such as lake trout and small-mouth bass.

On the other hand, when a lake is located in an area in which nutrients are released into the lake, the lake is nutrient-rich or **eutrophic.** These lakes support a great deal of plant life, which often chokes out other organisms. Such lakes have large blue-green algae populations, low DO content, and fish species such as carp and bullhead.

Figure 11.37 Ecological succession in a lake. (Wildlife Management Institute)

What is eutrophication? How can it be slowed?

Because nutrients tend to stay in a lake and accumulate, most lakes tend to become more eutrophic with time. Sediments are added by streams feeding the lake, also. Lake sediments become thicker and more recycling of nutrients takes place. Over hundreds to thousands of years, even an oligotrophic lake eventually becomes eutrophic. This natural successional process is called **eutrophication.** The amount of organic material and the levels of nitrates and phosphate increase. See Figure 11.37.

Pollution accelerates this natural process by increasing the nutrients in lakes. The nutrients come from the leaching of soil fertilizers

Figure 11.38 Lake Erie in the 1960s. Note the algae in the water and on the rocks. (Kenneth Mantai/Visuals Unlimited)

Define cultural eutrophication.

or dumping of nitrates and phosphates from treated sewage into waterways. Because this acceleration of eutrophication is caused by human activities, it is called **cultural eutrophication.** In a few decades it can produce the same effect that would normally take thousands of years.

When a lake becomes overloaded with nutrients, plant growth accelerates. Algal blooms cover the lake's surface. These large plant populations produce oxygen in upper layers of the water. But when the plants die they fall to the bottom and are decomposed by bacteria which use a great deal of the dissolved oxygen in the lower layers. As the DO levels of the bottom waters decline, trout, whitefish, and other deep-water species die from oxygen starvation. Fish that live in upper layers, such as perch, thrive and may increase, but overall the numbers of fish species decreases.

What natural characteristic of Lake Erie makes it a good candidate for pollution?

Of all the over-fertilized lakes in the world, Lake Erie is one of the largest and best known. The lake is 385 kilometers (240 miles) long, 80 kilometers (50 miles) wide, and has a volume of 450 cubic kilometers (109 cubic miles). Surely, such a large body of water is capable of handling and purifying an enormous amount of pollutants. However, Lake Erie, with an average depth of 17.7 meters (58 feet), is the shallowest of all the Great Lakes. Its shallowness is the root of Lake Erie's problems.

At one time Lake Erie was clear and filled with valuable fish. As large population centers developed around its shore, its pristine beauty was changed. Many factories poured wastes into its waters: Detroit's steel mills, paper factories, and automobile plants; Toledo's glass and steel industries; Cleveland's petrochemical and steel plants; Erie's paper mills; and Buffalo's flour mills and chemical factories. Large cities poured sewage, both treated and raw, into Lake Erie. Agricultural land between the cities added pesticides, herbicides and fertilizers.

The first symptom of a lake-wide problem was seen in the 1920s when the fish crop started to decline. By 1950, the catch—which once had been as high as 23 million kilograms (50 million pounds) annually—dropped to less than 450 kilograms (1000 pounds). The valuable species of whitefish, pike and sturgeon had been replaced by catfish, carp and smelt.

Because sewage dumped into the lake added nutrients, algae populations increased in the upper layers. As algae died and sank to the bottom, decomposers used most of the DO and the valuable fish died. Lake Erie was a graveyard for many fish species.

With the Water Pollution Control Act of 1972, the EPA spent billions of dollars on construction of municipal sewage treatment plants. Industries spent billions cleaning up their wastes. Non-point pollution from agricultural lands is difficult to curb. Though much still remains to be done, the trend has been reversed, and Lake Erie is recovering.

11.16 Pollution of Groundwater

Of growing concern to many people is the contamination of groundwater. Since groundwater flows slowly, it lacks the ability to purify itself. Soil particles are not effective in filtering out most pollutants found in water. Once these pollutants reach the groundwater it is almost impossible to clean up the water. Some engineers are investigating the possibility of pumping out an aquifer, cleaning the water and pumping clean water back in. If this were possible, it would be exceedingly costly. Preventing contamination in the first place appears to be the only effective solution.

Why can't groundwater purify itself?

Wastewater Treatment

?

How is wastewater from major cities treated?

Each American produces about 200 liters (53 gallons) of waste per day, including suspended solids, dissolved organic and inorganic materials, and microorganisms, such as viruses and bacteria. What happens to all those wastes we flush down toilets, sinks, garbage disposals and drains? To most of us, when wastes disappear down the drain, they are gone. Out of sight, out of mind!

A look at polluted rivers and lakes, however, reminds us that we cannot ignore the problem of what happens after we flush the toilet. We need to build wastewater treatment plants that treat and purify our wastewater, so that towns and cities downstream can safely reuse water from upstream users. (See Figure 11.40.)

The path of wastes from our sewers through a modern treatment plant will explain the problems and the advances in recently developed wastewater-treatment technology. After the toilet is flushed, wastes travel through a network of sewer pipes until they arrive at a wastewater-treatment plant. The plant consists of a series of tanks, screens, and filters that use both physical and chemical processes to remove wastes from the water.

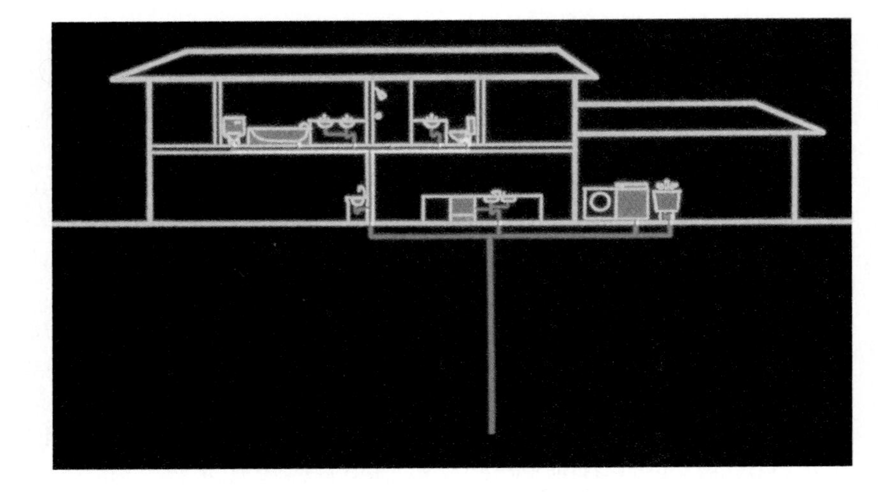

Figure 11.39 A home plumbing system. Where does wastewater go from here? (Metro Wastewater Reclamation District)

Figure 11.40 Aerial photograph of a large metropolitan wastewater treatment plant. (Metro Wastewater Reclamation District)

11.17 Primary Treatment

Describe primary treatment.

Sewage contains human wastes, paper, soap, detergent, cloth, food residues, microorganisms, and a variety of other substances. The first stage in wastewater treatment, called **primary treatment,** removes large solid objects and materials that settle out. Large objects such as rags and disposable diapers are screened out first. Then things like sand, grit, and coffee grounds settle to the bottom of a grit-removal basin.

In a large settling tank, called the primary **clarifier** (Figure 11.41), suspended particles settle to the bottom, and grease floats to the top. The grease is skimmed off, and the raw **sludge,** the bottom sediment, is removed. Primary treatment is diagrammed in Figure 11.42.

Figure 11.41 Primary clarifier.
(Metro Wastewater Reclamation District)

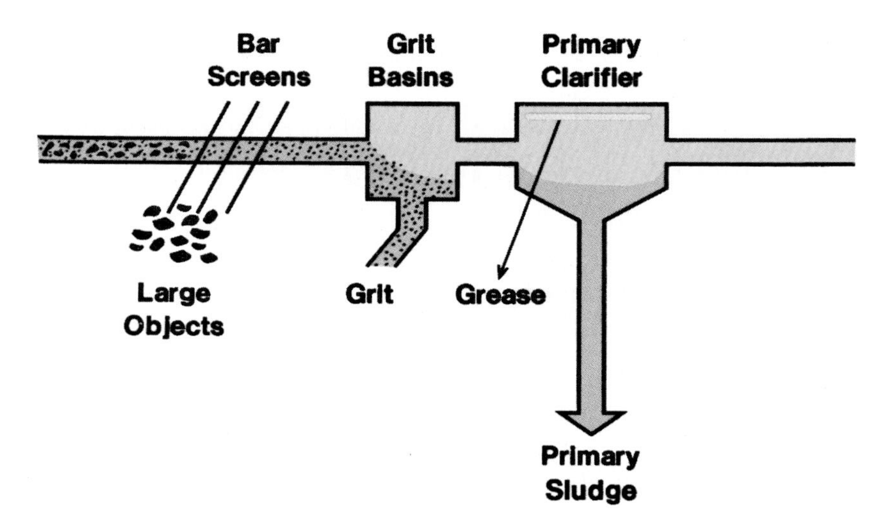

Figure 11.42 Primary treatment.
(U.S. Environmental Protection Agency)

For many years this was where sewage treatment ended. The liquid was simply discharged into lakes or streams. The discharge contains millions of microorganisms, some disease-causing, and large quantities of organic nutrients. These can destroy aquatic ecosystems.

11.18 Secondary Treatment

What is secondary treatment?

In modern wastewater treatment centers, the sewage goes through secondary treatment to remove the dissolved or suspended organic matter and to kill microorganisms. The liquid from primary treatment is pumped into large aeration tanks (Figure 11.43) where oxygen can work with microorganisms to decompose the organic materials. In the aeration tank, air (or in some facilities, pure oxygen) is bubbled through wastewater to create a swirling action which increases the biological activity. That is, the interaction of oxygen, microorganisms, and the organic nutrients occurs more rapidly. Microorganisms grow

Figure 11.43 An aeration basin.

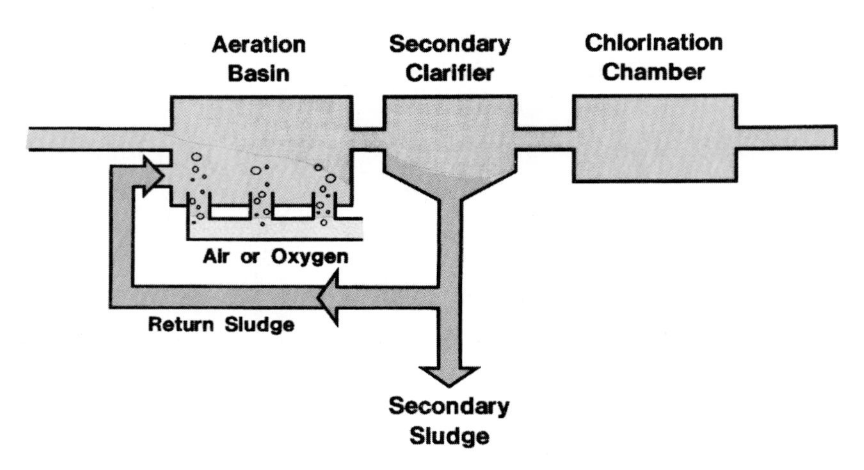

Figure 11.44 Secondary treatment. (U.S. Environmental Protection Agency)

and break down the organic matter. When the microorganisms complete their job of digesting the available food in the organic materials, they die and settle to the bottom of the tank.

The liquid from the aeration tanks then flows into the secondary clarifier (settling tank). Sludge settles to the bottom, and the liquid, still containing microorganisms, is treated with chlorine which kills 99% of the viruses, bacteria, and protozoans. This completes the secondary stage of treatment. In most cities, the liquid (effluent) is discharged into a nearby river or stream at this point. Figure 11.44 illustrates secondary treatment.

Another method of secondary treatment is called the **trickling filter** process. In this process, effluent from the primary clarifier is sprayed onto a bed of stones. The bed of stones, 1 to 2 meters deep, is covered with a slimy coating of bacteria and other microorganisms. Sewage is sprayed over the stones and a food chain of various organisms is started. Bacteria eat the various nutrients in the sewage, breaking it down into smaller components. The bacteria are then

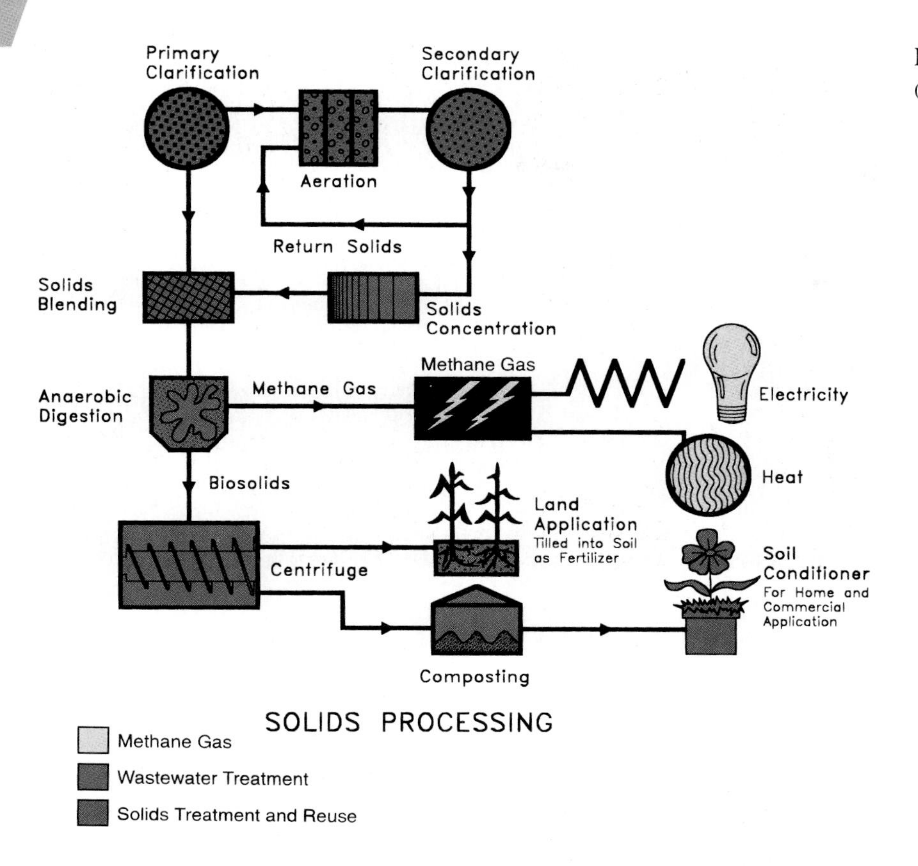

Figure 11.45 Solids processing.
(Metro Wastewater Reclamation District)

eaten by protozoans which in turn are eaten by worms, snails, flies, and spiders. After the trickling filter process, effluent flows into the secondary clarifier.

11.19 Tertiary Treatment

What is tertiary treatment designed to do?

Primary and secondary treatments remove more than 90% of all the solids and organic wastes. Chlorination eliminates most of the disease potential. However, most of the phosphates, nitrates, salts, radioactive materials, and pesticides that were in the original sewage still remain. Since high concentrations of these materials can cause severe ecological damage, many cities are now adding a third stage of treatment to remove some (usually not all) of these materials.

Tertiary treatments consist of a series of chemical or physical processes such as absorption, oxidation, or reverse osmosis for removing specific pollutants. The type and amount of tertiary treatment depends on local conditions and community goals.

11.20 Solids Processing

What is meant by solids processing?

Sludge resulting from sewage treatment must be further treated and digested. Figures 11.45, 11.46, and 11.47 all illustrate one possible approach to solids processing. First the sludge is decomposed in anaerobic conditions. The anaerobes break down the organic compounds into

Figure 11.46 Compost mixing machine turning compost. (Metro Wastewater Reclamation District)

Figure 11.47 Land application of biosolids. (Metro Wastewater Reclamation District)

harmless solids, organic acids, carbon dioxide, hydrogen sulfide, and methane. Since methane gas (CH_4) is flammable, it may be captured and used to operate generators or to heat buildings.

The final disposal of the sludge may be by incineration (burning), landfill, or composting. **Composting** is the breakdown (rotting) of moist organic matter in solid wastes by aerobic bacteria to form compost, a humus-like material that can be used as a fertilizer or a soil conditioner for lawns and gardens. Because the heat given off as composting occurs kills disease-causing organisms, compost can be used by gardeners and farmers as a fertilizer.

Properly done, the agricultural application of sludge reduces the need for chemical fertilizers. When wastewater is thoroughly treated with aerobic bacteria, the sludge can be used as a fertilizer without being composted. New technologies offer the prospect of producing sludge with fewer disease-causing microorganisms at a lower cost.

The Rivers Run Through It

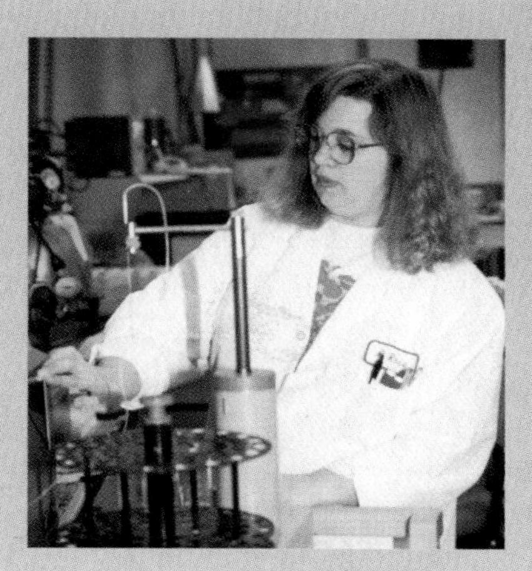

When Rebecca Rose reads newspaper articles and magazine stories about people who care about the environment, she is pleased to be part of the effort to protect Earth's most valuable resource: water. Rebecca, a lab technician at the Chicago Water Reclamation District (CWRD), tests water samples to determine the levels of industrial pollutants entering the waterways.

She works at the CWRD treatment plant for the Chicago area, in Stickney, Illinois. This area's waterway system—including the Illinois, Des Plaines, Chicago and other rivers—connects the Mississippi River and the Great Lakes. The water samples Rebecca examines come from industrial plants' effluent (waste material) pipes and from sewers. She may also test "lake watch samples" from Lake Michigan, collected after locks have opened to let water into the lake. Other samples of water and sludge come from release basins at water and wastewater treatment lagoons, and from Chicago's deep-tunnel project, which diverts rainwater into the waterway system to prevent flooding. The CWRD identifies the industries that exceed the limits for water pollution established by the Illinois EPA. Violators pay heavy fines.

In Rebecca's lab, testing is done for trace metals, especially heavy metals such as mercury and lead. Sometimes her task is to prepare the samples, and sometimes it's to run the tests themselves and monitor the results. She uses a number of different instruments and tests to measure what's in the samples. For instance, to identify certain metals, she uses flame atomic adsorption. To measure lead, she uses an Inductively Coupled Plasma instrument. The results go into a comprehensive report for the District's information system.

At other CWRD labs, technicians test samples for chemicals, bacteria, and other water pollutants. In addition to standard BOD tests, there is a COD (chemical oxygen demand) test that is faster at measuring the depletion of oxygen from the water. Other tests measure and analyze solids and nutrients such as ammonia and phosphates. Sludge from the District's treated wastewater is tested for safety before being sent out for use as a fertilizer on golf courses, landfills, and the ground covers along highways.

"My high-school chemistry teacher would never believe it if he knew what I'm doing now," jokes Rebecca. An average student in high school, she enjoyed her math and science classes but had no real interest in going on to college. Then, while working as a waitress and supporting two young children, she heard about job opportunities at the CWRD. She passed the Civil Service exam, and a year later was employed in an entry-level job at the District. Night-school classes (and a lot of late-night studying after working all day) led to an Associate in Science degree and to her present position.

Science is essential for Rebecca's work. Her early high school studies gave her basic knowledge about global science and scientific principles. College classes in chemistry, anatomy and physiology, algebra and trigonometry, and other subjects not only helped her qualify for advancement at the CWRD, but gave her a better understanding of her work in the laboratory.

Today Rebecca and her husband, a chemist, are active in promoting science education, and often judge projects at local science fairs. "Young people need to know more about their job options," Rebecca says. "No matter what they're interested in, and whether or not they want to go to college, the jobs are out there."

Figure 11.48 On-site sewage treatment.

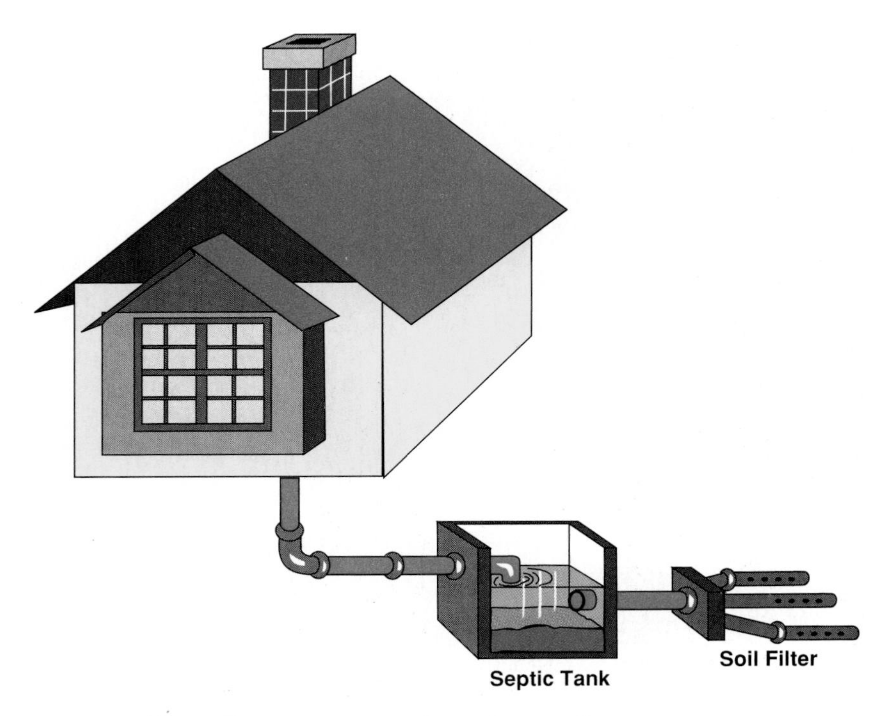

11.21 On-Site Sewage Treatment Systems

One third of all American families use on-site sewage-treatment systems. 85% of U.S. on-site systems use **septic tanks.** Most of the rest use aerobic tanks (with an air agitator). The purpose of the on-site system is to remove wastewater from its source, separate contaminants from the wastewater, and return an effluent to the soil for further filtration. This is all done on the property where the sewage originated. On-site disposal systems may offer economic advantages over municipal sewage systems if soil and water conditions are suitable and if a home is not close to a city sewer line.

How do on-site sewage-treatment systems work?

An on-site system has two parts: a sewage tank and a soil filter (leach field). See Figure 11.48. The sewage tank separates out the large solids as bacteria digest organic materials and cause scum and sludge to separate from the wastewater. Liquid effluent from the sewage tank flows into the soil filter, a network of porous pipes located in trenches covered with soil and turf. Gravel surrounding the pipes promotes even distribution of the effluent. This effluent contains high levels of bacteria and phosphorus, which must be removed or inactivated before reaching the water table.

The improper siting or construction of many on-site sewage treatment systems has caused groundwater pollution around the country.

Figure 11.49 The goal is to provide adequate quantities of high-quality water. (Copyright: Press Publishing, Ltd., Provo Utah. Used by permission.)

Homeowners must use care in selecting a contractor or know what they are doing if they do the work themselves.

The only maintenance required for a properly operating system may be the occasional removal of accumulated solids from the sewage tank. Most septic system problems can be reduced if homeowners are careful with their use of water. Garbage disposals should be used only sparingly, if at all. It is better to compost the garbage.

11.22 Solving Water Problems

Up to now, water management in the United States has mainly focused on arranging the nation's abundant supplies of fresh water to meet the needs of users. This "supply management" approach resulted in the building of large reservoirs and delivery systems, especially in the West. Increasing development costs, shortages of funds, government restraint, shrinking water supplies, polluted water, and a growing concern for the environment are forcing water managers and planners to rethink their strategies. We are moving into a time for water-demand management and conservation. The boxed section summarizes some of these strategies.

Water quantity and quality problems can be solved using a variety of strategies:

- **Technical solutions**—A variety of technical devices are available to both conserve water and avoid polluting it. These include ultra low-flush toilets, low-flow sink and showerheads; low-water landscaping, lined irrigation ditches, trickle irrigation systems, automatic car washes, dry cooling towers, and non-toxic chemicals that can substitute for toxic chemicals.
- **A water conservation ethic**—Clean water is such a valuable resource that wasting it is extremely harmful. The value of using resources wisely must be taught and practiced at home, at school, and in the workplace. Much water can be saved if citizens behave in a responsible way.
- **Economic solutions**—The price of a resource should fully reflect its true value. If water costs more, waste will shrink.
- **Water policy and water law**—The laws and policies of our nation determine who gets to use water and how it is used. Wise laws and policies can help resolve conflicts and promote the best use of resources.

Summary

What are some of the things you can do to reduce water problems?

Water is the most abundant compound in all living organisms. The resources of water on this planet are vast, yet the amount of fresh water available for human use is limited. Therefore, it is important to use this valuable resource wisely and conservatively. We must be careful not to waste or pollute our water resources, for economic growth and the quality of our life depend upon having enough water for our needs.

Some of our supply of usable fresh water has been set aside behind dams, in reservoirs. While this has made it possible for humans to live and farm in arid areas, it has not increased the total water supply. As the population grows, the demand for available water also grows.

Scientists and engineers have developed the technology to clean up polluted waters and to use less water in many industrial applications. In some areas, such as in Lake Erie and the Florida Everglades, people have worked to clean up the water and use more ecologically sound practices to restore natural habitats.

Wastewater can be treated so that the water becomes pure and can be reused. As the water is purified, many of the removed wastes can be set aside for recycling. In future years, as the population grows and pollution increases, more and more treatment and reuse of water will be necessary.

References

Academy of Natural Sciences. *Ground Water Contamination: Sources, Effect, and Options to Deal with the Problem* (Philadelphia: Academy of Natural Sciences), 1987.

Briscoe, John, and David de Ferrani. *Water for Rural Communities: Helping People To Help Themselves* (Washington, DC: World Bank), 1988.

Clarke, Robin. *Water: The International Crisis* (Cambridge, MA: The MIT Press), 1993.

Francko, D. A., and R. G. Wetzel. *To Quench Our Thirst: The Present and Future Status of Freshwater Resources of the United States* (Ann Arbor, MI: University of Michigan Press), 1983.

Gordon, Wendy. *A Citizen's Handbook on Groundwater Protection* (New York: Natural Resources Defense Council), 1984.

Gottlieb, Robert. *A Life of Its Own: The Politics and Power of Water* (San Diego: Harcourt Brace Jovanovich), 1988.

Meybeck, Michel, et. al., eds. *Global Freshwater Quality: A First Assessment* (Cambridge, MA: Basil Blackwell), 1990.

Natural Resources Defense Council. *Clean Water: Citizen's Handbook on Water Quality Standards* (Washington, DC: Natural Resources Defense Council), 1987.

Postel, Sandra. *Conserving Water: The Untapped Alternative.* Worldwatch Paper 67 (Washington DC: Worldwatch Institute), 1985.

———. *Water for Agriculture: Facing the Limits* (Washington, DC: Worldwatch Institute), 1989.

———. *Water: Rethinking Management in an Age of Scarcity.* Worldwatch Paper 62 (Washington, DC: Worldwatch Institute), 1984.

Reed, Sherwood C., et. al. *Natural Systems for Waste Management and Treatment* (New York: McGraw-Hill), 1988.

Rocky Mountain Institute. *Catalog of Water-Efficient Technologies for the Urban/Residential Sector* (Old Snowmass, CO: Rocky Mountain Institute), 1990.

U.S. Geological Survey, *Estimated Use of Water in the United States in 1990, USGS Circular 1081* (Washington, DC: USGPO), 1993.

Watson, Lyall. *The Water Planet* (New York: Crown), 1988.

End of Chapter Questions

Set A

1. Why must we carefully use our supplies of fresh water?
2. List two serious threats to groundwater supplies.
3. Name the two largest users of fresh water and indicate their approximate use by a percentage.
4. Describe the two major approaches for managing water.
5. What is desalination, and why is it of interest?
6. What is cloud seeding? List some potential problems related to cloud seeding proposals.
7. Trace the route of your drinking water through the hydrologic cycle.
8. What is the source of drinking water for your community? How is it treated?

9. How is water divided among agricultural, industrial and domestic users in your community? Who are the biggest users of water? What efforts are being made to conserve water in your community? What could be done?
10. What type of wastewater facility does your community have? Answer *either* a or b.
    a) Does your community provide tertiary treatment? How does your community dispose of sludge?

    OR

    b) If the wastewater from your home is piped into a septic tank, draw a map of your home and yard and mark the location of the septic tank and soil filter. Has the septic tank ever worked improperly? If so, what was the problem? When was the last time your septic tank was pumped? Where were the pumped wastes taken?
11. What are the greatest problems your community has in regard to:
    a) water quantity?
    b) water quality?
    c) pollution of streams or groundwater?
    d) treatment of special problems in your water supply?
    What steps has your community taken to solve some of these problems?
12. How is water being wasted in your community? In your school?
13. Give examples of point and non-point pollution sources. How can each of these be controlled?

Set B

14. Distinguish between natural eutrophication and cultural eutrophication and explain how eutrophication depletes the DO in a lake.
15. What is the relationship between DO and BOD of a river downstream from the point of effluent discharge from a wastewater treatment plant?
16. Discuss the benefits and ecological consequences of a water-diversion project.
17. If groundwater is a renewable resource, how can it be "mined" and thus depleted like a nonrenewable resource?
18. How does irrigation increase the salinity of water and soil? What solutions might be applied?
19. Explain how desalination plants may be used to increase water available for human use.
20. List various ways in which groundwater can become polluted. Why doesn't polluted groundwater repurify itself naturally as fast as surface water does?
21. Explain why land subsides when groundwater is depleted.
22. What causes salt intrusions to occur along coastal areas? What harm can be caused by these intrusions?

23. What practices led to problems in the Everglades? How is this area being restored?
24. What are the problems your community or state is facing in terms of water pollution? How are these problems being addressed and what progress has been made in solving them?
25. What can you personally and as a citizen do to solve some problems of water pollution?

Usibelli Coal Mine Inc.

Goal

To understand some ways of improving our ability to use our air and land

Resource Management: Air and Land

What is the use of having a house if you don't have a decent planet to put it on?

—Henry David Thoreau

Figure 12.1 Ecosystems can be damaged in three principal ways.

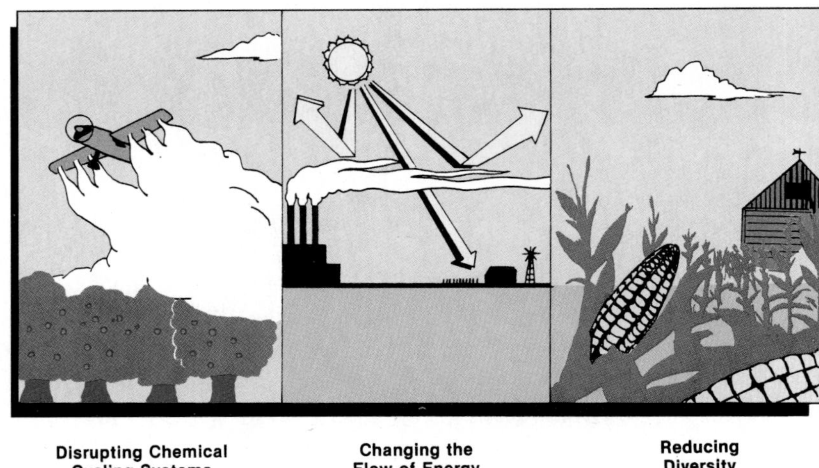

When humans had less impact on the environment, natural processes restored damaged ecosystems and countered the stresses that were placed on them. Winds and rains removed pollutants from the air. Flowing streams and decomposers acted together to purify dirty water. The natural movements of minerals and soil, along with the diversity of available vegetation and seeds, slowly restored land that had been damaged by fire, flood or human action.

A main factor in this partial restoration was time—the time for decomposers to break down the pollutants, and time for the surrounding ecosystem to advance into and restore damaged land. But, as the human population has become larger and more affluent, we have lost time as our ally.

?

How can ecosystems be damaged?

Ecosystems can be severely damaged in three principal ways. First, essential chemical cycling systems can be disrupted. Second, the flow of energy through them can be changed. Third, their diversity can be reduced. Modern societies, with their large numbers and large-scale use of energy and machines, are damaging ecosystems in all three ways. The widespread use of artificial fertilizers, herbicides and pesticides disrupts chemical cycles. Single-crop farming on great expanses of land is destroying plant diversity. The introduction of air pollutants, waste heat, and carbon dioxide (CO_2) into the atmosphere disrupts the energy flow through the ecosphere. As living organisms totally dependent on what the ecosphere provides, we must look carefully at what we are doing.

What human activity has the greatest impact on our environment?

In the past, keeping a family fed and housed was considered far more important than the environmental impact of those actions. As a result, we were left with many environmental problems. Human impact on the global environment comes from many sources. Modern agriculture uses pesticides, herbicides, and fertilizers. Mineral and other natural resources are removed from the ground. Energy is

Figure 12.2 Volcano—nature in action. Mount St. Helens with small ash burst, as seen from Harry's Ridge, five miles north of the volcano. (From United States Dept. of the Interior, U.S. Geological Survey, David A. Johnston Cascades Volcano Observatory, Vancouver, Washington. Photo by Lyn Topinka)

transported and utilized for human needs. Roads, highways, and airports are built to provide mobility. Each step in these processes has an environmental connection.

Good resource management demands the connection be examined scientifically and understood before an action is taken. Today, this is being done. The purpose of this chapter is to take a close look at some of the environmental implications of our attempt to achieve the "good life." We will look at some of the corrective measures we have taken, and can take. We will consider air and land quality, and methods of waste management.

Air Quality

The composition of Earth's air has remained much the same for millions of years. All modern living things evolved in that atmosphere and are dependent on it. When human activities change the air's composition, we may threaten the health or even the existence of some species, including our own.

  12.1 Air Pollution

It was one of the worst cases of air pollution in history. Poisonous gas, smoke and fumes polluted the once-sweet air of the Italian coastal city. The sky grew dark. Many died simply from breathing the air.

In this case, air pollution had come from a natural source—the eruption of Mt. Vesuvius that buried the city of Pompeii in the year 79 A.D. Volcanoes and fires have poured natural pollutants into the atmosphere for centuries. Wind adds dust, and plants add pollen and other vapors to the air. Wind and natural circulation, along with rain and gravity, can also remove these pollutants. Over time, natural forces establish a new state.

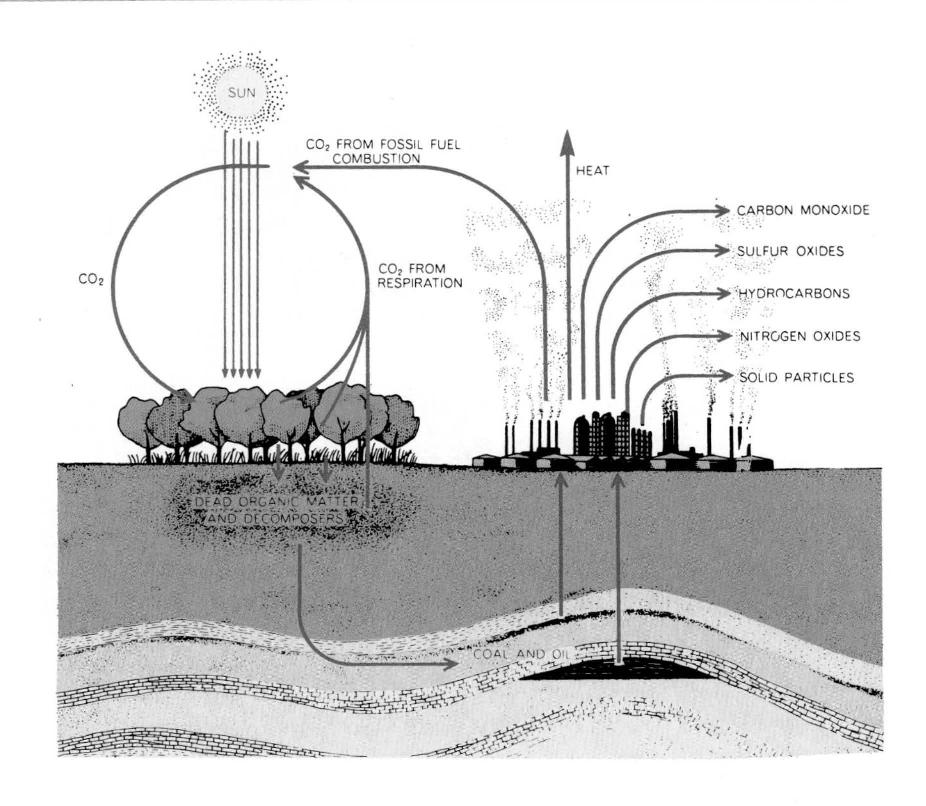

Figure 12.3 Energy cycle involved in the combustion of fossil fuels begins with solar energy employed in photosynthesis millions of years ago. A small fraction of the plants is buried under conditions that prevent complete oxidation. The material undergoes chemical changes that transform it into coal, oil and other fuels. When they are burned to release their stored energy, only part of the energy goes into useful work. Much of the energy is returned to the atmosphere as heat, together with such by-products of combustion as carbon dioxide and water vapor. Other emissions in fossil fuel combustion are listed at the right in the relative order of their volume. (From "Human Energy Production as a Process in the Biosphere," by S. Fred Singer, © 1970 by Scientific American, Inc. All rights reserved.)

Starting around 1800 with the Industrial Revolution, the air's composition was altered by the wide-scale combustion (burning) of fossil fuels. Today over 90% of the energy used each year in the United States involves the combustion of fossil fuels. Figure 12.3 summarizes the energy cycle for fossil fuels.

The five emissions (**pollutants**) listed at the right of Figure 12.3 cause the most concern. To emphasize the origin of these pollutants, the combustion equations from Chapter 6 are summarized in the boxed section.

An **air pollutant** is any substance in the air that is concentrated enough to harm humans or other animals, vegetation, or materials. Some familiar pollutants are smoke, carbon monoxide, and sulfur dioxide.

The ebb and flow of pollutants in our atmosphere is under increasing surveillance by the Federal Government's **Environmental Protection Agency** (EPA), the National Center for Atmospheric Research (NCAR) and National Oceanic and Atmospheric Administration (NOAA). These agencies either regulate pollution or monitor the air's composition.

Combustion (Burning Equations)

Oil:

oil + oxygen ——> CO_2 + H_2O + heat + wastes*

* wastes = unburned hydrocarbons, carbon monoxide (CO), NO_x, SO_x and some lead compounds (in the case of leaded gasoline)

Natural Gas:

natural gas + oxygen ———> CO_2 + H_2O + heat

Coal:

coal + oxygen ———> CO_2 + heat + wastes

More specifically,

coal (C) + oxygen (O_2) ——> CO_2 + heat + soot (unburned coal) + sulfur gases + nitrogen oxides + fly ash + CO.

12.2 The Big Five Air Pollutants

?

What is an air pollutant? What are the five major air pollutants in the United States?

Many substances pollute the air, but five cause most of the problems. These five are suspended particles (soot, ashes, dust, etc.), sulfur oxides (SO_x), nitrogen oxides (NO_x), carbon monoxide (CO), and unburned hydrocarbons (also called volatile organics) which are related to ozone (O_3). Carbon dioxide (CO_2) is not usually considered a pollutant, but you will read about possible problems associated with this gas later in this chapter.

a. Particulates

What are particulates?

Particulates are solid particles or liquid droplets suspended or carried in the air. Particulates are found mainly in automobile and truck emissions (our largest source), and in some industrial and combustion (power plants, heating) emissions. Particulates can directly damage the respiratory tract, can soil buildings and other materials, and can reduce visibility. In addition, they may contribute to long-term climatic changes.

Efforts to reduce air pollution have been most successful in the case of particulates. The installation of control equipment on industrial and power plant furnaces, and stricter regulations on the burning of solid wastes, are the major reasons for this reduction. Emission controls on automobiles have been important, also.

Figure 12.4 Particulates: effects on health and property.

b. Sulfur Oxides (SO_x)

Where do sulfur oxides come from?

Sulfur dioxide (SO_2) and other sulfur oxides are formed when sulfur-containing fuels are burned. Sulfur oxides are a by-product of the generation of electricity. This is because most electric power plants burn coal, oil or gas. All of these fuels contain some sulfur. In addition, automobiles also emit sulfur oxides. Metal ores can contain various amounts of sulfur. Therefore, metal smelters are also sulfur oxide sources.

Sulfur oxides do their damage as corrosive and lung-damaging sulfuric acid in smog. Sulfur oxides irritate respiratory passages and worsen conditions such as asthma, bronchitis, and emphysema.

Sulfur oxides are most effectively reduced by removing sulfur from coal before it is burned. Sulfur oxides can also be removed from smoke-stack emissions by using powdered limestone or trona. This process is called **scrubbing.**

c. Carbon Monoxide (CO)

Carbon monoxide is formed when carbon is not completely burned. It is a major problem in cities at higher elevations. Because of the lower oxygen content of the air, more CO (and less CO_2) is formed.

What causes carbon monoxide to form?

Carbon monoxide is a problem because it binds to the **hemoglobin** in our blood. Hemoglobin ordinarily carries oxygen to our cells. By reacting with hemoglobin, carbon monoxide causes oxygen deprivation (loss) in the body. Exposure to moderate concentrations of carbon monoxide causes headache and fatigue. Continued exposure to large concentrations can be fatal.

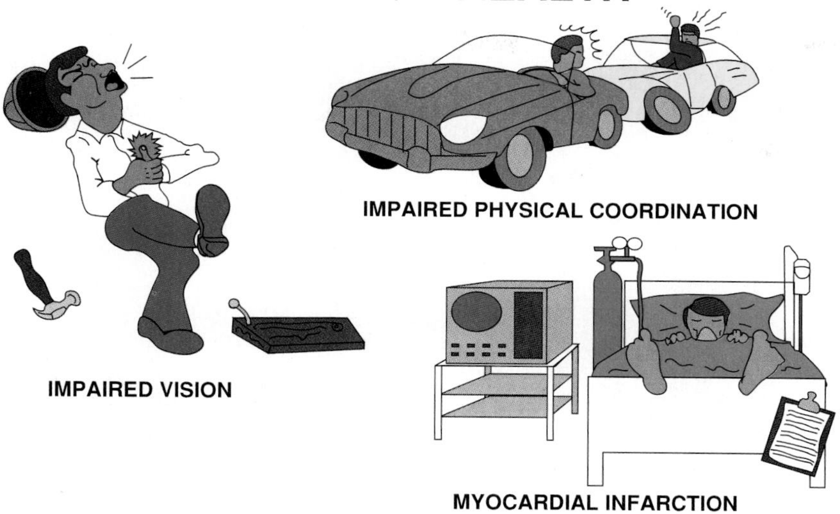

Figure 12.5 Carbon monoxide: effects on health.

Both improving emission-control systems on automobiles (through the use of catalytic converters) and increasing the oxygen content of fuels help reduce carbon monoxide levels.

d. Unburned Hydrocarbons

What causes the release of unburned hydrocarbons?

Unburned hydrocarbons (also called volatile organic compounds) come from incomplete combustion of gasoline and from evaporation of petroleum fuels, industrial solvents, paints, and dry cleaning fluids. They are most closely related to transportation, industrial processes, and home heating. The primary problem with hydrocarbons is their role in forming **photochemical smog.** They react with nitrogen oxides in sunlight and form ozone and other reactive chemicals. Catalytic converters are designed to break apart unburned hydrocarbons and change them into carbon dioxide and water. Federal emission standards, regulations, and technology have led to reduced emissions from the unburned hydrocarbons of automobiles.

e. Ozone

How is ozone formed in the lower atmosphere?

Ozone (O_3) is a highly reactive gas that is a pollutant when found in the *lower* atmosphere. It comes from a reaction involving sunlight and unburned hydrocarbons, but it also is naturally created by lightning. As a pollutant, ozone causes eye, throat and lung irritation. It may cause unwanted chemical reactions in various materials such as rubber.

Ozone in the *upper* atmosphere, on the other hand, is necessary for screening out ultraviolet radiation. More about that later.

Figure 12.6 Ozone: effects on health and property.

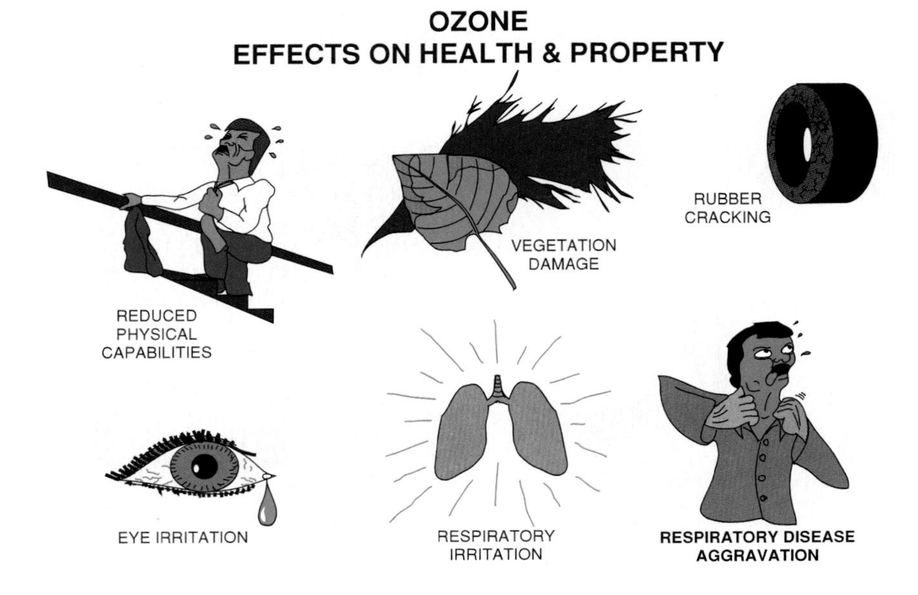

f. Nitrogen Oxides

Under what conditions will nitric oxide form?

Air is 78% nitrogen. At normal temperatures, nitrogen is relatively inert. (That is, it does not combine with other elements.) However, at the high temperatures associated with combustion, furnaces, and engines, some nitrogen gas (N_2) combines with oxygen to form nitric oxide (NO).

In the air, nitric oxide quickly reacts with additional oxygen to form nitrogen dioxide (NO_2) and/or nitrogen tetroxide (N_2O_4). These compounds are referred to as nitrogen oxides, symbolized as NO_x. Nitrogen dioxide absorbs light and is largely responsible for the brownish color of photochemical smog.

Smog originated as a term for the combination of smoke and fog in major cities. Smog was primarily industrial in origin. The term today also is applied to the brownish photochemical haze produced by the reaction between sunlight, atmospheric gases, automobile exhausts and industrial emissions. Most sunlight-driven chemical reactions involve nitrogen oxides and unburned hydrocarbons. The reactive chemicals produced not only harm living organisms, but even damage paint, rubber and other materials.

Catalytic converters are now designed to greatly reduce nitrogen oxides from automobiles. The converters include platinum and rhodium, which when heated by the exhaust, aid in stripping oxygen atoms from NO_x to release N_2 and O_2.

12.3 Temperature Inversion

The atmosphere around us is heated by the sun and by radiation from the Earth's surface. Under normal conditions, the air temperature drops steadily with increases in altitude. Air is warmer near the ground because it receives heat both from the ground and from sunlight. The air gets cooler and thinner at higher elevations.

Figure 12.7 City skyline enveloped in pollution. (National Renewable Energy Laboratory)

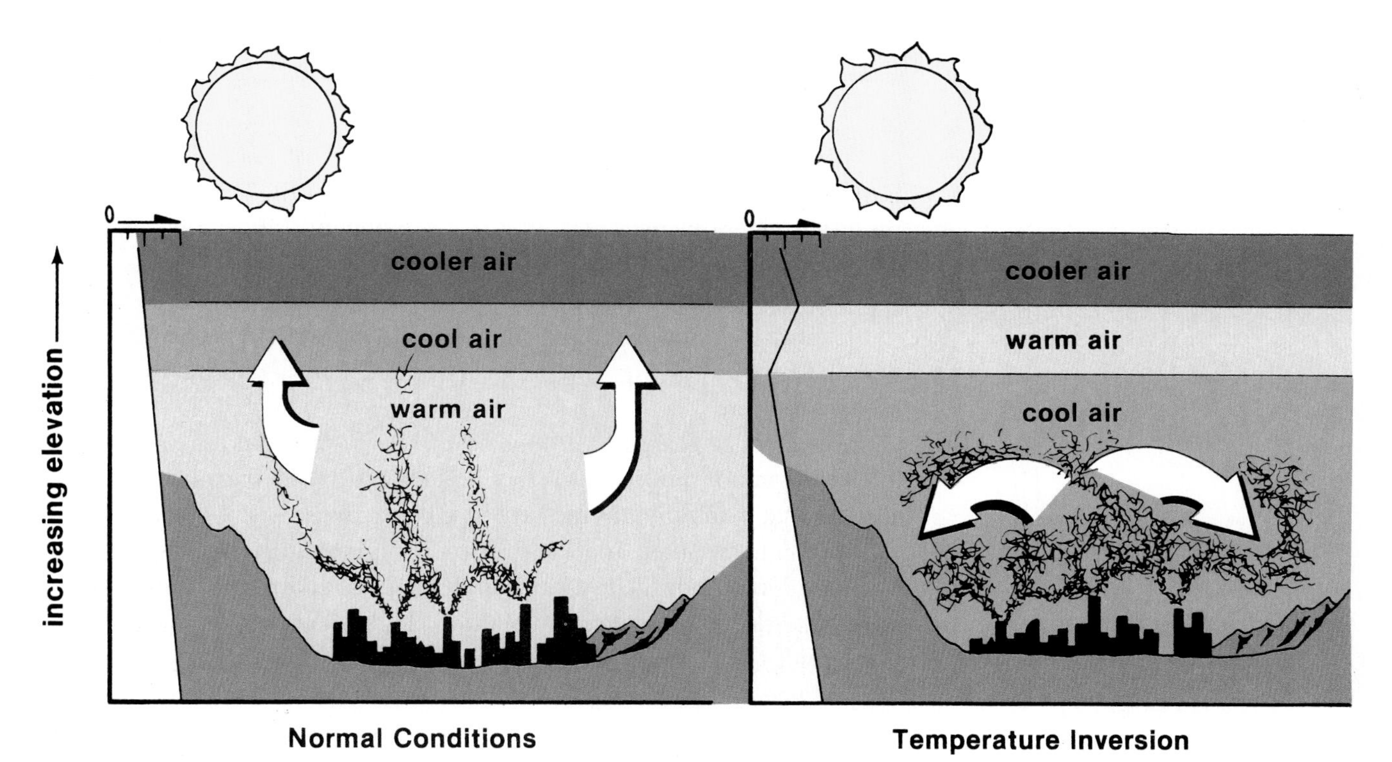

Figure 12.8 In a temperature inversion, pollutants are trapped in a layer of cool air that cannot rise into the warm air above it.

Polluted air given off by chimneys and smokestacks is generally much warmer than surrounding air. Under normal conditions, it is less dense than the air into which it escapes. Hence, it rises, spreads out, and becomes diluted. This is illustrated on the left side in Figure 12.8.

When polluted air is free to rise, its effects are short-lived. But when it is trapped above a land area by hills and mountains and a **temperature inversion,** the area may be polluted a long time.

?

What is a temperature inversion? Why do temperature inversions often create a health hazard?

Figure 12.9 The formation of sulfuric acid and nitric acid.

The Formation of Sulfuric Acid

STEP 1. The oxidation of sulfur when coal is burned:

$S + O_2 \rightleftarrows SO_2$

STEP 2. Further oxidation in the atmosphere:

$SO_2 + \frac{1}{2} O_2 \rightleftarrows SO_3$

STEP 3. Combination with water vapor to form acid:

$SO_3 + H_2O \rightleftarrows H_2SO_4$ (sulfuric acid)

The Formation of Nitric Acid

STEP 1. Nitrogen Fixation in hot engines and furnaces:

$N_2 + O_2 \rightleftarrows 2NO$

STEP 2. Further oxidation in the atmosphere:

$NO + \frac{1}{2}O_2 \rightleftarrows NO_2$

STEP 3. Combination with water vapor to form nitric acid and more NO:

$3NO_2 + H_2O \rightleftarrows 2HNO_3$ (nitric acid) $+ NO$

Temperature inversions arise when a layer of cool air near the Earth's surface is trapped beneath a layer of warm air. This holds back the usual air movement and dilution of pollutants (illustrated on the right side of Figure 12.8).

Normally, as distance from the ground increases, the temperature of the air drops. But in an inversion, above the lid of the cool layer is a thick layer of air having a higher temperature. This is referred to as the inversion layer.

Pollutants released at ground level rise in the cool air until they hit the inversion layer. Here they collect and build into the "brown clouds" that many of our cities are trying to prevent.

If a cold weather front moves into a region, the warm layer may be pushed away. Or, if intense sunlight can warm the cooler air at the Earth's surface, the inversion condition can be broken. However, during lengthy cold-calm periods, the pollutants may stay for several days. Since the pollutants are building up in a fixed volume of air, their concentrations can increase to harmful levels. To guard against this, traffic volume, industrial activity, and wood burning are carefully watched.

12.4 Acid Precipitation

Nitrogen and sulfur oxides in smog can cause great local damage. They also can harm living organisms far away from their source of emission. When the oxides combine with water vapor in the air, they form acids, as shown in Figure 12.9. Figure 12.10 illustrates "human-caused" acid rain production.

Figure 12.10 Human-caused production of acid rain. (From National Center for Atmospheric Research/National Science Foundation [NCAR/NSF].)

List some of the effects of acid precipitation.

Acid rain has created problems in lakes, soil and vegetation in North America, Japan, and regions of western Europe, especially the Black Forest in Germany. The acidic rainfall often occurs thousands of miles from the emissions, which are carried by the wind. Some experts think that an acidic haze over southern Alaska comes from Asia. Tall smokestacks built during the 1960s and 1970s to ease local air pollution may add to the acidity of rainfall in distant places by sending emissions high into prevailing winds. Thus, significant air pollution can occur even where there is no heavy industry. Some lakes in the eastern United States, Canada and Sweden are so acidic that fish populations have been severely reduced or destroyed. See Figure 12.11.

An acid is a substance with a high concentration of hydrogen **ions,** H^+. (An ion is an atom or group of atoms that has gained or lost electrons. It is positively or negatively charged.) Pure water, HOH or H_2O, is a combination of hydrogen ions and hydroxide ions, OH^-. Figure 12.12 shows how chemists measure acidity. They use a scale, called the pH scale, that ranks the acidity of a solution with a number from 1 to 14. Strong acids have the lowest pH values. (HC1, or stomach acid, has a pH of 1.5.) Weak acids have a pH of 4 or 5. Distilled water is neutral, with a pH of 7. If there are more OH^- ions than H^+

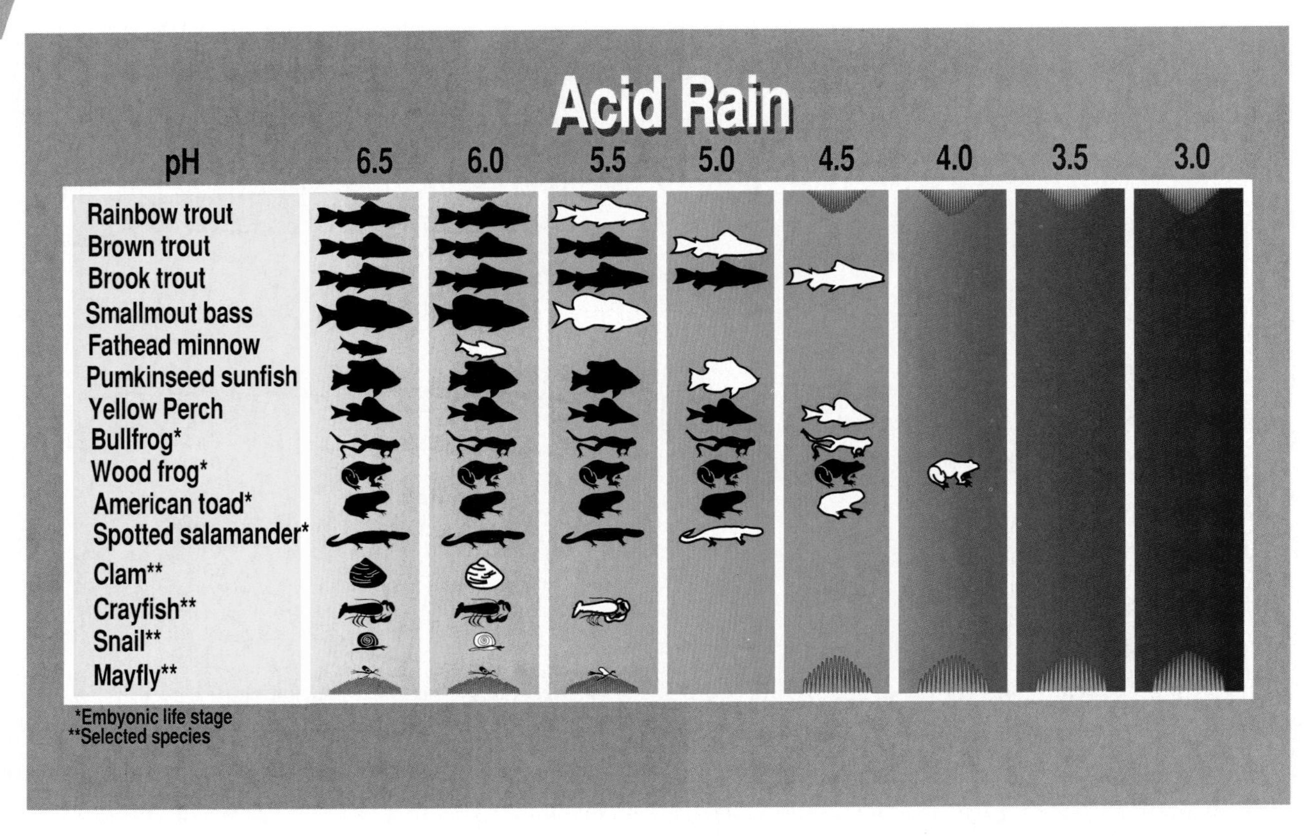

Figure 12.11 Acid rain: the effect on aquatic species. (From U.S. Department of the Interior [DOI], Fish and Wildlife Service [FWS].)

ions in a substance, its pH is more than 7. Strong bases (such as lye) have a pH of 13 or 14. Weak bases have a pH of 8 or 9. Mixing a base with an acid can create neutral substances.

Acid precipitation is any precipitation having a high concentration of sulfuric and/or nitric acid. Its pH value is always less than 5.6. Normal rain usually has a pH of 5.6 to 5.7. This is due to the carbon dioxide in the atmosphere, which reacts with water to form carbonic acid.

Acid precipitation can reduce the number of plant nutrients in the ground, resulting in less fertile soil. Crop yields suffer. However, in some cases, it can actually increase the nutrients in the soil by adding sulfur and nitrogen.

Some experts believe that acid precipitation will reduce timber yields. White pine seems to be particularly vulnerable.

?

List some of the ways we are attempting to reduce acid rain.

To combat the problem, scientists are trying to reduce the acidity of lakes and streams by dropping lime (a weak base) into the water. They also are conducting experiments aimed at breeding fish that are more acid-resistant.

We must keep in mind that natural forces—lightning, sea spray, volcanoes, decaying vegetation, and even rain forest ants—contribute to acidic precipitation. (See Figure 12.13.) Thus, the Earth has been

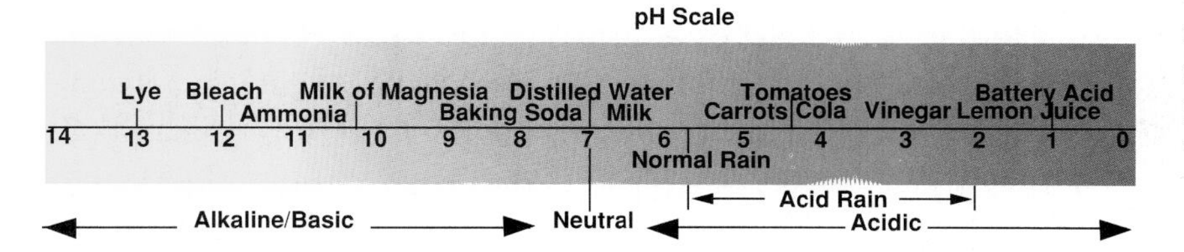

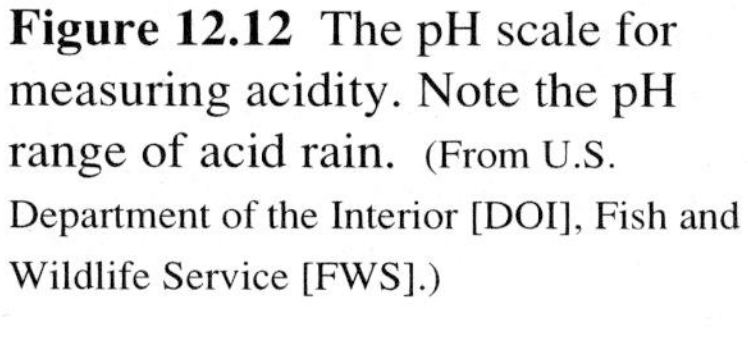

Figure 12.12 The pH scale for measuring acidity. Note the pH range of acid rain. (From U.S. Department of the Interior [DOI], Fish and Wildlife Service [FWS].)

Figure 12.13 Acid rain sources: natural and human-caused. Natural sources include thunderstorms, pine needles, volcanic eruptions, and even the activity of termites. (From Mineral Information Institute.)

living with acidic precipitation for millions of years. Probably the problem was more severe at some times than at others. Somehow, during those times, organisms adapted to the change.

This does not mean that we shouldn't lessen human production of acid rain. The technology exists to limit acid rain. Improvements in that technology are reducing the impact even more. For example, processes for removing the sulfur from coal before it is burned are being perfected. Unfortunately, technological solutions can be expensive.

12.5 Pollution Control and the Automobile

Why do we love our cars?

People will rally to fight pollution coming from power plants and industrial sources. In these cases, the "enemy" is perceived as *"them."*

The pollution problem is seen in a whole new light when it comes to automobiles. We Americans love our cars. We drive them, polish them, and often share our identity with them. To some, life is much less meaningful without them. Freedom, independence, power, prestige and individual worth are tied to a person's car/truck/four-wheel drive vehicle. This is one of the reasons it has been so difficult to expand mass transit, ride-sharing, or any other alternative mode of transportation in most areas. Only in cities where cars have led to great problems are people willing to use other ways of getting around.

This love affair with the automobile must be seriously considered if any attempt to reduce emissions from automobiles is to be successful. Two general approaches are promising: improving automobiles and fuels; and making driving less convenient and more expensive.

?

List some of the strategies that are being tried in an attempt to reduce/improve emissions from automobiles.

a. Improved Automobile Efficiency

Decreasing the total mass of the car is one of the most effective ways to improve fuel efficiency. Composite bodies (plastic and fibers) coupled with lighter ceramic engines may soon result in many automobiles that give from 40 to 60 miles per gallon or more. Cars with mileage ratings in this range exist today.

b. Special Traffic Lanes

The "fast lanes" can be designated for buses and high-occupancy vehicles (HOV) during rush hours, making driving less appealing.

c. Increased Automobile Costs

The cost of operating an automobile can be increased by raising the tax on gasoline, charging motorists fees for entering certain areas during rush hour, and increasing the cost of parking downtown.

d. Improved Fuels

We can develop cleaner-burning fuels for the internal combustion engine. Oxygenated fuels, which have oxygen built into them, reduce carbon monoxide emissions. When burned, they give off more CO_2 and less CO. Plant-based alcohol fuels add little CO_2 to the atmosphere in the long run, because photosynthesis by new plants can use the CO_2 produced by burning alcohol. Hydrogen may become an automotive fuel if a cheaper solar cell is developed.

e. Lowered Emissions

After-burners and the catalytic converter help control emissions from today's internal combustion engines. The **catalytic converter** oxidizes carbon monoxide to carbon dioxide, and unburned hydrocarbon to carbon dioxide and water. Catalytic converters can also break NO_x into N_2 and O_2.

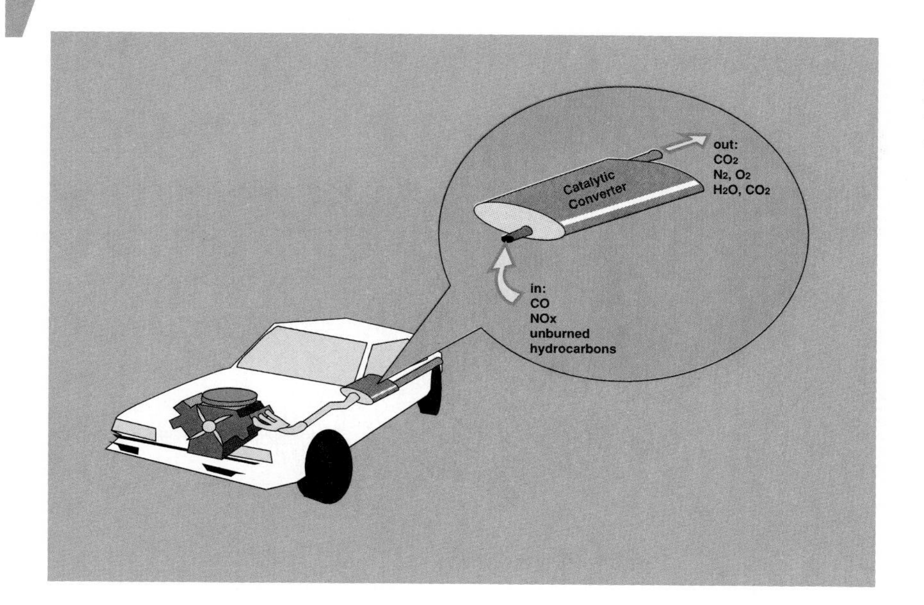

Figure 12.14 A catalytic converter changes engine exhausts into harmless carbon dioxide, nitrogen, oxygen, and water.

f. Smaller Vehicles

Small, quiet, and efficient electric cars and trucks for urban use would allow freedom of movement and greatly reduce transportation pollutants. Excellent batteries are available now, but light, small and tough bodies need to be designed and built with well-known composites.

g. Improved Engines

The internal combustion engine can be modified to lower emissions and improve gasoline mileage. A variety of new engine designs are being tested.

 12.6 Pollution Control and Electric Power Generation

Describe some of the measures being taken to reduce the negative impacts of electric power-generating plants.

The most striking success in controlling pollution from autos and industry has been in the reduction of particulate emissions. This residue, the visible particles—unburned carbon (soot), mineral ash and particles of tar—is what gives the blackness to smoke.

Because coal is usually the fuel in electric power plants, emissions from the plant's smokestacks were once a problem. Today, several processes are available for dealing with that source of pollution. By circulating the smoke between electrically charged plates (in a process called **electrostatic precipitation**), up to 99.5% of the total mass of particulate matter can be removed. Unfortunately, the remaining 0.5% contains the more hazardous fine particles, which manage to escape. See Figure 12.15a.

A **baghouse filter** can remove up to 99.9% of the particles, including the fine ones. A baghouse might be likened to a building-size vacuum cleaner. Exhaust gases are forced through fiber bag filters before they escape into the environment. See Figure 12.15b.

Figure 12.15a Electrostatic precipitator. The dirty air flows between negatively charged wires and grounded metal collecting plates. The particles in the air stream become charged and are attracted to the plates. The plates hold the accumulated dust until it is periodically knocked into hoppers. The clean air is pumped out through a stack. (American Lung Association)

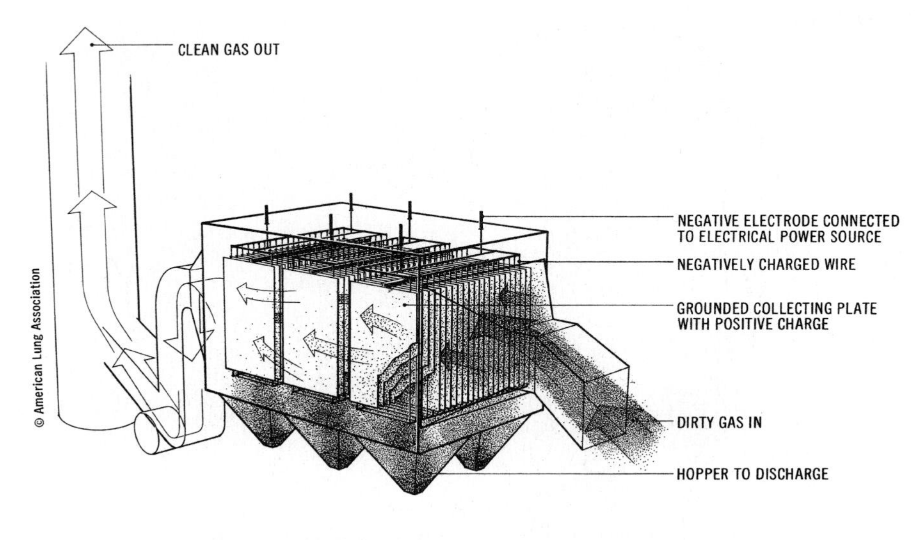

Figure 12.15b Baghouse. The dirty air is carried by pipe to the sides of the hoppers. From there the air passes up, into, and through the filter bags, and exits, clean, through vents in the walls and roof. (The cleaned air might also be vented through a stack.) The dirt trapped by the bags is periodically shaken into the hoppers, from which it can be removed. (American Lung Association)

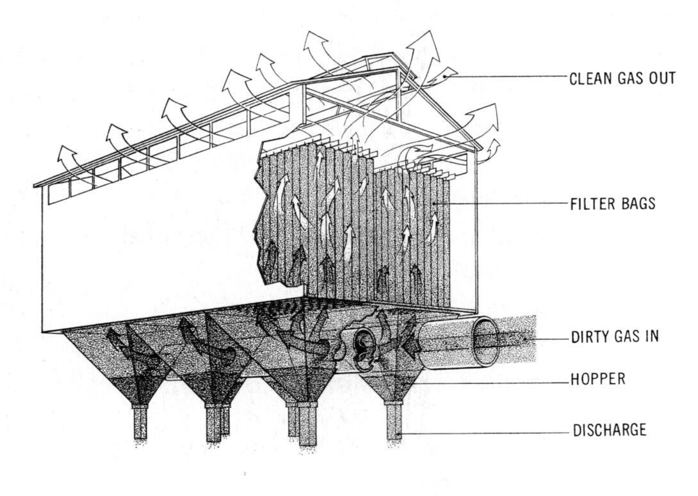

Sulfur dioxide is not removed by either the electrostatic precipitator or the baghouse filter. The **wet scrubber** can do that. It is illustrated in Figure 12.16. The scrubber forces stack gases through a chemical spray that absorbs SO_2. Scrubbers remove up to 99.5% of the particles and 80 to 95% of the SO_2, but they are extremely expensive to build and maintain.

Low-sulfur coals, like those found in the western United States, can be readily dry scrubbed. This process is well advanced and is economically feasible. Dry scrubbing is always combined with baghouse filtering.

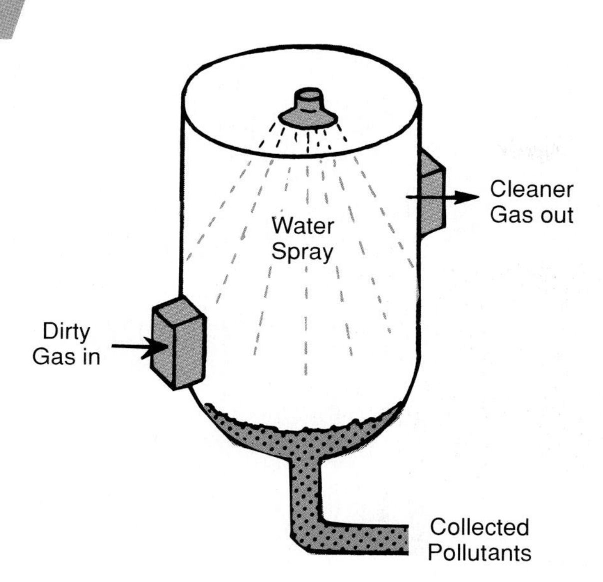

Figure 12.16 A wet scrubber. (From Public Service Company of Colorado.)

The major source of the sulfur pollutant is the sulfur impurity in coal. The most logical thing to do is to remove the sulfur from the coal before it is burned. Although some sulfur compounds can be removed by routine washing, most of them resist such simple removal. One of the advantages of coal gasification and liquefaction is the removal of sulfur before the gaseous or liquid fuels are formed.

Burning coal in the newer fluidized-bed furnaces also has advantages for similar reasons. Crushed calcium carbonate or limestone ($CaCO_3$) is added to the coal in the furnace, and the sulfur is removed as calcium sulfate ($CaSO_4$).

With all of these expensive efforts, there is still one more major problem—carbon dioxide. We haven't referred to it as a pollutant, because it is a normal part of the air. As fossil fuels are burned, carbon dioxide is formed and goes up the smoke stack. The implications of this fact will be discussed in the next section.

Pollution and Climate

When fossil fuels are burned, carbon dioxide (CO_2) is released into the air. Unmined coal, crude oil, natural gas, oil shale and tar sand deposits represent potential energy for powering future machines. They also represent billions and billions of future carbon dioxide molecules that are not in the atmosphere at the present time. Since burning is oxidation of carbon, burning carbon-containing fuel produces carbon dioxide. At present, fossil fuels are our primary source of energy. Burning them is the major energy conversion process. What are the implications of releasing all that carbon dioxide?

 12.7 The Greenhouse Effect

Why has the carbon dioxide content of our atmosphere increased?

The carbon dioxide content of the atmosphere has increased since the Industrial Revolution. Analysis of air trapped in the 1700s shows

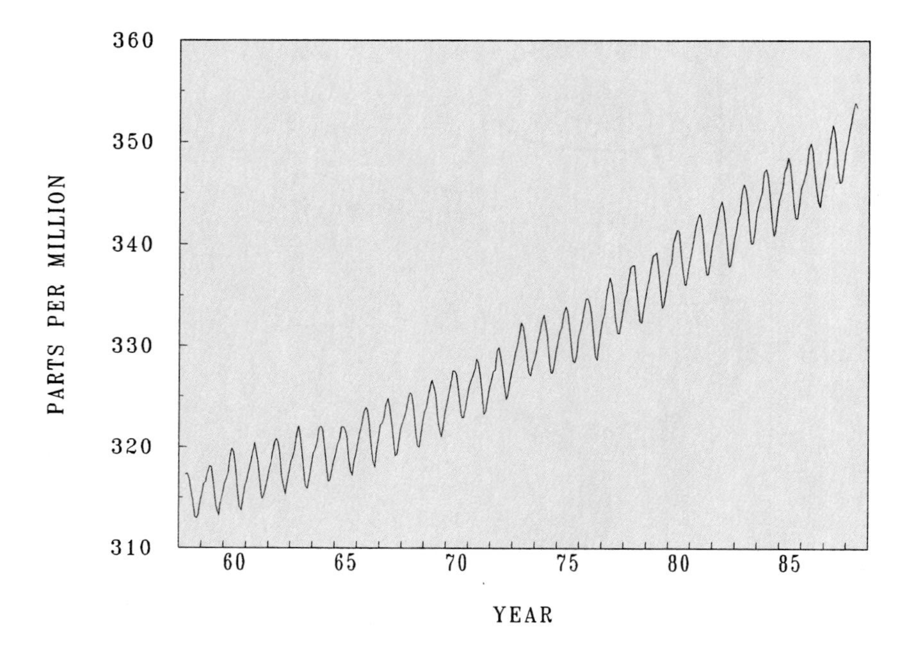

Figure 12.17 CO_2 concentration at Mauna Loa, Hawaii: 1958–1988. (From Charles D. Keeling, Scripps Institution of Oceanography and the Geophysical Monitoring for Climatic Change Laboratory, National Oceanic and Atmospheric Administration [NOAA].)

it had less carbon dioxide than today's air. The Mauna Loa Observatory in Hawaii has kept one of the longest continuous records of the changing CO_2 content of the atmosphere in more recent times. That record is illustrated in Figure 12.17.

Plants help control the amount of CO_2 in the atmosphere by using it for photosynthesis. Animals and humans breathe in oxygen and exhale CO_2. Plants use the CO_2 and give off oxygen. It is essential that we maintain plant growth to balance the effects of animal and human populations.

Carbon dioxide molecules allow passage of the visible and ultraviolet radiation of the incoming sunlight. But, they absorb the longer wavelength infrared (heat) radiated from the warm Earth. This traps heat in the atmosphere and may produce what is called the **"greenhouse effect."** This effect is similar to the heat build-up in a greenhouse or in a car with closed windows. See Figure 12.18. This effect is critical in maintaining temperatures suitable for life. However, CO_2 in the atmosphere is increasing. Some of the increase is due to the burning of fossil fuels. Some is due to land clearing and the related decrease in vegetation, as fewer plants are there to use the CO_2 molecules. Some of the increase is due to volcanoes. Some experts on the subject estimate that the Earth's mean temperature could rise 1.5° C to 4.5° C (2.5° F to 7.5° F) by the year 2050 if greenhouse gases continue to increase at the current rate. Such estimates are tied to computer modeling involving many variables whose connections are poorly understood. The predictions thus cannot be easily tested in the lab. They, however, imply changes we carefully watch for.

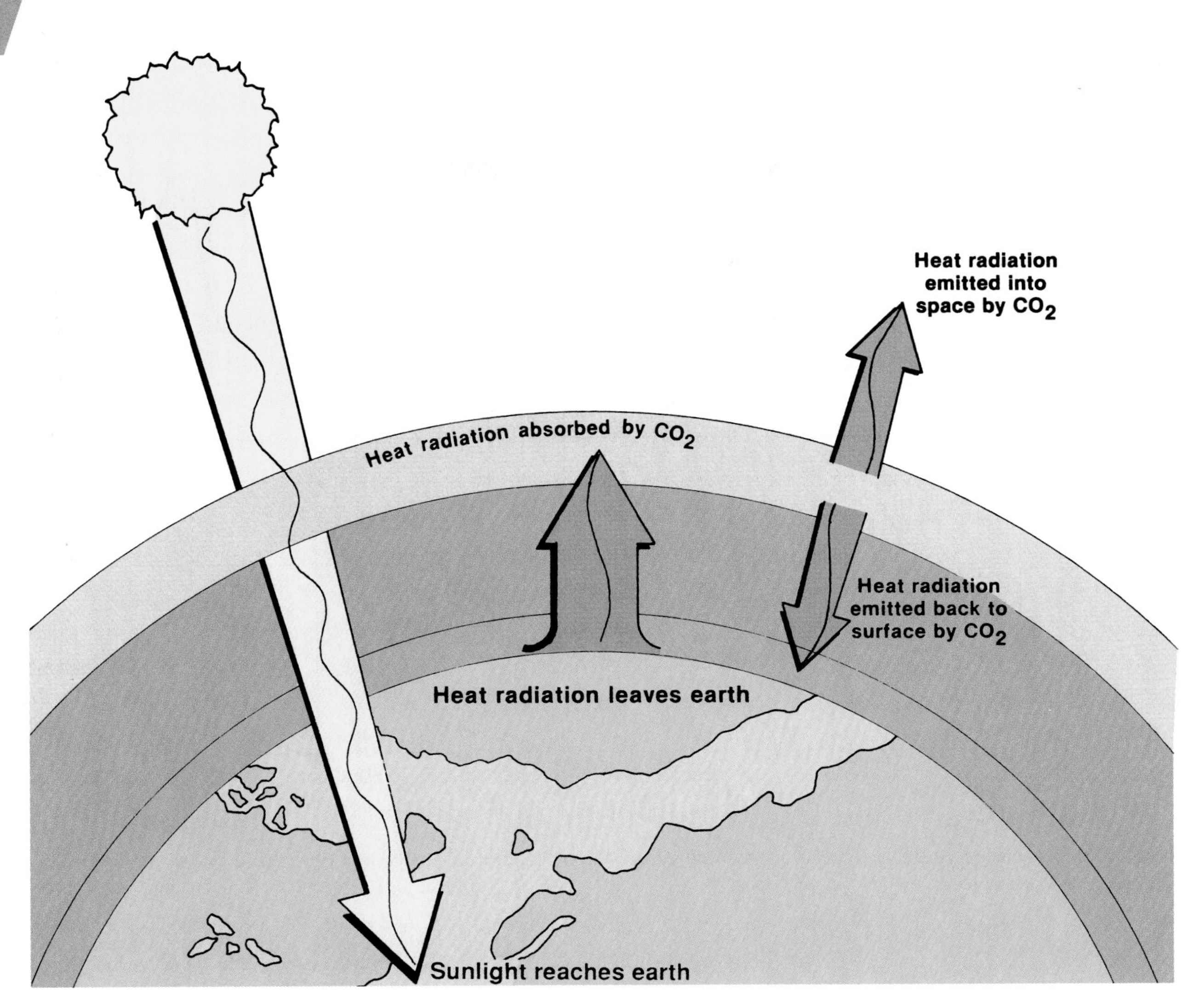

Figure 12.18 The greenhouse effect. (From National Center for Atmospheric Research/National Science Foundation [NCAR/NSF].)

How can the greenhouse effect result in a warmer Earth?

In addition to CO_2, methane and the **chlorofluorocarbons** (CFCs) have been shown to behave as greenhouse gases. Methane is produced as livestock manure decomposes and as termites break down dead wood. The CFCs have been used as refrigerants and for styrofoam. They were also used, until recently, as spray-can propellants.

Figure 12.19 shows average global temperature changes during the past century. When the CO_2 concentration data in Figure 12.17 (which covers 1958–1988) is compared to the same time period in Figure 12.19, one can see the reason for concern. Is this similarity scientific proof? Is CO_2 build-up the only possible explanation? Scientists, political leaders, and business executives will be debating this for the next decade. Examining some of the references cited at the end of this chapter can help you learn more about this issue. Are we debating

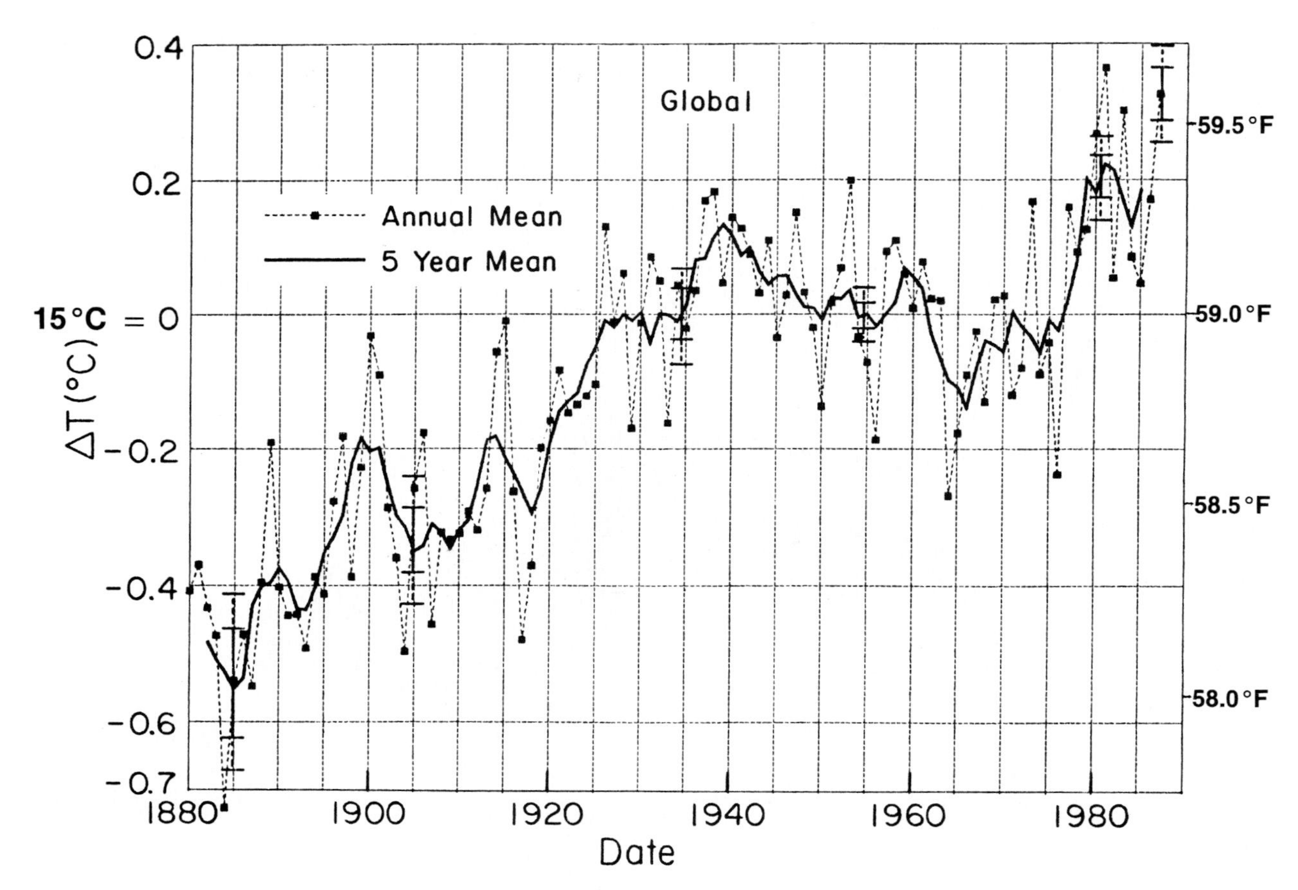

Figure 12.19 Average global temperature changes during the past century. (From American Geophysical Union © 1988; Fahrenheit scale added by author.)

when we should be taking action? That is something each one of us must decide. The collective opinion of the general public will help determine what action or lack of action we take.

Increased warming of the Earth by the greenhouse effect is only a hypothesis. There were other greenhouse warmings before modern times. It is too soon to tell if a permanent warming trend has begun. What does seem certain is that about half of the CO_2 produced by industrial processes since the beginning of the industrial age is still in the atmosphere. The turnover rate seems low. We must, therefore, look ahead carefully. If we get too much CO_2 in the atmosphere, it will be a long time before it can be removed by natural processes.

How much is too much CO_2?

How much CO_2 is too much? This question is also difficult to answer with certainty. One calculation predicts that a doubling of the CO_2 content would increase the atmospheric temperature at the Earth's surface two or three degrees. A temperature change of this size would cause significant changes in climate. Changes in climate could greatly influence the Earth's ecosystem and its food-growing capability. The very fact that we do not know the consequences is the

Figure 12.20 If the atmospheric conditions are met, the contrails produced by jet aircraft can grow and produce thin cloud layers. (Photo by John W. Christensen.)

strongest reason for proceeding with care. Analyzing and understanding what we are doing to our ecosystem must be one of our highest priorities.

If we fail to use new strategies and technologies, the fossil fuel age could be brought to a close by concerns related to the greenhouse effect or by acid rain rather than by the exhaustion of our fuel supplies. If, for instance, we require that the increase of the CO_2 in the atmosphere be held to 50% of its pre-industrial level, we will be able to burn only about 10% of the known fossil fuel reserves. It appears that our planet itself may "tell" us to concentrate on conservation, improve efficiency, and use the renewable resources of energy.

How can we lessen our use of the fossil fuels that may contribute to the greenhouse effect? Since burning alcohol wouldn't add to the greenhouse effect (assuming the alcohol is of plant origin), perhaps it should receive serious consideration as a major liquid fuel. Hydrogen fuel is another possibility.

12.8 The Effect of Particles on Global Cooling

?

How can particles in our atmosphere influence global temperature?

Human activity results in the release of huge quantities of particles—soot, dust and so on—into the atmosphere. Agricultural plowing plus wind creates dust. Clearing of land in general does the same. The constant movement of traffic, along with vehicle and airplane emissions, results in particle generation. Airplane emissions create new cloud layers which reflect sunlight that would have reached the Earth if the plane had not been in flight. There also are particulate emissions from industrial smokestacks, power plants and home chimneys. It has been speculated that an all-out nuclear war would create a giant particle effect. To these we must add all the natural sources: volcanic eruptions, dust storms, forest fires, and pollens.

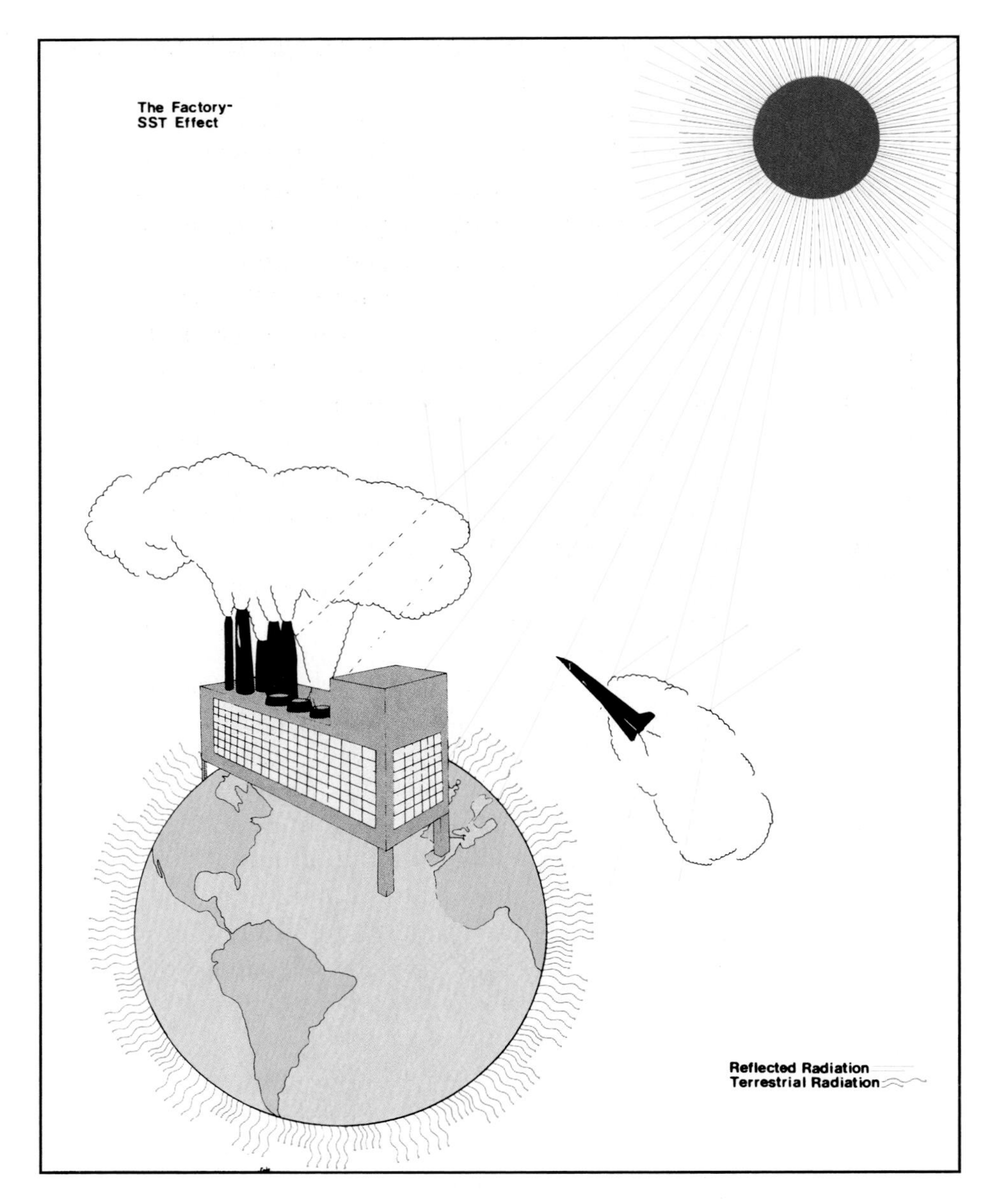

Figure 12.21 The effect of particles on incoming sunlight. (From Jennifer Cole.)

Particles can reflect sunlight back into space, reducing the amount of solar radiation that reaches the Earth's surface. The net result is cooling of the ground and atmosphere. Figure 12.21 illustrates this effect. (Some small particles in the upper atmosphere absorb sunlight and cause a warming of that region. It is generally believed, however, that the overall effect of particles in the atmosphere is cooling.)

Carbon dioxide may warm the Earth, particles may cool it. Might these two cancel each other? It is not yet known whether the particle effect will rival other events, such as the greenhouse effect. We do know that the Earth's weather machine is huge and complex. Humans are tampering with it in a variety of ways. The extent of this "weather modification" is just beginning to be understood.

12.9 Depletion of the Ozone Layer

?

Why is the ozone layer important?

While a layer of CO_2 and particles has been building up, the Earth's protective ozone layer has been thinning out.

The ozone layer surrounds Earth at an altitude of 12–35 miles. This layer is our first line of defense against the Sun's ultraviolet rays. The ozone can efficiently absorb ultraviolet light and thus prevent it from reaching life-forms on Earth. Ultraviolet rays cause sunburn and skin cancer, and have been linked to cataracts and other disorders.

What is ozone and how is it produced?

Ozone (O_3) is an oxygen gas that exists only rarely at the Earth's surface. It is produced during lightning storms and when sparks fly around powerful electrical equipment. It also is produced when sunlight acts on the ingredients that result in photochemical smog. Ozone is produced in the stratosphere when ordinary oxygen molecules (O_2) are bombarded with ultraviolet rays from the Sun. Ultraviolet radiation breaks apart O_2 molecules into free oxygen atoms (O). Some of the free oxygen atoms recombine with O_2 to form O_3.

Though ultraviolet radiation continually creates an abundance of ozone molecules, a variety of natural processes also destroy them. Until recently, these processes remained in balance.

In the 1960s, the group of **gaseous** chemicals called chlorofluorocarbons (CFCs) became very popular. Because they were nontoxic and inert, they could be used for refrigeration and for propellants in aerosol spray cans. They did what gases should do, but they didn't become involved in unwanted chemical reactions or make people sick. Unfortunately, when released, the gases rise into the stratosphere, where ultraviolet light can break them apart. Even worse, the resulting free chlorine atoms catalyze the destruction of ozone. Each chlorine atom produced could destroy 100,000 ozone molecules! See Figure 12.22.

This may be causing the reduction in the size of the ozone layer, especially over Antarctica. The change is shown in the satellite images reproduced in Figure 12.23.

About a dozen nations have agreed to sharply curtail the production of CFCs over the next decade. Let us hope that their action helps reduce the severity of the problem.

We also know that volcanic eruptions spew out great quantities of chlorine, which can also lead to ozone destruction. This has been going on throughout geologic time. We have no good data on these early depletions.

Land Quality

One of the most important reasons for the rapid growth of America into a great world power was its land. Natural resources of rich soil, hardwood forests, mineral deposits and abundant water were the assets contained on our continent.

When Europeans settled in America, they brought with them the concept of privately owned property. People could claim the right to own their own piece of land and develop it as they saw fit. Life,

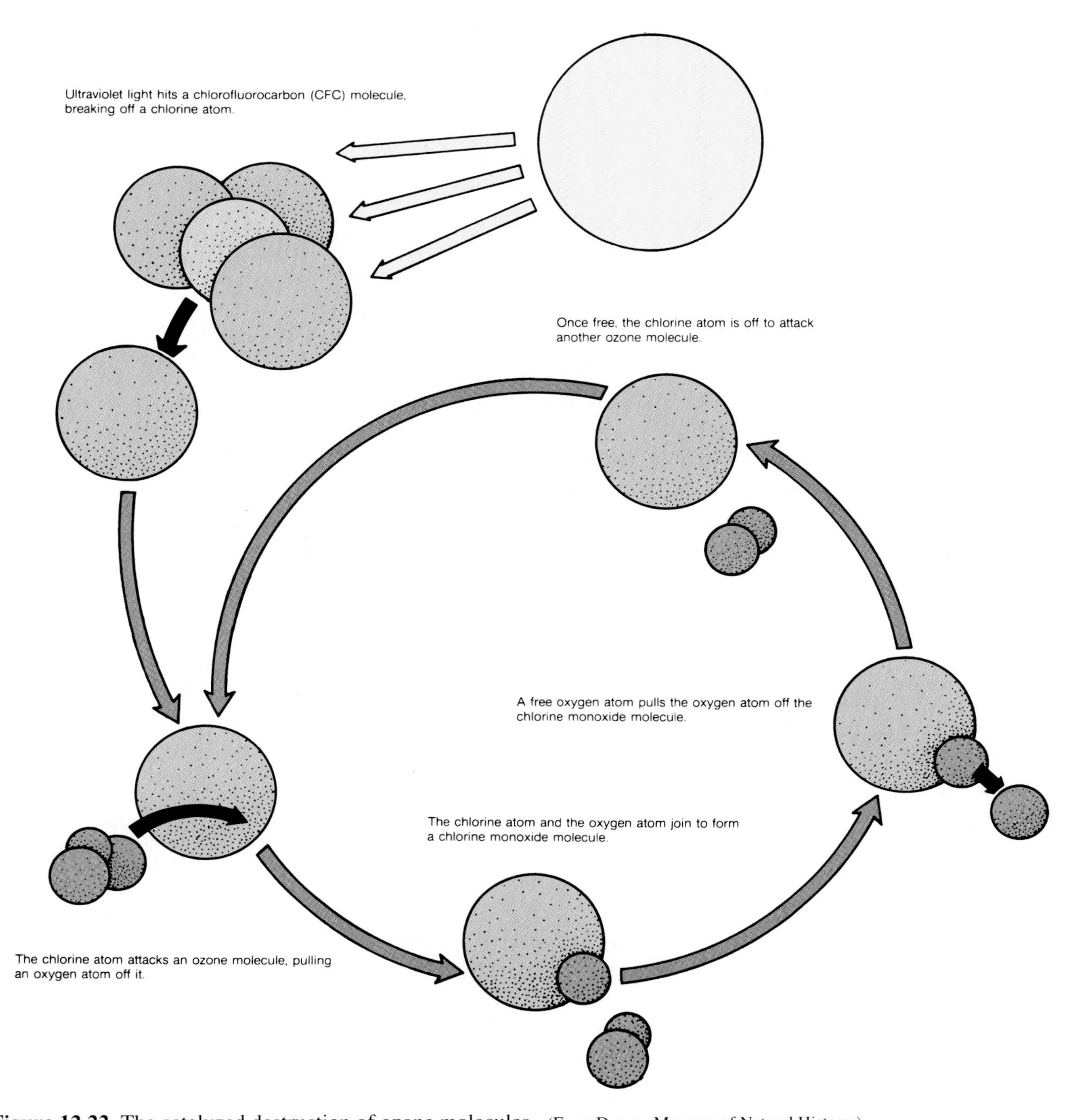

Figure 12.22 The catalyzed destruction of ozone molecules. (From Denver Museum of Natural History.)

liberty and private property all became linked within the American way of life. People also had the freedom to move and settle virtually anywhere in the country in pursuit of a better life.

What is land use?

Land use came to mean the use of land by human beings. Land-use priorities and decisions were made at the local level. Thus evolved the land-use patterns and practices that exist in America today. Western lands were acquired by purchase or treaty by the Federal government, which granted people land for settlement. The government also granted land to states, for schools and other purposes and to railroad

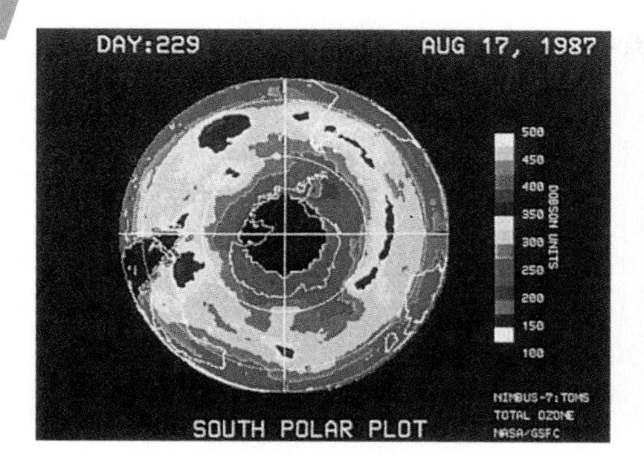

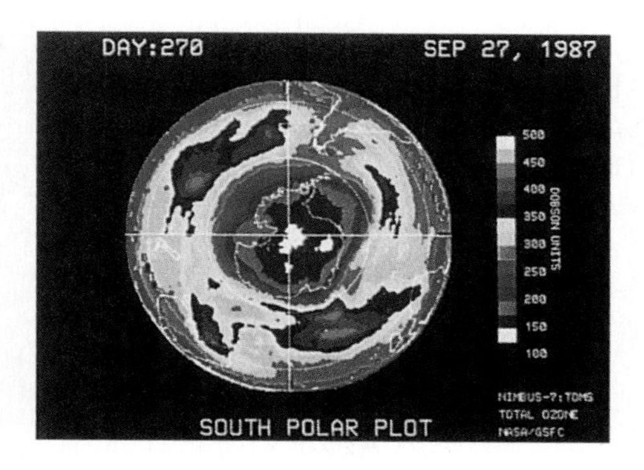

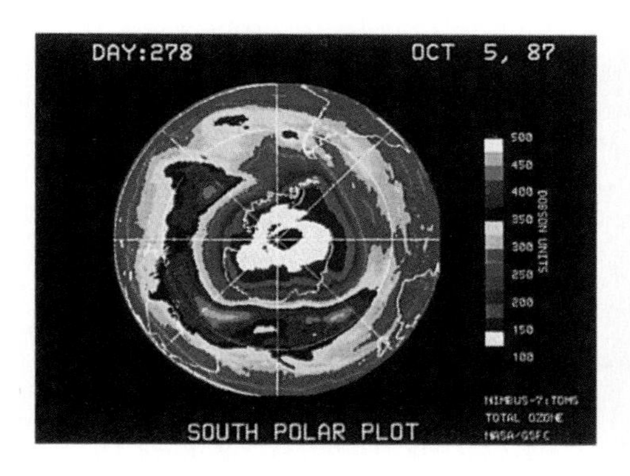

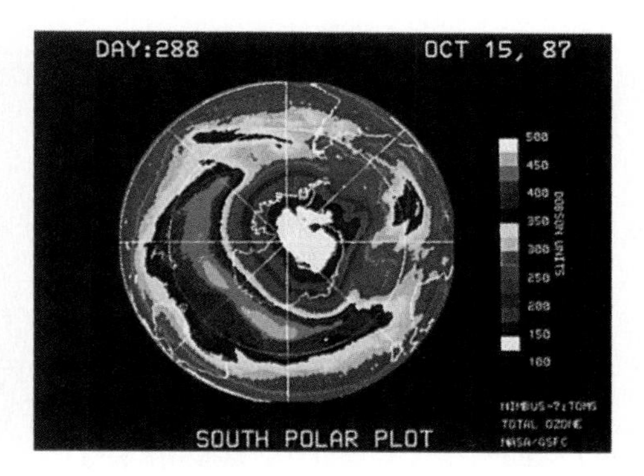

Figure 12.23 Growth and change in the ozone hole over Antarctica is shown in the satellite images for the time period from August 17 through October 15, 1987. Ozone concentration is measured in Dobson Units (DU). Concentration is indicated using a color scale. Low concentration of ozone corresponds to lower numbers on the Dobson Scale. (NASA/Goddard Institute for Space Studies.)

companies. Some grants went to individuals and companies for mineral development. Even today, the Federal government manages much of the land in the western states and regulates its use.

12.10 Present Land Use

Describe present land use in the United States.

Figure 12.25 shows how land in the United States is used. From this we see that over a quarter is forested (29%). Over a third is range and grassland (35%). Croplands cover another 17%, while deserts, swamps, and other lands amount to 12%.

Urban areas with populations of 2,500 or more account for only seven percent of the total. This doesn't sound like very much. However, it must be remembered that urban areas are not self-sustaining. They must be supported by vast farmlands, pastures, forests, estuaries and water drainage basins, as well as highway systems and industries.

In the entire history of the United States, less than 0.2% of the total land has been mined. Much of that tiny segment has been effectively reclaimed. See Figure 12.26.

Of the 2.3 billion acres in the United States . . .

- Farmlands cover 1.3 billion acres
- Urban areas use 34.6 million acres

Figure 12.24 Percent of Western States land area managed by the federal government. (From *Infowest Profile of the West,* edited by Philip M. Burgess, Jack A. Brizius, and Susan E. Foster. Western States' Strategy Center; © September, 1987.)

STATE	PERCENT
Alaska	89.5
Nevada	85.1
Utah	65.9
Idaho	62.5
Oregon	51.7
Wyoming	46.8
California	44.8
Arizona	43.9
Colorado	35.4
New Mexico	34.0
Montana	28.8
Washington	28.6
Hawaii	8.2
South Dakota	5.7
North Dakota	4.2
Nebraska	1.3

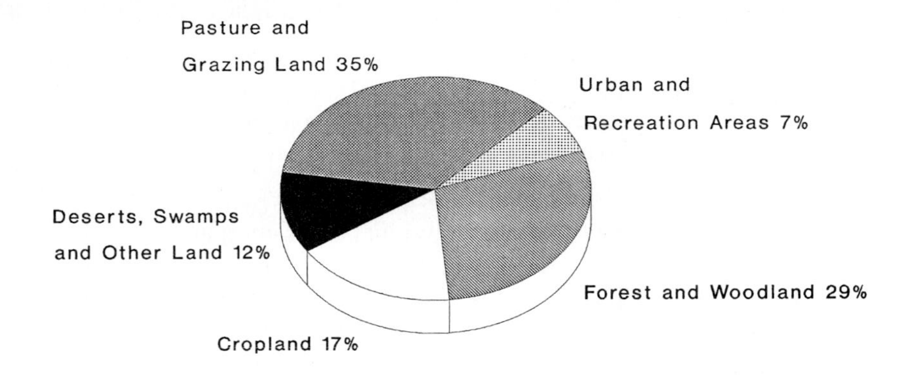

Figure 12.25 Present United States land use. (From Hammond Medallion World Atlas.)

- Highways cover 34 million acres
- Airports and railroads cover 6.5 million acres
- Mining uses less than 6 million acres
- Public lands (managed by the Federal government) total 525 million acres.

12.11 Present Land Use Decision-Making Structures

Land use is affected primarily by the resources it offers (forests, crops, minerals, water, location) and by government regulations. Almost 40% of all land in the United States is managed by the government, principally the Federal government. The highest concentration of Federal land is in the Far West—especially Alaska.

More than half of United States land is privately owned by individuals and corporations. The owners have considerable freedom to develop and use that land as they desire. This freedom, however, is not

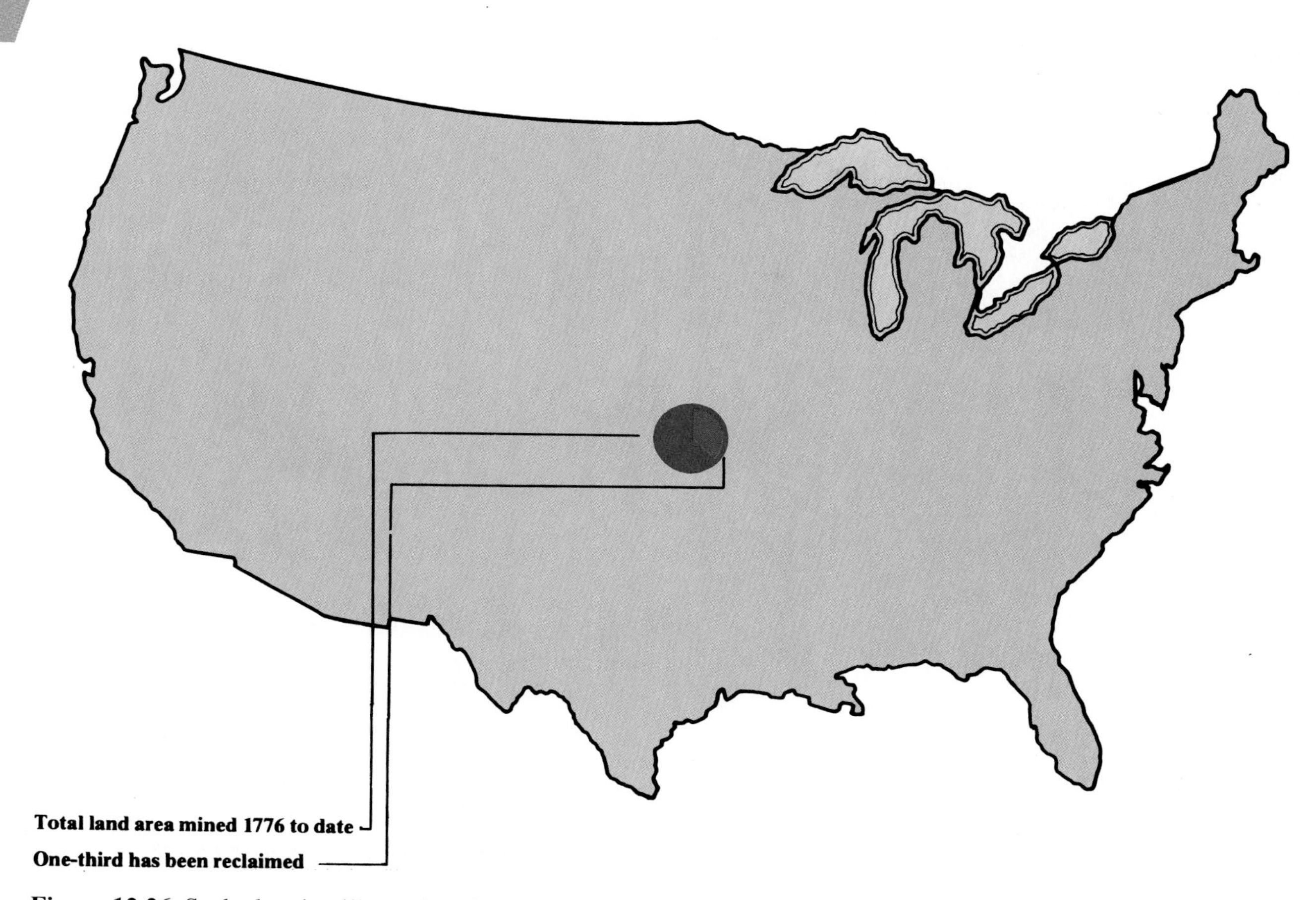

Figure 12.26 Scale drawing illustrating the total land area which has been mined 1776 to date. One-third has been reclaimed. (From USBM.)

total. Regulations such as zoning laws, subdivision standards, covenants and taxes all influence land use. You cannot use your land to diminish the enjoyment or opportunities of your neighbors.

Historically, for the most part, regulations for privately owned lands have been the responsibility of local governments. This seemed the best way to hammer out consistent, desirable use patterns. Agreements could be worked out between people who knew each other or had common interests, and zoning maps could reflect an overall plan. It was thought that responsible individuals would comply with the rules and that local governments would have the power to implement the goals.

?

How are most land-use decisions made in the United States?

Over time, Federal regulation of private lands and land use has increased. Flood plains, wetlands and water quality are examples of local land-use issues which, though perhaps administered locally, are now governed by Federal regulation.

The standard land-use decision-making model used throughout much of the United States is illustrated in Figure 12.27. If an individual or group wishes to use a parcel of land in a different way than stated in the current zoning laws, a request for a variation must be

A request for a change from agricultural to residential zoning.

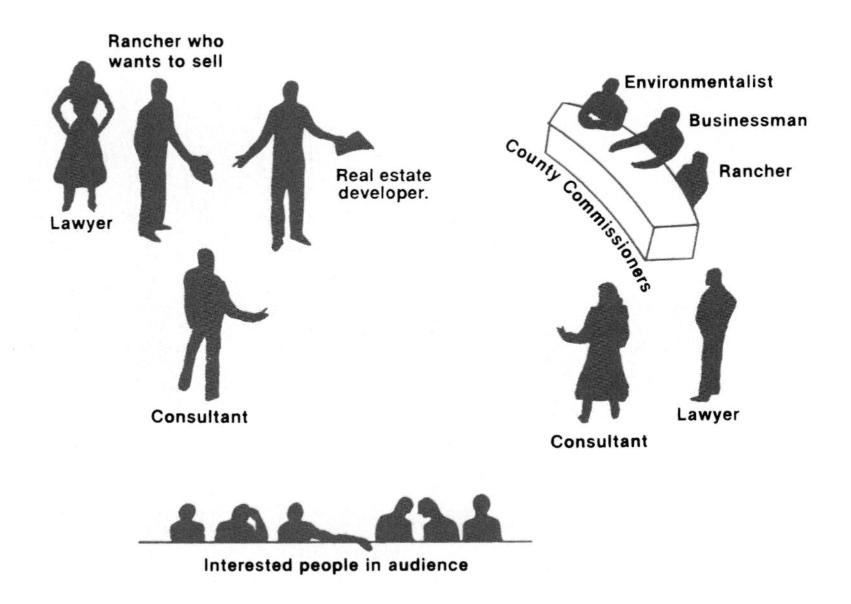

Note: All the commissioners have hidden agendas (not necessarily bad) on why they ran for the position they hold.

The public hearing is usually during the day. This is a poor time for receiving citizen input.

After hearing arguments from both sides, the county commissioners vote on the request. Majority rules.

Figure 12.27 The standard land-use decision-making model. (From John W. Christensen.)

made, and a public hearing held. After hearing arguments from both sides, the city planners or county commissioners vote on the request. Majority rules. Is this the decision-making model used in your region?

Many of our decisions about land use reflect an ancient attitude of man as the master of nature. This attitude regards private land as a commodity to be developed and used as the owner desires. The maximizing of profit or gain was often the top priority. Figure 12.28 traces this value from the frontier to the cities to the suburbs.

Currently, this ancient attitude is facing greater resistance as local citizens' groups are organizing and empowering themselves with an appeal for priority over and above landowners' profits. "Environmental impact mitigation" and "environmental sustainability" are the slogans for this new appeal. Citizen response contrary to landowners' development proposals has become so prevalent that planners nationwide have identified it as the "NIMBY" (Not In My Back Yard!) syndrome. The American Planning Association in Chicago, Illinois has emerged as a central information source for the expanding array of land-use issues which surround this ongoing controversy.

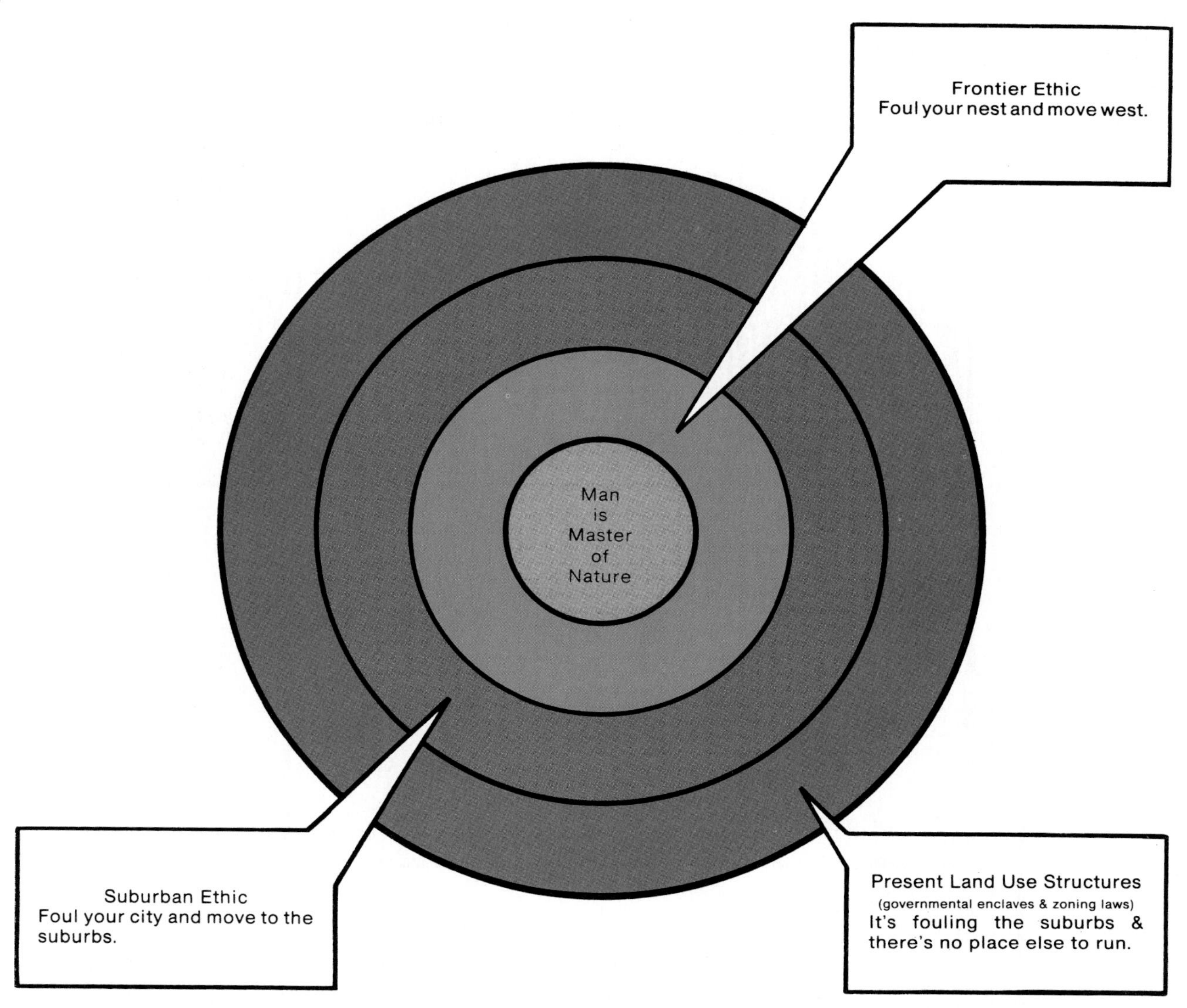

Figure 12.28 Land-use values. This model shows how the old belief that "man is master of nature" affects land use and behavior. In this model, land is thought of as a commodity. However, as the perimeter begins to collapse, the fundamental belief at the center is attacked. Make a new set of value rings starting with the belief "humans are partners with nature." (From John W. Christensen.)

 12.12 Future Land Use Planning

?

Why are new land-use decision-making models being proposed?

All too often, suburban and farmland development has been poorly planned and sprawling. Valuable marshlands were drained so farms could be expanded or more homes or office buildings could be built. Aquifers were drained for a few more years of high agricultural yields.

Cities and towns depend upon water rights which have long been in existence. New suburbs acquire their water in a variety of ways. State water laws usually control the method of acquisition. Figure 12.29 outlines a comprehensive land-use decision-making model. It should result in better decisions. Inspect it to see if it represents reality. Is there adequate opportunity for all sides of an issue and/or

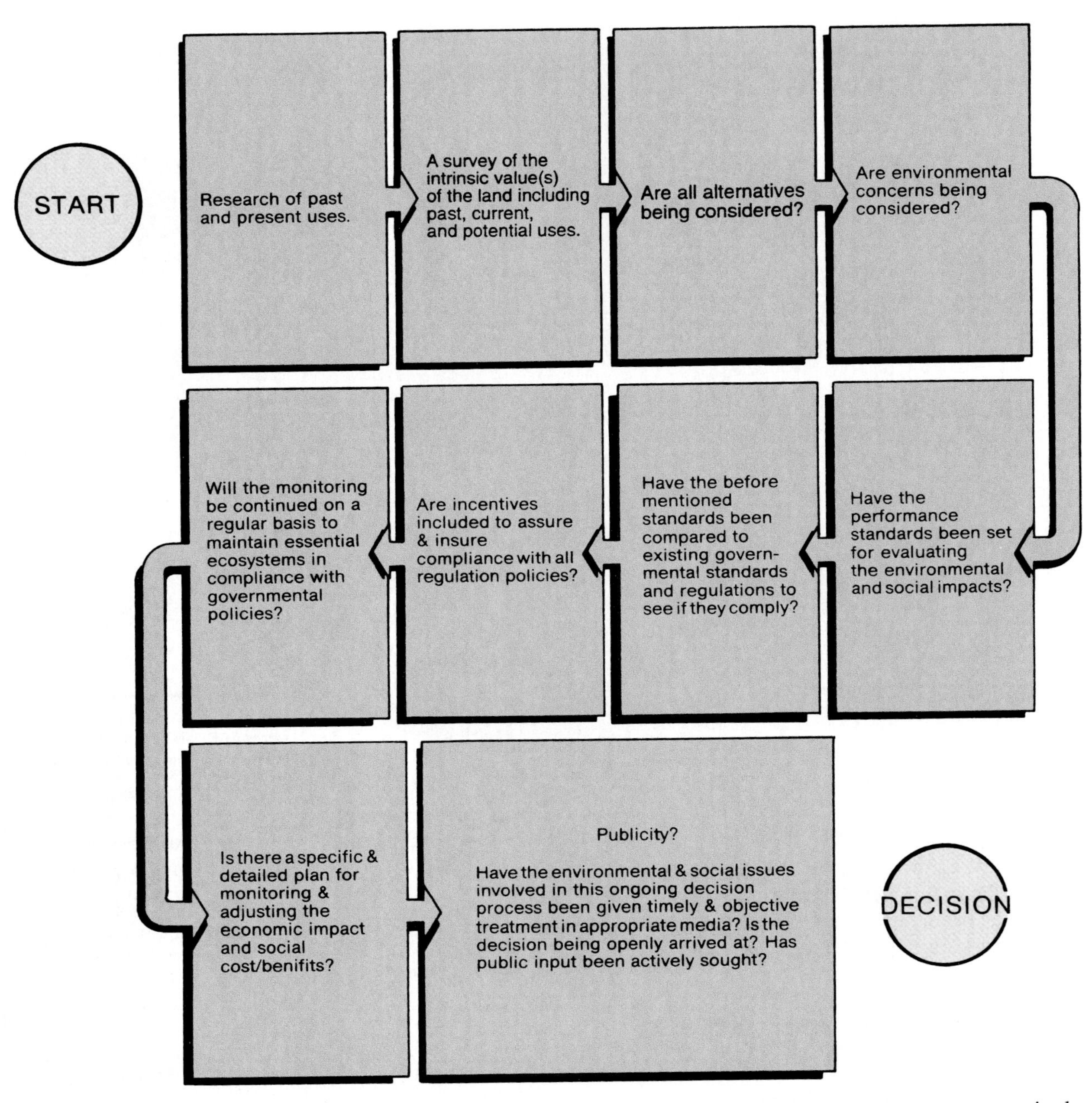

Figure 12.29 An idealized land-use decision-making model. The environmental impact statement process required by the Federal government fits the spirit of this decision-making model.

The Challenge of Compromise

science at work

No matter what your world view, saving the future of Earth and its people will require compromise—and that's the vocation of Diane Henderson, founder of DMH Land Use Planning in San Rafael, California. Working with city planners, land developers, and other professionals, as well as landowners, Diane's goal is to foster cooperation when development is planned in a community. Whether a project is large or small, Diane helps to plan growth that will have as few negative effects as possible on the community's citizens and environment. This work has a personal side for her, too—in addition to making a living at it, she often gets to watch over development projects in the area where she lives.

Diane especially enjoys the variety of her work. Working freelance means her role in every project is different. Planning takes many forms—in her home county of Marin, for example, she was part of a special staff guiding a large retail development project so that its changes would fit the requirements of everyone involved: business owners, city government, and environmentalists. In Salinas, California, she joined a planning team that was temporarily expanded to handle a high-priority development project. She has filled in as a city planning director until a new permanent director was hired. The locales of her work cover a broad range, too, from planning department counters to specific building sites, and even to a boat in the Sausalito Harbor, from which she can inspect developments along the coastline.

Varied projects mean varied tasks. As a planner, Diane has to understand the review process in a given city or county. Often she writes or collaborates on reports to planning boards. She works with local government officials and with many other professionals, such as transportation planners, architects, engineers, and attorneys—and, of course, with the area's citizens. To make development easier on the environment, she may suggest changes in bus service, installation of bike racks, and so forth. Sometimes her task is to answer questions for people who visit a planning department, seeking information. A big part of her work is communication and negotiation.

Variety is also reflected in the needs of the people Diane serves, and that's where the concept of compromise comes in. She wants to achieve the best possible outcome for everyone involved. Choosing her clients carefully, she will turn down a job if the people in charge don't want to consider environmental issues and the needs of the community. "Developers often need to be guided toward doing things right," she says. Always, however, her focus is to encourage cooperation. On all land-use projects, it's important for changes to be reviewed for their impact on the neighbors. This applies to an individual homeowner making changes to a house and its grounds just as much as the developer of a large shopping mall that is near other businesses, homes, and parks.

Diane has a B.S. from the University of California in Environmental Planning and Management. Although this particular degree is no longer offered, similar ones are. They involve studies in architecture, design, engineering, mapping, various sciences, sociology, and psychology—all tools that contribute to Diane's skill in planning and communication. She has taken additional classes from University of California Extension and the American Planning Association. Related paraprofessional careers in this field—planning technicians, for instance—are available to people having two-year degrees.

Diane says it's crucial that we "strike a balance between growth and protecting the natural environment." Growth and its problems are inevitable on our planet, so we must "provide for the future as well as preserve the past" as we search for global solutions to save Planet Earth.

Figure 12.30 Coal loading at a western U.S. mine. (AMAX Coal Industries, Inc.)

request to be considered? The challenge is to balance allowing private property owners to use land as they desire with protecting the community from wasteful or destructive misuse. The goal is to ensure a good quality of life for present and future generations.

12.13 Mined Land Reclamation

Strip mining affects land quality more than any other mining method. In this process, the soil and rock covering the mineral deposit are removed. The removed materials are called "overburden." Huge draglines and power shovels can remove as much as 60 meters (almost 200 feet) of overburden to get to the coal or ore, which can then be mined. Huge trucks haul the mineral away (Figure 12.30). When mining is complete, the overburden can often be put back into the empty cavity in preparation for **reclamation** (restoration). Although it is evident that strip mining disrupts the land, the land can be reclaimed. The record of reclamation in this country has not been a good one until recent years.

After years of controversy, a Federal strip mining law was passed in 1977. This, along with upgraded state laws, now assures that the past Appalachian devastation will not be repeated in new mining regions of the West. Today, based upon these laws and regulations, many mining companies, through hard work and the expenditure of many dollars, are reclaiming lands which can be used for other purposes. However, some mines developed from 1776 to the early 1950s have simply been abandoned and unreclaimed in accordance with existing laws and regulations.

Many examples of successful reclamation exist in this country and abroad. Overburden (top soil and rock) that was put aside during the mining period is replaced in the excavation area. Seed mixtures of good starter grass and native vegetation are planted, fertilized and watered. The steps in strip mining followed by reclamation are shown in Figure 12.31.

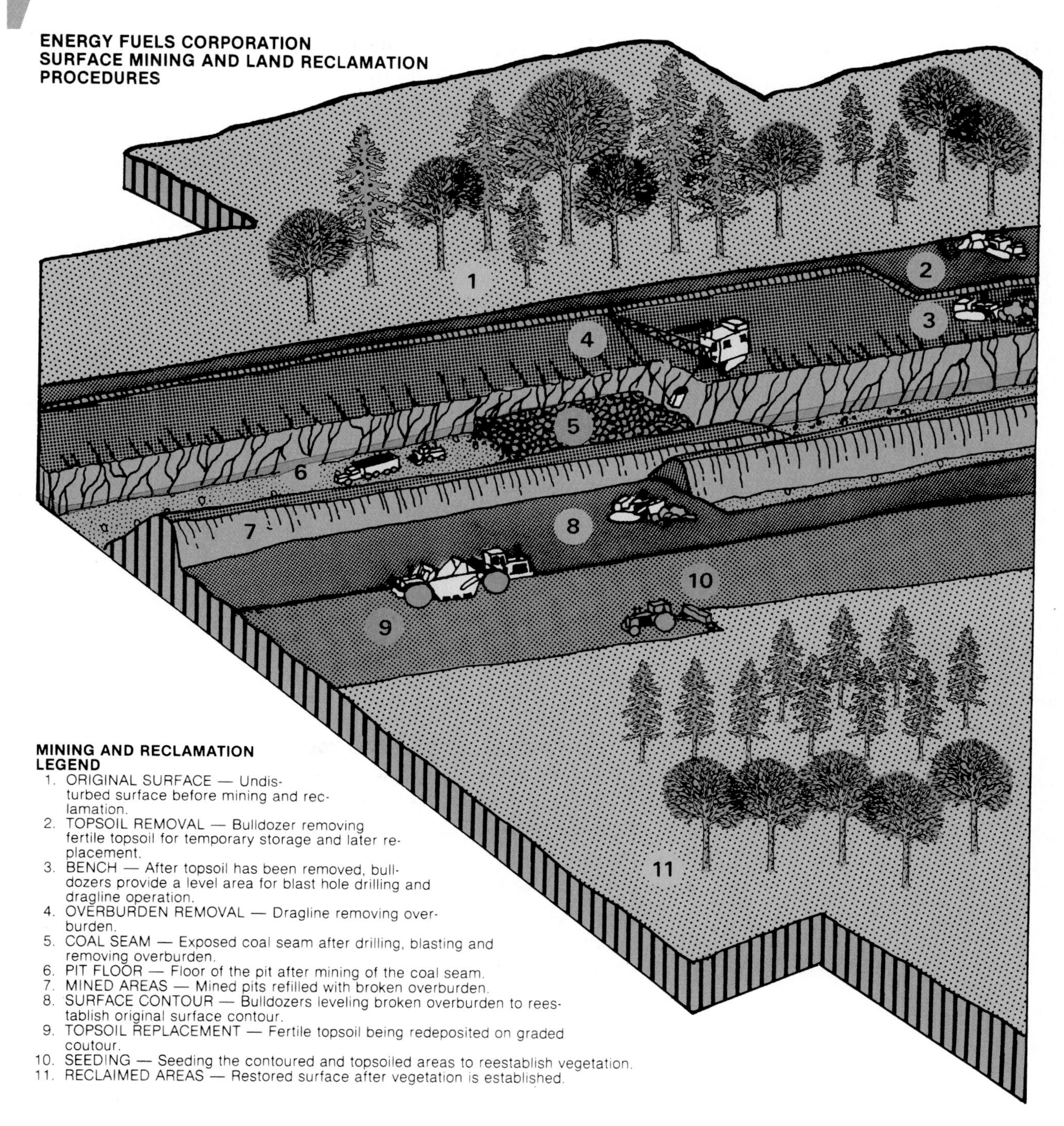

Figure 12.31 A modern surface mining and land reclamation procedure. (From Energy Fuels Corporation.)

How can strip-mined land be reclaimed?

Careful land reclamation adds to the cost of mining coal or other material. If the land is bulldozed to resemble its original contours and revegetated, the total cost may run as high as $20,000 per acre (1988 costs). In the arid West, where irrigation is required, the costs can be even higher.

How much more does mining coal cost since companies must reclaim strip-mined land?

This seems like a lot of money. To put it into perspective, however, do Problem 2 at the end of the chapter. From the calculation you will see that the cost of reclamation adds only a small percent to the total value of the coal.

Reclamation can and is being accomplished. It should be noted that we have used *coal* as an example in the previous paragraphs, but the mining sites of other resources, such as sand and gravel, can also be reclaimed. Sand and gravel excavations often make excellent fishing ponds or lakes.

The Problem of Waste

On March 22, 1987, a gigantic load—3,168 tons—of garbage from a New York City suburb was refused as landfill in Islip, New York. It was then acquired by National Waste Contractors, Inc., who hoped to sell it for methane extraction. The trash was loaded onto the barge *Mobro 4,000* and headed for Jones County, North Carolina. But, North Carolina officials ordered the barge away. By this time, it had become a symbol of our nation's mounting waste disposal problems.

For years we believed the saying "out of sight, out of mind" applied to all our waste products. We learned that matter couldn't be destroyed in the classroom, but in the real world it could. Bury it and it's gone. When it goes down the drain, it disappears. When the trash truck leaves the neighborhood, the trash leaves the planet. Classroom learning about the conservation of mass and reality didn't seem to connect.

What does the garbage barge story symbolize?

The journey of the *Mobro 4,000* finally made the connection between theory and reality. It traveled 6,000 miles in search of a dump. It was spurned by at least five states and three countries—Mexico, Belize and the Bahamas. It returned in failure to Gravesend Bay, off Brooklyn, on May 16, 1987. New York state and city officials huddled and negotiated until July 10, 1987, when an agreement was announced. The 3,168 tons of trash would be burned in a Brooklyn **incinerator.** Here it would be reduced to 400 tons of ash. The ash would then be trucked to the Islip municipal landfill.

12.14 Disposing of Our Solid Wastes

All living things make wastes. In nature, however, wastes are recycled. Natural wastes are **biodegradable,** meaning that microorganisms break down and change them into materials that can be used by the living.

Why do modern products pose a special disposal problem?

Modern societies interrupt natural chemical cycles. We produce metal alloys, glass products, plastics and a whole host of chemicals that are not biodegradable. Further, our wastes are discarded as a

Figure 12.32 The *Mobro 4,000* and its spurned cargo. (Jeffrey Cardenas/Sygma)

random mixture of organic products (paper, cardboard, food scraps) and inorganic materials (bottles, cans, plastics, chemicals, metals). This makes dealing with the wastes difficult.

The barge incident was a public statement that the problem is now one we **must** solve. Using natural processes is our key to that solution.

Much of our problem stems from the fact that, in the past, we got used to hauling wastes out of town to the public dump. Since hauling wastes was expensive (and time consuming), we didn't want to haul them too far. But, as the town grew, it surrounded the dump. Often it was converted to a park or other recreational use. A new dump was opened a few miles out of town. As the city grew, the story was repeated.

The old dumps often smelled bad and were breeding grounds for flies and rats. They sometimes caught on fire and burned for days.

What is the difference between a dump and a sanitary landfill?

Recently, new engineering has created *sanitary landfills* where newly dumped wastes are covered with soil at least once each day. This solved the rat, odor and fire problem. But, as time went by, the chemical makeup of the wastes changed. See Figure 12.33. New problems have arisen. The sanitary landfill approach is no longer an adequate solution.

An examination of Figure 12.34 explains why the chemical makeup of modern wastes is different now than in the early 1900s.

Most of the vast quantity of municipal solid waste is biodegradable. Much of the rest of it is paper, metal, and glass that could be recycled. Figure 12.35 summarizes municipal solid waste by type.

Distinguish between waste minimization and recycling.

This information indicates that waste minimization and a good **recycling** program have great possibilities. Some argue that Americans are too set in their ways and cannot be made to separate out their trash. Separating trash means putting paper products in one container,

Figure 12.33 Some modern products that contribute to the solid waste problem.

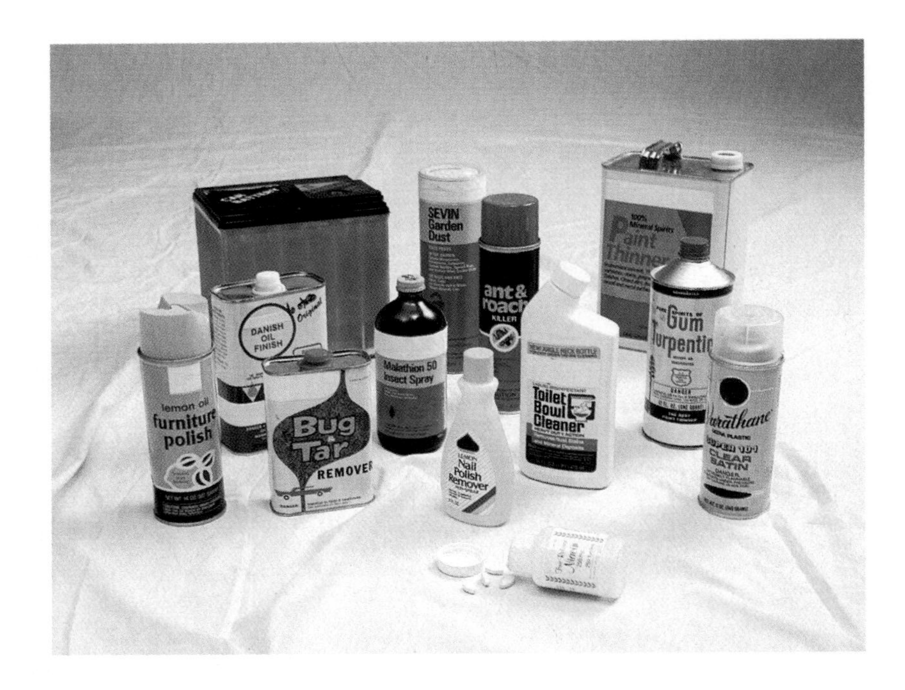

Figure 12.34 Modern technology has changed the composition of what we consume.

Item	Early 1900s	Today
Transportation	Horse and buggy wastes = manure and urine	Automobile wastes = exhausts, old batteries, used motor oil, chemical engine coolants, etc.
Sanitation	Out-house and wash basin wastes = abandoned toilet pits and dirty water.	Flush toilets and running water wastes = detergents, shampoos, toilet bowl cleaners.
Medication	No cure for serious infections. Peppermint and other natural remedies.	Powerful drugs and antibiotics. All kinds of chemicals to cure minor illnesses.
Pest Control	Fly swatter, sticky fly paper, cleanliness, soapy dishwater dumped on garden vegetables and plants, mousetraps.	Insecticides and repellents
Housecleaning	Mops and water, brooms, dust rags, a few waxes, homemade soap.	Chemical floor cleaners, oven cleaners, scouring powders, rug shampoos, furniture polish, spot removers, room fresheners.
Clothing	Most clothing made from organic fibers-wool, linen, cotton. Leather, animal fur.	Most clothing made of synthetic fibers which are washed in automatic washing machines with detergents and fabric softeners.
Packaging	Market basket, gunny sack, pack saddle.	Paper, cardboard, plastics, styrofoam.

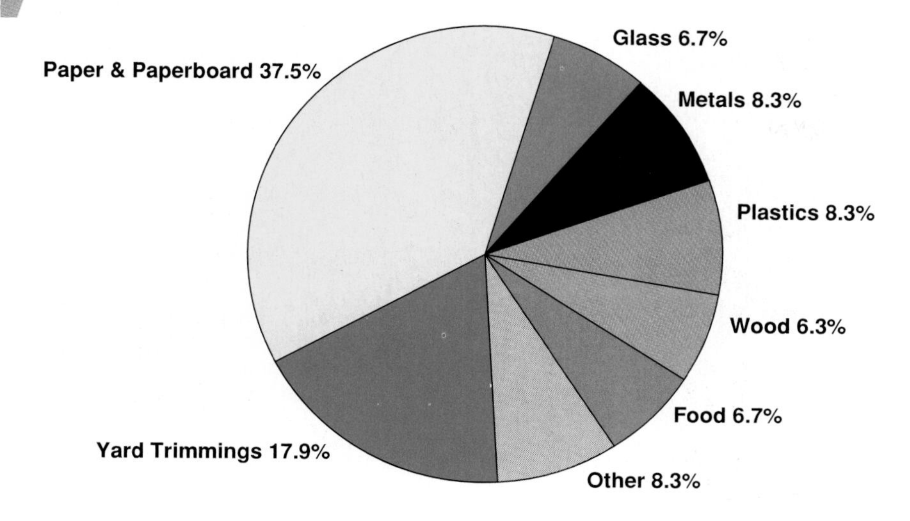

Figure 12.35 Gross discards of municipal solid waste materials, 1990. 100% = 195.7 million tons. (From EPA Report: *Characterization of Municipal Solid Waste in the United States: 1992 Update.*)

food scraps in a second, metal in a third, glass in a fourth, and so on. (Other separation schemes are possible.) We all seem to respond to financial incentives. Perhaps if the pickup charge for sorted trash was significantly less than that for unsorted trash, a meaningful behavioral change would result. Or, the return deposit on containers could be increased. Though plastics make up a small percent of municipal trash by weight, they take up a great deal of space. In addition, most plastics are not degradable. Some plastics can be recycled. The other category in Figure 12.35 may be a small percentage; but in today's society, it is a very significant one. Included in this category is hazardous waste.

12.15 Classifying Wastes

Because our wastes have such variety and some of our wastes are dangerous, it has become necessary to classify them. Once classified, mandated (legal) disposal procedures must be followed. Wastes are classified as:

?

Distinguish between nonhazardous and hazardous wastes.

a. Nonhazardous Wastes

1. **Biodegradable.** Substances which have their origin in living materials and which are broken down by the action of microorganisms. These substances include paper products, food wastes, wood, some fibers, and leather.
2. **Nonbiodegradable:** Discarded substances that are not biodegradable and that are not potentially dangerous to humans. These include glass, most metal products, and plastics. With time, chemical action corrodes many metal products.

b. Hazardous Wastes

Discarded chemical or biological substances that are potentially dangerous to humans. See Figure 12.36.

Figure 12.36 Municipal solid wastes mixed with liquid industrial wastes fill this unlined pit. The pit was later buried under 60 feet of refuse at a landfill, which is now a Superfund site. Codisposal is no longer considered to be an acceptable disposal practice. (EPA)

Figure 12.37 summarizes the types of hazardous waste. Hazardous wastes must be handled so they do not escape into the environment in concentrations that could be dangerous. We especially want to prevent them from getting into groundwater and municipal water systems.

?

What are some of the ways of reducing solid-waste problems?

12.16 Waste Management

Wastes in general, and hazardous wastes in particular, are dealt with in all of the following ways:

a. Reduction (Waste Minimization)

The quantity of wastes produced can be reduced in a variety of ways. Substitution reduces the demand for a hazardous substance. Recycling enables us to continually enjoy the benefits of a substance without having to dispose of it. Substances like DDT may be banned. People must be taught to purchase no more than they need. This automatically would reduce the quantity of waste.

b. Substitution

In some cases substitutes can be found. Many toxic insecticides have been replaced by synthetic substitutes that can be broken down into nontoxic materials. Nontoxic pigments, such as titanium oxide, have replaced the lead compound used in house paint. Lead is being phased out of gasoline as an octane booster. Certain organic compounds can accomplish the same thing.

Classification	Characteristics
a) *Highly flammable or explosive*	React chemically to produce fires, explosions or other violent reactions that may harm humans.
b) *Corrosive or reactive*	React chemically to eat away other substances including human flesh. Reactive materials combine with other things to become dangerous.
c) *Toxic*	Acts as a poison or causes cancer, birth defects, or other health problems.
d) *Infectious**	Cause living organisms to become diseased.
e) *Radioactive**	Can cause illness and increase a person's chance of developing cancer.

* Infectious and radioactive wastes are not legally defined as hazardous wastes in all cases. However, they fit the definition.

Figure 12.37 Hazardous wastes.

c. Recycling

Lead is a toxic metal. It is also a useful metal. The lead in automobile storage batteries can be recovered and reused. This way, the concentration of lead in our environment is partially controlled and does not increase. We also get much more use of the lead.

d. Chemical Alteration

Some toxic substances can be chemically altered (changed) to make them nontoxic. Nerve gases can be detoxified.

e. Labeling Instructions

Special and clear instructions, through proper labeling of hazardous materials, are essential to prevent improper use. We must be trained to read and follow these instructions. The first step in proper disposal is knowing what *proper disposal* means.

f. Placement Locations

Place wastes in specially designed, sealed landfills. Hazardous wastes cannot simply be buried because they may eventually seep into aquifers and end up in someone's drinking water. They must not be dumped down the drain. Sewage-treatment plants were not designed to handle them. Many toxic wastes will kill the microorganisms that make a sewer plant work. For these reasons, new municipal landfills are required by law to be constructed in such a manner that they prevent the escape of hazardous materials.

Figure 12.38 The U.S. Environmental Protection Agency projects that approximately half of our municipal solid waste will be either combusted, recycled, or composted by the year 2000. (From EPA Report: *Characterization of Municipal Solid Waste in the United States: 1992 Update.*)

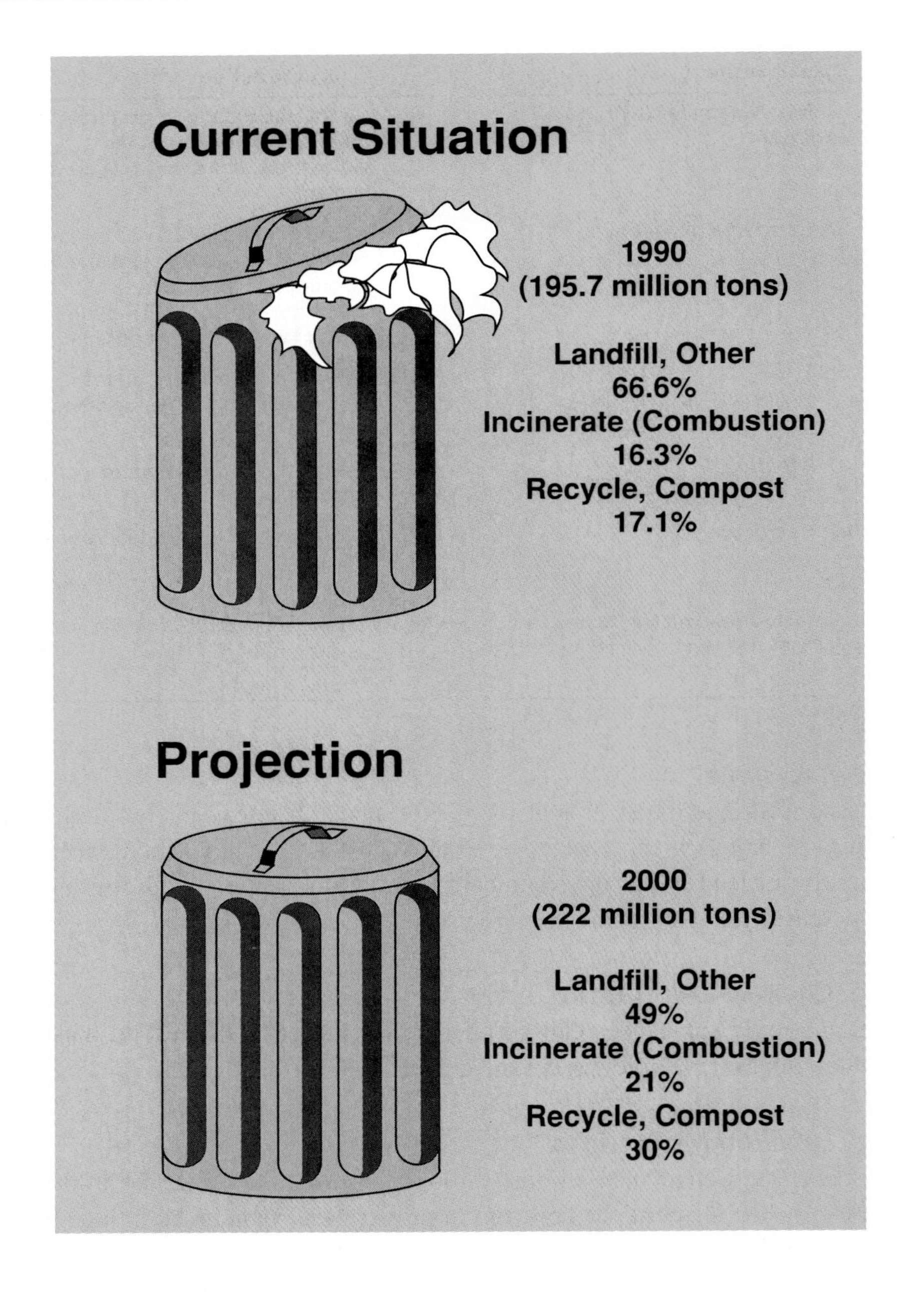

g. Incineration

Incineration is the burning of wastes under carefully controlled procedures. It is described in Section 12.17.

h. Regulation/Enforcement

It is essential to our well-being that the proper disposal of hazardous wastes be regulated and enforced. The Environmental Protection Agency (EPA) has been charged with this responsibility. Proper disposal is expensive, and there are always some who will try to avoid regulations. Unlicensed waste haulers are known as "gypsy haulers" and "midnight dumpers." Enforcement of our laws against them must be swift and effective.

i. Public Education

Whenever you buy a product, *you* take the responsibility to use and dispose of the product properly. If this attitude can be etched in people's minds and reflected in their behavior, we will have come a long way in dealing with our solid waste problems.

Our waste-disposal problem has greatly increased since World War II. Our nation's rapid industrial growth just after the war was matched by a surge in consumer demand for new products. The country seized upon new "miracle" products, such as plastics, nylon stockings, and coated paper goods, as soon as industry introduced them. Our appetite for material goods also created a problem: how to manage the increasing amounts of waste produced by industry and consumers alike.

As part of a general response to pollution, Congress passed the **Solid Waste Disposal Act** in 1965. It was the first Federal law to require safeguards and encourage environmentally sound methods for disposal of household, municipal, commercial and industrial refuse.

In 1970 Congress amended this law by passing the **Resource Recovery Act.** A third amendment, passed in 1976, gave us the **Resource Conservation and Recovery Act (RCRA).** The primary goals of RCRA are to:

Summarize waste-management legislation at the Federal level.

- Protect human health and the environment from the potential hazards of waste disposal
- Conserve energy and natural resources
- Reduce the amount of waste generated, including hazardous waste
- Ensure that wastes are managed in an environmentally sound manner

As our knowledge about the health and **environmental impacts** of waste increased, Congress revised RCRA, first in 1980 and again in 1984. The 1984 amendments—referred to as the Hazardous and Solid Waste Amendments (HSWA)—significantly expanded the scope of RCRA. HSWA was created in response to strongly voiced citizen concerns that existing methods of hazardous waste disposal, particularly land disposal, were not safe.

Problems associated with past mismanagement of hazardous wastes are covered by RCRA's companion law, the **Comprehensive Environmental Response, Compensation, and Liability Act of 1980 (CERCLA),** more commonly known as **Superfund.** It addresses the cleanup of inactive and abandoned hazardous waste sites.

The term "RCRA" (pronounced rick-ruh) is often used interchangeably to mean 1) the law, 2) the regulations, and 3) EPA policy and guidance. The law describes the waste management program mandated by Congress and gives EPA the authority to develop means to carry it out. The regulations carry out the Congressional intent by providing explicit requirements for waste management that are legally

Special Focus

What Do You Do with Used Paint Thinner?

Most people have cleaned a paint brush in paint thinner. What do you do with the thinner after the brush is cleaned? If you put the thinner in the trash, it may create a fire hazard on the garbage truck.

In a dump, the thinner may flow down into the soil and contaminate groundwater. Burning the thinner can release microscopic particles of paint pigments into the air. Some pigments are highly toxic. If you flush the thinner down the drain, the sewage treatment plant may not be able to handle it, and it may be discharged into the wastewater stream—ending up in the drinking water of someone downstream.

One thing that can be done is to let the pigment particles settle, then pour off the thinner into a new container for re-use. Industries that recycle waste could refine the thinner for re-use, or burn it, under controlled conditions, but this is not possible at home. Thinner can also be mixed with oil-based paints when the paints are collected for deposit in a hazardous waste site.

As time has passed, people have gained more experience with modern solvents, and have started to identify potential problems. Safer solvents are replacing the more hazardous ones of the not-very-distant past. Carbon tetrachloride, for example, was once used in homes as a dry-cleaning fluid and in fire extinguishers. Now we know it is toxic, and it is no longer sold for home use.

Source: *Hazardous Wastes from Homes,* Enterprise for Education, 1320 A Santa Monica Mall, Santa Monica, Caifornia 90401

enforceable. The Environmental Protection Agency (EPA) policy statements clarify issues related to the implementation of the regulations. Together, these three elements are all essential parts of the RCRA program.

12.17 Disposal of Municipal Solid Waste

What is municipal solid waste?

Solid waste from homes, office buildings, and restaurants is called **municipal solid waste.** Modern disposal techniques consist of five main strategies:

a. Recycling

The benefits of recycling have already been discussed. Recycling must be part of any modern municipal solid-waste program.

b. Biological Breakdown

The largest portion of municipal solid waste is biodegradable. As we described in Chapter 8, these materials can be broken down into liquid and gaseous fuels. To obtain full value from them, they should be separated from the other categories of waste.

c. Sanitary Landfills

Modern sanitary landfills cause little damage to the environment. The site is carefully selected and liners are used to prevent leaching of the

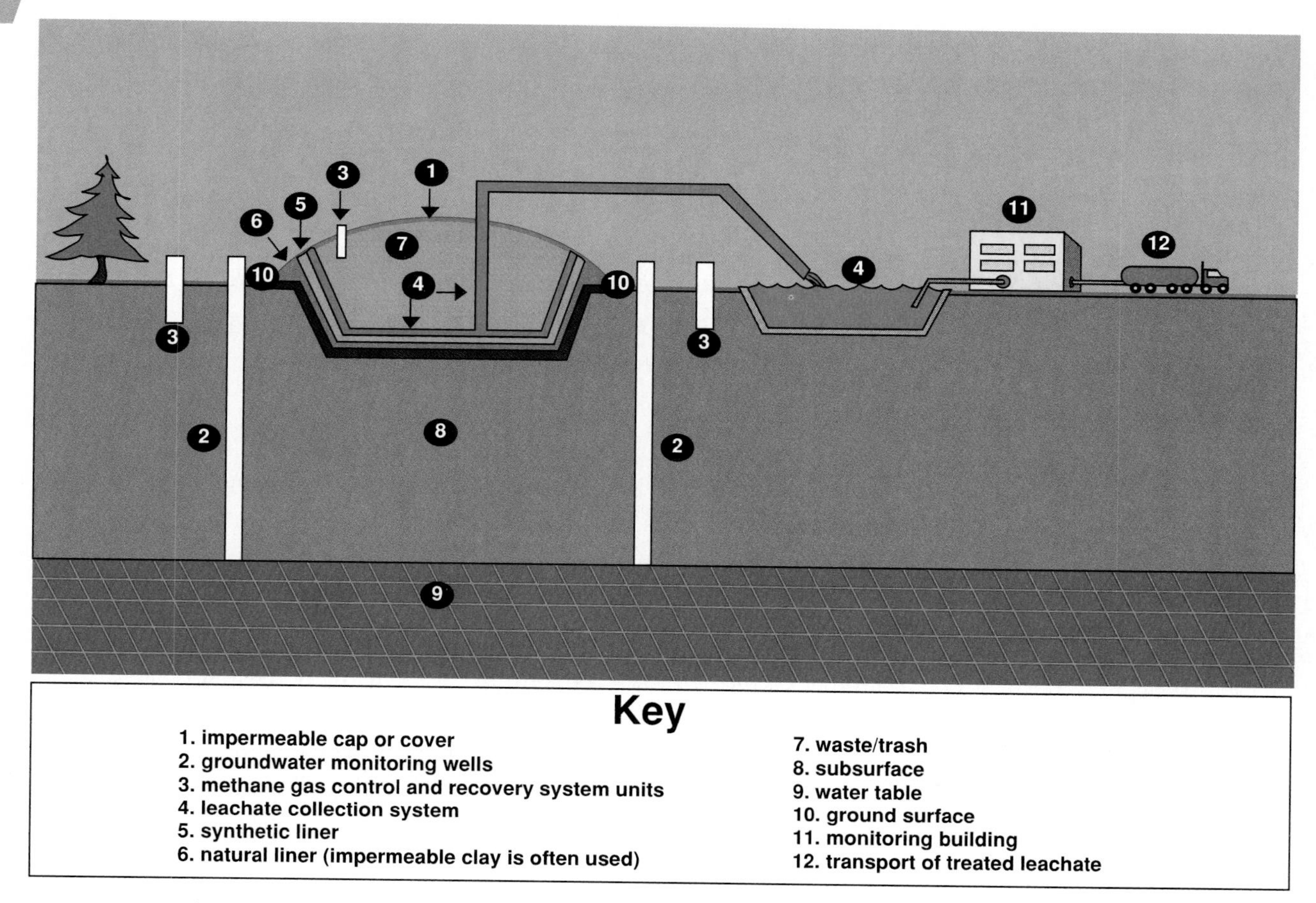

Figure 12.39 A modern sanitary landfill.

soluble portions of the wastes into groundwater. At these landfills, wastes are packed firmly together by heavy tractors and covered with soil each day. The soil cover prevents insects and rodents from getting into the refuse. It also greatly reduces fire danger and foul odors. Some landfills are designed to become a source of useful methane gas as the organic materials decompose.

d. Special Handling Procedures for Hazardous Wastes

The need for properly handling hazardous wastes has already been discussed. Industries are already carefully regulated. However, many cities and states do not have regulations that apply to households. Find out if your community has a hazardous-waste program. If it does, try to develop a plan to make more people aware of the program. If it doesn't, find out how one can be started. Many successful programs began with the concern of a single individual.

e. Incineration

Incineration is the process of burning wastes. This method is now preferred by many communities because they have run out of nearby potential landfill sites. Future landfill sites can become controversial

What are the disadvantages of incineration?

issues. Hauling solid wastes great distances is not only expensive, it also is a waste of energy. Advantages of incineration:

- Some valuable substances can be reclaimed from the ashes. To prevent the release of hazardous substances into the atmosphere, the products of incineration must be treated. Solid particles are removed and the gases mixed with chemicals. The remaining solids and ashes from the incinerator are taken to a hazardous-waste landfill.
- The huge reduction in volume.
- In some communities, the heat from municipal incinerators is used to produce steam. The steam used to drive the turbines generates electrical power.

The problem of waste disposal is monumental. However, if we are to continue to enjoy the products of modern technology, we must manage the wastes we generate.

12.18 Technology: Friend or Foe?

"If you are not part of the solution, you are part of the problem." This old maxim can also refer to an element of modern society that we seem to both love and hate. The element is **technology.**

What is technology?

Technology has several meanings. It includes the study of practical pursuits, such as agriculture; and of technical processes, such as the refining and working of metals. It can refer to all the products in a society, all the ways we use to make material products, or the ways we organize to get jobs done. The last definition may mean tangible objects and equipment, such as factories and assembly lines. Or, it may mean the so-called **social technologies**—that is, the ways we organize people to get a job done. Social technologies include charitable organizations, school faculties, labor unions, welfare services, taxes, the police, and many other private institutions and agencies of government.

?

Why is technology both part of the problem and part of the solution?

When we look at problems of energy and environment, it is tempting to suggest that technology has caused all our problems. After all, if we did not have factories and automobiles, we would not have so much air pollution. If we did not have electrical generating plants and fossil-fuel-burning equipment of various kinds, we would not be running short of petroleum and natural gas.

Those observations are partially true but over-simplified. Wood burning also pollutes the atmosphere. Before the use of fossil fuels, many forests near cities were cut down. This caused other economic and environmental problems. With today's large populations, we could not return to a major dependence on wood for fuel. We sometimes forget the benefits of technology. If we did not have the products of technology we would also be missing the health, safety, and convenience given by modern appliances, products, and conveyances. In fact, technology has given us a standard of living unimagined even a few centuries ago. We have gained many benefits. Pollution and resource depletion are the costs we are paying for those gains.

If technology has been part of the problem, if can also be part of the solution. Although we cannot realistically expect technology to solve all our problems for us, we can expect it to help us with some of them. In this chapter, you have read about some examples of ways in which modern technologies can help with our problems. Catalytic converters, scrubbers, and other devices can help us reduce and control air pollution. Reclamation techniques can lessen the negative impacts that mining can cause.

Such physical technologies are usually not very controversial, though there are some disagreements about economic matters like price and passing additional costs on to consumers. Using social technologies to address problems of energy and environment can, on the other hand, be very controversial. Why? Because we in this nation are very concerned about individual liberty. In fact, our Constitution guarantees us a great deal of freedom from unnecessary restraint through the law. Every time we try to legislate solutions to social problems, we know we are in for a battle—with good arguments on both sides.

A simple example may illustrate the point. Everyone knows that driving while intoxicated is a serious threat to life and welfare. It is estimated that over half of the traffic fatalities involve drinking drivers. What can be done? We already use some social controls in an attempt to solve the problem. Driving "under the influence" is illegal. Arrest and imprisonment may happen. Most states prohibit consumption of intoxicating beverages by anyone under the age of twenty-one. Tougher laws and better enforcement are certainly effective against the drinking driver.

Public education may be another solution. Some people favor voluntary choice over social control. They suggest that teaching people that negative health effects of alcohol consumption and the dangers of drunken driving will curb fatalities and accidents. This approach also preserves individual liberty and freedom of choice. Opponents of this approach are skeptical that voluntary choice can ever be as effective as social controls.

The same kind of controversy shows up in relation to matters of energy and environment. There is no doubt that social controls can be quite effective. The rationing of gasoline, heavy taxation of energy products, tax incentives for home energy improvements and solar use, fines to corporations for environmental contamination, and returnable bottle laws can all make a big difference in the amounts of energy consumed and the kinds of pollution released into the environment. But are those controls ethical? Are they legal? How much governmental regulation *can* business tolerate? How much *should* it tolerate? Are strict social controls defensible in a nation that is founded on the premise of liberty for all? Just how much control is too much? Is it ethical *not* to control for the benefit of society?

Can we as a society reach any consensus on how many controls and what kinds of controls we are willing to impose on our own behavior? Controlling corporations and government is one thing, but how about controls on personal choices like how many children to have, or how much food to consume, or how and when we can build a

Figure 12.40 "Someday, my boy, this will all be yours." (Cartoon by Bill Mauldin. Reprinted with special permission of North American Syndicate, Inc.)

fire in our fireplace? Are we as individuals willing to obey laws of that kind? Should we? Personal responsibility and moral judgment are the only practical ways for a free society to work and to remain free.

These are among the difficult questions of social technology that will demand answers now and in the future. The decisions we make about the wise use of both physical and social technologies may make a great deal of difference in the quality of life of future generations.

12.19 Conclusion

As a nation, and as earthlings, our choices and values demand that we assume personal responsibility and use good moral judgment in all that we do. We face a future unlike that of any generation before. We can no longer dump our wastes into remote soils, water or air, nor can we move to a new, unspoiled frontier. We have a new frontier—but it is different now. The "foul our area and then move on" practice no longer can be tolerated.

Where is the new frontier?

The new frontier is the frontier of the mind. It is a frontier of reconciliation. We must reconcile ourselves with our environment, the natural environment and the human environment. We must live with a knowledge that we are part of nature and nature is a part of us. We must be responsible for our own pollution. Most important of all, we must study and evaluate the effect of our own activities on our fellow humans, for we are all in it together. Only by working together can we build a future worth anything for ourselves and our children.

> Problems related to the wise use of our plant's air and land can be solved using a variety of strategies:
>
> - Education—understanding the problems and the full range of solutions available.
> - Modern technology—catalytic converters, electrostatic precipitators, scrubbers, high-mileage cars, lined landfills, substitute products, and hydrogen-powered automobiles.
> - Lifestyle changes—recycling, buying only what one needs, reusing materials, using pump-type spray containers, car pooling.
> - Laws and agreements—RCRA, HSWA, CERCLA, agreements regarding CO_2, design for recycling, and zoning laws.

Summary

Natural events or human actions can damage ecosystems by disrupting their chemical cycles, changing the flow of energy through them, or reducing their diversity. If the damage is not too great and enough time is available, natural processes can mend the damage. Today, unfortunately, change can occur too rapidly, and time is lost as our ally.

The human impact on the global environment comes almost entirely from agricultural practices and from our extraction, transport, and utilization of energy and mineral resources. Oil spills must be cleaned up, mined land reclaimed, nuclear wastes safely transported and stored, and combustion controlled. Cleanup and correction involve the use of new technologies, laws that regulate our behavior, and new attitudes about our relationship to others and our environment.

Acid rain can cause ecological damage to forests and lakes throughout the world. Progress is being made in combating it.

Carbon dioxide is normally not considered an air pollutant. However, the increase in the CO_2 content of the atmosphere (related to burning coal and hydrocarbons) may increase what is called the "greenhouse effect." This would result in a gradual warming of the Earth. Large numbers of particles in our atmosphere could reflect enough sunlight to cause some global cooling. At present, we don't know whether warming or cooling is occurring on a global scale.

The depletion of the ozone layer is another threat to our well-being. It is hoped that international agreements will lead to desired solutions.

Improper land use and waste disposal threaten soil and groundwater. Again, we can no longer tolerate thoughtless and selfish behavior.

Technology is both part of the environmental problem and part of the solution. It is true that laws restrict our options and freedoms. It also is true that we can continue to legislate more and more laws to deal with environmental problems. But can we continue having one layer of law upon another? The decisions we make concerning our use of technology and our behavior will have a definite impact on the quality of life for future generations.

References

Elkington, John and Jonathan Shopley. *Cleaning Up: U.S. Waste Management Technology and Third World Development* (Holmes, PA: World Resources Institute), 1989.

Fortuna, Richard C., and David J. Lennett. *Hazardous Waste Regulation: The New Era* (New York: McGraw-Hill), 1987.

Gore, Al. *Earth in the Balance* (Boston: Houghton Mifflin), 1992.

Goudie, Andrew. *The Human Impact on the Natural Environment,* Third Edition (Cambridge, MA: MIT Press), 1990.

Lehr, Jay H., ed. *Rational Readings on Environmental Concerns* (New York: Van Nostrand-Reinhold), 1992.

Levine, Joel S., ed. *Global Biomass Burning: Atmospheric, Climatic, and Biospheric Implications* (Cambridge, MA: MIT Press), 1991.

MacKenzie, James J. and Mohamed T. El-Ashry. *Airsick Crops and Trees* (Holmes, PA: World Resources Institute), 1988.

Mungall, Constance and Digby McLaren, eds. *Planet Under Stress* (New York: Oxford University Press), 1991.

National Academy of Sciences. *Acid Deposition: Long-Term Trends* (Washington, DC: National Academy Press), 1986.

National Academy of Sciences. *Policy Implications of Greenhouse Warming: Mitigation, Adaptation, and the Science Base* (Washington, DC: National Academy Press), 1992.

Ramade, Francois. *Ecology of Natural Resources* (New York: John Wiley), 1984.

Ray, Dixy Lee. *Trashing the Planet* (New York: Harper Perennial), 1992.

———. *Environmental Overkill: Whatever Happened to Common Sense?* (Washington, DC: Regnery Gateway), 1993.

Rothman, Tony. *Science a la Mode* (Princeton, NJ: Princeton University Press), 1989.

U.S. Department of Energy. *Environmental Restoration and Waste Management: Five Year Plan 1993–1997* (Springfield, VA: National Technical Information Service), 1991.

U.S. Environmental Protection Agency. *Characterization of Municipal Solid Waste in the United States: 1992 Update* (Washington, DC: NTIS #PB 92–207 166), 1992.

U.S. Environmental Protection Agency. *National Air Quality and Emissions Trends Report, 1991* (Research Triangle Park, NC: Office of Air Quality Planning and Standards), 1992.

U.S. Environmental Protection Agency. *What You Can Do to Reduce Air Pollution* (Washington, DC: EPA 450–K–92–002), 1992.

World Resource Institute. *World Resources* (New York: Oxford University Press), Annual.

End of Chapter Questions

1. List three ways in which ecosystems can be damaged severely.
2. Give one example of how twentieth century humankind is damaging ecosystems for each of the three ways listed in Question 1.
3. In what ways are energy consumption and mineral use related to environmental problems?
4. What is an air pollutant?
5. Complete the following chart for the five major air pollutants: (Do not write in book)

Air Pollutant	Main Source	Harmful Effects	Method of Eliminating

6. Hemoglobin in human blood combines more readily with carbon monoxide (CO) than with oxygen (O_2). What are the physiological effects on a human being exposed to high levels of atmospheric CO?
7. Explain how emissions of sulfur oxides (SO_x) might be reduced?
8. What are temperature inversions and why do they often create a health hazard?
9. What is acid rain, and what causes it?
10. List some of the things that motor vehicle manufacturers are doing in order to reduce the amount of air pollution produced by cars and trucks.
11. Electrical power plants use several different techniques to reduce their harmful emissions. To understand two of them better, make a chart like that shown below, on a separate piece of paper, and fill in your answers.

Device	Principle of Operation	Pollutant Reduced
Electrostatic Precipitators		
Scrubbers		

12. How does the ozone layer offer protection to living organisms on Earth?
13. What is the "greenhouse effect"? Why might it result in a warmer Earth?

14. Increased use of coal-fired electric generating plants may increase the amount of two types of pollution. Name them, and describe the problems each type can cause.
15. Why is it believed that increasing the particle load of our atmosphere will result in global cooling?
16. What is land use?
17. At the present time, how are most land-use decisions in the United States made?
18. How might land-use decision-making be modified in the future?
19. What happens to the overburden when strip mining methods are used?
20. Describe some of the social impacts related to the rapid development of an area rich in coal.
21. What are biodegradable wastes? Hazardous wastes?
22. What are some of the ways our solid wastes are being reduced?
23. Why is technology both part of the problem and part of the solution?
24. Where is the new frontier?
25. The world-famous spouting geysers, steaming hot springs, and bubbling mud pots of Yellowstone National Park could be destroyed or seriously damaged by a plan to develop geothermal energy near the park. In your opinion, should geothermal exploration and development be allowed in this area, or should it be banned? Develop logical arguments to defend your position, and relate your arguments to your own lifestyle and values.

End of Chapter Problems

1. Western coal seams are about 5 to 6 meters (15 to 20 feet) thick. Coal in the ground is worth about $15.00 per ton. It has a density of 1290 kg per cubic meter (81 pounds per cubic foot). There are 4033 square meters in an acre. What is the value of the coal taken from a 6-meter seam on an average acre?
2. If it cost $20,000 per acre to reclaim the strip-mined land in Problem 1, approximately what percent of the coal value (at the mine) goes for reclamation?

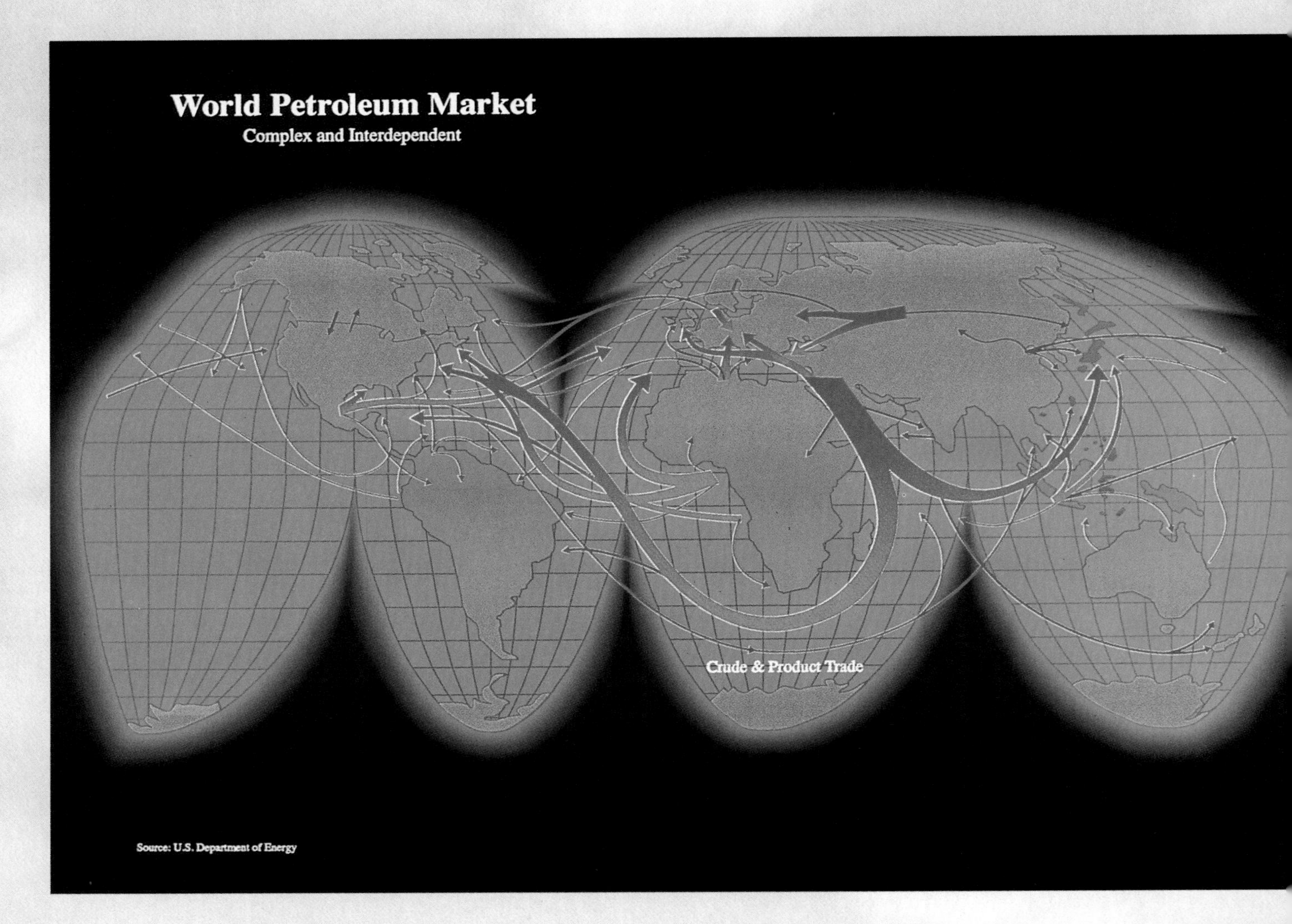
World Petroleum Market
Complex and Interdependent
Crude & Product Trade
Source: U.S. Department of Energy

Goal

To understand the basic principles of market economics and relate them to resource and environmental issues.

The Economics of Resources and Environment

There is no such thing as a free lunch.

—Anonymous

13.1 Introduction

Nearly everyone enjoys eating watermelon—especially when the temperature is high and the price of watermelon is low. Farmers are happy to grow watermelon to meet the demand, if they can make a profit doing so. So, summer after summer, watermelons are grown and eaten.

We eat watermelon without thinking about the effect on the environment or the economy. But growing watermelon requires resources, such as good soil, fertilizer and water. Farm laborers must plant, care for, and pick the melons. The melons must be transported to markets in vehicles, which require many resources to build and which use petroleum products as they run. The melons create a great deal of garbage in the form of rinds and seeds that must be discarded or recycled as compost. If discarded, they may require the use of an electric disposal. This may add to water pollution that must be cleaned up. If thrown out with the trash, they must be picked up by petroleum-using garbage trucks. Eventually they contribute to air or land pollution.

If too many watermelon are grown, or if the temperature drops, consumers may not buy enough melons for farmers to sell them at a profit. The melons may be left to rot in the fields. On the other hand, if farmers do not grow enough to meet the demand, they may be able to charge high prices to watermelon-hungry consumers.

?

Why study economics in a global science class?

All these facts about watermelon illustrate principles of economics. Economic issues, part of the social studies realm, are usually not dealt with in science classes. We will deal with economics for a number of reasons. One reason is that economics may be considered a science—like geology, biology, psychology or physics. Science is the attempt to understand the world around us by making and analyzing measurements. This broad definition makes economics a science. However, the main reason to include economics is that it influences resource use and the environment.

Current environmental and resource problems are, in part, a product of economic decisions. Manipulation of economic factors can play a major role in creating problems. The proper use of economics can also play a role in solving problems. To be ignorant of the basic principles of economics is to be ill prepared to study problems of energy, resources, and the environment.

Up to this point in the course, we have made many references to economics. We implied that environmental legislation has increased the price of energy. We indicated that economic factors are holding up the wide acceptance of solar contributions. We stated that decreasing supplies should cause the price of crude oil to increase in the years ahead. We talked about governmental policy in some of these areas.

In this chapter, we will clarify many of these matters. Before we do that, we must first have a general understanding of basic economics. That is where we will start.

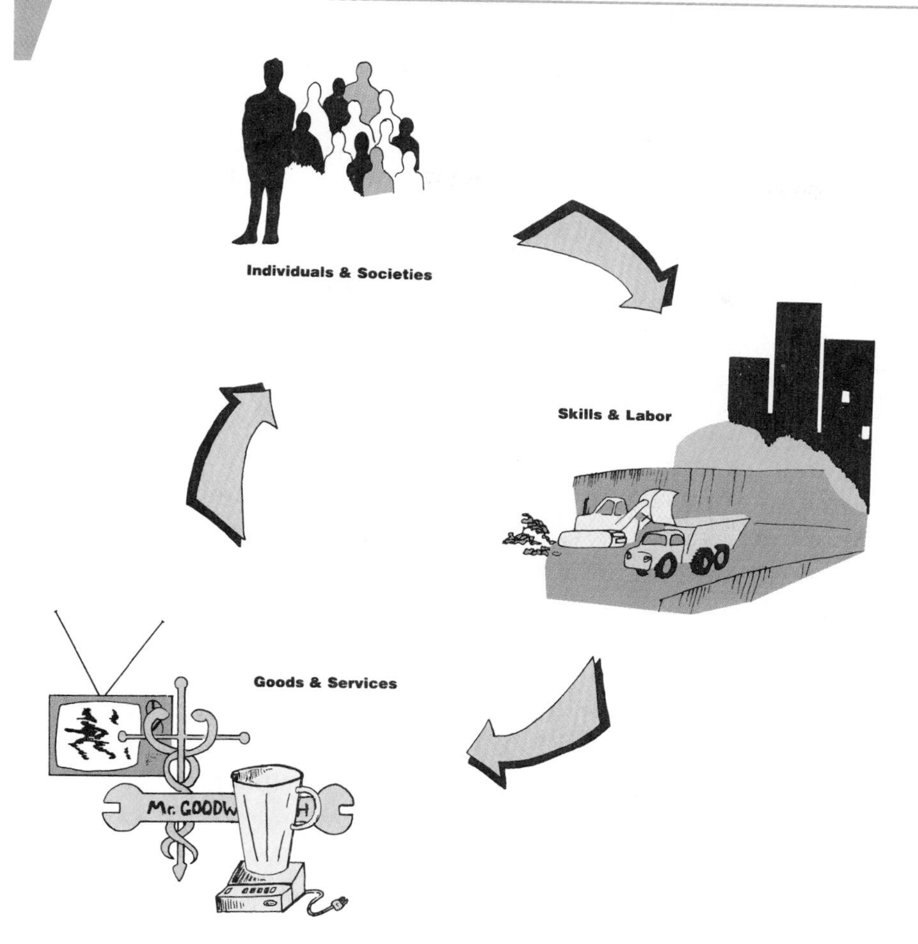

Figure 13.1 Economics: the study of the ways individuals and societies distribute their goods in an attempt to satisfy their wants.

13.2 What Is Economics?

What is economics?

Economics is the study of the ways individuals and societies distribute their goods in an attempt to satisfy their wants. Economics is a very broad field and is difficult to define. We will not consider all aspects of economics. We don't have enough time. Instead, we will define and develop those areas of economics that meet our needs for this course.

What are the basic economic questions?

Economics begins with an analysis of individual and group behavior. In doing this, economists have noted that every society must come to grips with three basic questions:

1. *What* economic goods will be produced, and in what quantities?
2. *How* will they be produced? What resources should be used? How should they be utilized in the productive process? What technology should be used?
3. *Who* should be allowed to use the economic goods? How much and under what conditions?

Goods are any things that are wanted to satisfy a need or to obtain pleasure. Since resources are limited and human wants virtually unlimited, the solution to the economic problem is not easy. The way the economic problem is dealt with varies from one society to another.

13.3 Beginning Assumptions

What are the beginning assumptions of market economics?

All sciences start with some beginning assumptions. Market economics is no exception. Here are three assumptions we need to consider:

> *Assumption No. 1:* People always want more, no matter how much they have. If they have enough of some things, they will want to acquire other things.
> *Assumption No. 2:* The Earth and its resources are finite.
> *Assumption No. 3:* People act purposely to maximize their satisfaction given the limited resources (and budgets) they have. Our behavior is based on self interest.

13.4 Scarcity: The Basic Economic Problem

What is the difference between a scarcity and a shortage?

As we have stated, human wants are unlimited but resources are limited. If we combine these two concepts we get the idea of scarcity. Thus goods are **scarce** if the desire for these goods is greater than the available resources or the means to produce them. Scarce goods are also called "economic goods."

The terms scarcity and shortage are commonly used as synonyms. In economics, though, scarcity and shortage are very different ideas. A **shortage** occurs if people cannot buy the full quantity of economic goods for which they are willing to pay the going price. For example, gold is scarce; not everyone can have all the gold they want at a price they can afford. However, there is no shortage of gold. You can buy all the gold you want, if you are willing to pay the market price.

With this in mind, we can easily see that most desirable things are scarce. However, most people get all the air they want without paying for it. If you go to the beach, you can carry away all the seawater you want, for free. Things such as non-purified air and seawater are referred to as "free goods."

13.5 Kinds of Resources

Name the four economic resources?

Resources are what individuals and societies have available to help them achieve their goals. Individuals and societies have limited resources with which to work. There are many different kinds of resources. Economists choose to divide resources into four groups: **natural resources, labor, capital,** and **enterprise.** It is important to understand each. See Table 13.1.

Enterprise may not seem like a resource, but management is one of the resources we use to achieve goals. People engaged in enterprise are called **entrepreneurs.** They pay rent for the use of natural resources, **wages** for labor, and interest for capital used in production. If they manage their affairs well, there will be money left over from the sale of the goods produced. This leftover amount is called **profit.** Profit is the reward for good business management. In a market economy, profit is needed to fund preparation for a better future.

Since resources are limited, only a certain number of goods can be produced, distributed, and consumed in a given amount of time.

Entrepreneur of Economics

science at work

"We can't predict the future, but if we understand the variables involved, we'll be prepared. We can plan a strategy to deal with change, instead of reacting to it after it happens." So says Walter Kieser, president of Economic and Planning Systems (EPS), an economics consulting firm in Berkeley, California. EPS studies practical economics solutions for local government planning departments, real estate development firms, and other agencies interested in what happens to a community when it is developed.

In helping its clients plan a project, EPS examines many issues from various viewpoints, but always with the goal of figuring out how development will affect the economics of a community. Is there sufficient demand for the product or service? How will demand be influenced by using the land for the project? By a change in the population numbers and/or income? On the supply side, what kind of local regulations and taxes must be considered? How will the project affect the community's resources—natural resources, labor, capital, and enterprise? What are the spillover costs to the local environment? What distribution mechanisms will be affected? In Walter's opinion, it's better to take a regional approach, and plan for the cumulative impact of several projects, rather than trying to solve a specific area's environmental problems after they have developed.

EPS studies proposals for many different locations. A recent one was for an island in the Caribbean, but most are in California and other western states. Examples are the city of Seattle's plan to revitalize an older downtown neighborhood, and the Alaskan government's need to analyze how increased tourism will affect their environment. Walter often travels to the site of the project to gather data and talk with public officials. His reports are used in city and county budgets, public financing proposals, and other documents used for planning.

In addition to using data gathered by other private and government agencies, EPS does many kinds of numerical analyses for their feasibility studies. They use tools such as financial modeling and forecasting to study what happened in the past and what is anticipated for the future. All of this information adds to understanding the relationships between supply and demand, cause and effect, and when changes occur in a community.

Walter is familiar with the philosophical conflicts that occur between economists and environmentists—but he thinks they *can* work together successfully. For instance, some of the economic value realized from building a resort in one area can be contributed to protecting wilderness in another area. As you know from reading this chapter, economics has a language all its own, but that doesn't have to be a barrier to understanding the economic impact of development in a community. Both sides—the changers and the changed—need to be involved early in the planning stage of the project, Walter says.

Walter's graduate work in public administration, political science, economics, and planning was very specific to his current career. But he uses much of his basic education, too—mathematics, especially. His interest in planning is a direct result of studying natural science. In quantitative biology, for instance, he learned about measuring the size and structure of populations, and the factors that influence those measurements. He says "the scientific method is fundamental to all human inquiry, to all analysis."

There are many opportunities for young people interested in economics. "This type of work will be increasingly important as the world confronts growing population size and related environmental problems," says Walter.

Table 13.1 Kinds of Resources

Group	Definition	How Resource is Paid For	Examples
Natural Resources	All natural materials that can be used in production ("gifts of nature")	Rent	Farmland, water, crude oil, forests, mineral deposits
Labor	Physical or mental work that produces things (from natural resources) for human use.	Wages	Mining, drilling, typing, cooking, serving food
Capital	Any human-made instrument of production (does not include money or other paper assets)	Interest	Tractors, shovels, hoists, draglines, pencils, buildings, tools
Enterprise	Process of organizing the other resources. (paying rent, wages, and interest)	Profit or tax revenue	Managing a business, administering a school

13.6 Resolving the Basic Economic Questions

What are the three basic economic questions?

As was stated earlier, economic analysis is concerned with three basic questions. Some economists refer to the questions as the "What, How, and for Whom" problem. Each society answers these questions in some fashion. Since there are limits to production, basic choices must be made. One way of gaining insight into the basic economic problems is to examine the various mechanisms which are used to distribute limited resources.

13.7 Distributive (Allocative) Mechanisms

Distributive mechanism: a technique for distributing a portion of the production of a society among its members.

How much of the total production does each person get to have or use? Or, how should goods be distributed (allocated)? Throughout history, quite a variety of answers to these questions have been tried. Some answers have been more successful than others. You probably have had experience with each. From both an efficiency and a fairness standpoint, some of the mechanisms listed below are better than others. For example:

a. Brute Force

Brute force.

This is basically the bully approach. Those who are strongest or most powerful take what they want (need) from the weak and helpless. This system, used under various conditions throughout history, has been the reason behind many wars.

b. Queuing

Queuing.

Queuing is based on the first-come, first-served idea. It is used at bakeries, ice cream parlors, and gas stations. Sometimes you must take a number and stand in line. As Americans learned during the so-called Arab oil embargo in the 1970s, waiting in a queue (position-in-line)

Figure 13.2 Free enterprise in practice.

Figure 13.3 How does Japan utilize its resources and resolve the basic economic questions?

Figure 13.4 Queuing for lunch.

can be very time-consuming. If this were the primary way of distributing resources, a society would be very inefficient. Those in line are not producing.

c. Random Selection

Random selection.

With the random (chance) approach, throws of dice or lottery systems could be used to make economic decisions. Unfortunately, the incentive to produce is lost. Why work hard when your reward is determined by chance? Toil and sweat may bring only a small reward. Poor performance gives an equal chance of hitting the jackpot.

d. Tradition

Those who have, keep, is the underlying philosophy. Tradition is still being used in many cases. Successful businesses are passed along from one generation to the next. Season tickets to football games are kept in the family. Farms, ranches, estates, and fortunes are held "close to the vest," thus eliminating any competition for the benefits to be derived.

e. Government

Government.

The Government often decides who gets what. But how this is best done is not obvious. The two common approaches involve "equal shares" and "need."

Equal shares.

> **Equal shares.** Everyone gets the same amount. At first glance, this simple system seems fair and efficient. However, individual needs are not identical. Babies need more milk than adults. Farmers need more tractors than musicians do. Not everyone likes yogurt.

Figure 13.5 What type of market allocation does this picture show? (From G. Asakawa.)

What do we mean by need?

Need. This approach is based on the philosophy "from each according to his or her ability, to each according to his or her need." However, it is difficult for governments to accurately and fairly determine other people's needs. Why not exaggerate your needs to get more for yourself? Why not send a lobbyist to Washington to make decision-makers aware of your special interest's situation? Why work hard if you're not included with the "needy"?

f. Market Economy

Market economics (free enterprise).

Market economy (free enterprise) is the system in which anyone is allowed to produce any product and attempt to sell it to others. The producer is allowed to keep the profit (or a portion of it) and use that profit to maximize his/her own happiness. How much product is produced is the decision of the producer and is determined by free market decisions.

Even though each of these systems is used to some degree in the United States, most economic decisions are made in the market place. Expected demand and price determine what is produced and who gets what.

The role of government in our economic system is also very important. Government is now involved greatly by regulating the safety, health, and well-being of workers and the products they produce.

 13.8 Basic Concepts of Supply and Demand

Supply and demand.

Have you ever wondered why certain products cost more during one season of the year than during others? Take, for example, the watermelon we considered earlier. During the winter months, there are few watermelons for sale and the price is high. In the summer they are cheap and plentiful. Why is this so? Does it cost more to grow and distribute watermelon in the winter than it does in the summer? We know that watermelon can only be grown during the summer months in most of the United States. This would account for the varying quantity for sale. But why the differences in price?

Questions about the price and quantity of products for sale can be partially answered through the economic laws of supply and demand. There has been a continuing battle between the consumers (who want to satisfy their wants at the lowest possible price for the quality they desire) and producers (who want to maximize their profits over short and long terms). The law of supply and demand is the basic system that attempts to resolve those differences.

?

What is the Law of Demand?

13.9 Demand

The **Law of Demand** basically works as follows: When a product is desired and the price is low, the demand will be very high. On the other hand, if the price is very high, the demand will be very low.

Chart 13.1 shows how **price** varies with the demand for watermelon at a certain grocery store. At any specific price per pound, so many pounds of watermelon will be sold. Thus at 50¢/pound, 800 pounds of watermelon will be in demand. This demand schedule can also be shown in graph form.

Chart 13.1 Demand Schedule for Watermelon*

Price/Pound	Quantity Desired
20¢	1400 pounds
30¢	1200 pounds
40¢	1000 pounds
50¢	800 pounds
60¢	600 pounds

*Demand and supply schedules for watermelon are attempts to show reality but are not of actual cases.

What is a demand curve?

To interpret the demand curve you must understand how it is built. (See Figure 13.6.) The graph shown should be labeled to indicate what we are studying—watermelon. The bottom line indicates quantity of an item (how much is being demanded). This is also called the horizontal or **X** axis. The vertical or **Y** axis indicates the price per quantity of what is being studied. Line **D** represents the demand for watermelon.

What determines the demand for products?

Now we can see how the Law of Demand works. Point Q_1 on the graph shows that at 30¢ a pound, 1200 pounds of watermelon will be sold. But at 50¢ per pound (see point Q_2) only 800 pounds of watermelon will be sold. Thus as the price goes up, the demand or willingness to buy goes down and vice versa.

Now that you have some idea about what a demand curve is, we need to discuss what determines or affects the demand for products. Note that the demand curve reflects the relationship between price and quantity consumed at a given location of a given commodity during a

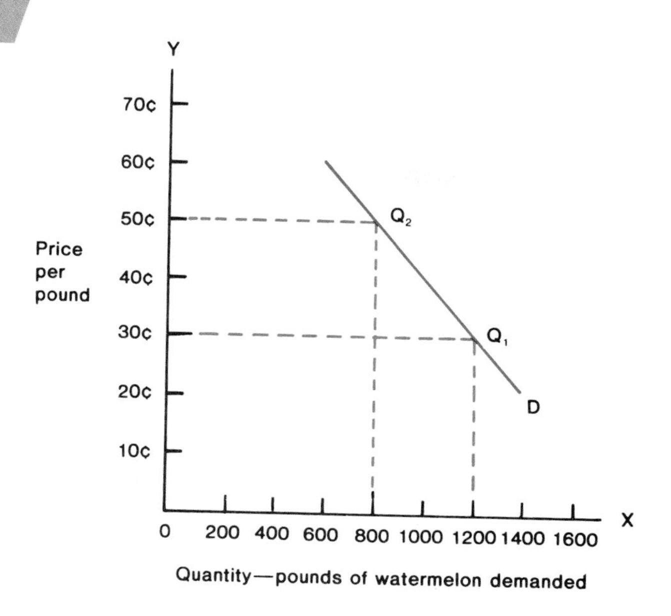

Figure 13.6 Demand curve for watermelon.

given period of time. Factors other than price or non-price components that affect demand generally fall into one of six categories. Specifically, demand for any specific product will change if:

1. consumer tastes and preferences change so that people are more or less favorably disposed toward the product.
2. consumer income increases or decreases.
3. price of similar or substitute goods increases or decreases.
4. number of consumers increases or decreases.
5. consumers expect their incomes or the price of goods to change in the near future.
6. longer or shorter time periods are considered.

What happens if the price of an item is held constant but the non-price components are allowed to vary? (See Figure 13.7.) In the case of watermelon, there might be a heat wave, or a movie star might popularize a "melon diet." That could lead to curve D_2. (An increase in demand usually causes a price increase.) On the other hand, a different kind of melon might become popular, or the watermelon might develop a disease. Curve D_3 might result. (If demand goes down, so will the price.) In all these cases, the price remains the same. Only the demand changes.

What is the demand for a product?

Now that you know something about demand curves, determinants of demand, and what happens when demand changes, let us review the definition of demand. *The demand for a particular product is the relationship between the price and the quantity desired if all non-price determinants remain constant.*

13.10 Supply

What is the Law of Supply?

Now that we have looked at the consumer's side of the market (demand), it is time to look at the producer's side. **Supply** refers to the amounts of goods a producer is willing to produce and sell in the

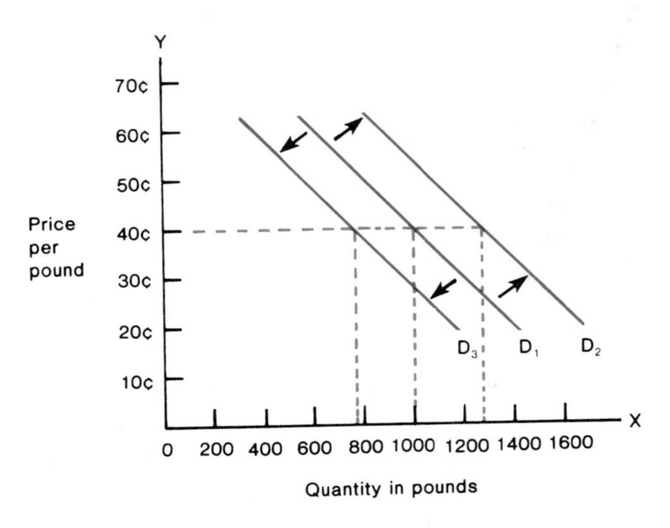

Figure 13.7 Change in the demand for watermelon.

Chart 13.2 Supply Schedule for Watermelon

Price/Pound	Quantity to Be Produced
20¢	300 pounds
30¢	600 pounds
40¢	900 pounds
50¢	1200 pounds
60¢	1500 pounds

market. The basic principle of the **Law of Supply** is that producers have a choice as to the amount they are going to sell on the market. In general, it works like this. For any specific good, if the price is high, producers will tend to produce as much as possible. If the price is low, they will produce less; or if the price falls below production costs, they may even stop production and sales.

What is a supply curve?

Chart 13.2 shows the supply schedule for watermelon at a certain grocery store. The grocer will supply so many pounds of watermelon at a specific price. Figure 13.8 shows this supply schedule in graph form. The graph is called the supply curve. The supply curve shows the maximum number of watermelon supplied at various prices. Examine Figure 13.8 and note line **S** (the supply line). Notice that producers will supply 1,500 pounds of watermelon at 60¢/lb. They will only supply 600 pounds of watermelon at 30¢/lb. Thus as the price goes down, the supply goes down and vice versa.

Just as there are several non-price determinants of demand, there are also several important non-price determinants of supply. As a result, the supply curve is the relationship between price and quantity

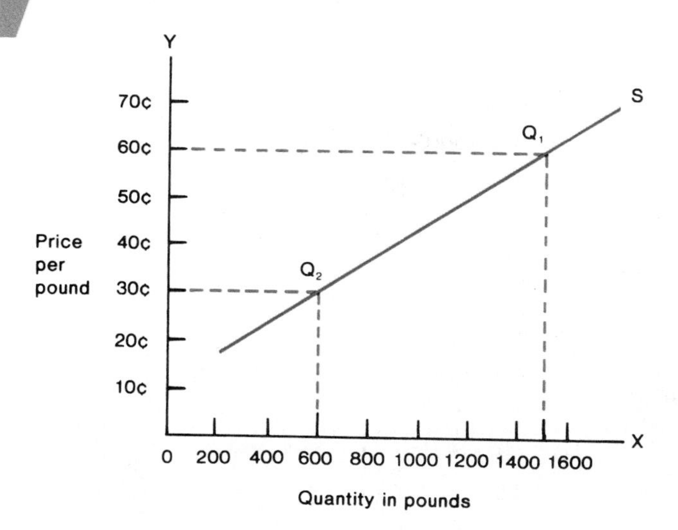

Figure 13.8 Supply curve for watermelon.

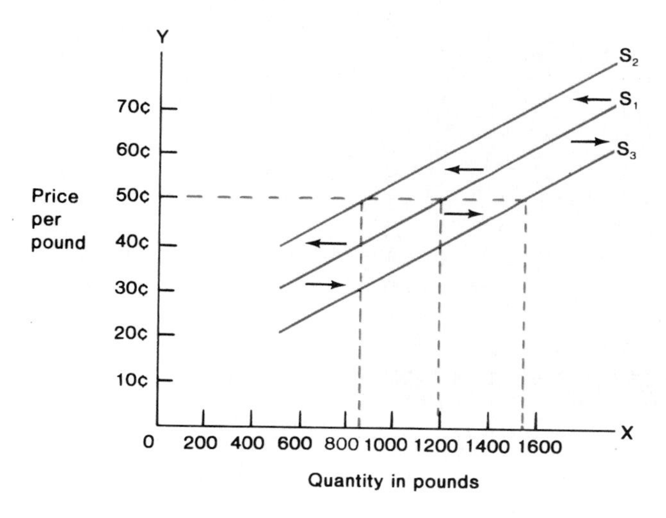

Figure 13.9 Change in the supply curve for watermelon.

supplied, keeping the non-price determinants of supply constant. The major non-price determinants affecting the curve are:

1. cost of resources
2. production technology
3. price of other producible goods
4. expectations
5. regulations and taxes or subsidies on producers
6. time

A change in any one or more of these determinants will cause the supply curve to shift. Any shift in the supply curve, with prices remaining constant, will result in the quantity of goods being produced to either increase or decrease (see Figure 13.9). A shift to the left (see line S_2) of the original (S) supply curve indicates a decrease in supply (perhaps caused by the lack of a needed resource). A shift to the right would indicate an increase in supply (perhaps a new technology results in lowering the resources needed). (See line S_3).

What are some possible non-price determinants of supply for watermelon?

Figure 13.10 The laws of supply and demand operate on a daily basis at the grocery store.

Chart 13.3 Supply and Demand Schedule for Watermelon

Demand		Supply	
Price	**Quantity**	**Price**	**Quantity**
20¢	1400 pounds	20¢	300
30¢	1200 pounds	30¢	600
40¢	1000 pounds	40¢	900
50¢	800 pounds	50¢	1200
60¢	600 pounds	60¢	1500

13.11 Market Equilibrium

In the real world, supply and demand curves don't exist independently of each other. They are plotted together to form a single market graph.

Let's see how this concept works. Chart 13.3 contains two schedules for watermelon, one for demand and one for supply.

When these schedules are put in graph form, they look like Figure 13.11. Line D on the graph represents the demand curve for a specific product and line S represents the supply curve. The two lines (D and S) intersect at point ME. This point is called **market equilibrium.** At market equilibrium the producer can supply an amount equal to demand at a price low enough to be acceptable to consumers but high enough so that producers can make an acceptable profit.

? What is market equilibrium?

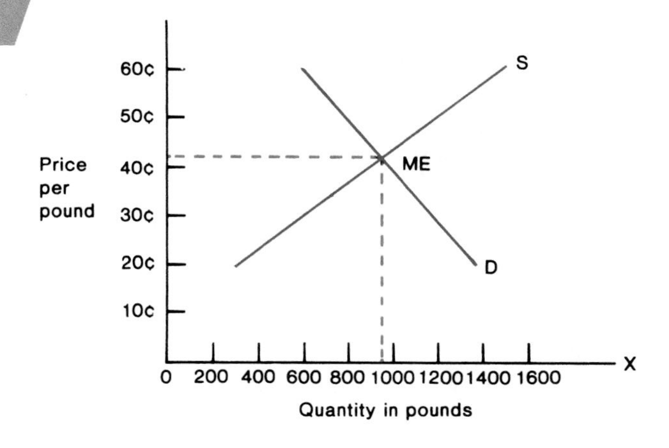

Figure 13.11 Supply and demand curves for watermelon.

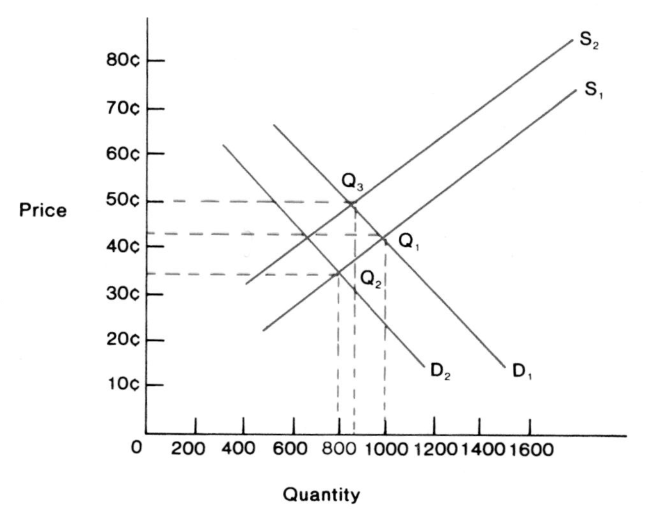

Figure 13.12 Changes in supply and demand.

13.12 Changes in Supply and Demand

What happens if the demand or supply curve changes or moves? We can see how it works by studying the graph. (See Figure 13.12). Notice Line D_2; this demand curve has moved to the left of the original demand curve (D_1), which indicates a decrease in demand. If the supply curve remains the same, the consumer will pay less for the product, but the producer will also produce less (point Q_2).

On the other hand, if the supply curve moves to the left (decrease in supply), the price will go up (point Q_3) if the demand curve stays the same. What will happen if both the supply and demand curve move?

Note: In the real world, changes are more complex than we have described.

How can surpluses and shortages be created?

What happens if the price of goods is too low or too high? In time, the market will correct itself and will change the price or quantity produced. But what happens if the price is artificially too high (meaning that the market does not control it)? We can see what happens when we examine Figure 13.13. We can see that if the price is set too low the producers will not produce as much as is demanded (point

BASIC CONCEPTS OF SUPPLY AND DEMAND

Law of Demand: The demand for a product or service depends on its price. Low prices lead to high demand; high prices lead to low demand.

Law of Supply: The quantity of goods and services offered for sale will vary with price. The higher the price the greater the quantity offered, and vice versa.

Graphic Representation of the Laws

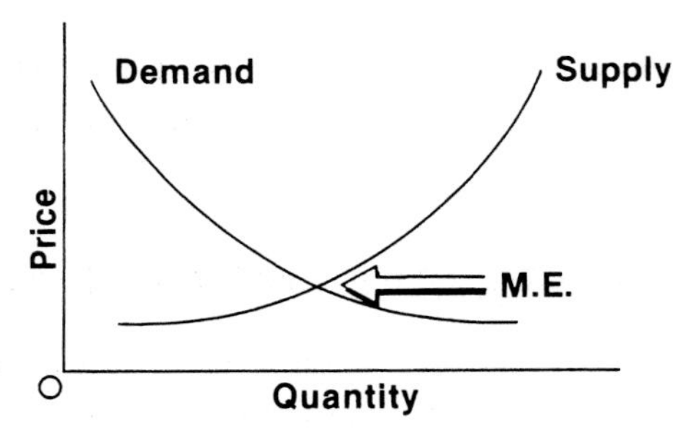

M.E. = Market Equilibrium. It is arrived at through the give and take of the market place.

Q_1). The same occurs in reverse if the price is set too high (point Q_2). The producers will produce more of the product than the consumer will buy. Most of the time it is the government (wage or price controls, price guarantees, ceiling prices, etc.) that sets an artificially low or high price and thus cause a **surplus** or **shortage.**

?
How is market equilibrium achieved?

In the real world, the market equilibrium price changes constantly because the conditions that determine it are not stable. Consumers change their minds. Advertising changes preferences. In addition, many of the non-price determinants of demand are out of the consumer's control. Income changes, new goods enter the market, and populations shift. On the supply side, technologies change, resources

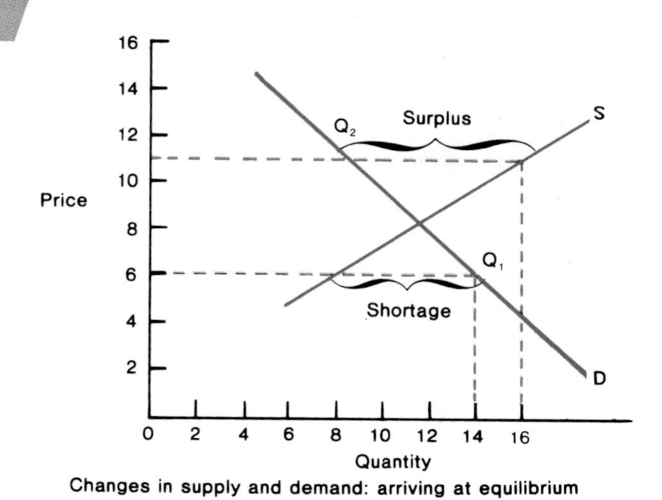

Figure 13.13 Surpluses and shortages in the market.

become more scarce, and governments may intervene. Thus a complex interplay occurs. This is what makes understanding and explaining the market so difficult.

13.13 Evaluating the Market (Free Enterprise) System

What factor makes the market system work?

As you have seen, the principles of supply and demand are quite simple. However, the actual functioning of the system is complex. Further, the whole system operates primarily on enlightened self interest. Consumers purposely act to maximize their personal satisfaction through the goods they obtain. Suppliers attempt to maximize their profits. **Competition** keeps suppliers from exploiting their customers. Suppliers must constantly be on the lookout for new and better ways to produce their goods. If they don't, their competitors will undersell them and still make a profit. In this way, competition guarantees that the market price is very close to the cost of producing an item.

Once goods are produced, how are they distributed? The answer is simple. Those who want the goods and can afford the price, get the goods. Those who can't afford the goods or are unwilling to pay the market price don't get them.

?

What are the major features of the market system?

The market system may seem unfair, cold, or impersonal. Cold as it may seem, however, there are some major arguments in favor of the market (free enterprise) system:

1. The major argument for the market system is that it is **efficient.** Resources are distributed among the people as efficiently and hence as cheaply as possible. Competition forces suppliers to adopt the most efficient methods of production and to sell goods as attractively and cheaply as possible.
2. The market system **emphasizes personal freedom.** No one tells you what you must buy or what you can or cannot have. Those decisions are made by the individual consumer.

a

b

Figure 13.14 The technology of photocopying has changed rapidly. This has resulted in fierce competition, and the consumer has benefited.

?

What problems are associated with the market system?

In spite of its efficiency and its emphasis on personal freedom, the market system also has some flaws. Briefly they are:

1. Markets can be manipulated and made non-competitive. When a few large firms dominate a portion of the market, they can work together to limit competition and keep the price of their goods high.
2. Since it takes money to make money, the free market can allow the rich to hold on to economic power. In some cases, tradition instead of free market forces determines who gets what.
3. Free market forces by themselves do not provide for social needs (such as schools and police protection), nor do they automatically absorb all the costs of goods. For example, the costs of pollution damages are not naturally included in the initial cost of a car, unless it has an emissions control system. Automobile producers did not voluntarily choose to include such systems. Another

Figure 13.15 Can you make a living selling old comic books? The owner of this store apparently thinks so. The give and take of the marketplace will provide the answer to our question.

Figure 13.16 The interplay between labor and management often leads to frustration and anger. (Jim Shaffer)

example would be a rapid shift to using solar energy. If solar options cannot, by themselves, compete economically with traditional energy sources, solar energy will not grow quickly in popularity.

4. Free markets tend to be unstable. Cycles of boom and depression or recession are common. Large numbers of people are hurt in these swings, affecting all classes from rich to poor. Competition breeds efficiency of production, but it also breeds stress.

5. The coldness of the market can cause alienation between the labor force and management. Each seems to be motivated by opposing interests, although this need not be the case. Many Japanese firms seem to have bridged this gap by promoting teamwork by workers and managers. The result is that both benefit.
6. Free markets fluctuate according to short-term factors. These factors include such things as crop failures, international conflicts and labor disputes. Long-term study and planning can often soften the blows of some of these short-term factors.
7. Free market forces by themselves do not provide for long-term planning. It is often difficult to fund needed research and development when the required funding cuts into short-term profits.

13.14 The Economic Role of the Government

?
Why does the government interfere with the economy?

Every human system has some inherent flaws. The free market system is no exception. Any system run by individuals, some of whom may be very selfish, can create problems. Thus some citizens have encouraged their governments to become involved in the economy and to interfere with and/or manipulate the free market. The government's role in our economy is the subject of great political and philosophical controversy. Like any other program of human creation, government intervention in our economic system has had varying degrees of success.

Our government has been given five main economic functions, with the goals of lessening the injustices and improving the benefits of the free market system:

1. *To ensure economic stability.*

   For businesses to function, contracts must be firm. Through their legislative powers, governments can establish rules for property ownership, standards for weights and measures, money standards and policy, and rules for legal agreements between parties.

How can the government help promote and maintain competitive markets?

2. *To promote and maintain competitive markets.*

   Competition is necessary for the free market to function efficiently. New production techniques and new products drive outmoded practices out of existence. Price increases conserve scarce goods and make sure they are used wisely.

   Unfortunately, it is possible to stifle competition and prevent free market forces from functioning. Firms can band together and control supply and demand. Supply can be restricted and then higher prices obtained. To prevent this, governments can pass and enforce antitrust laws.

How can the government change the distribution of resources?

3. *To change the distribution of resources in order to provide for public wants and needs.*

   As we mentioned before, the costs of both preventing pollution and pollution cleanup are not automatically included in the price of goods. To prevent innocent parties from having to pay for the

Figure 13.17 How is police protection paid for in your community? (Jim Shaffer)

pollution caused by others, governments have intervened. They may either force a supplier to eliminate or reduce a problem, or they may force someone to pay for the cleanup. The net result is that the cost of the good in question rises to reflect its true cost.

What wants and needs can the government help provide?

In other cases, the entire public may be taxed to provide goods and services that the market system would not provide equally to the entire population. For example, people want police protection, roads, schools, immunizations, and other goods and services. If a majority believes that everyone is entitled to these things, governments supply them.

4. *To promote fairness (equity) through the redistribution of income and wealth.*

How does government attempt to promote fairness through the redistribution of wealth?

So often we hear: "The rich get richer and the poor get poorer." It is true that to make money you generally must have money to invest. Because of this, those who are wealthy have a distinct advantage over those who are not. Not only do the poor find it difficult to work up the ladder of success, they have trouble saving for their old age, paying for emergencies, and providing opportunities for their children. To remedy some of this, our government provides such things as Social Security, Medicare, disaster relief, educational assistance, and so on. Further, the majority of our federal government's expenditures are financed with a progressive income tax. This means that those with higher incomes pay proportionately more in taxes.

Many observers say that some of the wealth of the industrial world is being redistributed on a worldwide scale through the actions of the OPEC oil cartel. This redistribution is relatively slow and non-violent. Indeed, inflation is less painful than revolution. It gets the job done without bloodshed or social and political upheavals. But for people on low or fixed incomes it can be disastrous. Some poor countries, like India, are unfortunately unable to benefit from this redistribution. In fact, their economic position is worsened by increases in the price of the energy they must import. On the other hand, some OPEC countries, like Kuwait, have become tremendously wealthy.

How does the government attempt to stabilize the economy?

5. *To stabilize national income, employment, and the price level.* Free markets have a tendency to go through cycles. Alternating periods of strong economic activity and recession are particularly hard on the poor. They have nothing saved to "tide them over." It would be helpful to control the economic cycle so that employment would constantly be high and prices relatively stable.

   Our government has a variety of mechanisms for stabilizing the economy. It can increase or decrease the money supply. Interest rates are manipulated for a variety of reasons. We will not explain these mechanisms further. It is sufficient for now to recognize that these stabilization activities exist and are a major effort of the federal government.

?

How do market economists view resources? How do scientists view resources?

13.15 Economics and the Energy Problem

As we explained earlier, economists view the world in terms of prices. Prices determine supply and demand. A graphic summary of the economist's viewpoint is shown in Figure 13.18a.

Most analysts of the energy problem view it from what a *Wall Street Journal* editorial termed the scientist's or "inventory-clerk's" perspective. These analysts try to tally up the resources in the Earth's crust. Their main concerns are with such questions as: How much do we have? How fast are we using it? How long will it last? In the inventory clerk's world, there are "gaps" between supply and demand. The graph that summarizes their concerns looks like Figure 13.18b.

How do these views differ?

The most striking thing about the inventory clerk's world is that prices never appear, but prices are always present! Prices are what influence quantity, surplus, shortage, supply, and demand. One cannot have these things without a price. Economists maintain it is the assumption that price will remain constant which causes the "gap" between supply and demand.

But, you ask, how can price remain constant or at some artificial level? This is where the conflict exists between the inventory clerks and the economists. Some maintain this is the cause of the energy dilemma.

Nearly every phase of the petroleum industry (part of the energy industry) is regulated. Further, government regulation of and assistance to the oil industry began shortly after its inception and has grown ever since. Much of this regulation and assistance was lobbied

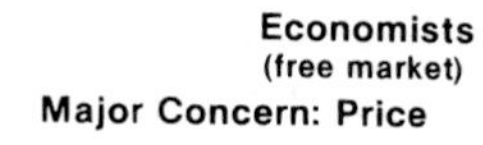

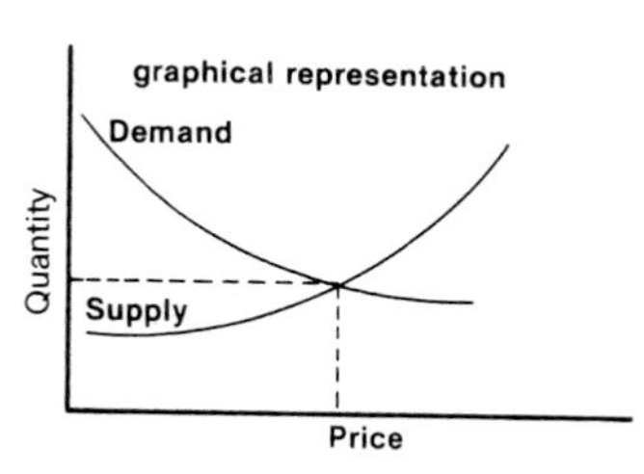

Major Assertion:
the assumption that price will or should remain constant causes the 'gap' between supply and demand.
-or-
Shortages and surpluses are caused by interference with free market forces.

Scientists
(inventory clerks)
Major Concerns: Reserves, Use Rates, Lifetimes.

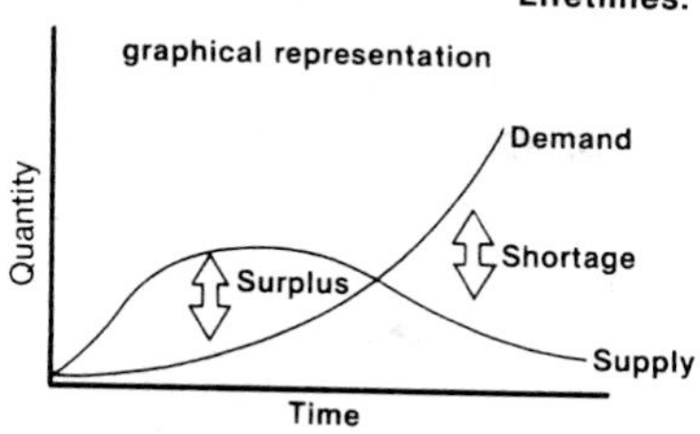

Major Assertion:
surpluses and shortages are the result of more factors than just price. International events, environmental factors and personal preferences and goals also can strongly influence consumption patterns

Figure 13.18 Two views of the energy problem: the economist's view and the scientist's view.

for by the industry itself. The regulations have become so complex that it is difficult for the average person to understand how they work, or why some of them are even there.

We stated earlier that one of the functions of government is to interfere with and manipulate some of the natural forces of the market place. In this way, it can accomplish certain societal goals that free market forces cannot. However, if the government or some other organization interferes with something as complex as the economic system, the full results of that interference cannot always be anticipated.

Figure 13.19 shows the approximate price for a barrel of crude oil from the Persian Gulf each year from 1970 to 1992. Although the graph is for Persian Gulf crude, it accurately reflects what has happened to the price of oil on the world market.

?

Why didn't U.S. demand for oil drop sharply in the 1970s when the price of world oil shot up?

With price increases such as those that occurred between 1973 and 1983, an economist would have predicted a dramatic drop in crude oil demand. There should have been no shortages of goods that were priced so high. But that is not what happened. What was the problem? There's more than one explanation.

First, Americans and the rest of the industrialized world had become so hooked on cheap energy that we just couldn't stop consuming. When energy was inexpensive, it made sense to use it. Because of the cheap energy era, we had a whole backlog of energy-inefficient vehicles, buildings, and machines that required constant "feeding." We had an energy-consumptive life-style. We were willing to sacrifice all sorts of other wants to get the fuel needed to run these things. Economists call this an inelastic (inflexible or unyielding) demand; an increase in price only slightly decreases demand. But that doesn't fully explain the consumption pattern.

The second reason for continued U.S. consumption in 1973-1983 was that we did not feel the full effect of the price increase. Our government purposely held down the price that could be charged for

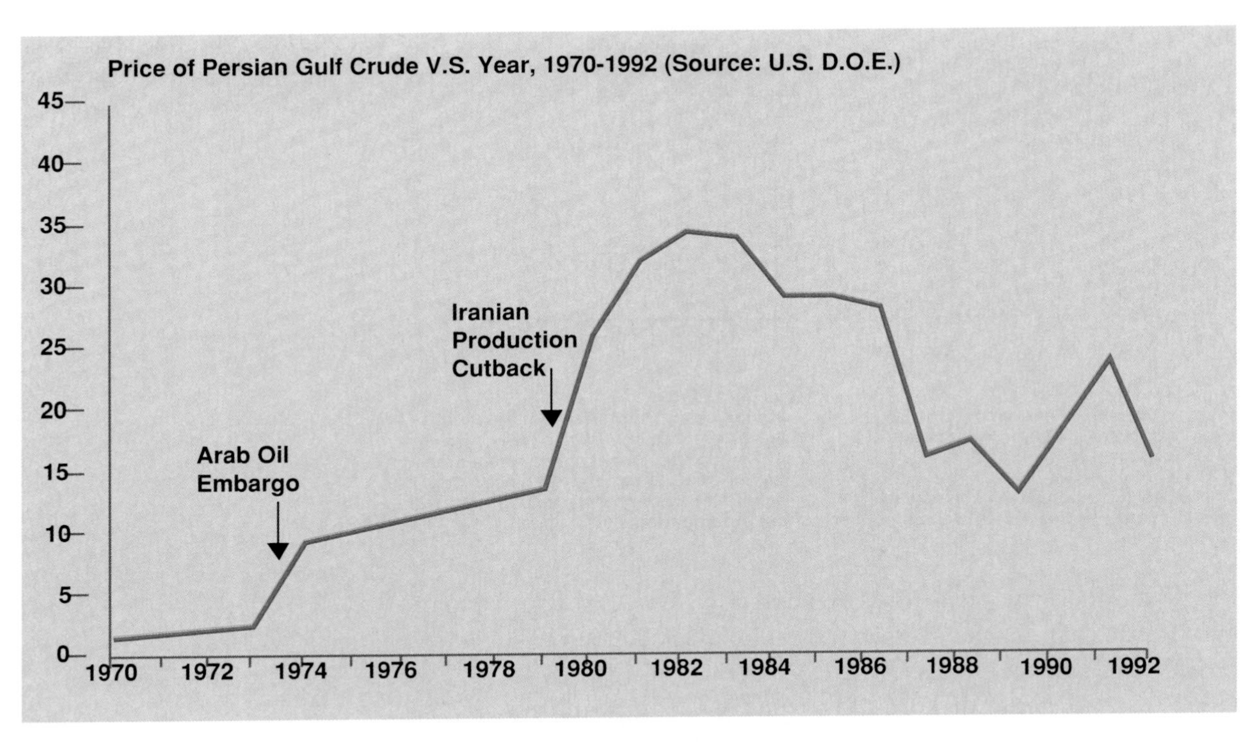

Figure 13.19 Price of Persian Gulf Crude vs. Year, 1970–1992. (Source: USDOE)

domestically produced crude oil. This was especially true of the oil wells that were producing before 1972. The weighted average price per barrel (old and new) for domestic crude was approximately $6.44 in January 1974. One can see from Figure 13.19 that this was about half of the average world price at that time. When imported crude was averaged in with domestic crude (along with other factors), the price we paid at the pump didn't fully reflect the world petroleum economy. **Subsidies** and regulations were used to hold energy prices well below economic and prevailing international levels. This way growth would not be seriously constrained. Thus, we had a shortage. People demanded more petroleum at the going price than industry was willing to supply.

We are now going through a period in which the price of domestic crude has been deregulated (allowed to rise or fall with supply and demand), and international production also is being curtailed. The free market can often be very cold and inhumane. Letting the price of gasoline rise could result in gasoline selling for $2.00 to $3.00 per gallon. Is this fair? Or, is this a way to promote conservation?

Why did we keep the price of gasoline artificially low for a time and allow shortages to persist? This gets back to why we allow government to interfere in the marketplace at all. One of the reasons is equity (fairness).

Probably the most significant occurrence related to the increased cost and uncertainty regarding petroleum supply was that the average

Figure 13.20 A gasoline rationing coupon. (From Jack Schneider, USDOE.)

fuel efficiency of cars driven in the United States increased by over 30% between 1973 and 1992. Conservation efforts by both industry and individuals have been rather remarkable.

Is it equitable to have the rich drive and the poor stay at home (or take the bus, or whatever)? It can also be asked: is it fair to have allocation by queuing (long lines at the gas station)? On the other hand, is it fair to hold a price artificially low and cause consumption of a resource at an unreasonable pace and then run out? Since queuing has little popular support and because brute force, tradition, and random selection have never been widely accepted as allocation systems in this country, we seem to have narrowed our options to two. Either the government will allocate gasoline in times of shortage using some sort of **rationing** system based on equal shares or need, or prices will be deregulated and the free market allowed to allocate based on ability to pay.

What are the arguments for and against rationing gasoline?

Would a rationing program be helpful?

It is estimated that a rationing program would cost approximately $1.2 billion per year (that's about 1.5¢/gallon) and take 8—12 months to set up. It would take some 33,000 federal, state and local officials to administer. However, rationing prevents long lines at gas stations, keeps stations open for regular hours, and forces you to make those hard choices on how you will use your transportation option. If you choose not to drive, you can sell your ration coupons on the "white market" to whoever will buy them.

You don't like rationing? Well, then, you'll have to take your chances with the free-market system, which will allow price to match supply. Those are all the choices you have.

13.16 Cartels and Monopolies

In the United States, the control of **monopolies** has been accomplished through the enactment and enforcement of antitrust laws. These include the Sherman Antitrust Act of 1890 and the Clayton Act of 1914. They are two of our most basic antimonopoly laws. The basic goal of such laws is to prevent firms from monopolizing the market—that is, conspiring to eliminate competition. The laws are designed to prevent interference with free market forces.

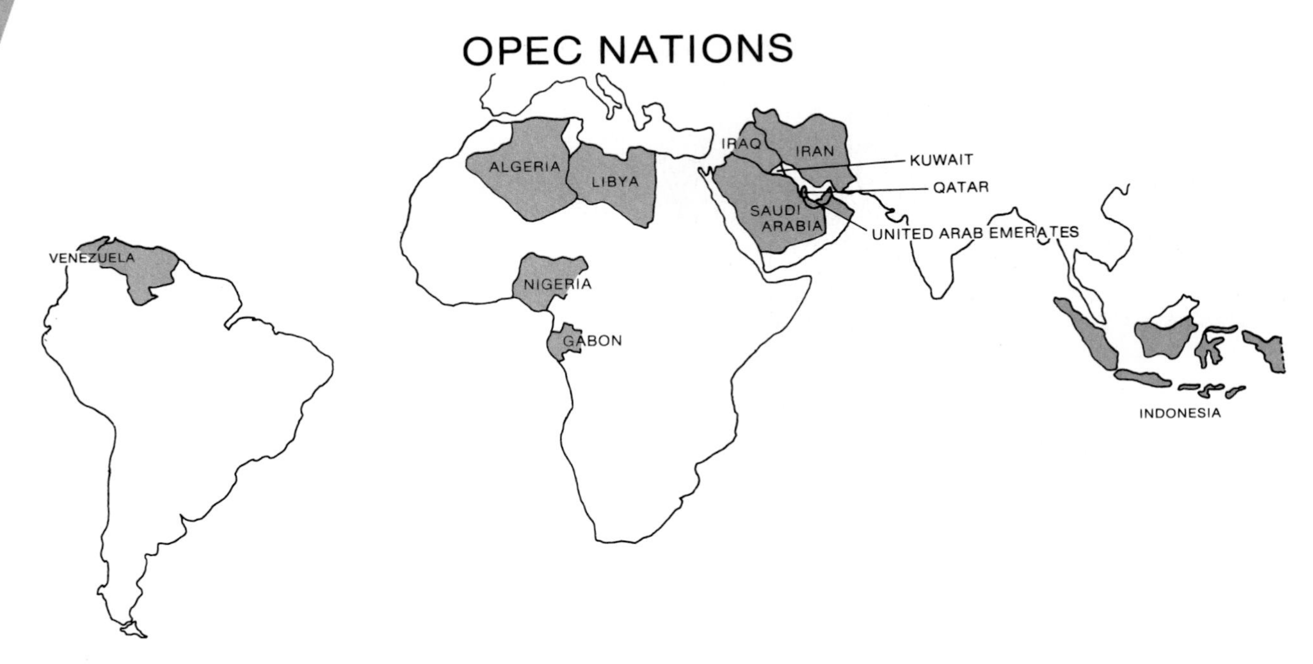

Figure 13.21 The OPEC nations.

What is a cartel?

Why is it difficult to deal with cartels?

International **cartels** are much more difficult to deal with. They consist of a voluntary combination of independent private enterprises or countries that supply the same commodities. Agreement is made to limit their competitive activities. This can be done by allocating customers, regulating quantity or quality of their output, fixing prices or terms of sales, or other methods. But how are the agreements to be enforced?

The Organization of Petroleum Exporting Countries (OPEC) international oil cartel is the most relevant example. OPEC was created in 1960 as the result of a Venezuelan initiative. Until recently, the group successfully maintained the high oil prices that began in 1973 and advanced member interests in trade and political matters with industrialized, oil-consuming nations. Cooperation among OPEC members has been unremarkable, but a unique combination of situations enabled them to work together. Nations that make up the membership of OPEC are Algeria, Gabon, Indonesia, Iran, Iraq, Kuwait, Libya, Nigeria, Qatar, Saudi Arabia, United Arab Emirates, and Venezuela. (See Figure 13.21.)

So far, oil-importing nations have been only moderately successful in breaking the cartel's power. Reducing imports, buying from non-member nations, developing energy alternatives, and emphasizing energy conservation practices seem to be the best way to minimize OPEC's influence.

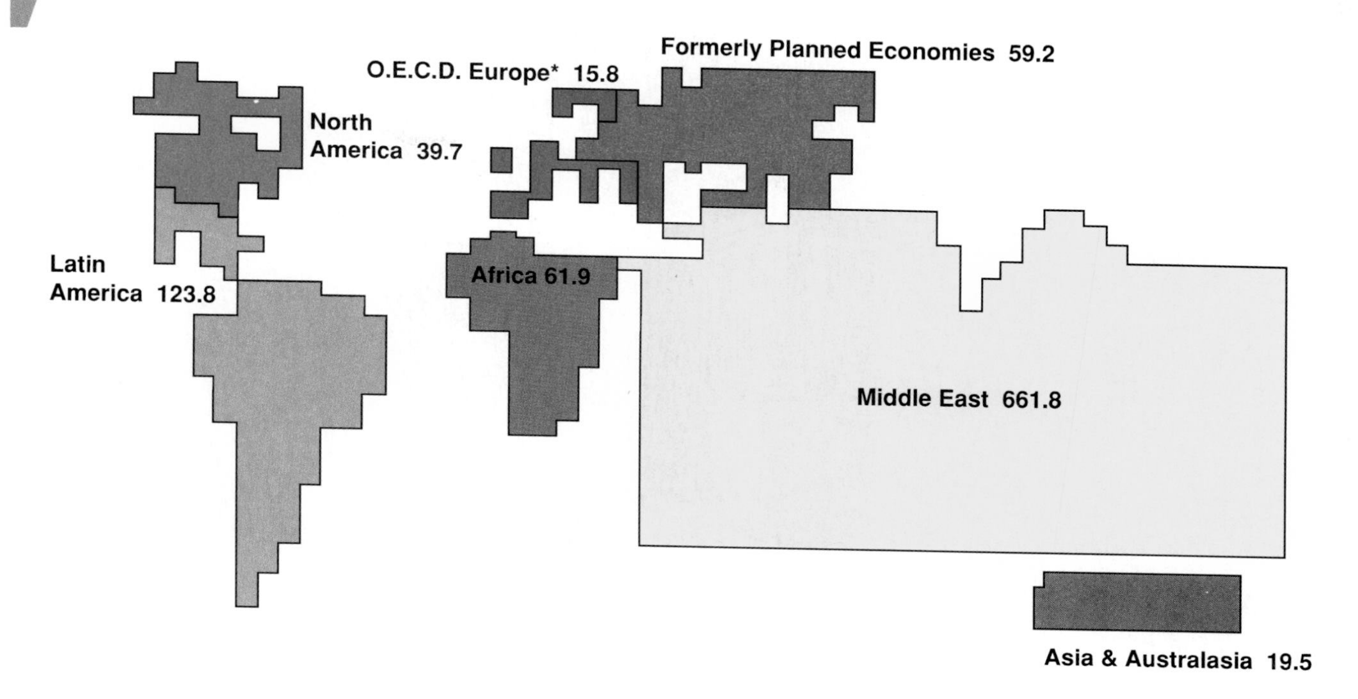

Figure 13.22 Proven oil reserves as of 1992 (billions of barrels). Regions are shown relative to the size of their proven oil reserves. (Source: BP Statistical Review of World Energy, June 1993.)

Historically, most cartels have not lasted long. Usually, some of the member nations or companies become dissatisfied with their share of total sales and profits. They will attempt to "go it alone" and break from the agreement. (Ecuador has done this.) Soon the cartel collapses.

O ver | Is this
P riced | a
E nergy | correct
C artel | statement?

OPEC has some advantages that make it harder to break up. A significant number of its most important members, those having the largest reserves of crude, have very small populations and few costly social programs. They have the problem of not knowing what to do with all their money. They would be better off having less income over a longer period of time. These countries actually increase their future earnings by keeping their oil in the ground. Further, other nations can do little to economically threaten them. We could refuse to sell them food, but other nations could satisfy that small need. They have the dollars to buy—so someone will sell.

Why is the OPEC cartel so tough to break up?

Iran, Indonesia, and Venezuela are notable exceptions. They have large populations and need significant income to deal with pressing social problems. In addition, Iran financed a bitter war with Iraq (also an OPEC member) for several years. International conflicts along with the significant production capabilities of Mexico and the North Sea, which are not in OPEC, could cause the cartel to collapse. However, it

Figure 13.23 The OPEC nations struggled during the late 1980s to maintain high crude oil prices. Internal conflicts made them their own worst enemy. (From Mike Keefe, *The Denver Post.*)

Figure 13.24 Tanker unloading crude oil. (USDOE)

is widely believed that the United States, Western Europe and Japan will import a growing percentage of the oil they will consume. This gives OPEC its power.

In terms of economic and national security, the best thing we can do is to avoid being vulnerable to short-term supply interruptions. Some experts believe that if we have an oil reserve in above-ground tanks (a storage capacity of about 60 days) and a shut-in petroleum producing capacity (wells that have been drilled but whose production is being held off) of approximately 0.5 million barrels per day, we could probably outlast most situations that produce supply interruptions. We should also continue serious efforts to develop alternative energy sources and improve the efficiency of the energy-consuming devices we use.

Figure 13.25 Government-supported wind-power research. Note the vertical axis wind turbine (Darrieus rotor) in the background.

13.17 Other Energy/Economic Issues

Other energy-related economic issues include:

a. Maintaining a Truly Competitive Market

The petroleum industry consists of five basic stages of production: exploration, development, production, refining, and sales. A *vertically integrated* company operates in all of these areas. There are certain economic advantages in doing so.

What is a vertically integrated oil company?

Some maintain that these economic advantages stifle competition. Should the federal government limit the extent of vertical integration of petroleum firms, or is this the most efficient way to utilize our petroleum resources?

Our large oil companies are becoming energy companies. In addition to selling oil and natural gas, they now own large reserves of coal, uranium, oil shale, tar sands, and land having geothermal potential. Does this diversification of oil companies slow the development of some of our future energy options? Might these companies promote the development of the options that will benefit them? Do our energy companies have the expertise for developing new energy resources? Are they the people most capable of leading us into a sane energy future? There are serious questions that our society and technology will resolve as time goes on.

Should oil companies be energy companies?

b. Financing an Energy Research and Development Program

In which future energy options are we most interested? How do we determine this? How shall research be financed?

A tax of one cent (1¢) per gallon on gasoline generates approximately one billion dollars in revenue annually. A billion dollars sounds like an enormous sum, but it cost the United States approximately 40 billion dollars to put a man on the moon, and it took 10 years to do it. Our peak spending for that was about $4.5 billion per year.

Some energy options—such as solar thermal energy conversion, photovoltaics, and fusion—require great investments at the beginning. Private industry is often reluctant to fund this costly research, as the potential for making a profit is too far into the future. Further, controlled nuclear fusion may never work. If research is to move forward, should the government help foot the bill?

Also, should industry be protected from drastic fluctuations in world petroleum prices if they are to pursue various energy options seriously? How much help (as subsidies or tax incentives) the struggling solar heating and cooling industry should receive is another issue. Don't look for large increases in solar applications until the economics are right. If the industry cannot compete economically, solar options won't be pursued. People won't sacrifice too much immediate happiness to pay for installing a solar panel.

Will government support be necessary to promote the development of some of our energy options?

Will governmental support be necessary to promote the research and development of some of our energy options? Some economists argue that if an industry cannot make it without subsidies, then that industry shouldn't make it at all.

c. Adjusting Our Economic Policies to Reflect the Fact That Fossil Fuels Are Expensive and Finite

What is the economic solution to waste?

The economic solution to waste is to raise the price of wasting. This is what the deregulation debate centers on. In the area of electrical energy consumption, we may need flat (or even inverted) utility rate structures rather than structures that give discounts to large users. Should we remove the subsidies and regulations that keep our cost of fuels so low? Why are we so slow to change the building codes that prevent the construction of energy-efficient homes and buildings? Progress is slow, but we are gaining on these issues. A freer economy and a more efficient government can do much to lessen the pains of the energy crisis and help us plan an energy future.

73 13.18 Economics and the Environment

In the past, the free market system actually made it profitable to pollute. Until the government interfered with the system, a manufacturer had only to pay the actual costs of production. Side effects of that production—smoke, chemical effluent, loud noise, and so on—often had a detrimental effect on the neighbors downstream or downwind. The manufacturer didn't have to pay. The costs or benefits that are external to the actual act of production or use that are passed on involuntarily to someone else are referred to as **spillover costs** or **externalities.**

Because pollution must eventually be cleaned up or related health problems treated, the consumer eventually pays for all costs, both direct and hidden. The problem then is how to deal with the spillover costs. Should they be openly added to the price of an item or service so that its market price reflects the true cost of producing it? If this is the case, the consumer who uses the product pays for the pollution it causes.

What are spillover costs or externalities?

True cost = actual (internal) cost + external (spillover) costs.

What is the true cost of an item?

Another possibility is to subsidize the manufacturer by allowing the pollution to continue and have the government do the cleanup. It is also possible to provide tax incentives that encourage the manufacturer to install pollution control equipment. In these cases, everyone pays.

Sometimes "jawboning," or preaching, at polluting industries results in their changing their ways. Industries are sometimes more responsive to ethical arguments if they can present themselves in their advertising as environmentally sound.

?

What are some of the ways we deal with polluting companies?

With proper laws on the books, individuals and groups can sue for damages in many cases. Often, the government sets pollution standards to keep pollution below a threshold (or maximum allowable) level. The regulations are monitored by government investigators. Violators are fined and required to correct polluting practices. Those who cannot comply with the regulations in a specified time period are prohibited from continuing operation.

Sometimes pollution charges are assessed a given manufacturer. The manufacturer simply pays the government for the pollution damage inflicted on the public. This technique generates public revenue, and is fairer and less expensive to enforce than the "monitor and sue" approach. The biggest polluters have the greatest incentive to change their ways. Unfortunately, it is difficult to estimate the charges to make for each pollutant.

All of the above-mentioned methods have been used at one time or another, with varying degrees of success. The most widely used of the methods is the regulation-monitor approach. This forces compliance. The costs of compliance soon appear as increased prices for the manufactured products.

From an international trade standpoint, it must be mentioned that environmental legislation often puts United States industries in a bind. We often cannot compete successfully with those foreign industries that are not required to clean up their products and facilities and the pollution they cause. Until environmental goals and laws become global in scope, the costs of responsible production will not be born equally.

How does international trade complicate pollution control?

As we mentioned earlier, pollution standards require that pollution levels be kept below some threshold point. Zero or extremely low pollution levels are not always necessary because natural chemical cycles can absorb some wastes. Also, the cost of removal increases rapidly as the standards become more stringent. The removal of the last few percent of any pollutant becomes prohibitively expensive.

Figure 13.26 This car is having a state-mandated emissions check. Who pays for the emission test? If the car fails the test, then what?

How much are we willing to pay for pollution control?

Does the public really want to pay for complete removal? Figure 13.26 illustrates the situation. As the pollution level drops, the costs of pollution-related damages fall. However, the costs of pollution removal increase. The low point on the total cost curve is usually the acceptable cost, the price the public is willing to pay for cleanup, and also the cost of the remaining damages they are willing to bear. We accept some discomfort to gain some other desired end.

? When does the acceptable-costs method of pollution reduction break down?

This technique of arriving at an acceptable cost works quite well for a small number of polluters. It must be remembered, however, that it does allow some pollution from each source. If the number of sources becomes large enough, we can still have a problem, even a very severe problem. You may reduce the polluting emissions from each automobile to a very low level, but if you put enough automobiles in a given area, you still have smog. If carried too far, the acceptable cost technique simply does not recognize the absolute boundaries or limits of the ecosystem in which we live. We deal with this larger problem in Chapter 14.

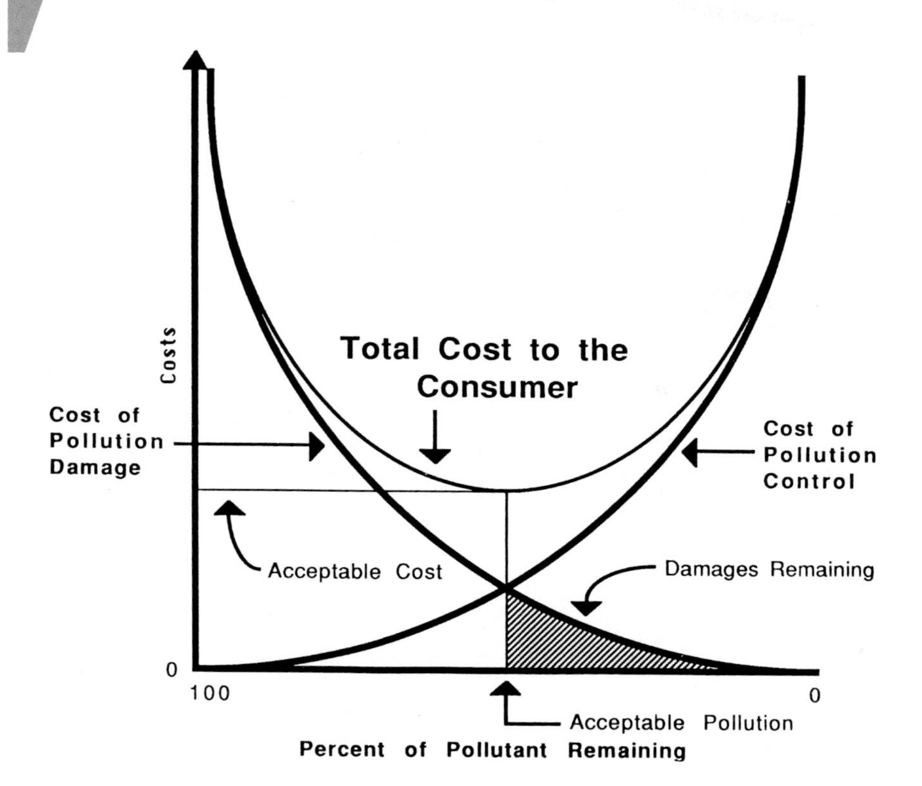

Figure 13.27 Trade-offs—balancing pollution and cleanup costs.

The economic arena offers a variety of strategies for dealing with problems related to resources and the environment. These include:

1. Allowing free market forces to function naturally. As resources become scarce, price rises and demand drops. The remaining resources are thus conserved.

2. Allowing governments to interfere with the free market in those areas where the market cannot, by itself, protect the environment or meet specific societal goals. Governments can:
   - **a.** promote and maintain competitive markets.
   - **b.** change the distribution of resources to provide for public wants and needs. This includes:
     - **1.** financing energy research and development.
     - **2.** subsidizing resources society desires to have developed, taxing resources society wants de-emphasized.
   - **c.** set goals for environmental cleanup.
     - **1.** regulation of individuals & businesses to clean up pollution.
     - **2.** enforcement: charging polluters and/or pay incentives to remove pollutants.

Economic and governmental strategies have a mixed record of success in dealing with resource/environmental problems. They are among the most controversial solutions to these problems.

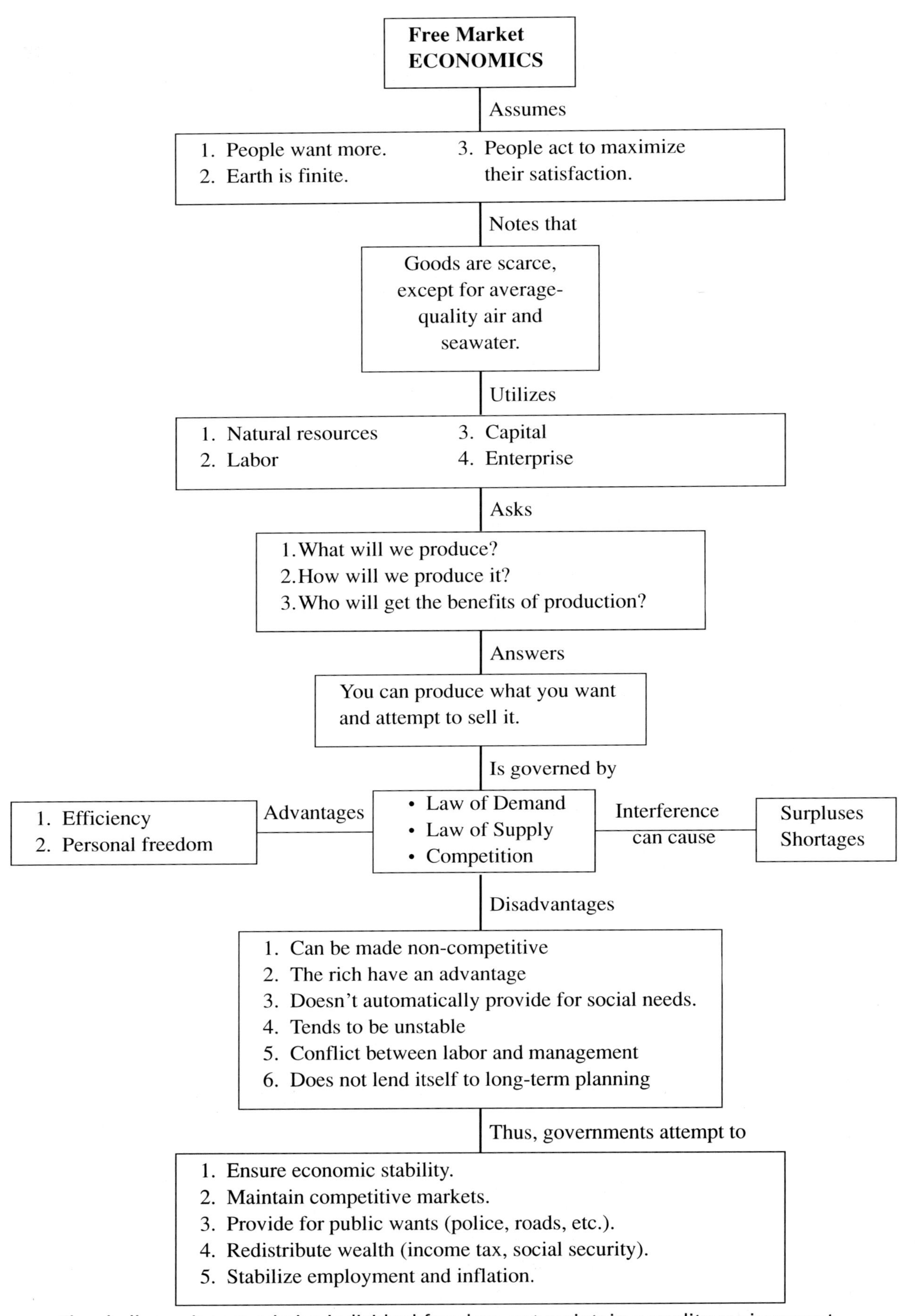

The challenge is to maximize individual freedom, yet maintain a quality environment

Summary

Economics is the study of the ways individuals and societies distribute their goods in an attempt to satisfy their unlimited wants. Individuals and societies have limited resources with which to satisfy wants. Economic resources include natural resources, labor, capital, and enterprise. Economic analysis is concerned with three basic questions regarding the use of resources: *What* economic goods shall be produced? *How* will they be produced? and, *Who* should be allowed to use the goods?

One of the best ways to gain insight into the basic economic problem is to examine distributive (allocative) mechanisms. These mechanisms include: brute force, queuing, random selection, tradition, government (equal shares, need), and the market economy.

In the market economy, if the price is low, the demand is high, and vice versa. Also, if the price is high, the supply is high, and vice versa. Producers and consumers interact in the marketplace. The interaction produces market equilibrium prices. At market equilibrium, the consumer is able to purchase the largest amount of a product at the cheapest price and the producer is able to sell the most at the highest price. Manipulation of free market forces can produce both surpluses and shortages.

The main advantages of the free market are its relative efficiency and its emphasis on personal freedom. The market system also has some flaws. These include: markets can be manipulated and made non-competitive, the rich have a competitive edge, free market forces do not provide for social needs, and market fluctuations make it difficult to do long-term planning.

Because of these flaws, citizens allow the government to manipulate the market. The goals of this manipulation are to: ensure economic stability, achieve competitive markets, provide for public wants and needs, promote fairness (equity), and stabilize the economy.

The interplay between energy supply and economic conditions is important to both individuals and societies. Freedom, conservation, equity and morality all tie into issues of rationing, dealing with cartels, and energy planning. Economic/environmental issues are similar to economic/resource issues.

The finiteness of Earth ultimately places limits on how to resolve economic/resource/environmental issues. This is the topic of Chapter 14.

References

Bowden, Elbert V. *Economics: The Science of Common Sense,* 7th ed. (Cincinnati: Southwestern Publishing Co.), 1992.

Brown, Lester R., et. al, *Saving the Planet: How to Shape an Environmentally Stable Global Economy* (New York, NY: W. W. Norton), 1991.

Byrns, Ralph T. and Gerald W. Stone, Jr. *Economics,* 5th ed. (New York: HarperCollins), 1992.

Chandler, William U. *The Changing Role of the Market in National Economies* (Washington, DC: Worldwatch Institute), 1986.

Cline, William R. *The Economics of Global Warming* (Washington, DC: Institute for International Economics), 1992.

Daly, Herman E. and Kenneth N. Townsend, eds. *Valuing the Earth: Economics, Ecology, Ethics* (Cambridge, MA: The MIT Press), 1993.

Editorial Staff. *The Wall Street Journal.* The "Energy Crisis" explained. May 27, 1977, page 10.

Gordon, Sanford D. and George G. Dawson. *Introductory Economics,* 7th ed. (Lexington, MA: D. C. Heath & Co.), 1991.

Kneese, Allen V. *Measuring the Benefits of Clean Air and Water* (Washington DC: Resources for the Future), 1984.

Tsongas, Paul E. *A Call to Economic Arms* (Boston: The Tsongas Committee), 1992.

End of Chapter Questions ?

Set A

1. What is economics?

2. Why study economics?

3. What are the basic economic questions?

4. What are the beginning assumptions of market economics?

5. Do you think that an economic system based on the assumption that people will readily and continually sacrifice some of their own happiness or wealth for the overall good of the whole (society, system) can succeed? Voluntarily? Efficiently? Justify your answer?

6. What is scarcity?

7. Name physical (tangible) goods that are not scarce.

8. In your opinion, could there be a gasoline shortage in the United States if gasoline sold for:

   a. $0.80 per gallon?

   b. $4.00 per gallon?

9. List the resources which are required to produce goods.

10. Once goods are available, what are the three basic economic questions all societies must answer?

11. What is an allocative mechanism?

12. After the three basic economic questions have been answered, a society must still distribute its goods. List six distributive mechanisms.

13. In your own words, state the Law of Supply and the Law of Demand.

14. Prepare a supply/demand curve for peaches. Use the data supplied below.

   a. According to your graph, what is the market equilibrium price of peaches?

   b. Assume the demand at each price dropped by one-half. What would the market equilibrium price become? (Use the original supply curve.) Prove your answer by plotting a new demand curve (D_2) on the same graph.

Supply and Demand Schedule for Peaches

Price/Pound	Quantity Demanded in Pounds	Quantity Supplied in Pounds
$0.90	1,500	10,250
.80	2,000	9,750
.70	2,750	9,000
.60	3,750	8,000
.50	5,000	6,750
.40	6,500	5,250
.30	8,250	3,500
.20	10,250	1,500

c. Assume the supply at each price dropped by one-half. What would the market equilibrium price become? (Use the original demand curve.) Prove your answer by plotting a new supply curve (S_2) on the same graph.

d. Given the changes in supply and demand, what would the price become? How does the new price compare with the original price? Why?

15. What is market equilibrium (ME) and how is it arrived at?

16. Why are neither consumers nor producers completely satisfied with the ME price?

17. How can surpluses and shortages be created?

18. What factors make the market system work?

19. List two features of the market system.

20. List five problems with the market system.

21. List five functions most governments are asked to perform in order to reduce problems that the market system cannot solve on its own.

22. Contrast how economists and scientists view resources.

23. Choose a position for or against gasoline rationing in the United States. Defend your position.

24. Why is (was) the OPEC cartel so tough to break up?

25. Should oil companies be allowed to be energy companies?

26. Will government support be necessary to promote the development of some of our energy options?

27. How can allowing only a very small amount of pollution to be emitted from each automobile lead to major environmental problems?

Set B

28. Assumptions are statements or ideas that are accepted as true (at least for a time) without proof. Do you believe the beginning economic assumptions listed at the start of the chapter? Why or why not?

29. Explain how a growing population and an increasing standard of living can cause additional demands for energy.

Inventory clerks

The inventory clerk's view of the energy problem:

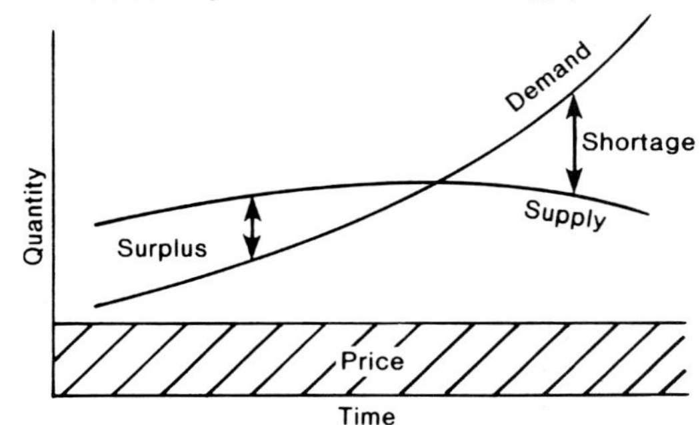

Economists

The economist's view of the energy problem:

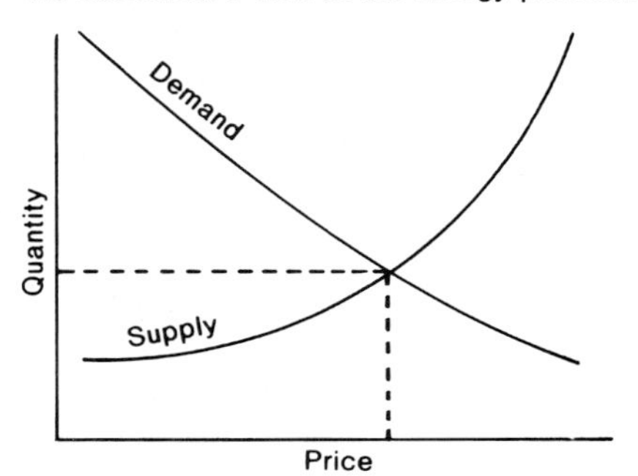

30. Explain how maintaining an artificially low price (price control) of a nonrenewable resource can shorten its depletion time.

31. Use the following two graphs to help you write a contrast of the "Inventory Clerk's" and the Economist's view of the world.

32. Why doesn't OPEC double the price of a barrel of oil every five years?

33. Explain how holding prices at an artificial low creates both shortages and waste. Also explain why there is no such thing as a shortage when free market forces operate. You may choose to sketch a graph as part of your explanation.

34. The Gizmo Manufacturing Company is located on the Moose Jaw River just one mile west of Edgerton, a town of 12,000 people. (Refer to map shown.) Two thousand people from town work at the Gizmo plant. Last fall, approximately 60 area people became very ill with intestinal problems, all at about the same time. An investigation traced the problem to beef from cattle raised on Joe Schmoo's farm. The problem with the beef was traced to a chemical found in the hay which was fed to the cattle. This chemical was also found in Moose Jaw River water, which was used to irrigate the hay field. The chemical was traced to Gizmo's effluent discharge into the Moose Jaw River. The following chart lists several possible actions that could be taken to deal with the problem. Comment on the potential effectiveness of each possible action.

Possible Action	**Comments**
Moral persuasion	
Suing for damages	
Prohibition (closing the plant)	
Direct regulation	
Payments and incentives to remove pollutants	
Pollution charges	

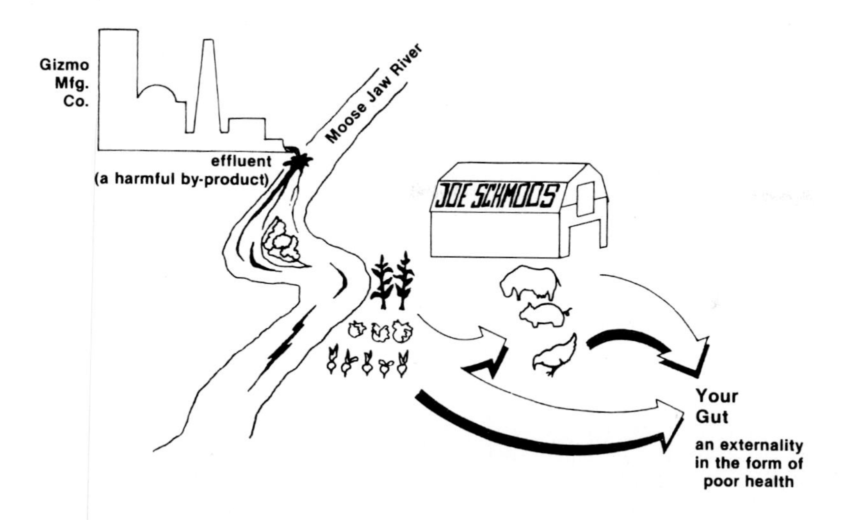

35. Explain how strict environmental regulations within the United States can damage American industry's ability to compete in international markets.

36. Suppose a survey of Americans revealed that half would cancel vacation plans if gasoline prices rose to $2.00 per gallon. Would this indicate that gasoline prices are "elastic" or "inelastic"? Explain.

37. Explain how the higher price of imported oil can affect the supply side of the *domestic oil market*. How can higher oil prices affect the demand for and the price of alternative fuels?

38. How might each of the following factors affect the financial outlook for solar heating equipment makers in the United States, nearly all of which are small entrepreneurial businesses? Give your reasons.

- **a.** Federal and state tax credits are available for solar investment.
- **b.** Major credit institutions tend to give loans to companies with proven "track records."
- **c.** Commercial banks prefer to make large loans rather than several small ones, which are more typical of small businesses, in order to lessen transaction costs.
- **d.** Federal authorization of a *Solar and Conservation Bank* would ease consumer financing of solar equipment purchases.
- **e.** Lenders are usually reluctant to make loans with terms greater than 10 years because interest rates can change quickly over long periods.
- **f.** Utilities can write no-interest loans to homeowners for the purchase of energy-conserving devices and materials.

Goal

To examine some predictions about our planet's future. To make some decisions regarding the best route into the future.

Options for the Future

Some men see the world as it is now and ask why.

I see the world as it never has been and ask why not?

—Cervantes (paraphrased)

Figure 14.1 The westward movement. (From Denver Regional Transportation District.)

How did growth help America become a major world power?

 14.1 Growth in a Finite System

Throughout most of U.S. history, Americans believed that growth was good and essential to the maintenance of a vibrant nation and a healthy economy. Growth was important in the evolution of America into a major world power, for three reasons. First, the human population in early America was small. Second, the space available seemed unlimited. Third, natural resources appeared almost limitless. As frontiers moved westward, the country grew, dreamed, and prospered. Opportunities abounded for those with an adventurous spirit. The frontiers called for development. Growth was the key.

As the expansion continued, so did the dream. (See Figure 14.1) The midwestern farmlands were developed, oil wells were drilled, and gold was discovered further west. When environmental problems appeared, the frontier motto was "foul your nest and move west." And so they did, all the way to the coast.

Around 1900, many people became worried about the growing immigrant population that crowded the cities. Progressive reformers encouraged birth control and sanitation. At the same time, others were concerned about the loss of forests that provided lumber and held soil in place. National forests were set aside. These steps seemed to help ease growth-related problems.

What evidence suggested possible problems related to growth?

By the 1960s, we could no longer ignore environmental issues. Parts of the country seemed filled with people. Smog was overpowering in many cities, and some rivers and lakes literally stank. For some, the dream had failed. Increasingly, Americans had to import several strategic metals and even petroleum. Something had gone wrong. In wounded bewilderment, many wondered if the system had failed. Intellectuals began re-examining our assumptions. Even the doctrine of growth was attacked.

In the atmosphere of the 1960s, it was only natural that the idea of "growth as the key to success" should be questioned; and it was, as we shall learn in the following pages. However, it is important to keep in mind that the assumptions upon which the following "no growth" philosophy are based are *only* assumptions, and many were shown to be false. Other assumptions must be given equal consideration. There is no instant solution. Thus, the following suggestions are yours to consider, ponder, and then use to form your own ideas.

14.2 The Limits to Growth Report

In 1970, the Club of Rome began a large-scale study of the growth question. The Club of Rome is a loosely-knit group of multi-national and highly respected scientists, scholars, and other assorted professionals. The Club's stated purpose is to develop ways of dealing with an ever more complicated world.

What is the Club of Rome?

Because of the worldwide scope and complexity of the growth issue, the Club hired an international team of scientists to head the study. The team was led by computer experts from the Massachusetts Institute of Technology (MIT).

The study group identified five basic factors that determine and, in their interactions, ultimately limit growth on our planet. They are:

?

What are the five factors that determine growth on the Earth?

- population
- agricultural production
- consumption of nonrenewable resources
- industrial output
- pollution

They identified three features that these five factors have in common:

?

What characteristics do the five factors have in common?

1. The factors are all **interrelated** and cannot be studied separately.
2. At the time of their study, the factors were all growing exponentially.
3. Since the Earth is finite, the factors all appear to have upper limits.

A simplified diagram of the interrelationships involved is shown in Figure 14.2.

Using data about the five factors and their growth rates, the scientists built a computer model to **simulate** the major ecological forces at work in the world. The model related all the important variables. For example, a rise in population is ordinarily accompanied by a rise in agricultural production, because more food is needed.

A variable is something that changes, or varies. Two of the variables studied were time and population size.

The Limits to Growth, a non-technical report of the findings, came out in 1972. The results of the simulation were startling. The

?

What is *The Limits to Growth* report?

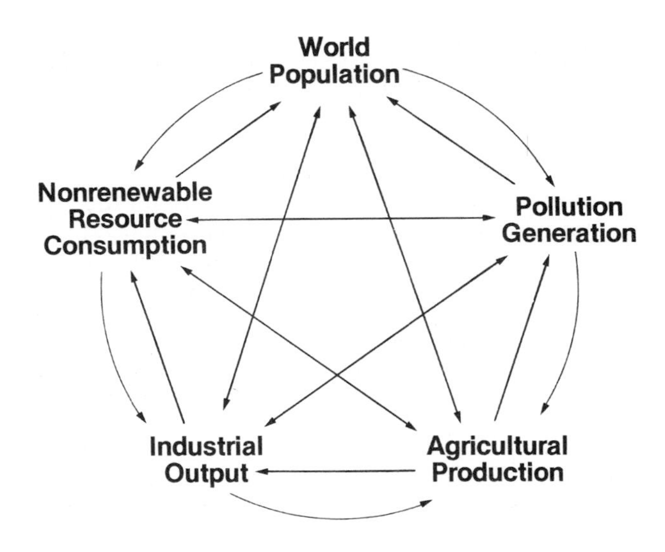

Figure 14.2 A simplified diagram of the Club of Rome's world model. Each arrow indicates that one factor influences another. For example, an increase in population size leads to increased industrial output.

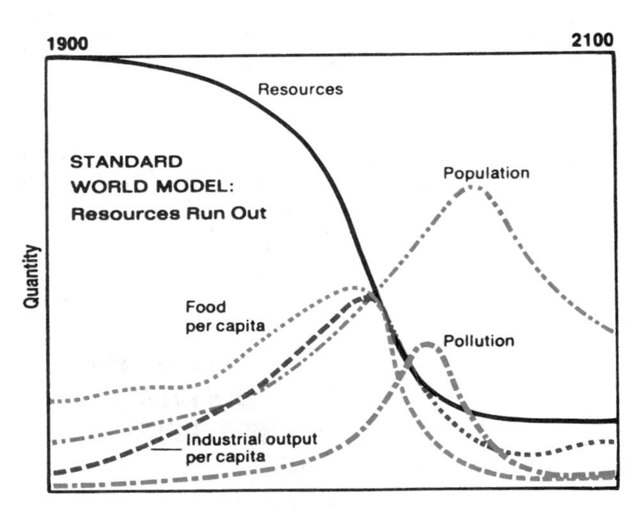

Figure 14.3 The standard computer run. (From *The Limits to Growth: A Report for The Club of Rome's Project on the Predicament of Mankind,* by Donella H. Meadows, Dennis L. Meadows, Jorgen Randers, and William W. Behrens III. A Potomac Associates book published by Universe Books, New York, 1972. Graphics by Potomac Associates.)

? What was the major conclusion of *The Limits to Growth* report?

basic finding was: *If there are no major changes in the physical, economic, or social relationships that have historically governed the development of the world system, the system will continue to grow exponentially until the rapidly diminishing resource base forces a collapse* (≃ 2020 A.D.). This conclusion, shown in Figure 14.3, illustrates the change in the five basic factors over time. The message was loud and clear. If we don't change our ways of doing things, we've had it.

14.3 Responding to the Prediction of Doom

Needless to say, the appropriate next question was, What should we do? The computer was asked a series of "what if" questions, and this is what it said:

1. *What if*—nonrenewable resources are discovered and developed in great abundance?
   Then—growth will continue and industrialization will expand. The rate of pollution generation will finally exceed the ecosystem's

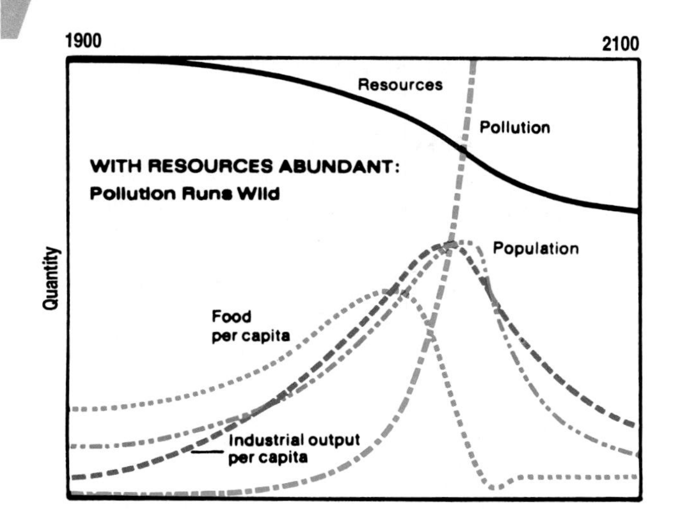

Figure 14.4 With resources abundant, pollution runs wild. (From *The Limits to Growth.*)

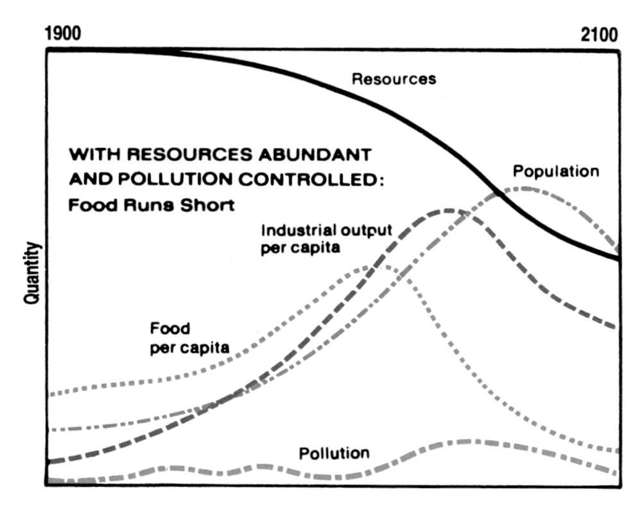

Figure 14.5 With resources abundant and pollution controlled: food runs short. (From *The Limits to Growth.*)

ability to cleanse itself. At this point, the ecosystem collapses. The death rate increases and food production declines. See Figure 14.4.

2. *What if*—nonrenewable resources are found in great abundance and the effectiveness of pollution control is increased by a factor of four? *Then*—population and industry will grow until the limit of arable land is reached; collapse then occurs. See Figure 14.5.
3. *What if*—nonrenewable resources are abundant, pollution control is effective, and agricultural productivity is increased? *Then*—population and industry grow to high levels. Although each unit of industrial production generates much less pollution, total production is so great that a pollution crisis finally brings an end to growth.
4. *What if*—nonrenewable resources are abundant, pollution control is effective, and effective birth control is available, but voluntary? *Then*—since the birth control is voluntary and does not involve any value changes, population continues to grow (but more slowly than before). Nevertheless, the food crisis is postponed for only a decade or two.

5. *What if*—world population is held constant after 1975?
   Then—the growth of industrial and agricultural output deplete the nonrenewable resource base and the system collapses.
6. *What if*—population and average living standards (in terms of material wealth) are held constant after 1975?
   Then—there is some hope, although lack of nonrenewable resource recycling would cause a decline in the nonrenewable resource base.
7. *What if*—population and average living standards (material wealth) are held constant after 1975 and recycling is effective?
   Then—the world can sustain itself far into the future.
8. *What if*—we wait until the year 2000 before we take effective action to deal with growth?
   Then—we waited too long.

? What two global factors must be controlled if growth is to stop?

The overall conclusion in 1972 was that without constraints, exponential growth would continue. Two factors dominated the situation: exponentially increasing *population* and *nonrenewable resource consumption*. In any program designed to produce a future world that is stable, the exponential growth of both of these factors would have to cease. Any combination of the variables influencing growth that did not stabilize both population and nonrenewable resource consumption would eventually lead to collapse.

The Limits to Growth study hit the world's thinkers like a bomb. It attacked some fundamental beliefs of modern-day society. It predicted a doomsday that was soon to be. There was hardly time to debate the study or make plans for a change. Either we were to accept the conclusions and change our values, or the world would collapse around us. It was repent or perish.

14.4 Criticism of the Limits to Growth Report

? What are the arguments against *The Limits to Growth* report?

Many criticized the study, and some flaws were found. The most serious charges were:

1. *The study sponsors (The Club of Rome) had hidden agendas.*
   Should an elitist group of technocrats be telling humankind what direction it ought to be taking? The Club members had already reaped the benefits of the growth they now abhorred. Maybe the way to ensure that one will make it alive through a revolution is to lead it.
2. *The assumptions determined the conclusion.*
   An assumption was made that the Earth and its resources were finite. It also assumed that nonrenewable resource consumption and population would grow exponentially. As in any simulation, the results depend on the initial assumptions. In this case, nothing could happen but collapse.

Figure 14.6 *The Limits to Growth* report.

3. *Skimpy and insufficient evidence was* ***extrapolated*** *years into the future.*
   The human inventive genius was ignored. We were assumed to be utterly incapable of adjusting to problems of scarcity. Would humans really sit by idly as technology stagnated, pollution built, and millions choked to death? (See Figure 14.7.) Couldn't we learn from experience to invent and adapt?
4. *Some important* ***variables*** *were not included.*
   As you know, pricing and behavior are linked. Pricing, however, was not a variable in the Club of Rome model. In the real world, rising prices would act as an economic signal to conserve scarce resources, provide incentives to use cheaper materials and/or substitutes, stimulate research efforts to develop ways to substitute or save on resources, and make exploration attempts more profitable. (Rationing could be used to accomplish some of these goals with less impact on the poor. Also, at present some minerals have no substitutes. Their prices could reflect their true value.) See Figure 14.8.
   The Limits to Growth model didn't assume that crowding was a variable that might limit population. Crowding might cause people to reduce their numbers before pollution, food shortages, and resource depletion overtook us. By ignoring crowding as a factor, the *Limits* study implied that crowding actually increases birth rates.
5. *The book told us what the world of the future should be like, but it didn't tell us how to get there.*
   The recipe for recovery was too generalized to be useful for policy-making. It is easy to say that population should be stabilized by

Figure 14.7 Free at last! (Reprinted with special permission of King Features Syndicate.)

Figure 14.8 Automobile "bumpers" used to be made of steel and chrome. Now, they contain aluminum, plastic, and synthetic rubber. (Jim Shaffer)

Figure 14.9 How do we get there from here? (Cover drawing by Folon; © 1966, The New Yorker Magazine, Inc.)

equating birth rates to death rates. It is a totally different level of reality to begin dealing with how this is to be done. The mechanisms for reducing population growth, redefining the good life, changing value systems and reordering priorities are what the problem is all about.

The Limits to Growth study only lightly touched on these issues. The above shortcomings in the study deserve serious study and thought. See Figure 14.9.

14.5 Accomplishments of the Limits to Growth Report

What were the beneficial results of *The Limits to Growth* report?

However, even with these faults exposed, *The Limits to Growth* study can still be praised *for* accomplishing the following:

1. It forced us to look at the direction in which we seem headed. It nailed down the fact that exponential growth is abnormal in a finite system. It put that fact in a time reference that hits us all—now. Every living thing reaches a limit beyond which it cannot grow. Trees reach a certain height. Animals and humans do the same. When growth continues beyond maturity, we call it obesity or cancer. Abnormal growth is dangerous.

Figure 14.10 The sustainable society. (From *The Limits to Growth*.)

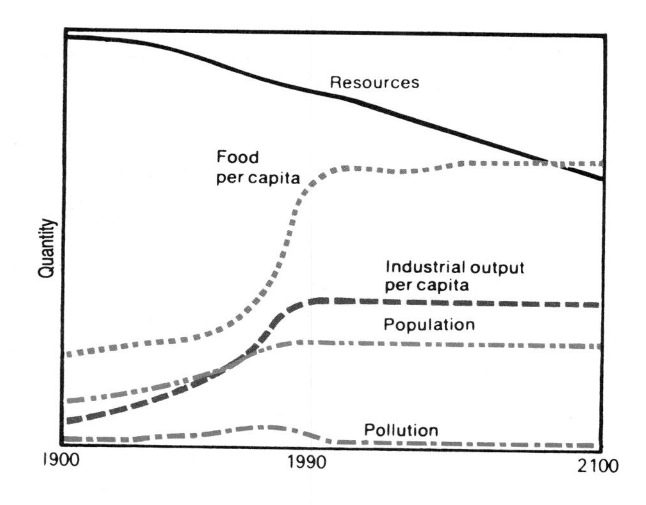

2. It pointed to recent historical evidence that there are limits to the five basic factors. The study organized and documented many of these signs.
3. It provided a glimpse of what the future might be like—if we chose their proposed road to survival. Figure 14.10 depicts that future.

Although the sketch of what a no-growth world would be like was vague, and the route to get there was not clearly defined, the idea of a **sustainable** future is of value in itself. Certainly, changes in our behavior are required if life as we know it is to survive on this planet. Though not the last word on predicting the future, *The Limits to Growth* was of value because it served to make us more aware of important issues.

What is *Beyond the Limits?*

14.6 Limits to Growth Revised

Twenty years after the release of *The Limits to Growth,* three of the original authors updated and improved their system dynamics computer model (called World3). They then assembled a team of researchers and writers to revise the original report. They rewrote the report and called it *Beyond the Limits* (1992).

Beyond the Limits does not foresee as dire a future as *Limits* projected. Instead, it advocates a cautious journey forward where waste is punished and moderation is rewarded.

The key conclusions of the new report are:

- Human use of many essential resources and generation of several pollutants have passed sustainable rates.
- Unless there are meaningful reductions in resource and energy flows, the world faces a sharp decline in food output, energy use, and industrial production.
- To avoid this decline, growth in resource consumption and population must be eased down at the same time as there is a

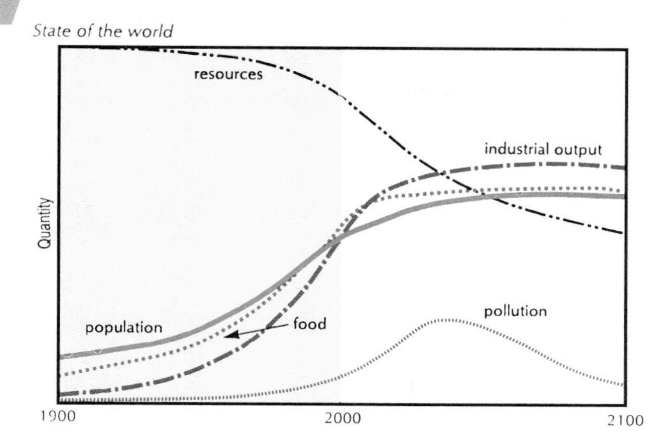

Figure 14.11 In this projected future, population and resources used per person are moderated starting in 1995. The desired family size is two children, and the standard of living is fixed to near European levels. Technologies increase the efficiency of resource use, decrease pollution emission, protect agricultural land, and increase land yields. The resulting society sustains 7.7 billion people at a comfortable standard of living with high life expectancy and declining pollution until at least the year 2100. (From *Beyond the Limits* by Meadows, Meadows, and Randers. Chelsea Green Publishing Company, Post Mills, Vermont. © 1992.)

rapid increase in the efficiency of resource and energy use. A sustainable society is technically and economically possible. See Figure 14.11.

The transition to a sustainable society must be made carefully. Issues of **equity** and quality of life must be boldly faced. We will have to learn to distinguish between growth and development. Growth means to get larger. Development means to make changes. There are limits to growth. There need not be limits to development.

75 14.7 Other Views of the Future

The 1972 release of *The Limits to Growth* triggered not only a heated debate concerning the growth issue, but also a series of other studies regarding the future of human life on Earth. The references at the end of this chapter list the major studies. These studies present different images of what the future holds.

What assumption is Simon making?

The *Limits to Growth* study argued that population size is shooting out of control. It concluded that population must be stabilized, and soon. But some thinkers disagree. Herman Kahn, who died in 1983, was the director of a "think tank", the Hudson Institute. Julian Simon is an economist associated with the Heritage Foundation. Julian Simon argues that the world would be better off with more people. The more people, the greater the knowledge base. The greater the knowledge base, the more likely we are to solve our resource/environmental problems. Herman Kahn and Julian Simon maintain that our lack of nonrenewable resources is only temporary. Improvements in our abilities to locate, extract, and use nonrenewable resources continues. Invention, substitution, and human ingenuity have no limits.

Some studies argue that pollution is not out of control and, in fact, our environment is now cleaner than in the 1960s. Lake Erie has been saved. Also, the overall quality of the air in many of the world's major cities is better than it was during that time period.

Some of the greatest differences of opinion are about how best to respond to the problems we face. Some advocate swift action coupled

Figure 14.12 The future as some technologists view it.

with strong governmental control. Some even call for a revolution. Others argue that problems are best solved by letting individuals respond to situations locally. They think that individual action coupled with a free market choice produces the best solution in almost all cases. Some studies advocate a complete redistribution of world economic and political power. This would lead to the resolution of the problem of inequities. Only then can the problems of population and resource depletion be adequately addressed.

What is a world view?

Why such different conclusions? Barry Hughes, in his book *World Futures: A Critical Analysis of Alternatives,* maintains that these differences are natural outcomes of differing world views. A world view is a comprehensive set of beliefs and basic assumptions about the way the world works coupled with the resulting "understandings" of complex events and processes. The world view you have leads to the solutions you propose to various problems. It dictates what you recommend as appropriate individual, social, and political behavior. Table 14.1 summarizes various world views with regard to global problems addressed in this course. It is a simplified version of the analysis done by Hughes.

Table 14.1 A Summary of Commonly Held World Views

Title	Assumption/Beliefs	Typical Forecasts	Recommendations
Technologists	• The global environment can be understood and controlled by humans. Humans are increasingly in control of the natural environment. • Technology is the key to a better future.	• Technological progress will steadily increase. • Environmental problems will be solved. • Resource limitations will be overcome.	• A governmental hands-off policy is best for most technological projects. • Research and development programs should be supported by governments.
Naturalists	• The universe is orderly and law-abiding. Humans are tied into the global environment. • The environment is more complex and delicate than most people realize. • Lifestyles consistent with natural laws are the key to a better future.	• Material wealth and technological progress will prove unsatisfying. • Environmental problems will appear faster than we can solve them, unless. . . . • Resource scarcities will intensify unless. . . .	• Selectively use and control new technologies. • Minimize rate at which resources pass through societies to conserve resources and limit environmental impact • Stabilize global populations.
Free-market Advocates	• Free markets benefit both producers and consumers. • Economic growth (betterment) occurs in stages.	• The gap between the rich and the poor will narrow over the next few decades. • The population problem will solve itself as a result of this. • Price mechanisms will solve energy and food problems.	• Globally, minimize government intervention in domestic and international economics. Intervention only hinders the natural solution.
Internationalists	• Free markets are unequally beneficial. • Economic benefits can be accelerated with help.	• The rich-poor gap will close only slowly. • Population might overwhelm resources in some countries and create a poverty cycle. • Agricultural and energy problems are long-term and might worsen.	• Wealthy nations should assist poorer nations with foreign aid and trade concessions.
Revolutionists	• Free markets are controlled by the rich. • Wealthy nations hold poorer nations in perpetual poverty.	• The rich-poor gap will not close; therefore, the population issue cannot be resolved, and agriculture and energy will remain problems for the poor.	• Poorer nations must either break away from the international system, and deny the rich the benefit of their natural resources; or, change via revolution must occur in the wealthy countries.

Figure 14.13 Different world views can lead to very different conclusions—even when the same data is used.

?

Why can futurists look at the same data and come to very different conclusions?

These views of the world and how it works differ greatly. Because of this, forecasts of the future differ greatly and so do recommended solutions to problems.

But, you ask, can't a look at the "facts" lead to movement toward a common viewpoint. The answer is—probably not. Facts are a nebulous thing. There are so many facts and bits of data to deal with that each of us has to decide which are important and which to toss out. Our world view helps us with that selection. The net result is that we cling to those facts that support our viewpoint. We ignore those that don't.

A second dilemma is that facts can be interpreted differently. The old story about the pessimist that looks at the glass of water and says it's half empty and the optimist that looks at the same glass and says it's half full applies here. We color our interpretations of data with our own perspective. Each of us is born with our own individual mental and physical abilities and characteristics. As we journey through life we each have a variety of unique experiences. As a consequence no one views the world in the same way as another. Thus, reasonable compromise is vitally important throughout our lives.

Finally, our data may be incomplete. Do we have enough data to predict, with certainty, a worldwide warming trend? How much data do we need? Have we been collecting data long enough to detect a cycle or trend of significance? A good scientific data base may only go back a hundred years. Is that long enough? Many of the environmental changes we are now monitoring are relatively recent concerns. Hence, accurate record keeping, in many areas, has been all too brief. In some cases, we have almost no data base at all. Blind extrapolation of insufficient data can lead to bizarre conclusions. See Figure 14.14.

At this point in the course, how should we proceed? The problem posed by conflicting world views makes it difficult. All these views cannot be correct. Only time will make that determination.

Figure 14.14 The dangers of blind extrapolation.

What we will do is move forward with the assumption that the Earth and its resources are finite. We will assume that natural laws govern how the world works and that humans are tied into the natural system. We will also assume that humans are clever, resourceful, and capable of acting in their own best interests. We will assume that we all want to live meaningful and productive lives. The story of human history seems to bear this out. With this in mind, we will return to our consideration of the sustainable world.

?

What assumptions does your author make about the world and how it works?

14.8 Life in a Sustainable World

No one likes the thought of world collapse and chaos. No matter what our world view, most people seem to desire stability, a clean environment, and reasonable comfort. A sustainable world is a worthwhile goal. However, the route to it is not agreed upon by all.

What would the sustainable world be like? Would life be boring? According to many futurists, a sustainable world would have the following characteristics:

?

What would a sustainable world be like?

1. It would be sustainable without sudden and uncontrolled collapse.

Figure 14.15 Photovoltaic panels are being tested for widespread utility applications. (USDOE)

2. It would be capable of satisfying the basic material requirements of *all* of its people. (Are *you* willing to settle for "basic material requirements?")
3. The average life expectancy could be about 80 years/person.
4. Material inequalities between groups of people would be fewer. (Most people would be neither very rich nor very poor.)
5. There would be more leisure time to devote to less-polluting and less-consuming activities.
6. Education, art, music, religion, basic scientific research, athletics, and social interactions would flourish.
7. Technical advances would continue, for the desire to improve quality of life would still exist. Scientific research would center on controlling pollution, finding alternative energy sources, developing improved contraceptives, developing better recycling techniques, improving conservation practices for energy and resources, enhancing human relations, and improving mental, physical, and spiritual health.
8. Incentive would be there. Instead of wealth, the incentive would be a better quality of life.

14.9 Conflict Resolution

This is a time when violence is not strength and compassion is not weakness. We are civilized.
— King Arthur (in Camelot)

A test of how civilized the Earth's people are is to measure the number of violent disputes that occur at a given point in time and compare that number to the number of disputes that are settled peacefully during the same time period.

?
What does it mean to be civilized?

Figure 14.16 We must learn to reduce violence in all aspects in our lives—our personal interactions, in athletics, and in the ways our governing bodies settle disputes. (David Klutho/Sports Illustrated.)

A look at events around the world clearly indicates that humans need to improve their ability to *resolve* conflicts. Conflicts occur between individuals, between groups of people (governments, industries, communities), and between regions or nations.

Why is world cooperation important?

We know that global collapse can be avoided. We also know that to avoid collapse, major conflicts must be resolved. The degree of cooperation required to achieve sustainability is greater than humans have yet achieved.

Is it reasonable to expect that the rich nations of the world will make short-term sacrifices to achieve long-term benefits? Will people act in their own best interests if they must forego too much immediate pleasure? Can we build a new global economic order? This order would feature industrial specialization corresponding to regional capacities and the most effective utilization of labor, capital, and available resources. Each region would maximize the economic and human resources which it has. Growth would stop in some regions and continue in others because some regions are still in need of development to meet the material needs of their people. Growth would be carefully controlled. Birth control would be a high-priority item.

The current crises are not temporary. They are tied to certain historical patterns of change. Cooperation among nations has been the exception rather than the rule. For the blueprint to succeed, our ability to **foresee** and **forestall** will be taxed to the limit.

The role international organizations, such as the **United Nations (UN),** can play is not clear. Although attempting some small military efforts, it is more a debating society than anything else. It is not a world government nor a major military power. It is a meeting place for countries large and small. It is a forum for communications, debate, and occasionally reconciliation. At present, it is the major system we

Figure 14.17 The United Nations was formed in 1945 under a permanent charter that was ratified by 51 countries. Is it an effective organization for promoting stability and peace? Can it be? (UN Photo #10395 by Y. Nagata.)

have for resolving international conflict. When people speak in a civilized forum, the likelihood that they will fight is reduced. Who knows? Sometimes they may even listen to each other.

14.10 Sustainable Economics

What is sustainable economics?

A nation or a world that is not growing must operate under an economic system that has a different set of goals than the economic systems that are prevalent in today's world. A sustainable world must have a sustainable **economy.** A sustainable economy is one in which both the number of people and the flow of resources are maintained at some desired, **sufficient** level. It is an economy that recognizes the fact that the world is a complex but finite system that has evolved with reference to a fixed rate of solar input. It views humans as fallible creatures, ultimately dependent on what a finite ecosystem can provide.

One person who has provided a description of a sustainable economy is Herman E. Daly, an economics professor at Louisiana State University and an economist with the World Bank. The following paragraphs are based on his description.

The free market is allowed to control the transfer of goods and services. However, the free market is placed under certain restraints. The restraints are necessary because the free market is incapable of keeping the consumption of resources below ecological limits, conserving resources for future generations, preventing overpopulation, or avoiding gross inequities in wealth and income distribution. To remedy these flaws, three economic **mechanisms** are to be established:

A mechanism is a way to accomplish something.

The three mechanisms that might make sustainable economics work.

?

1. A mechanism for maintaining constant population.
2. A mechanism for limiting the rate at which resources pass through the economy.
3. A mechanism for reducing poverty and thus building commitment to the system.

These three mechanisms can come about by government policy and laws, or they may be the result of education, which brings about changes in personal preferences, beliefs, and values.

14.11 Maintaining a Constant Population

How might population be stabilized?

Some modern social forces in the United States, and to varying degrees in other developed nations, may bring about a stabilization of population. These include: (1) the demand for new roles by women, (2) the promotion of the benefits of smaller families and/or the choice to begin a family at a later age, (3) the demand by many women for control over their reproductive functions, (4) the widespread availability of birth control devices and information, (5) a comfortable standard of living, and (6) the removal of the **tax incentives** for having large families.

The population situation in the *less-developed countries* (LDC) is difficult for those of us in the *more-developed countries* (MDC) to comprehend. Many people hope that the **demographic transition** will work for them as it has for us. The demographic transition is a phenomenon seen in populations of some industrializing nations. As industrialization proceeds and wealth accumulates, population growth slows. However, a decline in death rate usually precedes the decline in birth rate, producing a period of rapid growth before stabilization. The demographic transition is thought to occur because children are more important to family budgets in the agricultural economies of LDC than in the MDC. In most LDC, parents look to their children to care for them in their old age. Because many infants and children die, large families ensure that some will survive long enough to care for their parents. The better medical care in developed countries leads to survival of more children making large numbers of children unnecessary.

It is not known if a demographic type of transition will occur without significant industrialization. It is believed by some that population will always stabilize when living standards reach a level when basic human needs are met and life becomes enjoyable and meaningful to both men and women.

Figure 14.18 This 1958 Buick Riviera Special is representative of the Americans cars of the late 1950's and 1960s—heavy, large, much chrome, and low mileage. It averages 12 to 15 miles per gallon.

Although a topic of debate, it may be that the wealthy nations (MDC) will have to help the poorer nations (LDC) while their populations stabilize. They may need help with population control, with industrial development, and with financial assistance.

 14.12 Values Regarding Resource Use

People have beliefs and attitudes about everything. This includes our natural resources and how we should use them. The pioneers who settled America had basic beliefs (values) about how natural resources should be used. These values served their needs well. The nation they established grew, became great, and provided a comfortable and meaningful life to most of its people. But the situation of most Americans today is different than that faced by the early pioneers. In many cases, this requires a change in some of our values. The values of our ancestors do not always meet our present needs. This is especially true in the case of natural resources.

Values can change over time.

Early pioneers believed that man was master of nature. To them, the natural environment was hostile and needed to be tamed. They had to cut down forests to grow food and build roads. Today, we realize that we are partners with nature. Nature provides us with the food, air, soil, water, and minerals we need to both stay alive and live a quality life. We can work with nature to make sure that these benefits will always be with us.

We used to think that bigger was better. The tasks of the early pioneers were large, and they required large tools. However, this is not always the case. A large, heavy car can waste valuable resources. Often a smaller car can be faster, more comfortable, and more fuel efficient than a larger one.

When America was being developed, it appeared that our resources would never run out. However, the settlement of the nation has shown that there are limits. The Earth is only so big.

We once thought that the wastes of society could simply be buried, and this caused them to be gone. We now realize that the conservation of mass applies to everything.

Large families were the norm in early America. Life on the farm was hard, and many hands were necessary to get the job done. Today, children are usually not an economic gain. They add to our lives in other ways. American couples now have two children on the average.

It was once believed that material wealth was a measure of your success as an individual. Rich people and families were highly regarded simply because they were rich. The gathering of land and belongings became a goal in itself. This helped fuel the economy. Much evidence supports the observation that wealth, in and of itself, does not guarantee happiness.

A look at the space photo of the Earth forces us to realize, once again, that we are all on this planet together. To survive into the future, we must use our natural resources with care. With a resource-use ethic, our resources can sustain generation after generation on our planet.

14.13 Promoting the Wise Use of Natural Resources

How might we limit the use of renewable and nonrenewable resources?

It is important that we understand the interactions and limits of the ecosphere. These limits determine the maximum and best levels of economic activity. How much waste can a given lake, river, or ocean absorb without undergoing irreversible ecological damage? How much pollution can a given volume of air absorb and still be able to cleanse itself? Our present environment demonstrates that limits exist, but we need to know what they are. More research is needed on environmental impact and pollution control.

Even with limited knowledge, we can see that producing and using goods produces pollutants. Probably the most effective way to limit pollution is to limit use of the resources (renewable and nonrenewable) needed for making goods.

How can the flow of resources through an economy by slowed? There are many ways. Some of the ways could involve significant governmental interference in the market and restrictions on personal freedom. This is not, however, a necessary requirement. Conscious individual choice can lead to intelligent and prudent use of materials if people understand how this benefits them—and if they believe other people will also cooperate. The free market, itself, can promote conservation. Finally, new technologies and inventions can produce the same result.

First, nonrenewable resource flow could be limited through government control. Governmental action might include the required use of biomass fuels or the placement of high taxes on materials we want to conserve. The advertising of products that contain scarce resources could be banned.

Figure 14.19 EPA tests indicate the 1989 Honda CRX HF can average over 50 mpg in over-the-road driving. What mileage rating do you foresee for automobiles by the year 2000? How do high-mileage cars reduce the flow of resources? (Courtesy American Honda Motor Co., Inc.)

Second, we may simply choose to allow the free market to function. Increased scarcity causes prices to rise. Higher prices encourage conservation. They also enable mining companies to develop lower grade ore deposits because the potential for profit is now there. Higher prices also stimulate the search for new ore bodies and substitute materials.

Third, individuals can make conscious efforts to conserve, eliminate waste, choose products in which materials are used wisely, and recycle and reuse when possible.

Fourth, technology can also play a significant role. In many ways, the technological solutions are the preferred solutions because they enable us to continue doing many things we have grown to enjoy and yet reduce resource consumption. Technology can bring us the energy-efficient automobile (lighter in mass due to its composite body) that can be battery-powered (electric) or have a computer-monitored ceramic engine that uses specialty fuels. Technology also enables us to extract more completely the resources we mine, and to find or develop substitutes for many of the materials that may become scarce.

In the attempt to achieve a more stable world, one of the great debates will center on what role government should play in dealing with our natural resource issues. Even now, it is unclear whether we have a national energy plan. Certainly natural resources are directly affected by governmental laws, rules and regulations.

The role of the government in making resource policy.

The government, in cooperation with the business community and an informed public, can play an important and affirmative role in formulating and carrying out a national natural resource strategy. Because of its nature, some people think the government is best equipped to reconcile conflicting interests, balance various national

Figure 14.20 The government can play an important role in guiding a national strategy for using natural resources. (Architect of the Capitol.)

Figure 14.21 Arctic energy development. (From Atlantic Richfield Corporation.)

needs, formulate policies, set objectives, establish appropriate incentives for the private sector to achieve those objectives, monitor progress, and provide leadership. How well our government performs these functions will, in large measure, determine our future.

As you can see, the matter of a resource policy is complex. There is no *one* best road to follow; no *one* best solution that is fair to all. That is what makes policy development so difficult. Solutions come from ideas. Dialogue, debate, and compromise bring results. Irrational behavior brings nothing but panic. See Figure 14.22.

Figure 14.22 The panic of irrational thought. (Gene Bassett. Scripps-Howard Newspapers.)

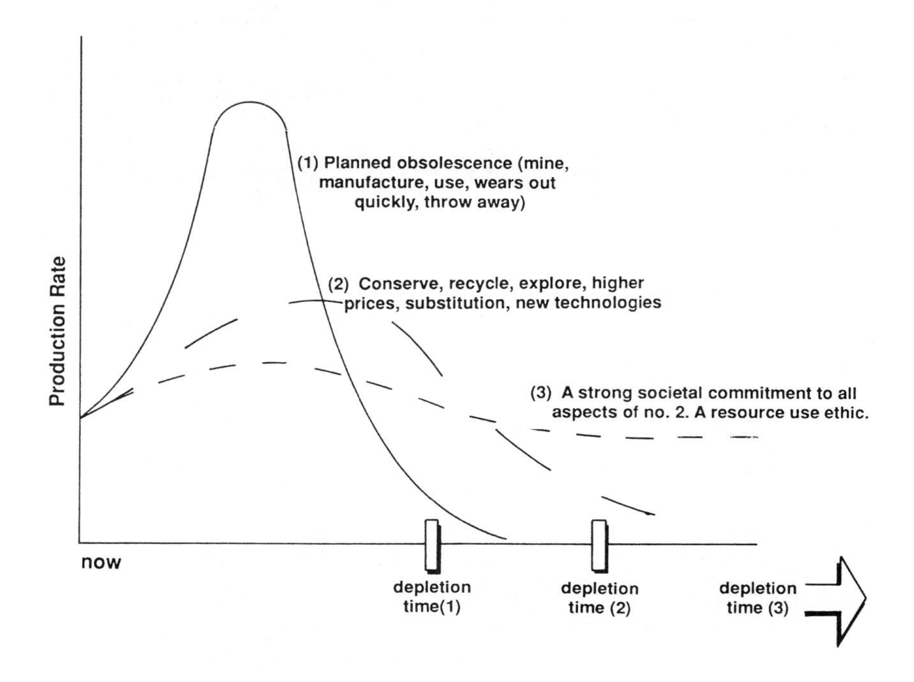

Figure 14.23 The shape of a resource depletion curve for a nonrenewable resource depends on human attitudes. Which curve is most likely to represent our future?

Wise resource use offers exciting possibilities for the future. Figure 14.23 illustrates this. **Curve 1** is the familiar resource depletion curve. **Curve 2** shows how some commitment to conservation, recycling and research and development buy us time and new possibilities. **Curve 3** illustrates the dream. A nonrenewable resource use ethic assures prudent use. Proper application of economic forces stifles waste. Invention and substitution could enable us to change materials that are not economic today into valuable raw materials in the future. In that way, our total supply of useful resources could even increase.

Which curve we follow is yet to be determined. You will help to determine its course.

Remember not to write in your textbook. Use a separate piece of paper for your answers.
Did you complete the table?

In Table 14.2, we list ten of the most important natural resource options that we have. Next to those, we briefly outline the political issues that center on those options. Filling in the rest of the table is up to you. The opinions you express, as you fill out the chart, constitute

Table 14.2 Natural Resources Options

Resource Options	Political Issues	Effectiveness Rating (1 to 10)*	What the United States Should Do (and How)
1. Slow the flow of natural resources through the world economy (use less, greater efficiency).	Economic disruption. Unemployment. Retraining. Use of leisure time. Price and/or tax incentives. Government regulation. Education of the public. Free market interactions.		
2. Invest in more public transportation.	Effect on auto industry and auto-related businesses. Access for elderly and disabled. Are there better ways to transport people?		
3. Recycle metals.	Economic incentives. Creating new behavioral patterns.		
4. Reduce population growth.	Reproductive freedom. Religious opposition. Reversing some present economic incentives.		
5. Live more simply (lifestyle change).	Redefining the "good life." Economic readjustment. Preference for non-consuming activities.		
6. Increase exploration and development of natural resources.	Terms of access to resources. Producers' economics. Environmental impact.		
7. Resolution of coal development uncertainties.	Air pollution. U.S. strip mining. Mine safety.		
8. Resolution of nuclear program uncertainties.	Siting and licensing of plants. The breeder program. Safeguarding plutonium. Spent fuel handling and storage.		
9. Research and development of alternative energy sources.	Choice of priorities. Role of the government.		
10. International cooperation.	Energy trade controls. Economic impact of rising energy prices. Technology and emergency supply sharing.		

*1 = Most-Effective Option 10 = Least-Effective Option

Desert Drama

science at work

Much of California is so dry that only pipelines from the mountains and from other states make agriculture and large cities possible there. But even the piped-in water is no longer enough. During years of drought, little snow falls on the mountain peaks. In every year, the population grows larger and requires more water. Californians must give up many of the water-wasting practices of the past if they are to have enough water for basic needs.

In 1988, the third year of what was to be a very long dry spell for California, Kate Jackson started experimenting with growing cacti and succulents. People looking for ways to conserve water in their gardens find lots of ideas at Kate's Desert Theatre, near Watsonville, California. There she displays and sells her "unthirsty" plants.

In a water-saving landscape, a top layer of gravel, lava rock, or California gold rock takes the place of grass (which needs more water). This layer helps raise the planter bed and reduce erosion. Low-maintenance plants are planted sparsely on this background. Kate says her water-thrifty plants, in soil that is weed free and contains good drainage and nutrients, require only infrequent but thorough watering to keep them thriving.

Desert Theatre has a cast of many. There are five varieties of cacti, which are easy to care for and good in coastal climates. There are euphorbia, opuntia, hanging epiphyllum, and more. Many exotic species are imported from Australia (Kate's birthplace), South Africa, Madagascar, the Canary Islands, and South and Central America. Kate has five greenhouses on an acre of land, including three display beds where her customers can see sample landscapes.

What makes a plant suitable for light watering? Some can conserve water in stems or leaves and use it economically through dry seasons. Some are deep-rooted and can get water from far down in the ground. Many have hairy or thick leaf surfaces, which reduce water loss. A few have dormant stages in which they don't need any water at all.

A nurse and midwife for several years, Kate also has some experience in landscape installation. Desert Theatre is the result of combining her interests in plants, art, and photography. She reads a lot to keep up on new gardening ideas and techniques, as well as environmental issues, and suggests that interested young people look for horticulture programs at community colleges. By the way, there was an unexpected benefit from all that studying for her R.N.: Because Kate learned the origins of medical and pharmacology terms, she can easily translate all those Latin and Greek plant names!

The workday starts at 5:00 A.M. for Kate. After doing "business" chores, she is always busy outdoors with watering and fertilizing, propagating and potting, to maintain her stock of plants. She also gives lectures, to educate people about breaking away from more typical, water-hungry gardens. To do this, she tells people about her low water bills, even at peak growing times. But her most effective arguments are the dramatic displays of her attractive and exotic plants.

Not every method of conserving water is pleasant. But the Desert Theatre demonstrates that with a creative approach, people can use less water without sacrificing the beauty of their natural environment. As the population continues to expand and available resources to shrink, we will need to apply such creativity in many areas of life.

your own natural resource policy. The soundness of your opinions is an indication of how well thought out and workable your plan may be. The collective decisions of our people and our leaders on these issues will be our national resource plan. It should evolve from sound national debate and introspection, not just happen at random. You can be part of formulating a positive attitude on national natural resource issues, if you choose to.

?
What should be our resource policy?

 14.14 Limiting Inequities

?
How might inequities between people be minimized?

Mechanisms for limiting gross inequities in wages and accumulated wealth are built on the concept of **enoughness.** To many, any attempt to limit wages and wealth borders on socialism or communism. Labels aside, the concept of enoughness recognizes that humans are finite. Thus, they are limited in how much they can eat, and how much they can handle at any one time. A person can travel only so fast and be in only one place at one time. The idea of enoughness recognizes that a given individual or family can only handle and enjoy a fixed number of goods. Possessions, beyond that, are mere greed. For each individual, there is a state of adequacy.

Establishing a state of sufficiency.

For a sustainable economy to exist, the issue of equity must be faced. One idea is to use maximum and minimum income levels. A maximum income could be enforced through a progressive income tax (without loopholes). As your income rose, you'd pay more tax until you reached the point where all your income, beyond the allowed maximum, went for taxes. A negative income tax plan could be used to assure a minimum income. Each household would report its total earnings on a tax form (as we do today). If the amount reported is over the level established as the basic poverty line, a tax is due the government. If, however, the total income is below the poverty level, the family would receive a check from the government to bring it up to the minimum. Would such an approach do away with welfare and the costly bureaucracy necessary to administer it?

Most people, giving the plan some thought, would agree that the concept of enoughness is a truism. The problem is that part of our human nature causes us to desire (and take when we can) more than enough for ourselves. In addition to wanting more than we need for ourselves, we also want to pass on material goods to our children.

What is the South Indian Monkey Trap?

We're like the monkey caught in the South Indian monkey trap. The South Indian monkey trap is an ingenious device, for it traps monkeys because of their own greed. It consists of a hollowed-out coconut fastened to a stake by a chain. The coconut is filled with rice. There is a hole in the coconut just large enough for the monkey to put its extended hand through, but not large enough for the withdrawal of a fist full of rice. The monkey is trapped, intact, by its inability to reorder its values. It cannot realize that freedom is worth more than a fistful of rice.

How are we like the trapped monkey?

We seem caught in a similar trap. The selfish part of our human nature causes us to hold on to the old values that offer us the remote

Figure 14.24 The South Indian monkey trap.

—Ryon Packer

possibility of accumulating wealth (things) beyond what we can enjoy. We hold on to growth and miss the freedom that a life in harmony with our fellow humans and nature would allow. However, there is a part of human nature that causes us to love our environment and show compassion for the condition of our brothers and sisters. It is this part that we might draw on to help create a balance.

The issue of equity must be handled with care. Successful societies don't reward laziness. If creativity and work are not rewarded, people won't work.

?

The challenge is to maximize both stability and freedom.

 14.15 Maximizing Stability and Freedom

Because we are human and imperfect, if programs as outlined are ever established, it will take cooperation of a very unusual kind among private citizens, corporations, and government. This type of cooperation will be required if we are to maintain a stable world that recognizes both finiteness and the full potential of human beings. It is difficult to visualize, in a completely stable world, freedom being the same as the freedom we experience today.

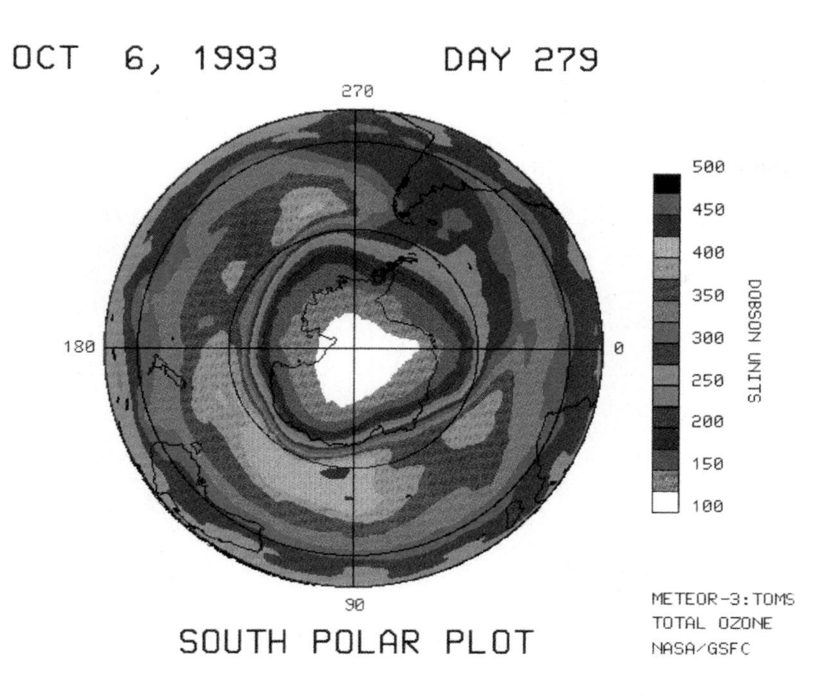

Figure 14.25 The expanse of the ozone hole over Antarctica is shown in this satellite image. Ozone concentration is indicated using a color scale. The ozone layer in the upper atmosphere filters out most of the sun's ultraviolet radiation. Increased ultraviolet radiation is associated with elevated skin cancer rates and a whole host of negative impacts on nature such as stunted plant growth and lower resistance to disease. (NASA/Goddard Institute for Space Studies.)

No one likes to consider giving up freedoms for any reason. Thus it is only natural to ask, "What alternatives are there to the sustainable world pictured in the preceding section?" In those sections proper credit is not always given to the resourcefulness of the human mind.

Suggestions and hints of a new way of living are beginning to appear, all leading toward stability. As examples: The Japanese have voluntarily made a two-child family the norm; the Chinese are trying to make a one-child family the norm; environmental pollution is now unacceptable in the United States and Canada; automobile engines may shortly be made from ceramics to conserve metals. Automobiles can be made to use much less gasoline than thought possible not many years ago. Even though petroleum resources are finite, reserves are still being discovered. The consumption of the last drop of oil may well be several centuries down the road, particularly given our *creative* efforts to conserve and develop alternative sources of energy. International agreements seem to be changing resource-use patterns resulting in reduction in the size of the ozone hole. See Figure 14.25.

As new technologies, political frameworks, and philosophical conceptions spread, there is a good chance that exponential growth will be materially slowed. This should give the ingenuity of humans a chance to reorder our world. At the same time, we should be able to preserve the opportunity to strive for true freedom for all people. Herein lies an alternative to government-imposed programs for preserving the future.

14.16 Possible Futures for Humankind

The future will happen. What *kind* of future we have depends a good deal on how we face the important issues we have been discussing.

Figure 14.26 Some people just don't want to face the issues.
(Reprinted by permission of Tribune Media Services.)

Unfortunately, some people don't want to face these issues. See Figure 14.26. Those attitudes will lead to a future just as surely as wise planning also leads to a future.

Should we try to live more simply?

Can the good life be redefined? Can people be taught to prefer more efficient cars? Is an attic fan almost as effective as an air conditioner? Can hiking in the woods become more enjoyable than a drive through the forest? Can listening to or playing good music become preferable to snowmobiling or water skiing? What forms of recreation do you prefer?

?

Almost all of us will spend our entire lives on planet Earth.

If we assume the laws of science will continue to hold true—that mass and energy are conserved and that disorder steadily increases—then it is probably safe to say the vast majority of us are bound to this planet. With almost all of us bound to Earth, the laws of human ecology take on new meaning. The interplay of human actions and natural forces seems to imply that humankind can follow a course that will lead to any one of six possible outcomes. These outcomes are outlined in Figure 14.28.

Note that each graph has a solid line to depict a pattern for stable or unstable growth (-) in relation to resource limit or carrying capacity K (—). In this case, as before, we are referring to *the world's carrying capacity for humans:* the size of the human population that can be supported on a long-term, sustainable basis by the world's resources. As we pointed out previously, carrying capacity cannot be defined unless a standard of living and a role of technology are first specified. The two seem to be inversely related. Although you cannot accurately calculate a world carrying capacity for humans, you can compute some rough estimates of it based on a variety of assumptions (as in *The Solar Input* lab and in *Beyond the Limits*) and draw appropriate conclusions. With these ideas in mind, let's take a look at the graphs.

Figure 14.28a is the optimistic view. It assumes that humans realize their predicament in time and take those measures that allow us to slowly ease into a steady-state world. Possibly rising costs and the change in values that result will become self-limiting mechanisms. They may force stabilization of population size and resource use.

Figure 14.27 Wind surfing is relatively nonconsuming. The wind provides the energy. You provide the challenge. (Mark Müller)

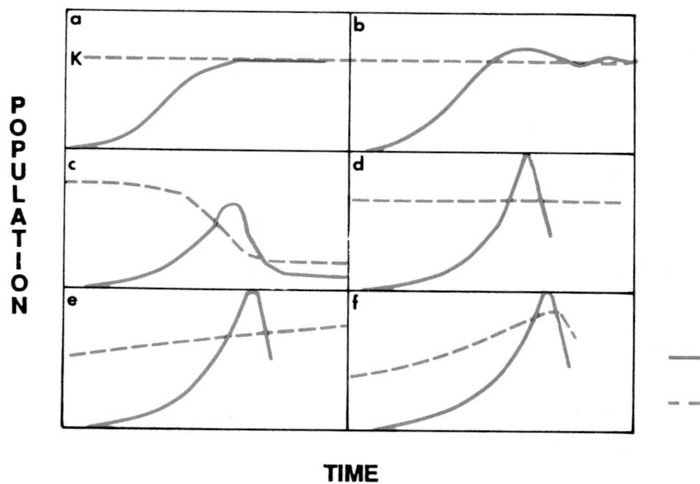

Figure 14.28 Patterns of stable and unstable growth.

Figure 14.28b assumes that humans react to uncontrolled growth, but not quite soon enough. Hence, for a time, we overshoot our limits. Readjustment, however, allows stabilization to take place. Fortunately, the overshoot wasn't too severe, and the ecosystem experiences no permanent damage.

Remember the story of the Kaibab deer in the laboratory manual?

Figure 14.28c assumes that humans react to uncontrolled growth, but not until our limits have been exceeded and some ecological damage has been done. The earth's carrying capacity is permanently lowered. An equilibrium is eventually established, but at a lower level than before.

In Figure 14.28d humans continue their consumptive patterns of exponential growth until the Earth can no longer satisfy them. Civilization then experiences a sudden and irreversible collapse.

In Figure 14.28e technological advances and planet management result in a steadily increasing carrying capacity. However, growth in both population and human demand is more rapid than the growth in carrying capacity. The limits are overshot and a collapse occurs. We may or may not survive.

Figure 14.28f is a slight modification of Figure 14.28e. Again, technological advances and planet management result in an increased carrying capacity. However, growth in population and material well-being overshoot and damage the limiting factors. As a result, both collapse.

Which of these patterns most closely reflects our future? We do not know. Perhaps there will be some unexpected turn of events that will dramatically alter our future and cause us to rapidly move in a completely new direction. Who knows?!

By taking this course you may have caught a glimpse of a world that has never been. You may have caught a vision of a world that could be, a world where human beings might live in harmony with each other and their environment.

Summary

Growth was important as America evolved into a major world power. The population had to increase so that every region of the nation could become productive and utilize its resources. For a time, all the results of this expansion seemed positive. But eventually some problems appeared. Smog appeared in many of our major cities, many rivers and lakes literally died, and large sections of land became eroded and useless. Waste accumulation became overpowering. For many, hopes and dreams ended in despair. The westward migration was over.

In the early 1970s, the doctrine of growth came under serious attack. The attack was based largely on *The Limits to Growth* study. This study identified five factors that determine and, in their interactions, ultimately limit growth on our planet. They are: population, agricultural production, consumption of resources, industrial output, and pollution generation. These five factors have three things in common: they are all interrelated; at the time of the study, they were all growing exponentially; and they all appear to have upper limits.

The Limits to Growth study predicted that if human behavior doesn't change, we are headed toward a global collapse. There is only

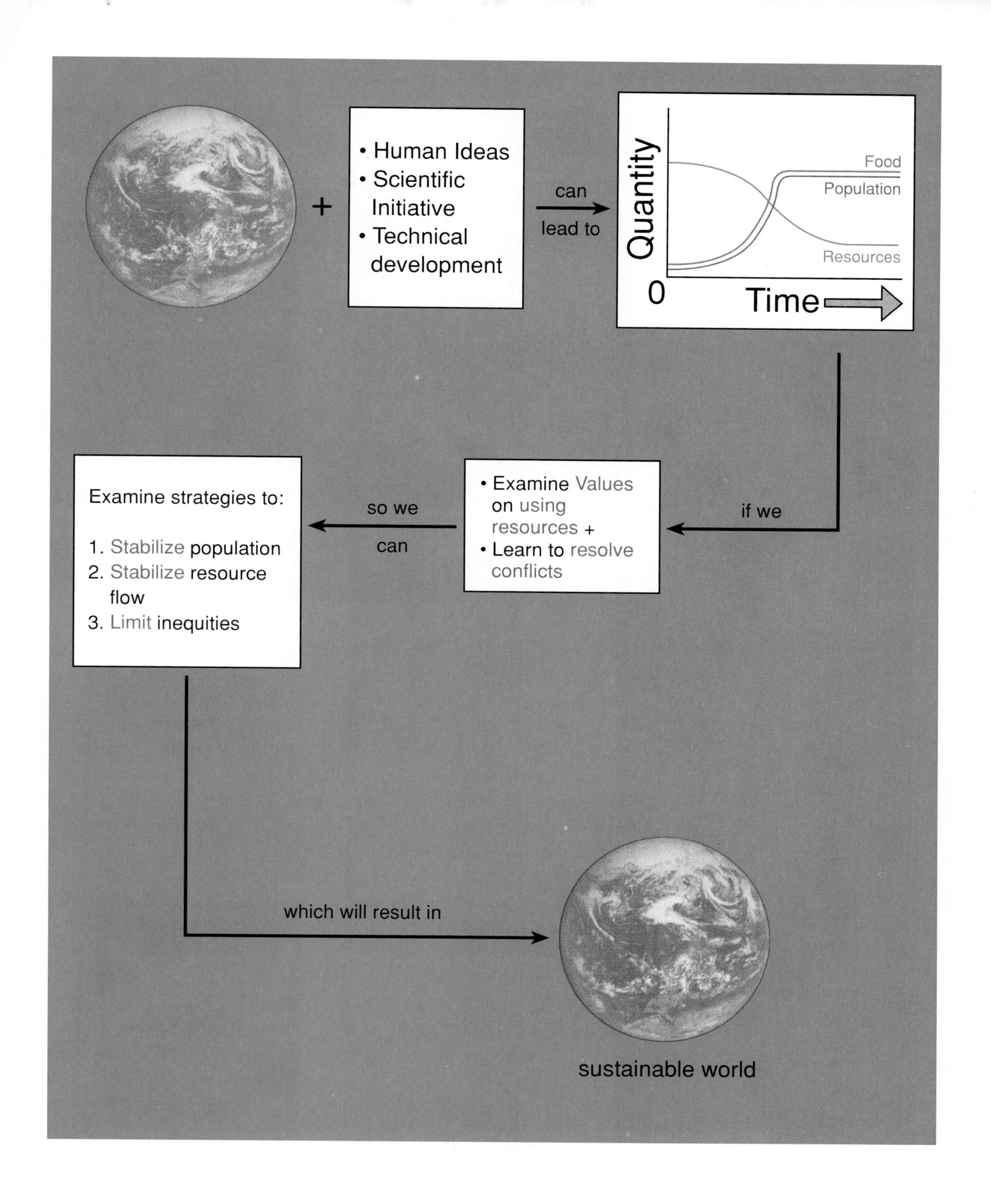
+
• Human Ideas
• Scientific Initiative
• Technical development
can
lead to
Quantity
Food
Population
Resources
0
Time
if we
• Examine Values on using resources +
• Learn to resolve conflicts
so we
can
Examine strategies to:
1. Stabilize population
2. Stabilize resource flow
3. Limit inequities
which will result in
sustainable world

There's no place like home.
— Dorothy

one way to prevent it—population and resource consumption must be stabilized. Growth in population and resource depletion must cease. Our perception of what is meaningful in life must be re-focused.

The study was interesting, but it was attacked for several reasons: the rich were telling the poor they had to give up their dreams of wealth accumulation; economics was not considered as a tool for modifying human behavior; and, the result was fixed, because growth in a finite system has to fail. The study also was vague in spelling out how a sustainable world could be achieved.

The *Limits to Growth* was praised for forcing us to look at the direction in which we seem headed, documenting evidence of environmental stress, and providing a glimpse of what a sustainable (steady-state) future may be like.

A sustainable system must have a sustainable economy. This economy must have a way to control the flow of the physical resources that pass through it, a way to achieve a stable population, and a way for limiting inequities between members of the population. The greatest threats to human survival are ignorance, selfishness, and greed. We have seen that instituting a steady-state system could mean sacrificing some freedom. We have also seen that the world is beginning to curtail growth. Human ingenuity must be brought into play to preserve freedom and the opportunity for individual fulfillment.

The world we are being asked to shape is like no other. It involves a general realization that we're all passengers on a wonderful, but fragile, spaceship. We're part of everything and everything is a part of us. Why not make a personal commitment to help build a better tomorrow?

References

Baily, Martin N., et. al. *Growth with Equity* (Washington, DC: Brookings Institution), 1993.

Blinder, Alan S., *Hard Heads, Soft Hearts: Tough-Minded Economics for a Just Society* (Reading, MA: Addison-Wesley), 1987.

Brown, Lester R. *Building a Sustainable Society* (New York: W. W. Norton), 1981.

Brown, Lester R., and others. *Vital Signs: The Trends that are Shaping Our Future* (Washington, DC: Worldwatch Institute), 1993.

Club of Rome. (See Meadows, *The Limits to Growth*).

Cole, H. S. D., and others, eds. *Models of Doom; A Critique of The Limits to Growth* (New York: Universe Books), 1973.

Daly, Herman. *Steady-State Economics*, 2nd ed. (Washington, DC: Island Press), 1991.

———. Review of *The Ultimate Resource,* by Julian Simon. *The Bulletin of Atomic Scientists* 38:39, 1982.

Durning, Alan. *How Much is Enough?* (New York: W. W. Norton), 1992.

Falk, Richard A. *A Study of Future Worlds* (New York: Free Press), 1975.

Forrester, Jay W. *World Dynamics,* 2nd ed. (Cambridge: Wright-Allen Press), 1973.

Freeman, Christopher, and Marie Jahoda, eds. *World Futures: The Great Debate* (New York: Universe Books), 1978.

Hardin, Garrett, and John Baden, eds. *Managing the Commons* (San Francisco: W. H. Freeman), 1977.

Harman, Willis W. *An Incomplete Guide to the Future* (New York: W. W. Norton), 1979.

Heilbroner, Robert L. *An Inquiry into the Human Prospect.* (New York: W. W. Norton), 1991.

Herrera, Amilcar O., and others. *Catastrophe or New Society? A Latin American World Model* (Ottawa: International Development Research Centre), 1976.

Hughes, Barry B. *World Futures: A Critical Analysis of Alternatives* (Baltimore: The John Hopkins University Press), 1985.

Kahn, Herman, and others. *The Next 200 Years: A Scenario for America and the World* (New York: Morrow), 1976.

Leontief, Wassily and others. *The Future of the World Economy* (New York: Oxford University Press), 1977.

MacNeill, Jim, et. al. *Beyond Interdependence: The Meshing of the World's Economy and the Earth's Ecology* (New York: Oxford University Press), 1991.

Meadows, Donella H., and others. *The Limits to Growth* (New York: Universe Books), 1972.

———. *Beyond the Limits* (Post Mills, VT: Chelsea Green), 1992.

———. *Groping in the Dark: The First Decade of Global Modeling* (New York: John Wiley), 1982.

Miles, Ina. World views and Scenarios. In *World Futures: The Great Debate,* edited by Christopher Freeman and Marie Johoda (New York: Universe Books), 1978.

Olson, Mancur and Hans H. Landsberg, eds. *The No-Growth Society* (New York: W. W. Norton), 1974.

Pestel, Eduard. *Beyond the Limits to Growth* (New York: Universe Books), 1989.

Pirages, Dennis, ed. *The Sustainable Society* (New York: Praeger), 1977.

Repetto, Robert, ed. *The Global Possible* (New Haven: Yale University Press), 1985.

Rolston, Holmes, III. *Philosophy Gone Wild* (Buffalo: Prometheus), 1989.

Rostow, W. W. *The World Economy* (Austin: University of Texas Press), 1978.

Schipper, Lee and Stephen Meyers. *Energy Efficiency and Human Activity: Past Trends, Future Prospects* (New York: Cambridge University Press), 1992.

Scientific American Magazine. *Managing Planet Earth* (New York: W. H. Freeman), 1990.

Simon, Julian L. *The Ultimate Resource* (Princeton University Press), 1981.

Smith, Emily T. Growth vs. Environment *Business Week,* pp. 66–75, May 11, 1992.

United Nations Conference on Environment and Development. *Agenda 21, Rio Declaration, Forest Principles* (New York: United Nations), 1992.

World Commission on Environment and Development. *Our Common Future* (New York: Oxford University Press), 1987.

End of Chapter Questions ?

Set A

1. In the United States, the growth ethic had its origin deep in our history due to three main facts. List them. When the United States was founded:
   - **a.**
   - **b.**
   - **c.**
2. How did growth help America become a major world power?
3. What is *The Limits to Growth* report?
4. *The Limits to Growth* report identified five basic factors that determine and, in their interactions, ultimately limit growth on our planet. List them.
5. The five factors to be listed above have three common characteristics. List them.
6. Use Figure 14.3 to estimate the date of occurrence of the following:
   - **a.** Amount of food per person begins to decline
   - **b.** Industrial output per person (standard of living) begins to decline
   - **c.** Resource level is at 50% of 1900 values
7. Give two reasons why per capita food production drops off at about 2010.
8. What was the major conclusion of *The Limits to Growth* study?
9. What two factors must be controlled if growth is to stop?
10. What would a sustainable world be like?

11. What kind of government do you think we would have if we were actually moving toward a sustainable world?
12. What seem to be the necessary motivations of individuals as well as corporations in a sustainable world?
13. What are some of the arguments for and against *The Limits to Growth* study?
14. What is *Beyond the Limits*?
15. Why do futurists look at the same data and come to such different conclusions?
16. List four social forces at work in the United States today that are reducing the growth of our population.
17. What is sustainable economics?
18. What are the three mechanisms required for a sustainable economy?
19. Compare the concept of enoughness with your present lifestyle.
20. What is the one most important factor that will determine whether a sustainable economic system will work?
21. What changes might cause one to spend more time in sports (or recreation) and less time driving?
22. What should be our resources policy? (See Table 14.2.)
23. Why is a democratic decision to locate a nuclear power plant in a particular low-population area not a "fair" decision?
24. Which line on Figure 14.23 do you think most accurately depicts human use of nonrenewable resources? Explain why you feel the way you do.
25. Describe the ways we (on the Earth) are like passengers on a spaceship.
26. Why will most (practically all) humans never leave the Earth—even for a short period of time?
27. How can we make things better?

Set B

28. When our country was young, we grew and prospered as a result of the so-called "frontier ethic." What factors made practice of that ethic possible? How did belief in that ethic eventually get us into trouble?
29. *The Limits to Growth* study group identified five basic factors that determine through their interactions the ultimate limits to growth on our planet. Review the factors. Give at least two examples of what is meant by "interactions." (HINT: If one factor increases or decreases, what happens to the others?)
30. Which (if any) of the criticisms of *The Limits to Growth* study change the major *ideas* which the model is attempting to demonstrate?
31. Carefully examine Table 14.1. Which world view most accurately describes how you view the future? Can you identify the experiences in your past that have caused you to hold that view?

32. What might we gain, and what might we lose if our system were based on Sustainable Economics?

33. How are we like the monkey caught in the South Indian monkey trap?

34. Imelda Marcos, widow of deposed Philippine dictator Ferdinand Marcos, had 2,700 pairs of shoes. How does this illustrate the concept of enoughness?

35. Do you believe that human beings will act in their own best interests (if they know what their interests are) even if some sacrifice and limitations are involved? Why or why not?

36. Do you agree that individuals and societies usually do what they *want* to do when they can, but that they wait to do what they *have* to do until they must? If this is, indeed, an attribute of human nature, how might it affect our ability to "get the job done?" Which curve in Figure 14.25 best reflects this attribute?

37. One prominent United States Senator has suggested that Congress is totally incapable of planning for the future. Do you agree with his assertion? Who or why not? What concerns should we have if the Senator is correct?

38. If humans achieve a stable world, which mechanism will be more effective: government-imposed programs or human choice and resourcefulness? Defend your answer.

Appendices

1. Scientific Notation
2. International System (SI) Units
3. SI Unit Prefixes
4. Common Conversion Factors (Related to Energy and Resources)
5. Table of Energy Conversion Factors
6. Practice Problems that Involve Converting Units
7. Useful Data Regarding Energy Production Facilities.

Appendix 1

Scientific Notation

In the study of resource/environmental problems, very large and very small numers are regularly encountered. For example, the total power incident from the sun at the top of the Earth's atmosphere is 173,000,000,000,000,000 watts. It would be difficult to deal with such numbers if we didn't have a special method for handling them. Scientific notation is the method for doing just that. Learn it well. With scientific notation, problems which look almost impossible to solve become relatively simple.

Most of what you need to know about scientific notation involves four ideas. These are:

1. A system for multiplying and dividing combinations of ten.

The following is a partial list of powers of ten:

$10^0 = 1$

$10^1 = 10$

$10^2 = 10 \times 10 = 100$

$10^3 = 10^2 \times 10 = 1000$

$10^4 = 10 \times 10 \times 10 \times 10 = 10{,}000$

$$10^{-1} = \frac{1}{10} = 0.1$$

$$10^{-2} = \frac{1}{10^2} = \frac{1}{100} = 0.01$$

$$10^{-3} = \frac{1}{10^3} = \frac{1}{1000} = 0.001$$

2. A way of writing any number involving powers of ten.

Any number can be written as the product of a number between one and ten and a number which is a power of ten.

ex. $769 = 7.69 \times 10^2$

$5{,}200{,}000 = 5.2 \times 10^6$

$0.124 = 1.24 \times 10^{-1}$

$0.0000003 = 3 \times 10^{-7}$

3. A system for multiplying numbers.

In multiplication, exponents of like bases are added.

$10^2 \times 10^3 = 10^{2+3} = 10^5$

$10 \times 10 = 10^{1+1} = 10^2$

$(4 \times 10^4)(2 \times 10^{-6})$

$= 8 \times 10^{4-6} = 8 \times 10^{-2}$

4. A system for dividing numbers.

In division, exponents of like bases are subtracted.

$$\frac{10^2}{10^5} = 10^{2-5} = 10^{-3}; \frac{8 \times 10^2}{2 \times 10^{-6}} =$$

$$\frac{8}{2} \times 10^{2+6} = 4 \times 10^8.$$

After studying the four ideas, practice using scientific notation by doing these problems.

1. Express the following in scientific notation.

a. 720

b. 32,600

c. 1006

d. 59,000,000

e. 0,831

f. 0.02

2. Evaluate the following and express the results in scientific notation.

a. 1700×340

b. $220 \times 35{,}000$

c. $40 \div 20{,}000$

d. $61{,}900 \div 0.48$

e. $\frac{3.17 \times 7{,}230}{0.000289} =$

f. $\frac{(16{,}000)(0.0003)(2.4)}{(2{,}000)(0.007)(0.00051)} =$

Answers to the above problems appear below. Note that the answers to all the problems in this text are never given to more than three figures.

7.2×10^2, 3.26×10^4, 1.006×10^3, 5.9×10^7, 8.31×10^{-1}, 2×10^{-2}.

5.78×10^5, 7.7×10^6, 2×10^{-3}, 1.29×10^5, 7.93×10^7, 1.61×10^3.

Appendix 2

International System (SI) Units

Names, symbols, and conversion factors of SI units used in this text:

Quantity	Name of Unit	Symbol	Conversion Factor
Distance	meter	m	1 km = 0.621 mile 1 m = 3.28 ft 1 cm = 0.394 in. 1 mm = 0.039 in 1 μm = 3.9×10^{-5} in. = 10^4 Å 1 nm = 10 Å
Mass	kilogram	kg	1 tonne = 1.102 tons 1 kg = 2.20 lb 1 gm = 0.0022 lb = 0.035 oz 1 mg = 2.20×10^{-6} lb = 3.5×10^{-5} oz
Time	second	sec	1 yr = 3.156×10^7 sec 1 day = 8.64×10^4 sec 1 hr = 3600 sec
Temperature	kelvin	K	273° K = 0° C = 32° F 373° K = 100° C = 212° F
Area	square meter	m^2	1 m^2 = 10^4 cm^2 = 10.8 ft^2
Volume	cubic meter	m^3	1 m^3 = 10^6 cm^3 = 35 ft^3
Frequency	hertz	Hz	1 Hz = 1 cycle/sec 1 kHz = 1000 cycles/sec 1 MHz = 10^6 cycles/sec
Density	kilogram per cubic meter	kg/m^3	1 kg/m^3 = 0.001 gm/cm^3 1 gm/cm^3 = density of water
Speed, velocity	meter per second	m/sec	1 m/sec = 3.28 ft/sec 1 km/sec = 2240 mi/hr
Force	newton	N	1 N = 10^5 dynes = 0.224 lbf
Pressure	newton per square meter	N/m^2	1 N/m^2 = 1.45×10^{-4} lb/in^2
Energy	joule	J	1 J = 0.239 calorie
Photon energy	electronvolt	e V	1 eV = 1.60×10^{-19} J; 1 J = 10^7 erg
Power	watt	W	1 W = 1 J/sec
Atomic mass	atomic mass unit	amu	1 amu = 1.66×10^{-27} kg

Customary Units Used With the SI Units

Quantity	Name of Unit	Symbol	Conversion Factor
Wavelength of light	angstrom	Å	1 Å = 0.1 nm = 10^{-10} m
Acceleration of gravity	g	g	1g = 9.8 m/sec^2

Appendix 3

SI Unit Prefixes

Prefix	Abbreviation	Factor by Which Unit is Multiplied
exa	E	10^{18}
peta	P	10^{15}
tera	T	10^{12}
giga	G	10^{9}
mega	M	10^{6}
kilo	k	10^{3}
hecto	h	10^{2}
centi	c	10^{-2}
milli	m	10^{-3}
micro	μ	10^{-6}
nano	n	10^{-9}
pico	p	10^{-12}
femto	f	10^{-15}
atto	a	10^{-18}

1 thousand = 10^3
1 million = 10^6
1 billion = 10^9
1 trillion = 10^{12}
1 quadrillion = 10^{15}
1 quintillion 10^{18}

Appendix 4

Common Conversion Factors
(Related to Energy and Resources)

Weight

1 short ton	contains	2,000 pounds
1 metric ton	contains	1.102 short tons
1 long ton	contains	1.120 short tons

Conversion Factors for Crude Oil (Average Gravity)

1 barrel	contains	42 gallons
1 barrel	weighs	0.136 metric tons (0.150 short tons)
1 metric ton	contains	7.33 barrels
1 short ton	contains	6.65 barrels

Conversion Factors for Uranium

1 short ton (U_3O_8)	contains	0.769 metric tons
1 short ton (UF_6)	contains	0.613 metric tons
1 metric ton (UF_6)	contains	0.676 metric tons

Conversion Factors for Energy

1 calorie = 3.968×10^{-3} Btu = 4.184 joules
1 kilocalorie = 1000 calories = 1 dietic Calorie
1 Btu = 252.0 calories = 772 ft · lbs. = 1055 joules
1 foot · pound = 1.285×10^{-3} Btu = 0.3239 cal.
1 joule = 0.2389 cal. = 0.7376 ft · lb.
1 ton of TNT = 1.04×10^9 cal. = 4.14×10^6 Btu
1 barrel of oil = 5.8×10^6 Btu
1 kilowatt · hour = 3413 Btu = 860,000 cal. = 1,000 watt · hours
1 therm = 100,000 Btu

Very Large Energy Units

1 Exajoule (EJ) = 10^{18} joules
1 Quad = 10^{15} Btu
1 Quad (Q) = 1.06 Exajoules (EJ).

Fuel Related Conversion Factors

1 kilowatt-hour	3,413 Btu's
1 short ton of coal	25,000,000 Btu's
1 bbl crude oil	5,800,000 Btu's
1 gallon of gasoline	125,000 Btu's
1 gallon of No. 2 fuel oil	140,000 Btu's
1 cubic foot of natural gas	1,031 Btu's
1 therm of gas (or other fuel)	100,000 Btu's
1 cord of wood	20,000,000 Btu's

1 gram fissionable U-235 = 74,000,000 Btu
1,000 k Wh = 0.123 metric tons of coal (heating value).
1 metric ton of peat = 0.3 to 0.45 metric tons of anthracite or bituminous coal.

Coal (per 2,000 lb. ton)
Anthracite = 25.4×10^6 Btu
Bituminous = 26.2×10^6 Btu
Subbituminous = 19.0×10^6 Btu
Lignite = 13.4×10^6 Btu

Required to generate 1 kWh of electricity
1 kilowatt · hour = 0.88 lbs. of coal
= 0.076 gallons of oil
= 10.4 cu. ft. of natural gas

Appendix 5

Table of Energy Conversion Factors

The following table summarizes the relation between several common energy units. Careful use of this table can aid in the solution of those problems that require the conversion from one unit to another.

Unit	Btu	ft · lb	joule	cal.	kWh
1 British thermal unit =	1	778	1055	252	2.93×10^{-4}
1 foot · pound =	1.29×10^{-3}	1	1.356	0.324	3.77×10^{-7}
1 joule =	9.48×10^{-4}	0.738	1	0.239	2.78×10^{-7}
1 calorie =	3.97×10^{-3}	3.09	4.19	1	1.16×10^{-6}
1 kilowatt · hour =	3413	2.66×10^6	3.6×10^6	8.6×10^5	1

Appendix 6

Practice Problems That Involve Converting Units

We all know that multiplying a quantity by 1 doesn't change that quantity. The procedure for converting values of physical quantities from one unit to another is built on this idea. The multiplication of both the numerator and denominator of a quantity by equal quantities produces no change in the original quantity. This can be illustrated as follows.

The average radius of the Earth is 3959 miles. How many feet is this?

$$d = 3959 \text{ miles} \times \frac{5280 \text{ ft.}}{5280 \text{ ft.}} \text{ or}$$

$$d = 3959 \cancel{\text{miles}} \times \frac{5280 \text{ ft.}}{1 \cancel{\text{mile}}} = 2.09 \times 10^7 \text{ ft.}$$

Note that units cancel the same as numbers.

Examine the problem above carefully. Then solve the following problems. The use of a pocket calculator is helpful in solving these problems, but it is not essential. What is essential is that you set the problems up carefully so you know what you are doing.

1. Make the following conversions:
   a. 15 Btu = ______ kWh.
   b. 1720 joules = ______ cal.
   c. .07 kWh. = ______ Btu
   d. 2.3×10^4 ft · lb. = ______ joules
   e. 596 cal. = ______ ft · lb.
   f. 1 gal. gasoline = ______ cal.
   g. 1 cord of wood = ______ bbls. of oil
   h. 1 ton of TNT = ______ bbls. of oil
2. World crude oil production is projected to peak at approximately 34 billion barrels per year around the year 2000. How many barrels a day is this? How many gallons a day is this? If the world population reaches 6 billion by the year 2000, how many gallons per day per person is this production?
3. In 1979, the U.S. consumed approximately 79 Quads of energy. This amount of energy is equivalent to the consumption of how many barrels of oil a day? If the population of the U.S. was 221 million that year, convert the consumption to gallons per day per person.
4. The energy represented by the gasoline in the tank of a typical automobile (15 gallon capacity) is equivalent to the energy content of how many pounds of coal?

5. A large oil shale plant (called a retort) can produce 100,000 barrels of synthetic crude oil a day. The energy stored in this crude oils is equivalent to the energy stored in how many short tons of coal? How does the energy production of a large oil shale plant compare with the production of a large coal mine? (See the information in Appendix 7).
6. The energy released when 1 gram of U-235 completely fissions is equivalent to the energy stored in how many pounds of coal? How many short tons of coal is this?
7. **a.** If it requires the burning of .88 pounds of coal to produce 1 kilowatt · hour of electricity, how many tons of coal are consumed at a 500 megawatt electric power generation plant each day (when the plant is in full operation)? *Note*

   1 kilowatt × 1 hour = 1 kWh.

   1 kilowatt × 2 hours = 2 kWh.

   6 kilowatts × 3 hours = 18kWh.

   b. If a railroad coal car holds 50 tons of coal, how many cars of coal are consumed at a 500 megawatt plant in one day?
8. How many automobiles with 15 gallon gasoline tanks can be completely filled up each day by an oil refinery that produces 20,000 bbls. of gasoline per day?

Appendix 7

Useful Data Regarding Energy Production Facilities

Comparative Sizes:

Large Coal Mine	10–20,000 tons/day
Large Electric Generating Plant	500–1,000 megawatts
Large Coal Gasification Plant	500×10^6 ft.^{3}/day
Large Oil Shale Plant	100,000 bbls./day
Typical Oil Refinery	50,000 bbls./day

NOTES: 1. All these operations have approximately the same energy output/day.

2. All these operations cost about the same to build, i.e., approximately 1 to 2 billion dollars.

Glossary

A

abiotic nonliving.

abortion the intentional termination of an unwanted pregnancy.

abrasives substances which can be used to rub or wear away, especially by friction.

acid (rain) precipitation any precipitation having a high concentration of sulfuric and/or nitric acid. Any precipitation that has a pH value of less than 5.6. Acidic precipitation includes acid rain, acid snow, acid sleet, acid hail, acid fog, and dry pollutants which form acid when they encounter moisture. All of these forms of precipitation are naturally acidic due to the carbon dioxide in the atmosphere. Generally, rain has a pH of 5.6 to 5.7. The average pH of a rainstorm in the Northeast (USA) is 4.0.

acidic soil the common soil in humid climates, characterized by an abundance of iron oxides and clay minerals deposited in the *B-horizon* by leaching.

active solar those techniques for collecting, storing, and releasing solar energy that require some outside source of energy for fans and/or pumps.

aerobic able to live and grow only if free oxygen is present.

affluence abundance, especially of riches, materials, wealth. A state of prosperity.

air pollutant any substance in sufficient concentration in the air to produce a "harmful" effect on humans or other animals, vegetation, or materials.

alcohol a colorless, volatile, flammable, organic liquid that is formed by the fermentation of biomass.

alkaline soil the common soil in arid climates, characterized by accumulation of calcium carbonate in the A-horizon.

allocative mechanism a technique for distributing part of the production of a society among its members.

alloy a metal that is a mixture of a metal(s) with a nonmetal or another metal.

alpha particle the nucleus of a fast moving helium atom ($^{4}_{2}He$).

alpine growing on mountain heights above the timber line; as alpine plants.

alternative breeder a breeder reactor that contains a much lower inventory of fissionable material than breeders at present.

ambient surrounding; outside; as the *ambient* air.

anaerobic able to live and grow in the absence of air or free oxygen.

anaerobic digestion the biochemical decomposition of organic matter by anaerobic bacteria.

annual plants terrestrial plants that die off each year during periods of temperature and moisture stress but leave behind seeds to germinate during the next favorable climatic season.

anthracite the most highly metamorphosed form of coal. Anthracite has a high energy content. It is black, hard and glassy.

anticline an upward fold of sedimentary rocks. The layers slope down, from the top on all sides.

appropriate technology a strategy for approaching the energy future based on the general belief that "simpler is better" and that sources should be matched to end use tasks.

aquifer a porous and permeable formation that stores and transmits enough groundwater to supply wells.

armature the part of an electric generator that revolves, consisting of a series of coils of insulated wire surrounding a laminated iron core.

asthenosphere the zone of the Earth that geologists believe flows like thick tar.

atmosphere the layer of air surrounding the Earth.

atom a small piece of matter that is composed of protons, neutrons and electrons.

atomic number the number of protons in an atom's nucleus.

attitude in geology, the position or angle of a rock layer in relation to a point of reference.

B

background radiation normal radiation in the lower atmosphere from cosmic rays and from Earth sources.

bacteria single-celled microorganisms that lack chlorophyll. Some bacteria are capable of causing human, animal or plant diseases; others are essential in pollution control because they break down organic matter in air and water.

baghouse an installation containing thousands of heat-resistant fiberglass bags to control particulate emissions. A baghouse works as a room-size vacuum cleaner.

beta particle a fast-moving electron (°β) that can penetrate a few millimeters of aluminum or about 100 centimeters of air.

bioconversion a general term that refers to the transformation of solar energy to chemical energy during photosynthesis.

biodegradable decomposing quickly as a result of the action of microorganisms.

biofuels fuels produced from recently-living material.

biological control use of naturally-occurring predators, parasites, bacteria, and viruses to control pests.

biological oxygen demand (BOD) amount of dissolved oxygen gas required for bacterial decomposition of organic wastes in water.

biomass the total weight or mass of all living matter in a particular habitat or area.

biome a large ecosystem characterized by a distinctive type of vegetation and maintained under the climatic condition of the region.

biosphere (see ecosphere)

biotic living.

birth control all methods for controlling conception or impregnation.

bitumen hard or semisolid material occurring as natural asphalt.

bituminous coal a soft intermediate grade of coal. The most common grade of coal.

breeder reactor a reactor that both produces and consumes fissionable fuel, especially one that produces more than it consumes.

brute force an allocative mechanism in which the strong or powerful obtain the major share of the production because they take it for themselves.

Btu (British thermal unit) the amount of heat required to raise the temperature of one pound of water one Fahrenheit degree.

C

calorie the amount of heat necessary to raise the temperature of one gram of water one Celsius degree. One thousand calories are known as a kilocalorie (Calorie). 1 kilocalorie = 1 Calorie = 1000 calories. Food value is measured in Calories. Food Calories are a measure of the energy content of various foods.

capillary action the movement of liquids in narrow tubes that is the result of adhesion, cohesion, and surface tension. The movement is referred to as capillarity.

capital any man-made instrument of production. Capital resources include tractors, tools, shovels, and buildings.

carbohydrate any of various compounds of carbon, hydrogen, and oxygen (as sugars, starches, cellulose), most of which are formed by green plants and which constitute a major class of animal foods.

carbon cycle a chemical cycle in which the element carbon is circulated in various forms through the ecosphere.

carbon dioxide (CO_2) a gaseous molecule containing one atom of carbon and two atoms of oxygen, formed by respiration in animals or the complete combustion of fossil fuels.

carbon monoxide (CO) a gaseous molecule containing one atom of carbon and one atom of oxygen, formed by the incomplete combustion of fossil fuels.

carnivore an animal that uses other animals as a food source.

carrying capacity the maximum number (population size) of a given organism that a given ecosystem can support.

cartel a voluntary combination of independent private enterprises or countries that supply like commodities and agree to limit competition.

catalytic converter a device added to the exhaust pipe of an automobile that converts the air pollutants carbon monoxide (CO) and unburned hydrocarbons to carbon dioxide (CO_2) and water. The newer converters also break down nitrogen oxides.

cell a group of atoms and molecules interacting in an organized way to exhibit life.

cementation a uniting or joining together, as with cement.

ceramics one of the most important classes of materials on which modern societies rely. Ceramics are a class of inorganic, nonmetallic products which are subjected to high temperatures during manufacture. They are of interest because of their resistance to the action of chemicals and their ability to withstand high temperatures.

chain reaction a series of reactions in which each reaction causes one or more new reactions to occur. A reaction that stimulates its own repetition.

chaparral a biome characterized by a dry climate with little or no summer rain. Vegetation is dominated by shrubs that have adapted to regrow rapidly after the fires that occur frequently during the dry season.

chemical energy the energy that is stored in the chemical bonds that hold molecules together.

chemical sedimentary rock rock that was formed by chemical precipitation, usually from seawater.

chlorofluorocarbons (CFCs) organic molecules consisting of chlorine and fluorine bonded to carbon. Used as spray-can propellants and coolants. Previously thought to be inert but now known to destroy the stratospheric ozone layer.

chromosome a centrally-located thread-like cell structure that contains hereditary material (genes).

circuit the path an electric current follows as it moves through wires and electrical devices.

clarifier a tank in which partially treated wastewater is allowed to separate into settleable solid, liquid and floatable components.

clastic rock a sedimentary rock formed from particles (clasts) that were mechanically transported.

cleavage the tendency of some minerals to break along smooth, flat, parallel surfaces.

climax community a community that remains stable over a long period of time. Climax stage of succession.

closed system a system where nothing enters or leaves. Hence, a system that must use and reuse everything in it.

cloud chamber a device in which the tracks of charged atomic particles, such as cosmic rays or radioactive emissions, are displayed. It consists of a glass-walled chamber filled with a supersaturated vapor, such as alcohol. When charged particles pass through the chamber, they trigger a process of condensation, thus producing a track of tiny liquid droplets, much like the vapor trail of a jet plane.

cloud seeding dispersion of small particles (condensation nuclei) into the atmosphere to stimulate cloud formation and precipitation.

coal a black or brownish-black organic solid primarily carbon but containing varying proportions of hydrogen, oxygen, nitrogen, and sulfur. Coal releases energy when burned and is a widely used natural fuel.

coal gasification a process for converting coal into a synthetic fuel similar to natural gas. The process involves applying heat, pressure and steam to pulverized coal.

coal liquefaction a process for producing a synthetic crude oil by adding hydrogen to coal.

coal seam a layer or stratum of coal.

coarse-grained large visible crystals or particles.

coliform bacteria a normally harmless type of bacteria that resides in the intestinal tract of humans and other animals and whose presence in water indicates that the water may be contaminated with disease-causing organisms found in untreated human and animal waste.

combustion the production of heat and light energy through a chemical process—usually oxidation. Burning is combustion.

community a group of populations living in a given area.

composite plastics plastics combined with fiberglass for added strength.

compost relatively stable decomposed organic material.

Comprehensive Environmental Response, Compensation and Liability Act (CERCLA) the Federal law that addresses the cleanup of inactive and abandoned hazardous waste sites. It is sometimes referred to as Superfund.

conchoidal a type of rock or mineral *fracture* that produces a shell-shaped curved surface. It is often seen in quartz and obsidian.

coniferous trees cone-bearing trees, mostly evergreens that have needle-shaped or scale-like leaves.

conservation a careful preservation and protection of something; especially the planned management of a natural resource to prevent waste.

Conservation Law a law which states that in a closed system some quantity of mass or energy remains conserved (unchanged) forever.

Conservation of Energy (Law of) energy can neither be created nor destroyed. It can, however, be transformed from one form to another.

Conservation of Matter (Law of) matter can neither be created nor destroyed. It can, however, be rearranged.

consumers individuals or groups that buy/use resources, goods, and services.

consumptive use a use which consumes or uses up a resource.

contact metamorphism baking, or changes, that occur when molten rock comes in contact with solid rock.

continuous mining a method of mining in which the continuous mining machine cuts or rips coal from the face and loads it onto conveyors or into shuttle cars in one continuous operation.

continuous resources those resources that renew themselves and hence are always available if used sensibly.

control rod a rod, plate, or tube containing a material that readily absorbs neutrons, used to control the power of a nuclear reactor. By absorbing neutrons, a control rod prevents the neutrons from causing further fission.

convection the transfer of heat by the mass movement of the heated particles, as in air or liquid currents.

conversion factor a number which enables you to change from one measurement unit to another.

cooling pond a lake or pond used to cool heated water from an electric power plant or factory.

cooling system the system for removing heat from the core of a nuclear reactor and transferring it to the steam generator.

cooling tower a device used to remove excess heat from water used in industrial operations, notably in electric power generation.

core the center of the Earth. (see Figure 1.1)

cosmic rays radiation of many sorts; mainly atomic nuclei (protons) with very high energies, originating outside the Earth's atmosphere. Cosmic radiation is part of natural background radiation.

critical mass the smallest mass of fissionable material that will support a self-sustaining chain reaction under stated conditions.

crude oil unrefined petroleum. Petroleum as it is taken from the ground.

crust the upper part of the lithosphere. (see Figure 1.1)

crustal abundance pertaining to the average concentration of a particular element or isotope in the Earth's crust.

crystal a form of matter in which the atoms, ions, or molecules are arranged regularly in all directions to form a regular, repeating network.

cultural eutrophication (see eutrophication)

current the flow of charged particles through a conductive material.

D

deciduous trees trees, such as oak and maple, which lose all their leaves during part of the year.

decomposers the tiny organisms (such as bacteria, fungi, and some protozoa) that break down the complex compounds in dead animals and plants.

decomposition reduction of the net energy level and change in chemical composition of organic matter because of the actions of aerobic or anaerobic microorganisms.

dehydrate to remove water from; to dry.

demand the quantity of a good or service which people are willing and able to buy at various prices. Demand is influenced by advertising, prices of other goods, etc.

demographic transition a phenomenon witnessed in the populations of many industrialized nations. As the standard of living increases, both birth and death rates decline. Gradually zero or low population growth is achieved. The decline in death rate usually precedes the decline in birth rate, producing a period of rapid growth before stabilization occurs.

demography the study of human populations.

desalination the removal of salt, especially from sea water, to make it drinkable.

desertification the process by which arid lands become transformed by loss of vegetation and soil into barren desert.

deuterium an isotope of hydrogen whose nucleus contains one neutron and one proton and is therefore about twice as heavy as the nucleus of normal hydrogen, which is only a single proton. Deuterium is often referred to as heavy hydrogen.

developed countries countries characterized by high standard of living, low population growth rate, low infant mortality, excessive material consumption, high per capita energy consumption, high per capita income, urban population, and high literacy.

developing countries countries characterized by low standard of living, high population growth rates, high infant mortality, low material consumption, low per capita energy consumption, low per capita income, rural populations, and low literacy.

diffuse to spread out, to mix by diffusion as in gases and liquids.

digestion biochemical decomposition of organic matter. Digestion of sewage sludge takes place in tanks where the sludge decomposes, resulting in partial gasification, liquefaction, and mineralization of pollutants.

dipolar having two equal but oppositely charged ends.

disseminated deposit a deposit of ore in which the metal is distributed in small amounts throughout the rock, not concentrated in veins.

dissolved oxygen (DO) amount of oxygen gas (O_2) dissolved in a given quantity of water at a given temperature and atmospheric pressure.

distributive mechanism (see allocative mechanism)

diversity the physical or biological complexity of a system. In many cases it leads to ecosystem stability.

doubling time the amount of time it takes a growing quantity of something to double in number or volume.

E

Earth the grand oasis in space.

earth-sheltered home a home which combines passive strategies with underground placement. These homes are usually open to light on the south side, with the other walls and floor placed in the ground. Some earth-sheltered homes have earthen roofs, others do not.

ecology the study of organisms in their homes. The study of the relationships of living organisms with each other and with their environment.

economics the study of ways that individuals and societies distribute their goods in an attempt to satisfy their unlimited wants.

ecosphere the global ecosystem. The biosphere. The sum total of all the various ecosystems on the Earth.

ecosystem any area of nature that includes living organisms and non-living substances interacting to produce an exchange of materials between the living (biotic) and non-living (abiotic) parts.

effervesce to give off gas bubbles, as carbonated beverages.

efficiency the efficiency of a machine or, more generally, of any process in which some energy or work is put in and some combination of useful work or energy comes out. Efficiency is the ratio of the desired output (work or energy) to the input.

efficient to accomplish with the minimum use of time, energy, money, or effort.

effluent a discharge of pollutants into the environment, partially or completely treated or in their natural state. Generally used in regard to discharges into water.

electric power transmission the method by which electric power is transferred from the power generating plant to where the power is to be used.

electrical energy a special kind of kinetic energy. Electrical energy is the energy of electrical charges, usually electrons in motion.

electromagnetic induction the production of electric current in a closed circuit caused by a change in the magnetic field that passes through that circuit.

electromagnetic wave a wave of energy radiated into space by the sun, a light, or an antenna.

electrons the tiny, negatively charged particles that orbit or migrate about the nucleus of an atom.

electrostatic precipitator a device used for removing particulates from smokestack emissions. The charged particles are attracted to an oppositely charged metal plate, where they are precipitated out of the air.

element one of the approximately 108 known chemical substances that cannot be divided into simpler substances by chemical means. A substance whose atoms all have the same atomic number.

energy the ability to move matter around. That something which is necessary to maintain life and a vibrant society.

energy content the amount of heat energy released by the combustion (or reaction) of one unit mass of that fuel.

energy conversion (see energy transformation)

energy quality the ability of an energy source to do useful work as measured by the ease with which it can be transformed to mechanical energy or electrical energy. Energy quality is also referred to as energy usefulness.

energy transformation the process of changing energy from one form to another. Example: a match transforms chemical energy to heat energy.

enoughness having sufficient food, clothing, shelter, possessions and money to satisfy all the reasonable wants of an individual.

enterprise the process of organizing the economic resources of nature, labor and capital in an attempt to both fulfill a need and obtain a profit.

entrepreneur one who organizes, manages and assumes the risks of a business or enterprise.

entropy a measure of the degree of disorder of a situation. A measure of energy's gradual degeneration to a useless condition.

environment the sum of all external conditions and influences affecting the life, development and ultimately the survival of an individual organism or population.

environmental impact the total effect of an environmental change, either natural or human-made, on the ecology of an area.

Environmental Protection Agency (EPA) the Federal agency empowered to determine environmental standards and enforce Federal environmental laws.

enzyme organic catalysts produced in plant and animal cells that regulate chemical reaction rates in those cells.

equal shares a form of distribution where everyone is given the same amount of some good or service.

equilibrium a stable state of a system. A state of balance or equality between opposing forces.

equity that which relates to fairness. The general principles of fairness and justice.

estuary coastal regions such as inlets or mouths of rivers, where salt and fresh water mix.

eutrophication accumulation of nutrients in a lake or pond due to human intervention (cultural eutrophication) or natural causes (natural eutrophication). Contributes to the process of succession.

evaporation the process of changing from a solid or liquid state to a vapor or gas.

evaporites chemical sedimentary rocks consisting of minerals precipitated by evaporating waters, especially salt and gypsum.

evapotranspiration the combination of water evaporation from the Earth's surface and transpiration from plants.

evolution a process of continual change in organisms caused by changes in successive generations.

exponential growth growth which starts slowly but has the potential to shoot out of control rapidly. Growth that is characterized by doubling in a fixed amount of time.

exponential lifetime (T_e) an estimate of the amount of time the reserves of a resource will last, assuming they are consumed at an exponentially increasing rate.

externalities costs (or benefits) that are external to the actual act of production, or uses that are passed on involuntarily to someone else.

extinction the total loss of a species worldwide.

extrapolate to estimate a quantity beyond the known base of data by assuming the present trends will continue.

extrusive rock rock formed from lava or from other volcanic material spewed out onto the surface of the Earth.

F

family planning process by which couples determine the number and spacing of children.

famine the situation in which people in a given area suffer from lack of access to food sufficient for good health. This may be due to drought, flood, earthquake, or political/economic conditions.

fault a crack in the crust of the Earth along which rocks have moved.

fermentation the breakdown of complex molecules in organic compounds caused by bacteria. The souring of milk is an example.

fertile material a material, not itself fissionable, which can be converted into a fissionable material by irradiation in a reactor. There are two basic fertile materials, Uranium-238 and Thorium-232.
fertilization (conception) the fusion (uniting) of egg and sperm which begins embryonic development.
fertilizer a substance that makes the land or soil capable of producing more and healthier vegetation or crops.
fine-grained barely visible crystals or particles.
finite having bounds or limits. Not infinite, subject to limitations.
First Law of Thermodynamics energy cannot be created or destroyed. It can, however, be transformed from one form to another. This is also known as the Law of Conservation of Energy.
fission the splitting of a heavy nucleus into two nearly equal parts (which are nuclei of lighter elements) accompanied by the release of a large amount of energy and generally one or more neutrons.
fission fragments the two nuclei which are formed by the fission of a nucleus. Also referred to as radioactive waste.
fissionable isotopes isotopes that can be fissioned (split) by neutrons to release nuclear energy. Nuclear fuel.
flat plate collector a device for collecting solar energy and converting it into heat.
flotation separation of ore constituents by binding in a froth, then skimming the froth from the liquid.
fluidized-bed combustion a method of producing heat from low-grade coal. Air is blown into a bed of sand, or of powdered coal and limestone, causing the bed to churn almost like a boiling fluid. The bed is heated red-hot by the injection and ignition of a start-up gas, and more ground or powdered coal is slowly fed in. Steam is generated in boiler tubes laid in the bed, and the exhaust gases are captured under pressure and used to drive a gas turbine.
foliation a parallel or nearly parallel structure caused by a parallel arrangement of platy minerals.
food chain the sequence transferring energy in the form of food from one organism to another.
food web a complex, interlocking series of food chains.
foot · pound the amount of work done or energy used when a force of one pound acts through a distance of one foot.
foresee to see beforehand, to see into the future.
forestall to hinder or prevent by doing something beforehand.
fossil fuels the remains of once-living plants and animals that can be burned to release energy. Examples are coal, oil, natural gas, oil shale and tar sands.
fracture zone a crack in the earth's crust where plates slide past each other horizontally.
free enterprise (market) an economic system in which individuals are free to start and operate their own businesses in a competitive environment.
fuel cell a device for converting chemical energy directly into electrical energy without combustion.
fusion the formation of a heavier nucleus from two lighter ones (such as hydrogen isotopes), resulting in the release of energy.

G

gamma rays high-frequency electromagnetic radiations that have an indeterminate range in matter. They are very penetrating.
gangue the fraction of ore rejected as tailing in a separation process. It is usually of no value but may have some secondary commercial use.
gaseous diffusion a method of isotopic separation based on the fact that gas atoms or molecules with different masses will diffuse through a porous barrier (or membrane) at different rates.
gasohol a mixture of gasoline and alcohol. The alcohol is generally formed from the fermentation of spoiled or inferior wheat and other grains.
generator a device for converting mechanical energy into electrical energy.
geologic analogy a method for estimating the quantity of a resource in a region prior to exploratory drilling. It consists of comparing the region to a known region of similar geology.
geologist one who studies the make-up, structure, and history of the earth's crust, including rock layers, fossils, and mineral content.
geothermal energy energy originating in the Earth's crust, especially in volcanic regions.
germplasm the substance in seeds by which hereditary characteristics are transmitted.
global science the study of how individuals and societies use their living and non-living resources and influence the environment in their attempts to satisfy human wants.
glucose a variety of sugar less sweet than cane sugar, occurring naturally in fruits and honey.
goods anything that is wanted to satisfy a need or obtain pleasure.
gradient the rate of change of temperature, pressure, etc. A diagram or curve representing this.
grasslands found in both temperate and tropical regions and characterized by periodic drought, flat or slightly rolling terrain, and large grazers that feed off the lush grasses.
greenhouse effect the trapping of heat in the atmosphere. Incoming solar radiation penetrates the atmosphere, but outgoing radiation (heat) is absorbed by water vapor, carbon dioxide, and ozone in the atmosphere. This is re-radiated toward the Earth, causing a rise in temperature.
gross primary productivity the total organic matter fixed during photosynthesis.
ground water water below the water table.

H

habitat the specific region in which an organism lives.
half-life the time it takes half the atoms of a particular radioactive substance to disintegrate to another nuclear form.
hazardous wastes potentially harmful solid, liquid, or gaseous waste products of manufacturing or other human activities.
HCl hydrochloric acid.
heat capacity the quantity of heat required to raise the temperature of a body (object) one degree.
heat density a synonym for energy content.
heat energy a form of kinetic energy that flows from one body to another because of a temperature difference between them. The effects of heat energy result from the motion of molecules.
heat engine any device that converts heat energy into mechanical energy.
heat pump a device that transfers heat from a cooler region to a warmer one using mechanical or electrical energy.
hemoglobin the red coloring matter of the red blood corpuscles. Hemoglobin carries oxygen from the lungs to the cells and some carbon dioxide from cells to the lungs.
herbivore a plant-eating animal.
horizons layers found in most soils.
human ecology the study of the growth, distribution, and organization of human communities and how they interact with other humans, other species and with their environment.
humus decaying organic matter that increases soil fertility, aeration, and water retention.
hydrocarbon any of a vast family of compounds containing carbon and hydrogen in various combinations; found especially in fossil fuels.
hydrologic cycle the water cycle.
hydrogen storage any technique for producing and storing hydrogen as a fuel source. The production usually involves electrolyzing water because water is plentiful, and electricity is difficult to store.
hydropower techniques for converting the gravitational energy of water stored behind a dam to electrical energy.
hydrosphere the surface water on the Earth.

I

igneous rock rock that solidified from a molten state.
immiscible liquids liquids that cannot mix.
impermeable not permitting the passage of fluids such as water.
incineration the burning of household or industrial waste.
inequity lack of justice or fairness; an instance of injustice or unfairness.
infiltration the movement of ground water or hydrothermal water into rock or soil through joints and pores.
insectary a place where insects are raised, especially for study or for the purpose of breeding natural predators to control pests.
in situ in the natural or original position or location.
insulation a nonconducting material used to retard the flow of heat.
integrated pest management (IPM) a pest-control strategy based on natural forces, such as the use of natural insect enemies, weather, crop rotation, use of pest-resistant plants, and carefully applied doses of pesticides.
interdependent mutually dependent. Depending on each other.
interrelated the idea that in an ecosystem everything is mutually related to everything else.
intrusive rock igneous rock that forced its way in a molten state into surrounding (country) rock before it cooled.
ion an atom or molecule that has lost or gained one or more electrons and has become electrically charged.
ionizing radiation radiation which has enough energy to dislodge one or more electrons from an atom, forming ions. These ions can react with and damage living tissue.
isotope one of two or more atoms with the same atomic number (the same chemical element) but with different mass numbers. The nuclei of isotopes have the same number of protons but different numbers of neutrons.

J

Joule the amount of work done or energy used when a force of one newton acts through a distance of one meter.

K

kerogen the solid organic matter of high molecular weight contained in oil shale. When heated (retorted), kerogen breaks down, yielding synthetic crude oil and hydrocarbon gas.
kilowatt-hour a common unit of electrical energy. The energy expended when 1000 watts of electrical power are used for one hour.
kinetic energy the energy possessed by a moving object. Energy of motion.

L

labor the physical and/or mental productive ability of people.
land use the use of land by human beings.

laser fusion an approach to nuclear fusion in which a small solid sphere crammed with deuterium and tritium is bombarded with powerful laser beams in an attempt to drive the fuel inward to the point where the nuclei fuse.

laterite a distinctive soil formed in humid regions, characterized by high alumina and iron oxide content and produced by rapid weathering of feldspar minerals.

lava magma that pours out onto the Earth's surface.

Law of Demand a law of economics saying that the demand for a product or service depends on its price. Low prices lead to high demand; high prices lead to low demand.

Law of Limiting Factors the single needed physical or chemical factor that is most deficient in an ecosystem determines the presence or absence and population size of a particular species.

Law of Supply a law of economics saying that the quantity of goods and services offered for sale will vary with price. The higher the price, the greater the quantity offered for sale; the lower the price, the less offered for sale.

leaching the process of extracting or removing a soluble substance from a material or rock layer by causing water to filter through the material or layer.

lead time the time span from when a project is first proposed to when it is completed.

legume any of a large group of plants characterized by true pods enclosing seeds. Because of their ability to store up nitrates, legumes are often plowed under to fertilize the soil.

lifetime calculation a calculation done for the purpose of determining how long a resource will last.

lignite a very soft low grade coal formed by the burial of peat.

limiting factor a factor such as temperature, light, or water that limits the ability of an organism to grow and be productive.

Limits to Growth, The a nontechnical report of the findings of the Club of Rome's study of growth on our planet. The report came out in 1972.

liquefaction to change into a liquid.

lithosphere the solid portion of the Earth's crust.

load the electrical devices (appliances, light bulbs) in an electric circuit that the current operates. The load offers resistance to the flow of current.

loam a soil that is a sandy and clayey mixture.

longwall mining a method of subsurface mining in which a narrow tunnel is cut and then supported by movable metal pillars. After the ore is removed, the roof supports are moved forward, allowing the earth behind them to collapse.

M

macro of or involving larger quantities or objects.

magma molten rock beneath the Earth's surface. Magma is a supersaturated solution containing nonvolatile minerals and volatile constituents.

magnetic confinement fusion a fusion process in which tritium and deuterium are heated to a plasma that is confined in a chamber by means of electromagnetic forces.

magnetic field a region in space in which a magnet or compass needle will experience a force.

magnetohydrodynamics (MHD) the science that deals with the interaction between a magnetic field and a flowing ionized gas. MHD offers the possibility of more efficient electric power generation.

malnutrition the state of poor health in which an individual's diet lacks one or more of the essential vitamins and nutrients, especially protein.

mantle a thick shell of the Earth below the asthenosphere that behaves like a solid.

marine of the sea or ocean; inhabiting, found in, or formed by the sea.

market a situation in which buyers and sellers communicate with one another concerning the exchange of goods and/or services.

market economy an economic system in which most of the businesses are owned and operated by private citizens. Most economic decisions are made by individual producers and consumers through buying and selling in the market.

market equilibrium the point where the consumer is able to purchase the largest amount of a product or service at the cheapest price, and the producer is able to produce the most at the highest price.

mass a number that measures the quantity of matter. It is obtained on the earth's surface by dividing the weight of a body by the acceleration due to gravity.

mass number the number of protons plus neutrons in an atomic nucleus.

matter anything that occupies space and has mass.

mechanical concentration any concentration of a mineral caused by the movement of a fluid.

mechanical energy the energy of an object as represented by its movement, its position, or both.

mechanism any system, means, or strategy for doing something.

meltdown an event at a nuclear reactor if a pipe ruptures or there is some other major interference with the normal cooling system. This would allow the reactor's hot fissionable fuel to quickly overheat. The fuel could quickly form itself into a heavy, white-hot blob of molten metal that could penetrate through the reactor and melt its way down through the basement of the plant and into the ground. Large quantities of contaminated steam and other vapors would be released into the environment.

metabolism the chemical reactions that take place in an organism as food is utilized.

metamorphic rock sedimentary or igneous rock in which the minerals or texture or both have been changed by high temperature and pressure without melting.

methodology the application of the principles of reasoning to scientific and philosophical inquiry. The science of method or orderly arrangement.

micro of or involving smaller quantities or objects.

microorganisms any living things of microscopic size; examples include bacteria, yeasts, simple fungi, some algae, slime molds, and protozoans.

mill a building or collection of buildings containing machinery for separating the valuable portion of an ore from the waste rock.

mineral any naturally-occurring crystalline inorganic material. A naturally-occurring substance or phase with a characteristic internal structure determined by a regular arrangement of the atoms or ions within it, and with a chemical composition and physical properties that are either fixed or that vary within a definite range.

moderator a material, such as ordinary water, heavy water or graphite, used in a reactor to slow down high-velocity neutrons, thus increasing the likelihood of further fission.

molecule a group of atoms hooked together in a particular way.

monoculture cultivation of one plant species (such as wheat or corn) over a large area. Highly susceptible to disease and insects.

monopoly the market condition that exists when one company or group is the only producer of a good or service. This condition demands that consumers pay whatever price is asked.

muck broken rock coming from a mine or tunnel. Muck may or may not contain valuable minerals.

municipal solid wastes combined residential and commercial solid waste materials generated in a given municipal area.

mutation a sudden fundamental change in heredity producing a new individual unlike its parents in some way.

N

natural gas a gas mixture that is trapped in many places in the upper strata of the Earth. Natural gas is mostly methane and ethane. It can be found alone but is often found with petroleum.

natural resources the materials that nature provides which can be used in production. Natural resources are often called gifts of nature.

natural selection the process by which the individuals in a population that are best suited to their environment survive and pass their characteristics on to their offspring.

need a lack of something essential, desirable or useful. A condition requiring supply or relief.

net energy the difference between total energy produced and total energy used.

net primary productivity that part of the total or gross primary productivity of photosynthetic plants that remains after some of this material is used in the respiration of those plants. The remaining net productivity is available for harvest by animals (including humans).

neutron an uncharged elementary particle with a mass slightly greater than that of the proton and found in the nucleus of every atom heavier than ordinary hydrogen.

niche all the physical, chemical, and biological factors a species needs to survive, stay healthy, and reproduce in an ecosystem.

nitrogen cycle a chemical cycle in which the element nitrogen is circulated in various forms through the ecosphere.

nitrogen oxides (NO_x) gases formed in great part from atmospheric nitrogen and oxygen when combustion takes place under conditions of high temperature and high pressure; e.g., in internal combustion engines; considered major air pollutants.

no-till a method of cultivation in which the soil is left undisturbed to reduce soil erosion, lower labor costs, and save energy.

non-point source a source of pollution in which wastes are not released at one specific, identifiable point but from a number of points that are spread out and difficult to identify and control.

nonrenewable resources resources that are not replaced or regenerated naturally within a reasonable period of time. Examples: fossil fuels, minerals.

nuclear energy the energy liberated by a nuclear reaction (fission or fusion) or by radioactive decay.

nuclear fuel cycle all of the steps involving the use of a nuclear material, starting with the removal of ore from the ground and ending with the eventual disposal of related waste materials.

nuclear proliferation (see proliferation)

nuclear reactor a device in which a fission chain reaction can be initiated, maintained, and controlled.

nuclear waste equipment and materials (from nuclear reactions and operations) which are radioactive and thus not usable.

nucleon a nuclear particle; a proton or neutron in the nucleus of an atom.

nucleus the small, positively-charged core of an atom. The nucleus contains nearly all the atom's mass. Both protons and neutrons are found in all nuclei, except that of ordinary hydrogen, which consists of a single proton.

nutrient an element or compound that is needed for the survival, growth, and reproduction of a plant or animal.

nutrition nourishing or being nourished by taking in and assimilating food.

O

ocean thermal energy conversion (OTEC) an energy option which utilizes temperature differences between surface waters and ocean depths to vaporize a working fluid and generate electricity.

oil (see crude oil)

oil shale a sedimentary rock containing kerogen. Heated kerogen yields synthetic crude oil, which can be processed into gasoline and other petroleum products.

oligotrophic lake a lake with low dissolved plant nutrient (nitrate and phosphate) content.

omnivore an animal, such as a human, that can use both plants and other animals as food sources.

ore a mineral or mineral aggregate containing precious or useful metals and that occurs in such quantity, grade and chemical combination as to make extraction commercially profitable.

ore body a more or less solid mass of ore that may consist of low-grade as well as high-grade ore and is of different character than the adjoining rock.

organ a group of tissues performing a similar function. Examples: the heart, the lungs.

organ system a group of organs performing a similar function. Example: the digestive system.

organic derived from living organisms; the branch of chemistry dealing with carbon compounds.

organic farming a method of producing crops and livestock naturally by using organic fertilizer (manure, legumes, compost, crop residues), crop rotation, and natural (biological) pest control (good bugs that eat bad bugs, plants that repel bugs), and environmental controls (such as crop rotation) instead of using commercial, synthetic fertilizers, pesticides, and herbicides.

organism any living thing.

overburden material of any nature that covers a deposit of useful materials or ores that are to be mined.

oxisol the common soil in very wet regions. Oxisols are deep red. All but the most insoluble materials have been leached away. Lack of soluble minerals means this soil does not support abundant plant growth.

oxygen (O) an element that is found free as a colorless, tasteless, odorless gas in the atmosphere; or combined in water, in most rocks and minerals, and in numerous organic compounds. It can combine with all elements except the inert gases, is active in life processes, and is involved especially in combustion processes.

ozone (O_3) a highly reactive molecule made up of three atoms of oxygen. High in the atmosphere ozone forms a layer that filters out harmful ultraviolet radiation, thus protecting life on Earth. Ozone is also formed at the Earth's surface as a damaging component of photochemical smog.

P

particulates solid particles and liquid droplets suspended or carried in the air. Particulates include soot, ashes, dust, etc.

passive solar those techniques for using solar energy to heat an enclosure that require no nonsolar energy for fans or pumps.

peat a mixture of plant fragments formed from partly decayed vegetation that is slowly built up in swamps.

pedalfer a common soil type in humid regions, characterized by an abundance of iron oxides and clay minerals deposited in the B-horizon by leaching.

pedocal a common soil type of arid regions, characterized by accumulation of calcium carbonate in the A-horizon.

pegmatite an igneous rock with extremely large grains (more than a centimeter in diameter). It may be of any composition but most frequently is granite.

permafrost a permanently-frozen aggregate of ice and soil occurring in very cold regions.

permeable open to passage or penetration by fluids, especially by water or crude oil.

petroleum an oily, flammable liquid that may vary from almost colorless to black and occurs in many places in the upper strata of the Earth. It is a complex mixture of hydrocarbons and is the raw material for many products.

photochemical smog a complex mixture of air pollutants (oxidants) produced in the atmosphere by the reaction of hydrogen and nitrogen oxides under the influence of sunlight. Photochemical smog produces localized dead spots, yellowing, and growth alterations in plants. It is an eye and respiratory irritant in humans.

photon a small bundle of radiant energy. A photon carries a quantum of electromagnetic energy.

photosynthesis the process by which plants use sunlight to combine carbon dioxide, water and various minerals into carbohydrates (such as glucose).

photovoltaic cell an electronic device that converts sunlight directly into electrical energy.

photovoltaic effect the ejection of electrons from the surface of a material that is exposed to visible light.

pillar the mass of coal or ore left to support the ceiling of a mine.

placer a deposit of gold or other metal-bearing alluvial gravel.

plasma an electrically neutral gaseous mixture of positive and negative ions. Sometimes called the "fourth state of matter" since it behaves differently from solids, liquids and gases.

Plate Tectonics Theory the theory that there are six large crustal plates, and many smaller ones, that move around on the surface of the Earth.

platy made of flat, broad, thin sheets.

pluralistic containing many parts, views, or features. A pluralistic society contains many nationalities, religions, and customs.

plutonium (Pu) a heavy radioactive, man-made metallic element with atomic number 94. Its most important isotope is fissionable plutonium-239, produced by neutron irradiation of uranium-238. It is used for reactor fuel and in weapons.

point source (of pollution) easily discernible source of pollution, such as a factory.

pollutant something that pollutes; especially a harmful chemical or other waste material discharged into the water or atmosphere.

pollution the presence of matter or energy whose nature, location, and/or quantity produces undesired environmental effects.

population all the organisms of the same type living in a certain area.

population histogram graphical representation of population by age and sex.

porosity the percentage of space between soil or rock particles.

porous full of pores or tiny holes which can be occupied by fluids such as water or crude oil.

potential energy stored energy. Energy that is due to the position or configuration of a mass.

precipitation the process by which water vapor molecules condense to form drops or ice crystals that are heavy enough to fall to the Earth's surface.

predator an organism that lives by preying on other organisms.

prey an animal taken by a predator as food.

price the value, in monetary terms, placed upon a good or service.

primary consumer first consumer organism in a given food chain.

primary productivity the rate of creation of organic matter by photosynthetic plants.

primary succession the sequential development of communities in a bare or soilless area that has never been occupied by a community of organisms.

primary treatment the first stage in waste water treatment in which the floating or settleable solids are mechanically removed by screening and sedimentation.

priorities a preferential ranking of goals, projects, or actions.

producers organisms (such as plants) that synthesize organic substances from inorganic substances.

profit the amount of revenue left for a producer after all costs of production are paid.

proliferation the process of growing or increasing rapidly in number or amount.

proteins the principal organic substances within cells. Proteins contain carbon, hydrogen, nitrogen, oxygen and usually sulfur. Proteins are synthesized from raw materials by plants but assimilated as separate amino acids by animals.

proton an elementary particle with a single positive electrical charge and a mass approximately 1837 times that of the electron. Protons are found in all nuclei.

protoplasm the living part of a cell.

pumped storage reversible pump turbines use surplus electric power to lift water into a reservoir when demand is low and then use it to generate power when it is needed.

pyrolysis to heat, for the purpose of breaking up, in the absence of air. Chemical decomposition by heat.

Q

quad (Q) a large quantity of energy equal to one quadrillion Btu. $1Q = 10^{15}$ Btu.

queuing to line up or wait in a line, especially of persons or vehicles.

quota a limit placed on foreign imports or resource production. Also, in communist countries, a production goal for a factory or industry.

R

R-value a measure of a material's ability to stop heat from passing through it. The higher the R-value, the greater the resistance to heat flow.

radiant energy the energy of electromagnetic waves, including light.

radioactive waste materials which are radioactive and for which there is no further use.

radioactivity the spontaneous transformation of an atomic nucleus during which it changes from one nuclear species to another, with the emission of particles and energy.

random selection a form of distribution in which the products of a society are allocated by drawing lots or some other mechanism based on chance.

randomness a measure of the disorder or chaos of a situation. Also an indication of the degree of degradation of an energy supply.

rationing the process of distributing or dividing up a commodity in short supply in an equitable manner, or so as to achieve a particular objective.

real world lifetime (T_{rw}) the amount of time the reserves of a resource actually last under real world conditions.

recharge in hydrology, the replacement of ground water by infiltration of water from the atmosphere.

reclamation the process of restoring to cultivation, useful purpose, or original state.

recycling the process by which waste materials are transformed into new useful products in such a manner that the original products may lose their identity.

refining the process by which a mineral concentrate is brought to a fine or a pure state.

renewable resource a resource that can be used continuously without being used up.

renewal time the time it takes a depleted resource to be restored to its original condition.

rent payment received by an individual or group for the use of a natural resource.

replacement deposit a deposit of ore minerals by hydrothermal solutions. The minerals were first dissolved in the hot solution and then substituted for some other mineral in the surrounding rock.

reserves the amount of an identified resource that can be extracted profitably with existing technology under present economic conditions. Reserves are a subclass of resources.

reservoir a source or place of residence of some valuable material.

residual enrichment a mineral concentration process in which a material of no value is dissolved away, leaving behind a valuable substance.

resistance opposition to the passage of electric current, causing electric energy to be transformed into heat.

resolve to work out, to come to a decision.

Resource Conservation and Recovery Act (RCRA) the federal law that regulates hazardous waste generation, storage, transportation, treatment, and disposal. The emphasis is on resource conservation.

resource depletion curve a plot of production rate versus time which represents the complete production cycle of a resource in a given region.

resources identified and unidentified deposits of a mineral that can be economically recovered with existing technology or which may become economically recoverable when prices rise or mining technology improves.

respiration the oxidation of food by organisms that releases usable energy, carbon dioxide, and water.

retort a vessel in which substances are distilled or decomposed by being heated in the absence of air.

rift an opening made by splitting.

rock the basic solid material of the Earth's crust. Rock is a collection of minerals.

rock-forming minerals the minerals that make up the most common rocks in the Earth's crust.

room-and-pillar mining a method of underground mining in which a series of rooms are cut and pillars (columns) left standing to support the roof. Once a particular area is mined out, the pillars are systematically removed and the roof allowed to fall.

S

salt dome a solid mass of salt that was once fluid and flowed into fractures and other weaknesses in surrounding geologic structures. Oil and gas traps formed against the side of this salt, in faults caused by the movement of salt, and in arched formations above the salt.

sanitary landfill an engineered method of solid waste disposal on land in a manner that protects the environment. Waste is spread in thin layers, compacted to the smallest practical volume and covered with soil at the end of each working day.

scarcity the condition that exists when the desire for a good or a service is greater than the available resources or the means to produce it.

scrubber a device used in controlling particulate and/or gaseous emissions. The process involves washing impurities out of the stream of flue gas and carrying them off in a slurry of ash and water.

Second Law of Thermodynamics (Form 1) in any conversion of energy from one form to another, there is always a decrease in the amount of useful energy.

Second Law of Thermodynamics (Form 2) heat cannot by itself flow from cold to hot. It spontaneously flows from hot to cold.

Second Law of Thermodynamics (Form 3) in any closed system, randomness always tends toward a maximum.

secondary consumer animals that obtain their food by feeding only on plant-eating animals.

secondary enrichment a mineral concentration process in which a valuable substance is dissolved and carried to a new location where it is redeposited in a concentrated state.

secondary solar sources of solar energy that involve the conversion of wind, warm water, and biomass into energy forms more useful to humans.

secondary succession the sequential development of communities in an area in which the natural vegetation has been removed or destroyed but the soil or bottom sediment is not destroyed.

secondary treatment waste water treatment, beyond the primary stage, in which bacteria consume the organic parts of the wastes. The biochemical action is accomplished by the use of trickling filters or the activated sludge process. Customarily, disinfection by chlorination is the final stage of the secondary treatment process.

sediment any matter or mass deposited by water or wind.

sedimentary rock rock made up of fragments of other rocks and minerals, usually deposited in water.

seed bank a facility in which a variety of seeds are kept under ideal conditions for the purpose of preserving genetic diversity.

seismic of or having to do with an earthquake.

selective advantage a biological trait that enables an organism to survive in a particular environment better than other similar organisms.

semiconductor a material, such as silicon, whose electrical conductivity can be greatly increased by exposing it to heat, light, or voltage.

septic tank a tank in which waste matter is putrefied and decomposed through bacterial action.

severance tax a tax on the taking and use of natural resources, imposed at the time the mineral or other product is extracted or severed from the Earth.

sewage the total of organic waste and waste water generated by residential and commercial establishments.

shortage the market condition which occurs when people cannot buy the full quantity of an economic good or service they desire at the going price.

shrublands lands covered with bushy, woody plants having several permanent stems instead of single trunks.

silica a hard, glassy mineral found in a variety of forms, as in quartz and sand.

simulate to imitate, to look or act like.

slough a place of deep mud or mire. A swamp, bog, or marsh.

sludge solid organic material produced during sewage treatment.

smelting the fusing or melting of an ore in order to separate out the metal it contains.

smog a combination of fog and smoke. The term is now also applied to the photochemical haze produced by the action of sun and atmosphere on automobile and industrial exhausts.

soft technology (see appropriate technology)

soil loose weathered material at the surface of the Earth, in which plants can grow.

soil conservation strategies to reduce soil erosion and to prevent depletion of soil nutrients.

soil erosion movement of topsoil and other soil components from one place to another, usually by wind and flowing water.

soil profile the layers in a particular sample of soil.

solar cell (see photovoltaic cell)

solar collector a device for collecting solar energy and converting it into heat.

solar energy energy from the sun that is received by the Earth.

solar input the amount of solar power received by a square meter of land on a clear day when the sun is directly overhead.

Solar Thermal Energy Conversion (STEC) the name given to those strategies for concentrating and collecting enough solar energy to make large quantities of steam.

Solid Waste Disposal Act (1965) the first federal law to require safeguards and encourage environmentally sound methods for disposal of household, municipal, commercial, and industrial refuse.

solution mining a method of removing soluble materials from underground deposits by pumping hot water down a drill hole and recovering the salt by evaporation of the resulting brine.

solvent a medium, usually liquid, in which other substances can be dissolved.

source bed the layer of rock that was the origin of a valuable material.

spillover costs the costs (or benefits) external to the actual act of production or use of a product that are passed on involuntarily to someone else.

static lifetime (T_s) an estimate of the amount of time the reserves of a resource will last, assuming both the quantity of the reserve and the use rate don't change.

steady state a balanced condition in a system because a substance (or energy) is entering and leaving at the same rate.

steady state economics an economic system that can operate in a non-growing environment. In a steady state economy, both the number of people and the stock of available resources is maintained at some desired, sufficient level.

sterilization any procedure by which an individual is made incapable of reproduction.

stockpile a reserve supply of a raw material.

stockwork a condition in which an ore is deposited regularly throughout a mass of rock.

strata layers of rock, especially layers of sedimentary rock.

strategic minerals minerals which are essential to the economic and military strength of a nation.

stratigraphic trap a trap for underground fluids that results from the orientation of the layers or strata. Stratigraphic traps occur when an upward-sloping porous layer is pinched between two non-porous layers.

strip mining a mining technique used when the deposits of a resource lie relatively near the surface. Overburden is stripped away, the resource removed, and overburden from an adjoining area (as it is mined) placed in the void that was formed.

structural trap a trap for underground fluids that is the result of the geologic structure. Anticlines, salt domes, and fault traps are all examples.

subbituminous coal a form of coal produced at pressures and temperatures greater than those that produce lignite but less than those required for bituminous coal.
subduction zone the shear zone between a sinking oceanic plate and an overriding plate.
subsidence the act or process of sinking or settling to form a depression.
subsidy a government grant to a private enterprise considered of benefit to the public.
succession the natural replacement of one biotic community by another.
sufficient enough, as much as is needed.
sulfur oxides (SO_x) pungent, colorless gases formed primarily by the combustion of fossil fuels, considered major air pollutants. Sulfur oxides may damage the respiratory tract, as well as vegetation.
superinsulation a strategy for the design of a building for the purpose of providing superior comfort for its inhabitants along with much lower heating/cooling bills.
supply the amount or quantity of goods or services available for purchase at a given price.
surface mining another term for strip mining.
surface tension a property of liquids in which the exposed surface tends to contract to the smallest possible area.
surface water water falling on the surface of the Earth which runs off into lakes and streams. It stays on the surface.
surplus a quantity or amount over and above what is needed or used.
sustainable able to continue indefinitely.
sustainable agriculture agriculture that maintains the quality of soil and water resources so that it can continue indefinitely. Organic farming strategies are maximized.
syncrude crude oil that requires some human intervention in its production rather than crude that is pumped from the ground.
synthetic fuels fuels which involve some type of human intervention (technology) to produce. Examples are oil shale, coal gasification, and tar (oil) sands.
system efficiency the overall efficiency of a process that occurs in a series of steps. The efficiency of a system is equal to the product of the efficiencies of the various steps in the process.

T

tailing the inferior or refuse material separated as residue in the milling process.
tar sands a sandy geologic deposit containing a heavy oil or tar-like fuel too thick to be pumped to the surface, but which can be mined and treated to obtain synthetic fuels.
tax incentive tax cuts that either encourage people to work and spend or accomplish some action advantageous to the public.
technology applications of science that provide objects used for human sustenance and comfort. The application of scientific knowledge for practical purposes.
temperature inversion the situation that results when a layer of dense cool air is trapped under a layer of thinner warm air. The warm gaseous pollutants cannot rise through the warm air, so they accumulate at the boundary between these layers.
terracing construction of small earthen embankments or terraces on hilly or mountainous terrain to reduce the velocity of water flowing across the soil and reduce soil erosion.
terrestrial pertaining to or consisting of land, as distinguished from water.
tertiary treatment waste water treatment beyond the secondary, or biological, stage that includes removal of nutrients such as phosphorus and nitrogen and a high percentage of suspended solids. Tertiary treatment, also known as advanced waste treatment, produces a high-quality effluent.
texture (rock) the size and arrangement of mineral grains.
thermal mass a mass of material, such as rock or water, that can absorb solar radiation in the daytime and then radiate away heat at night. Inside a building, thermal mass tends to moderate indoor temperatures.
thermal pollution an increase in water or air temperature which disturbs the ecology of the area. Most often, thermal pollution is associated with electric generating plants which require large amounts of cooling water to remove waste heat.
thorium (Th) a naturally radioactive element with atomic number 90 and, as found in nature, an atomic weight of approximately 232. The fertile thorium-232 isotope is abundant and can be transmuted (changed) to fissionable uranium-233 by neutron irradiation.
tidal energy the kinetic energy of the ocean's tides that can be converted to electric energy.
tilth tilled land; land which has been cultivated and prepared for raising crops.
tissue a group of similar cells performing a similar function. Examples: muscle tissue, blood tissue.
tradition the practice of handing down stories, beliefs, customs, etc. from one generation to another.
transform fault a plate boundary along which two plates slide past each other.
transformer an electrical device that is used to step-up or step-down voltage. When voltage goes up, current goes down. When voltage goes down, current increases.
transition a passing from one condition, form, stage, etc. to another.

transpiration the process by which moisture is carried through plants from the roots to the leaves, where it changes to vapor and escapes to the atmosphere through leaf openings.

trickle irrigation supplying irrigation water through tubes which drip or trickle water onto the soil at the base of each plant. Also called drip irrigation.

trickling filter a form of secondary sewage treatment in which aerobic bacteria degrade organic materials in wastewater as it seeps through a large vat filled with crushed stones.

trimester a term or period of three months. One-third of a normal human pregnancy.

tritium a radioactive isotope of hydrogen with two neutrons and one proton in the nucleus. It is man-made and is heavier than deuterium (heavy hydrogen).

tundra treeless, boggy regions of both low average temperature and low average annual precipitation. There is both alpine tundra and arctic tundra.

turbine a bladed, wheel-like device which converts the kinetic energy of a gas or liquid into the mechanical energy of a rotating shaft.

U

unburned hydrocarbons air pollutants which come from the incomplete combustion of gasoline and from the evaporation of petroleum fuels, industrial solvents, and painting and dry cleaning activities.

undernourishment a state of poor health in which an individual is obtaining too little food.

unit train a long train of approximately one hundred cars, all of which carry the same product (usually coal).

United Nations an international organization established immediately after World War II for the purpose of working for world peace, security and the betterment of humanity.

uranium (U) a radioactive element with the atomic number 92 and, as found in ores, an average atomic weight of approximately 238. The two principal natural isotopes are uranium-235 (0.7% of natural uranium), which is fissionable, and uranium-238 (99.3% of natural uranium), which is fertile. Natural uranium also includes a minute amount of uranium-234. Uranium is the basic raw material of nuclear energy.

uranium enrichment any process in which the relative abundance of uranium-235 in a sample is increased from 0.7% to some higher value.

useful energy energy which can easily be transformed to do mechanical or electrical tasks.

V

value the worth of a thing in money or goods at a certain time; market price.

variable anything changeable; a thing or quantity that changes or can change.

vein deposit a mineralized zone or belt lying within boundaries clearly separating it from neighboring rock.

vitamins organic molecules that are needed in small quantities in the diet of higher animals to perform specific biological functions.

volatile evaporating rapidly; diffusing freely into the atmosphere.

voltage a measure of the electrical force for driving an electric current.

W

wages money received by an individual from an employer in exchange for physical or mental labor.

water budget a water balance. It accounts for the income, storage, and loss of water over an area.

water cycle the total process by which water is circulated through the ecosphere.

water diversion a method for increasing the supply of fresh water in a water-poor area by bringing in water from a water-rich area.

water table the top of a saturated soil zone.

watt · hour If the potential difference across a portion of an electrical circuit is one volt, a current of one ampere flowing continuously through that portion for one hour will furnish one watt · hour of electrical energy.

weathering the natural process of breaking down rocks.

wet scrubber an antipollution device that uses a liquid spray to remove pollutants from a stream of air.

wilderness an area where the biological community is nearly undisturbed by humans.

windbreaks rows of trees or hedges planted to partially block wind flow and hence reduce soil erosion and water loss on cultivated lands located in high-wind areas.

wind generator a generator operated by the wind's rotation of turbine blades that radiate from a shaft. Wind generators can be a cheap source of electricity if used properly.

work the transfer of energy that involves a force acting through a distance.

Index

Definitions are provided on pages indicated in **boldface type.**

E

F

G

H

I

J

K

L

M